W9-CSA-945

Springer Series in Electrophysics
Volume 11

Edited by Walter Engl

Springer Series in Electrophysics

Editors: Günter Ecker Walter Engl Leopold B. Felsen

Volume 1 **Structural Pattern Recognition** By T. Pavlidis

Volume 2 **Noise in Physical Systems** Editor: D. Wolf

Volume 3 **The Boundary-Layer Method in Diffraction Problems**
By V. M. Babič, N. Y. Kirpičnikova

Volume 4 **Cavitation and Inhomogeneities** in Underwater Acoustics
Editor: W. Lauterborn

Volume 5 **Very Large Scale Integration (VLSI)**
Fundamentals and Applications
Editor: D. F. Barbe 2nd Edition

Volume 6 **Parametric Electronics** An Introduction
By K.-H. Löcherer, C. D. Brandt

Volume 7 **Insulating Films on Semiconductors**
Editors: M. Schulz, G. Pensl

Volume 8 **Theoretical Fundamentals of the Ocean Acoustics**
By L. Brekhovskikh, Y. P. Lysanov

Volume 9 **Principles of Plasma Electrodynamics**
By A. F. Alexandrov, L. S. Bogdankevich, A. A. Rukhadze

Volume 10 **Ion Implantation Techniques**
Editors: H. Ryssel, H. Glawischnig

Volume 11 **Ion Implantation: Equipment and Techniques**
Editors: H. Ryssel, H. Glawischnig

Volume 12 **Fundamentals of VLSI Technology**
Editor: Y. Tarui

Volume 13 **Physics of Highly Charged Ions**
By R. K. Janev, L. P. Presnyakov, V. P. Shevelko

Volume 14 **Plasma Physics for Physicists**
By I. A. Artsimovich, R. Z. Sagdeev

Volume 15 **Relativity for Engineers**
By J. van Bladel

Ion Implantation: Equipment and Techniques

Proceedings of the Fourth International Conference
Berchtesgaden, Fed. Rep. of Germany,
September 13–17, 1982

Editors: H. Ryssel and H. Glawischnig

With 474 Figures

Springer-Verlag
Berlin Heidelberg New York Tokyo 1983

Dr. Heiner Ryssel
Fraunhofer-Institut für Festkörpertechnologie,
Paul-Gerhardt-Allee 42
D-8000 München 60, Fed. Rep. of Germany

Dr. Hans Glawischnig
Siemens AG, Balanstraße 73
D-8000 München 80, Fed. Rep. of Germany

Series Editors:

Professor Dr. Günter Ecker
Ruhr-Universität Bochum, Theoretische
Physik, Lehrstuhl I, Universitätsstraße 150,
D-4630 Bochum-Querenburg,
Fed. Rep. of Germany

Professor Dr. Walter Engl
Institut für Theoretische Elektrotechnik,
Rhein.-Westf. Technische Hochschule,
Templergraben 55,
D-5100 Aachen, Fed. Rep. of Germany

Professor Leopold B. Felsen Ph.D.
Polytechnic Institute of New York,
333 Jay Street, Brooklyn, NY 11201, USA

Conference Chairmen: H. Glawischnig (Siemens) and H. Ryssel (IFT)

International Committee: D. Aitken (AIT); E.H. Bayer (IBM); J. Cecil (Veeco/AI); G. Dearnaley (AERE); F. Ferrari (Univ. Trento); H. Glawischnig (Siemens); P.R. Hanley (Varian); P. Mazzoldi (Univ. Padova); C. McKenna (Hughes); E. Pásztor (AS Hungary); P.H. Rose (Eaton); H. Ryssel (IFT); P.J. Scanlon (Univ. Kingston); K.G. Stephens (Univ. Surrey); T. Tokuyama (Hitachi); S.C. Tsou (AS China); L. Wegmann (Balzers); J.R. Winnard (IBM); A. Wittkower (Eaton); J.F. Ziegler (IBM)

Program Committee: M. Bruel (LETI); F. Ferrari (Univ. Trento); H. Glawischnig (Siemens); G. Götz (Univ. Jena); H. Kranz (IFT); E.F. Krimmel (Siemens); C. McKenna (Hughes); W. Nachbauer (Valvo); H. Runge (Siemens); G. Ryding (Eaton); H. Ryssel (IFT); L. Wegmann (Balzers); J.R. Winnard (IBM); J.F. Ziegler (IBM)

Local Organizing Committee: M. Bleier (IFT); M. Forster (IFT); P. Glawischnig; K. Haberger (IFT); M. Holtschmidt (Siemens); H. Kranz (IFT); F. Krimmel-Fanti; A. Meyer; H. Platzdasch (Siemens); B. Schmiedt (IFT); E. Traumüller (IFT)

Sponsors: Siemens AG; Fraunhofer-Gesellschaft; Region 8 of IEEE; Appl. Implant Technology; Varian; Veeco; Eaton; High Voltage Engineering; Electrostatics International; Balzers; Atomica; Brookhaven Instruments; Haefely; Tennelec; Whickham Engineering

---

ISBN 3-540-12491-8 Springer-Verlag Berlin Heidelberg New York Tokyo
ISBN 0-387-12491-8 Springer-Verlag New York Heidelberg Berlin Tokyo

Printed in Germany

Offset printing: Beltz Offsetdruck, 6944 Hemsbach/Bergstr.
Bookbinding: J. Schäffer OHG, 6718 Grünstadt.
2153/3130-543210

Preface

The Fourth International Conference on Ion Implantation: Equipment and Techniques was held at the Convention Center in Berchtesgaden, Bavaria, Germany, from September 13 to 17, 1982. It was attended by more than 200 participants from over 20 different countries. Several series of conferences have dealt with the application of ion implantation to semiconductors and other materials (Thousand Oaks, 1970; Garmisch-Partenkirchen, 1971; Osaka, 1974; Warwick, 1975; Boulder, 1975; Budapest, 1978; and Albany, 1980). Another series of conferences has been devoted to implantation equipment and techniques (Salford, 1977; Trento, 1978; and Kingston, 1980). This conference was the fourth in the latter series. Twelve invited papers and 55 contributed papers covered the areas of ion implantation equipment, measuring techniques, and applications of implantation to metals and semiconductors.

A school on ion implantation was held in connection with the conference, and the lectures presented at this school were published as Vol. 10 of the Springer Series in Electrophysics under the title *Ion Implantation Techniques* (edited by H. Ryssel and H. Glawischnig). During the conference, space was also provided for presentations and demonstrations by manufacturers of ion implantation equipment.

Once again, this conference provided a forum for free discussion among implantation specialists in industry as well as research institutions. Especially effective in stimulating a free exchange of information was the daily get-together over free beer at the "Bier Adam".

Many people contributed to the success of this conference. Valuable guidance was provided by both the international committee and the program committee. The members of the local organizing committee, and especially the conference secretary, Barbara Schmiedt, are to be commended for their indefatigable efforts to make this conference in the beautiful Alpine county of Berchtesgaden as pleasant and effective as possible.

The fifth conference in this series is scheduled to take place in Jeffersonville, Vermont, July 23-27, 1984, under the chairmanship of Robert Brown of IBM, Burlington. This conference will continue the trend towards greater user participation, and calls for papers dealing with practical aspects of equipment and techniques in the field of ion implantation.

Munich, January 1983 *Heiner Ryssel and Hans Glawischnig*

Contents

Part I Ion Implanters

Part II Ion Sources

Part III Implanter Subsystems

Part IV Special Implantation Techniques

Part V Ion Beam Lithography

Part VI Measuring Techniques

Part VII Implantation into Metals

Part VIII Implantation into Semiconductors

Part IX Transient Annealing

Part I

Ion Implanters

Physical Limitations of Ion Implantation Equipment

P.R. Hanley

Varian Associates/Extrion Division, Blackburn Industrial Park,
Gloucester, MA 01930, USA

1. Introduction

When the physical limitations of ion implantation systems are examined, several constraints related to the generation, analysis and scanning of energetic ion beams can be readily identified which will clearly limit the performance of this equipment. These constraints will probably be relevant to most applications of the ion implantation technique.

The most notable success of ion implantation has been in semiconductor wafer fabrication where the installed base of equipment exceeds 1,000 systems worldwide. For this application, the handling time per wafer is as fundamental a physical limitation as the time to implant a wafer and may well be more restrictive. Wegmann [1] noted that wafer handling may have been the deciding factor in the relative success of a particular equipment design being widely accepted for industrial production applications.

Because the reproducibility of implanted dose from wafer to wafer and the uniformity of dose across the wafer are two of the major advantages of ion implantation, uniformity considerations limit the minimum time required to implant a wafer as discussed by Turner [2]. As semiconductor doping applications have extended to the high dose region above 1×10^{15} atoms/cm^2, high beam powers have become common. Freeman [3] proposed scanning a batch of wafers through a stationary beam to reduce the temperature rise resulting from the kinetic energy lost by the ions when stopping in the wafer. Recent developments reported by Current, Perloff and Gutai [4] suggest that the allowable temperature rise during implantation may be considerably less than was previously believed. Dopant activation appears to be highly sensitive to the temperature during implantation for the case of high dose implants. Several other dose-rate dependent effects may operate to limit the practical application of this equipment, such as photoresist outgassing and insulator charging.

Although some of these effects may prove to be unimportant in the newer applications such as insulator formation by implantation and metallurgical materials modification, they will probably operate to limit the maximum performance of implanters designed specifically for semiconductor doping. It is likely that an entirely new generation of equipment using considerably higher beam currents will be required to economically pursue these new applications where the required doses are typically one or two orders of magnitude above the highest doses presently used for doping. This discussion will be primarily directed to ion implantation for semiconductor applications, specifically the doping of silicon wafers up to 150 mm in diameter with the common dopants of boron, phosphorous, arsenic and antimony. The results of these specific analyses will then be generalized to other applications of ion implantation.

2. Implant Parameters

The ion implantation process affords precise control of several physical parameters which are of critical significance to the doping of semiconductors. Energy and dose can be independently selected to control with excellect predictability the dopant concentration as a function of depth for the implanted species in the substrate. This major advantage of ion implantation over thermal diffusion has contributed prominently to the acceptance of implantation as an industrial process. Measuring the charge incident on the wafer allows the dose to be precisely reproduced, wafer to wafer and day to day. The fact that each ion carries a positive charge enables the dopant atoms to be accelerated to a precise energy, analyzed, and scanned uniformly across the wafer.

2.1 Species Selection

Ion beams which are to be used to dope semiconductors are subjected to analysis prior to scanning the ion beam over the wafer. By passing the ion beam through a magnetic field, the ions are dispersed according to their momentum and unwanted ion species are rejected at a defining slit. Therefore, an ion can be selected in the dimension ME/q^2 where M is the ion mass, E is the ion energy and q is the ionic charge number.

Analysis of the ion beam is necessary because the extracted beam usually contains several atomic and molecular ion species which are produced by ionization of the feed gas as well as sputtered ions from the discharge chamber; specifically the filament and arc chamber. It is the presence of these heavy metal contaminants which is the primary motivation to analyze ion beams for semiconductor applications. When the feed gas is changed to obtain a different ion species, a strong memory effect is usually present because of the residual pressure of the prior feed gas. A typical mass spectrum is shown in Figure 1 for BF_3. The presence of a $^{31}P^+$ next to the $^{11}B^{19}F^+$ peak is attributed to memory effect in the source from a previous implant.

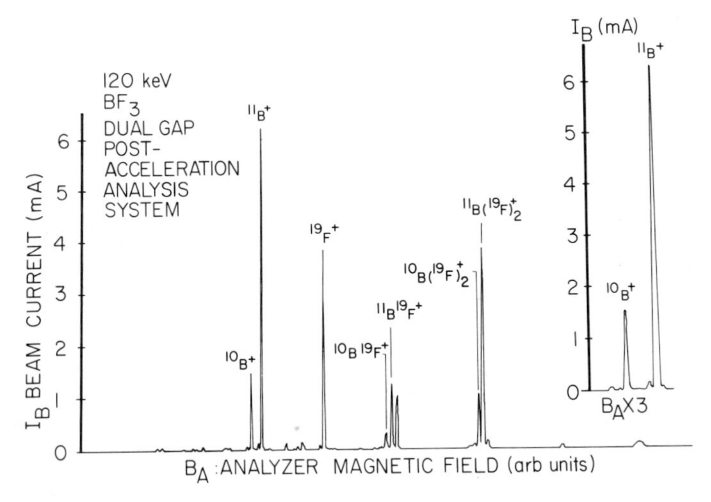

Figure 1. Mass Spectrum. Beam Current as a function of analyzer magnetic field for BF_3 at 120 keV in a dual gap post-acceleration analysis system

Undesirable molecular ions with the same momentum as the desired species can occasionally be selected by the analyzer: the classic case being $^{12}C^{19}F^+$ ions which are selected as well as the desired $^{31}P^+$. Another example is the fact that doubly charged beams like $^{75}As^{++}$ have nearly the same momentum as $^{75}As^+$ of half energy which have dissociated from the diatomic molecular ion $^{75}As_2^+$ by collisions with residual gas molecules in the high gas pressure region immediately after the ion source. As is well known in mass spectrometer design, the only way to avoid this problem is to add another dispersive element in the form of a an electric field which selects ions in the dimension E/q or by passing the ions through a velocity filter such as a crossed field analyzer (refer to Jamba [5]).

In the early days of implantation, the relative merits of performing analysis prior to the final acceleration (pre-acceleration analysis) or after the final acceleration (post-acceleration analysis) was a subject of some controversy [1]. Packaging considerations aside, post-analysis systems offer a major benefit when implanting with molecular ions to minimize the range of a given species. A typical example is implantation with BF_2^+ to make shallow boron junctions. If molecular ions collide with residual gas molecules and dissociate after analysis, then this can have undesirable consequences in pre-analysis systems where most of the energy gain is obtained after analysis. The molecular ion fragments (some of which are typically monatomic ions of the desired dopant species) are accelerated to energies comparable to the total energy and penetrate to far greater depths than the desired molecular ion. (Consider implanting with BF_2^+ at an energy of 135 keV where 35 keV acceleration is provided before analysis and 100 keV after analysis. The dissociated B^+ fragment would be accelerated to 108 keV which would have a much larger range than the BF_2^+.) This can only be avoided by minimizing the residual gas pressure in the acceleration region.

Although memory effects in the ion source can be easily avoided by analysis, cross contamination from sputtered components of previous implants are considerably harder to avoid. This effect has been identified in high dose As implants which are particularly susceptible to P cross contamination. Fair and Meyer [6] have reported that the co-diffusion of P in a high concentration As background in Si results in significantly enhanced diffusion. This effect is commonly observed in high current batch process machines where the wafers are mounted on a disc and the beam is scanned across the disc or the disc across the wafers. In either case, a substantial fraction of the implanted As ions incident on the surface of the disc sputter previously implanted P atoms from the surface. Sputtered low energy atoms are deposited on the surface of the wafers and then driven at anomalously high diffusion rates by subsequent high temperature processing. These effects can be avoided by thin screening oxides which can be etched away prior to subsequent thermal treatment. When implanting through an oxide is undesirable, this cross contamination can be avoided by dedicating discs to a given ion species. Secondary ion mass spectrometry has shown that this cross contamination phenomenon can be avoided in a dual end station system by isolating the vacuum system of one end station from the other by an isolation valve while the implant process is proceeding. It is interesting to note that simply dedicating an end station is not sufficient to avoid cross contamination if the end station vacuum systems are pumping in parallel on the beam line during implantation. Cross contamination effects have been observed under these conditions which were eliminated by isolating the end stations; an effect attributed to the migration of sputtered neutrals through the vacuum system [7].

Modern implanter systems are now constructed with a careful selection of materials used on slits, apertures and wave guide liners to avoid the sputtering of undesirable atoms like Fe and Cr on the surface of the wafers. In post-analysis systems, the sputtered ions from the analysis region do not receive further acceleration as in a pre-analysis system. The addition of a neutral trap formed by introducing a deliberate angular offset in the beam line can minimize neutral atoms which are sputtered from the materials of the wave guide liners and slits. Sodium contamination has been observed in a double mechanical scanned system which is closely coupled to the analyzing region with a short beam line in a pre-analysis configuration [8]. Subsequently it was found that sodium contamination was reduced by the incorporation of a neutral trap into this equipment.

Although the above phenomena represent difficulties in determining the precise identity of the implanted species, most of the problems discussed above can be eliminated or minimized with clever design. It is likely that some type of analysis will be required for most semiconductor processing and there is no evidence that this need for analysis will place fundamental physical limitations on the ultimate performance of equipment designed for this application. For metals applications (where the presence of trace impurities would probably not be significant and where the beam currents will have to increase proportionately to the required dose, i.e. one or two orders of magnitude), the need for an additional crossover at the rejection slit may impose a significant physical limitation which should probably be avoided.

2.2 Energy

The ballistic nature of the implantation process allows the dopant depth distribution to be designed [9]. Until recently, this ability has been severely restricted by the need to anneal the implant damage and activate the implanted dopant by high temperature processing in a furnace. Recent advances in annealing technology have been developed which minimize the redistribution of the implanted dopant [10]. As device geometry shrinks, the trend in high dose implantation will be towards shallower junctions [11].

Earlier n-channel MOS source and drain implants were done through relatively thick screening oxide layers which had the beneficial effect of minimizing contamination problems. Recently, a study of the characteristics of MOS devices for As^+ implants through various thicknesses of screen oxide has been reported [12]. This work investigated the effect of oxygen-recoil induced damage clusters on device performance. It was shown that thick oxides produce more recoils and higher leakage currents. Therefore, it is likely that future screening oxides will be thinner and this may cause a trend towards lower energies for n-channel source and drain implants.

It is possible to form concentrations of dopants in silicon above the solubility limits. Implantation is not subject to equilibrium solubility considerations as dopant atoms can remain in metastable sites in the lattice. During activation and annealing, concentrations that are above the solubility limit will either redistribute deeper in the silicon until they can be activated or they will cluster [10]. This is the basis of the predeposition implant process, which (except for the need to penetrate a screening oxide) can be done at relatively low energies [13] [14]. Consequently, most of the high dose implant applications are accessible to relatively low energy machines.

Historically, the serial process machines rated at 200 keV have adequate energy to perform the majority of implants that are required. Supplemented by high current batch process machines up to 120 keV, most of the routine implants required today in Si can be performed. These energies are readily obtained by air insulation in pre-acceleration systems up to 200 keV and in high current post-acceleration systems up to 120 keV. Techniques of pre-acceleration analysis with air insulation can be extended up to the 400 keV and perhaps to 500 keV range. For higher energies, air insulation becomes impractical because of the large sizes involved. Production applications are emerging to implant p wells at energies at or above these levels. Other specialized implantations may require energies approaching the MeV range. A broad range of pressurized accelerators in both single-ended and tandem configuration are capable of producing relatively large quantities of common dopants with current ranges of up to 100 uA which would allow economically practical implants at doses of 1 x 10^{14} atoms/cm^2 with this type of equipment. There is no limit in practice up to the several MeV range to the energy that can be achieved with ion implanters and development of higher energy machines requires only a demonstrated need in the market.

2.3 Dose

The reproducibility of the implanted dose of the desired dopant species depends on the fact that each atom carries a charge and the total charge incident on the wafer can be measured by integrating the beam current to the specified dose. Usually, the wafer and its supports form the end of a deep biased Faraday cup preceded by a beam limiting grounded aperture. Proper Faraday cup design will minimize leakage of secondary electrons and secondary positive ions. Less common are sampling techniques such as corner cup integration where Faraday cups are located at the corners of the ground mask over which the ion beam is scanned in two dimensions by transverse time-varying electric fields. The beam is monitored in four individual small Faraday cups and their currents can be compared as a useful monitor of the scan uniformity and the adequacy of overscan. Another sampling method described by Ryding and Farley [15] has been applied to a dual mechanically scanned batch process implanter of the disc type. Although full-time measurement systems may be preferable in theory, good dose uniformity results have been demonstrated by both full-time and sampling methods. Electron flood devices are now in use which provide a source of low energy electrons, either from direct extraction from a filament or by secondary electrons which are formed from bombarding the Faraday walls with energetic primary electrons [16]. Circulating electron currents can be as high as an order of magnitude above the ion beam currents that are being measured, and thus provide an excellent test of the adequacy of the Faraday design to suppress electron leakage, as reported by Turner [17]. Consequently, the design of the Faraday system itself will probably not be a fundamental limitation on the dose reproducibility and uniformity of semiconductor implanter equipment. In most of the other applications, dose reproducibility and uniformity are not so stringent, and these considerations will be relatively less important.

The major physical constraint to the performance of a dose system lies in its inability to detect a neutral atom of the desired dopant species. Some charge exchange with the residual gas of the vacuum system as the beam passes through the implanter is inevitable. The higher the beam current the more difficult this residual vacuum is to control. In pre-analysis systems without a neutral trap, there is direct line of sight between the exit of the analyzer and the wafers to be implanted. When scanning is accomplished by a dual mechanical system which moves the wafers in two dimensions with respect to a stationary beam, the dose uniformity across the wafer will be unaffected by the presence of neutrals, but the total dose will be higher than the charge measured by the integrator. The measured sheet resistance for a given dose setting will decrease as the beamline pressure increases. This is a fundamental limitation in systems that do not incorporate a neutral trap.

In pre-analysis configurations where the beam is scanned by two-dimensional time-varying electric fields, and where a neutral trap is incorporated in the scanner, neutralization of the beam in the region after scanning will produce dose changes similar to those observed in the batch machine but the uniformity will not be affected. Similar considerations apply to hybrid magnetic-mechanical scanning systems for neutralization which occurs downstream from the last bending element [18]. Although careful designs of differential pumping systems can minimize this effect, neutralization of the primary ion beam may be a limiting consideration in photoresist applications of high dose implanters.

2.4 Temperature

When wafers are implanted with high power ion beams, the temperature rise of the wafer must be held within typically 100 C° to preserve the integrity of the resist pattern. Considerable progress has been made on this problem recently which will be reported by Smith [19]. Techniques now exist to maintain the temperature rise during implantation within acceptable limits for very high power beams which will be mentioned in Section 6. These breakthroughs have eased an important constraint in the use of serial process implanters for high dose photoresist applications.

3. Throughput Considerations

The dominant economic performance parameter of an implantation system is throughput in wafers per hour. When the present generation of high current batch process ion implanters was being designed, Rose [20] argued that doses greater than 1×10^{15} at/cm^2 (100 mm diameter wafers) were inaccessible to the high current machines of that time which delivered 2 mA of useable beam. In 1978, serial process implanter systems typically produced scanned beam currents of 0.5 mA so this argument should logically apply to these systems at doses that would be lower by a factor of four. For this case, the implant is clearly beam-current limited. From the equation for implant time (t in seconds),

$$t = eDA/I,$$

where e is the charge in coulombs per atom, D is the dose in atoms/cm^2, A is the implant area in cm^2 and I is the current in coulombs/second. (For $D = 1 \times 10^{15}$ and I = 0.5 mA, the implant time is 29.4 seconds.) From the relationship for throughput (TP in wafers/hours),

$$TP = 3600/(t_i + t_v + t_h),$$

where t_i is the implant time, t_v is the vacuum pump down time, and t_h is the wafer handling time, all in seconds. For serial process implanters, (circa. 1978), t_v and t_h sum to approximately eight seconds and with the calculated value of t_i we can see that the throughput would be 96 wafers per hour. This is a reasonably high throughput compared to 200 wafers/hour at the mechanical handling limit, and the implant is clearly accessible to this type of equipment. Rose's argument is a practical one: as the dose increases up to 1×10^{16} atoms/cm^2, the implant time increases and the throughput reduces to the point where the process is uneconomic.

3.1 Serial Process Systems

The throughput performance of serial process implanters that were at the state of the art in 1978 is plotted in Figure 2. This figure should be compared to Figure 1 from the paper by Namba [11] which relates applications in semiconductor device processing to the required ion dose. As can be seen from this comparison, all of the first and some of the second generation applications can be economically addressed by this type of equipment. For doses near 1×10^{16}, the throughput drops to 12 wafers per hour which is clearly uneconomic. In 1978, serial process machines typically required minimum implant times of 10 seconds to achieve the specified dose uniformity across the wafer. This is related to the type of scan control used to program the two-dimensional time-varying electric fields. In 1980, Turner [2] reported on improved crystal controlled scan generator which gave the specified uniformity for five second implants. This development increased the throughput at the mechanical handling limit to 275 (100 mm) wafers per hour. Subsequently in 1981 the scan beam current of these machines was increased by a factor of three to 1.5 mA for P^+ and As^+ for energies above 120 keV. These machines could then compete quite successfully with batch process systems up to doses of 3×10^{15} atoms/cm^2. The present generation of high current batch process ion implanter systems are designed to address the portion of the throughput-dose space indicated by the shaded area. The developments in 1981 on serial process systems have reduced that area still further.

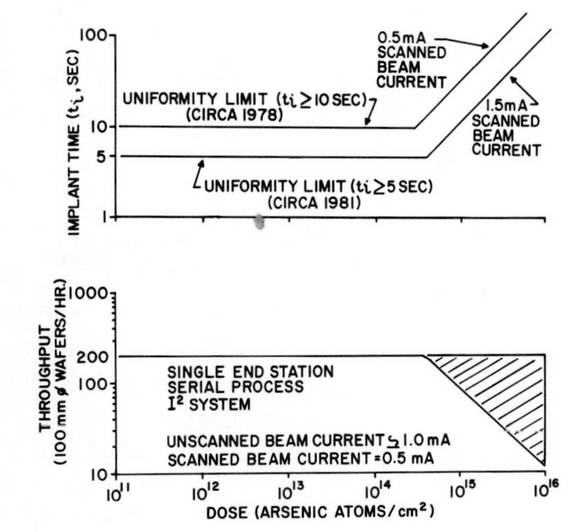

Figure 2. Throughput as a function of dose. Single end station serial process ion implanter system (circa 1978) with casstte to cassette autoloaders

An important question to consider is if further developments will allow serial process to compete economically with batch process at high doses, or if physical limitations will preclude the further development of these systems beyond their present capabilities.

3.2 Batch Process Systems

The present performance of batch process systems is compared to serial process systems in Figure 3. The throughput-dose space has expanded in both dimensions. Maximum doses for n dopants are now typically 2×10^{16} at/cm^2. The wafer handling limits have been extended for both serial and batch machines up to 350 and 400 (100 mm diameter) wafers per hour, respectively. Both these systems employ dual end stations to achieve higher throughputs at the mechanical handling limit. The current shown on the serial process system is the same as in 1981 at 3 mA unscanned and the equivalent current for the batch process system has increased to 12.5 mA. In the beam-current-limited region the throughput difference at a given dose is nearly proportional to the difference in unscanned beam current and the small discrepancy is caused by the higher scanning efficiency of the dual row disc used in the batch system. On this figure, the shaded area represents the portion of the throughput-dose space which can be accessed by increasing the beam current of the batch process system. The region above and to the right of the 3 mA limitation of the serial processing system represents the region of that space accessible to the serial process system if the beam current can be increased.

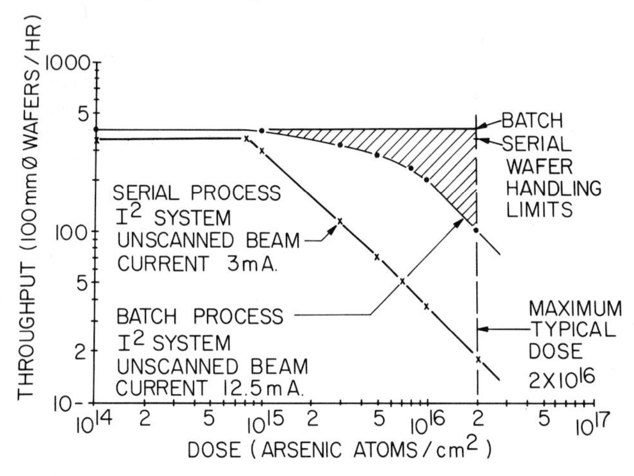

Figure 3. Throughput as a function of dose. Comparison for dual end Station ion implanter systems with cassette to cassette autoloaders $^{75}As^{+}$ at 120 keV for 100 mm ø wafers

3.3 Wafer Handling and Pumping

Serial process implanters are limited in their pump down time by the desorption of water vapor from wafers entering the vacuum system and from the lock materials which are exposed to ambient atmosphere. Conventional gravity fed load lock systems expose the lock materials for a minimum time to atmosphere, resulting in a minimum adsorption of water vapor. The dominating desorption is from the wafer itself, and the vacuum cycle time is strongly influenced by the lock roughing time. Once the lock is opened, the vacuum burst into the system typically pumps down in less than two seconds and the implant is allowed to proceed. Since there are two locks and an implant platen, parallel operations are possible. The exit lock can vent, unload and pump down while the platen is loading and implanting. The entrance lock can load and pump down while the wafer is implanting and dumping. The average time to complete a handling and venting cycle is eight seconds per wafer; and for a ten second implant, the throughput is 200 wafers per hour. By reducing the minimum implant time to five seconds the throughput can be increased to 275 wafers per hour.

The mechanical handling limit of a serial process ion implanter can be increased by employing a dual end station as described by Turner and Dinaro [21]. In this system, a single lock is employed for each end station and the lock is exposed to air during unloading and loading. Independent wafer and cassette transport is provided for each end station so that operations can proceed in parallel. For this system, the cycle time is 10.25 seconds and includes an allowed time for implant which exceeds the minimum required for uniformity. Pump down is performed by a multiple expansion tank and a cryo panel is used for pumping condensables. Wafer handling time is slightly longer than in the gravity fed load lock system described previously, but now the implants can proceed in foreground while the alternate end station is unloading, reloading and roughing in background. The result is a throughput of 350 wafers per hour which will be essentially independent of wafer size providing that 25 wafers can be loaded into the cassette.

For a dual end station batch process system, similar handling wafer constraints will apply. For a given throughput, the number of vacuum cycles will be inversely proportional to the batch size (N). In these systems, the entire implant disc and chamber are opened to ambient during unloading and loading. Therefore, larger batches will require the chamber to be open for a longer time for wafer handling which will increase the time to pump down, as shown in Figure 4. These two effects have to be carefully balanced and represent a fundamental limitation on the throughput of batch process systems. If the implant could be performed with no loss of dose reproducibility at 2×10^{-5} torr, then this constraint could be eased considerably.

For a batch of 25 wafers, typical values of t_v and t_h each are 210 seconds with an autoloaded system. Therefore, for a 30 second minimum

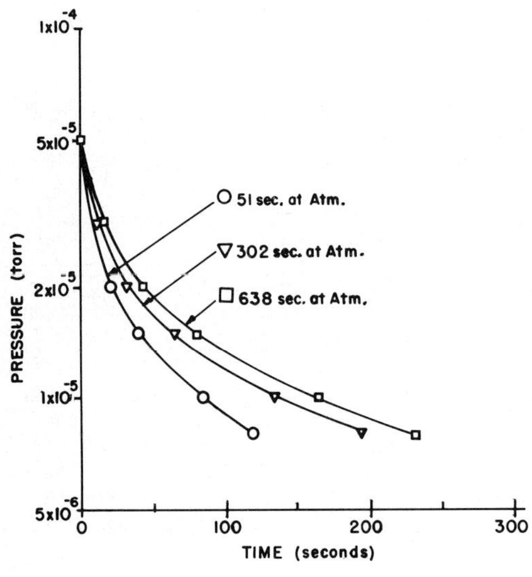

Figure 4. Pressure as a function of time. Pumpdown of a cryopumped batch end station (N=25) after exposure to atmosphere

implant time (which represents the period of one scan cycle at the minimum acceptable scan rate) throughput can be shown to be:

$$TP = 3600 \times z \times N/(t_i + t_v + t_h)$$

where z is the number of end stations, N is the number of wafers per batch and the other symbols are as previously defined. For this example of t (cycle) = 450 seconds, z = 2, and N = 25, the throughput is 400 wafers per hour. These timing considerations are shown in Figure 5 for three different relationships between t_i and $t_v + t_h$. For $t_i \ll t_v + t_h$, the implanter is idling while the loading and vacuum cycles are being completed (represented by Δ_{vh}). When $t_i = t_v + t_h$ the system is perfectly matched and the implanter is being used 100% of the time as are the handler and vacuum systems. When $t_i > t_v + t_h$, the handler and vacuum stations are idling (represented by Δ_i) while the implanter is proceeding. Although this diagram was developed for the batch system, it applies equally well to the serial process dual end station system.

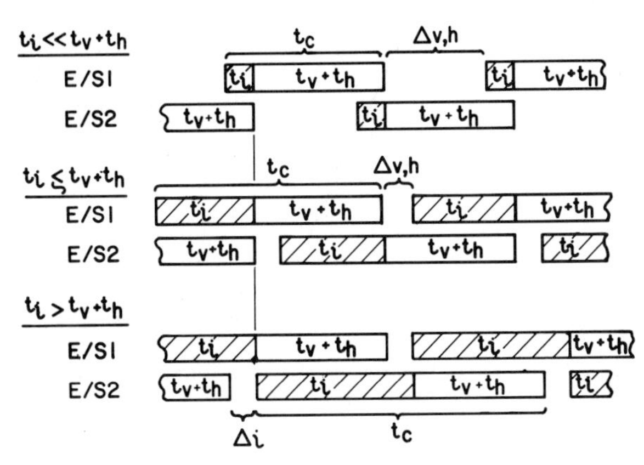

Figure 5. Timing chart. Illustrating the relationships between t_v, t_h and t_i for a dual end station implanter

It was previously stated that wafer handling time may be as fundamental a physical constraint as implant time. Handling time per wafer is very similar in gravity fed serial, dual end station serial, and dual end station batch systems and the average is approximately eight seconds per wafer. If a time and motion study is performed on the wafer handling, it appears likely that there will be diminishing returns in trying to further improve the wafer handling limit of ion implantation systems. Considerable improvements remain to be made in the vacuum pumping performance of batch process machines, and it is likely that this performance will be considerably improved when the next generation of ion implanter systems is developed.

3.4 Beam Current

Wegmann [1] believed that the steady increase in beam currents that has been observed might eventually be limited not by the ion sources but by

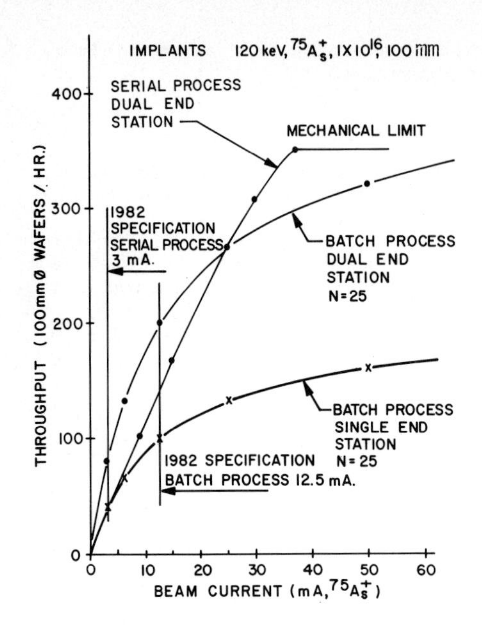

Figure 6. Throughput as a function of beam current. Comparison of the effect of beam current on throughput of single batch, dual batch and dual serial end station ion implanter systems. For a direct comparison, the single end station batch system calculated is identical to the dual system in all other parameters

wafer cooling. It now appears that wafer cooling will not be the limitation. A related question might be: How much beam current is enough? Figure 6 illustrates throughput in 100 mm wafers per hour at a dose of 1 x 10^{16} atoms/cm^2 as a function of unscanned beam current of As^+ for batch and serial systems. The relative benefits of increasing beam current are dramatically illustrated. In the case of the batch process machines, typical systems have a beam current specification of 12.5 mA. If this current were to double to 25 mA, the throughput of these machines would only increase by 33%. If the current were doubled again to 50 mA, the throughput would only increase by 60% for a current increase of a factor of four. For infinite beam currents, the throughput would only increase by 100%. Conversely, for the serial process dual end station system, a beam current increase of a factor of 10 would result in a gain of nearly a factor of 10 in throughput. Clearly, the batch process systems are approaching or are at a point of diminishing returns for further increases in beam current, while considerable gains remain to be achieved in serial process systems. The physical parameters which govern the beam optics of ion implantation systems will now be examined to identify constraints limiting beam current.

4. Ion Optical Limitations

Each of the ion optical elements in an ion implanter system places physical restraints on the performance of the system, as each of these elements has a finite aperture. The beam size must be carefully matched to the available aperture in all of the elements to avoid interference which would reduce the available current. An additional complication is caused by the fact that most systems must operate over a dynamic range of at least one order of magnitude of energy and with dopant ions whose mass varies by an order of magnitude (from boron to antimony). In order to perform high quality implantations at low dose, the beam current must have a dynamic range of at least three orders of magnitude. Finally, the ion beam must be presented to the scanning system such that the beam can be uniformly averaged over the wafers without significantly deteriorating in optical quality. Taken together, these requirements place severe constraints on the ion optical design.

4.1 Ion Source and Extraction Optics

Ion sources were recently reviewed by Aitken [22]. Most modern implanter systems use hot cathode arc discharge ion sources where the ionizing electrons are thermionically emitted from a directly heated filament and accelerated to an arc potential of approximately 100 volts. These electrons initiate and sustain the discharge by ionizing molecules of a feed gas, and the discharge is immersed in a magnet field applied along the length of the filament. Ions are extracted from the side of the arc chamber from a slit parallel to the filament and with dimensions which range from 1 to 3 mm in width and from 10 to 90 mm in length depending upon the current desired. Positive ions are typically extracted from the discharge by a three-electrode ion extraction system whose dimensions are highly asymmetric to match the asymmetry of the arc chamber slit. As might be expected, the extracted ion beam is strongly divergent across the narrow dimension of the slit (which is defined as the X direction), and weakly divergent in the dimension along the length of the slit (which is designated as the Y direction). The coordinate Z is reserved for the axial dimension along the beam line. In order to perform a parametric analysis of the performance of the source-extraction system, it is necessary to have a quantitative comparison of the properties of the ion beam as the source parameters and extraction geometries are varied. This type of quantitative comparison can be provided by an automated emittance measuring device, as described by Thompson, Honjo and Turner [23]. Figures 7a and 7b are the results of measurements made on a relatively small slit geometry which delivered a beam of Ar^+ at approximately 10 mA. The 20% intensity contours are labeled A through E.

The most striking feature of these emittance measurements is the high degree of asymmetry in size and angle which is evident by comparing the X-X' and Y-Y' results. By shaping the contours of the facing positive and negative electrodes in the three-electrode ion extraction system, it is

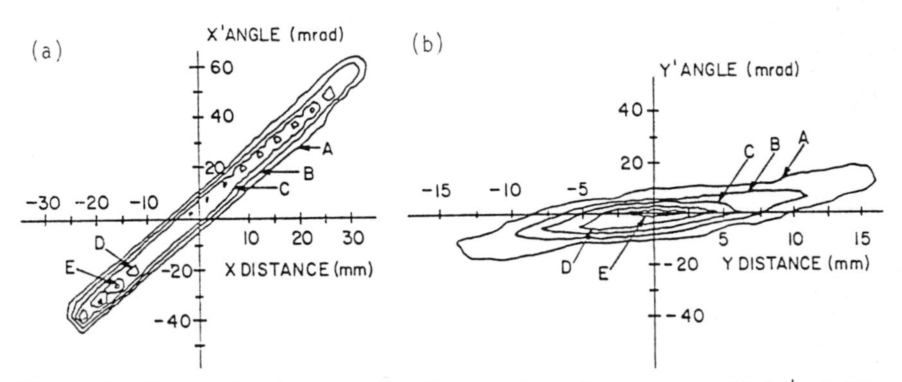

Figure 7. Measured emittance of a Freeman-type ion source. 40 Ar^+ at 35 keV with Arc V = 78V, Arc I = 3.0 A, Extraction I = 13 mA, Source Magnet = 0.9 A, unanalyzed. a. Dispersive plane of analyser, measured before analysis. b. Y-Y' plane, normal to X, where Z is the axial coordinate

possible to dramatically alter the divergence angle of the beam extracted from the source. This effect can be used in the low divergence Y direction to force the beam to be net convergent thereby eliminating the need for additional focusing in this plane [18]. The extraction optics in the X-Z plane can be modeled by computer calculations which include the effects of space charge expansion [23]. A typical calculation is shown in Figure 8a for a model of the source which was measured in Figure 7. An equivalent emittance plot in the X-X' plane is shown for this calculation in Figure 8b which should be compared with Figure 7a. There is reasonable agreement between the calculated and measured values which enables computer modeling to proceed with some confidence. Ion sources which are routinely used in production can produce in excess of 20 mA of Ar^+ from a slit 2.5 mm wide and 40 mm long. Measurements of ion beams extracted from these types of sources suggest that it may be possible to increase beam current from these systems up to 50 mA for a representative species like Ar^+. Therefore, it is unlikely that high current ion implanters for semiconductor applications will be physically limited by the beam current available from the ion source.

For applications where the required dose is one or two orders of magnitude above that required for semiconductor dopants, different ion source geometries will probably be required. Sources which use microwave power to produce ionization in a discharge chamber with subsequent

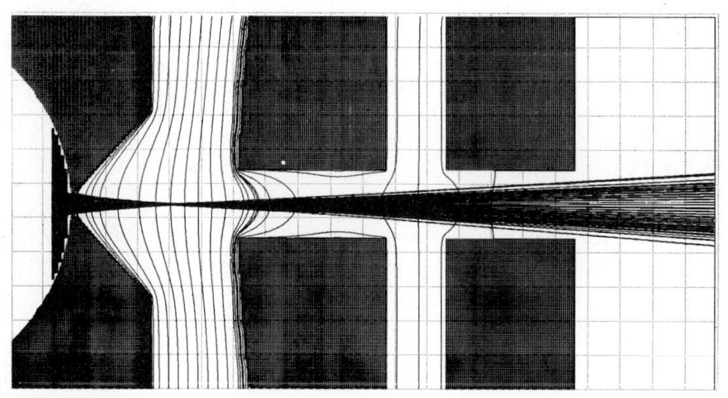

a

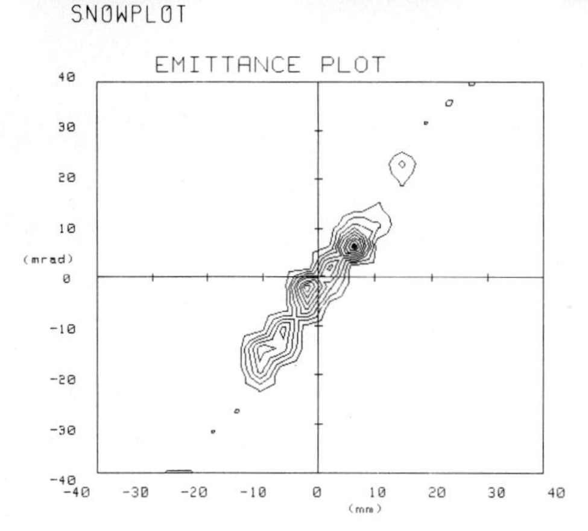

b

Figure 8. Space charge calculations of the extraction region compared with measurements. a. Extraction region calculations. b. Calculated emmittance in the X-X' plane

extraction from a slit may offer some advantages for high current applications [22]. Multiple aperture sources are practical for currents up to 100 mA and these may be suitable for use with unanalyzed implanters for metallurgical applications.

4.2 Acceleration

If the beam current of an implanter system is measured over a broad dynamic range in energy, a characteristic curve is produced. Figure 9 compares the beam current as a function of energy for pre- and post-acceleration analysis systems. At the maximum energy, the beam current is relatively insensitive to changes in energy. At about 2/3 of the maximum energy, the beam current becomes proportional to $E^{3/2}$. This functional dependence is the result of the ion beam expanding under its space charge forces until it intercepts the finite apertures of the optical elements. In the region where the current is insensitive to energy, the beam is emission limited from the ion source. For both the pre-acceleration and post-acceleration analysis systems that are shown, beam currents are measured after transport through the entire optical system. The optical transmission efficiency can be estimated by summing the measured beam currents on target of all the individual ion species and comparing this value with the extraction power supply current drain. For a properly operating system, these efficiencies can be as high as 80 or 90%.

Secondary electrons are created by collisions of the edge of the primary beam with slits and apertures, and by collisions with the residual gas. These low energy electrons are trapped in the potential well of the ion beam and tend to screen the self-forces exerted by the ions within the beam. Consequently, one of the major advantages of post-acceleration analysis systems which do not employ transverse electric fields for

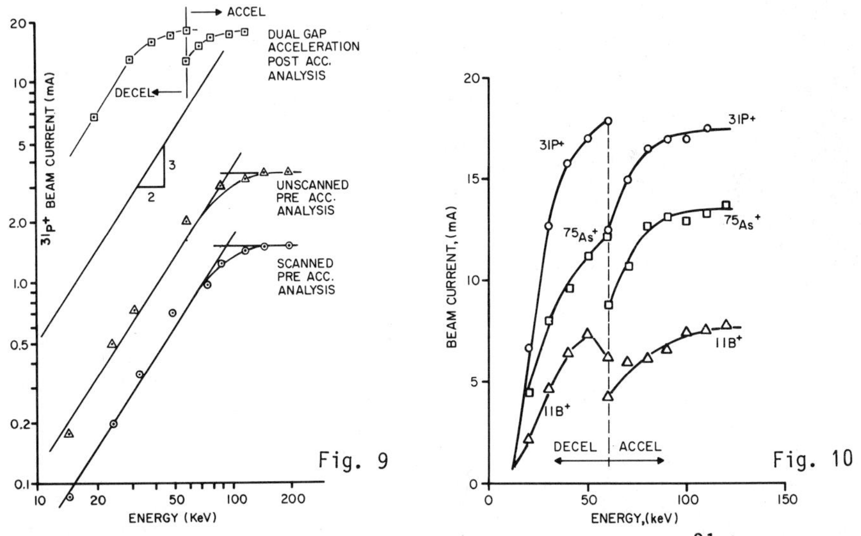

Figure 9. Beam current as a function of energy. Measured $^{31}P^{+}$ beam current for pre-and post-acceleration analysis ion implanter systems

Figure 10. Beam current as a function of energy. Measured beam current for a post-acceleration analysis ion implanter system illustrating the effect of a dual gap (ACCEL-DECEL) accelerator

scanning is that the beam can be effectively space-charged compensated from source to Faraday. The negative extraction electrode forms an electron reflector near the source and the negative bias on the Faraday cup provides an electron reflector at the opposite end. This configuration works well up to energies of 60 or 80 keV. For higher energies, voltage breakdown problems can occur in the high field region between the source and the extractor. In order to avoid this problem, an additional electrode can be inserted between the positive source and the negative electrode. It is important that the grading of this intermediate electrode be maintained by a low impedance for charges of either sign, as it is subject to bombardment by positive ions from the source and by electrons from the negative electrode. Performance of this configuration is shown in Figure 10 for the common dopants [24]. In this example, DECEL mode applies an independent constant voltage between the positive and negative electrodes. The ion energy is independently established by controlling the potential between the positive electrode and ground. (Refer to Figure 8a.) The ACCEL mode has two electrodes inserted between the positive and negative electrodes. The first is held at a potential such as to maintain a constant extraction field between this electrode and the source, the second electrode is grounded, and the negative electrode then acts as an electron barrier. The performance of this configuration is shown on the right-hand side of Figure 10. This technology operates well up to 120 keV and may well be able to be extended to higher energies. In this case, the ion source and extraction electrodes constitute a non-uniform field multiple-gap acceleration tube. This system now begins to resemble the post-acceleration analysis systems of an earlier era, but at significantly higher beam currents than were previously thought possible.

Pre-acceleration analysis systems employ an extraction and analysis module similar to the single-gap version of the system described previously. Space charge compensation is an important aspect in these machines in the region between the negative extraction electrode and the entrance to the acceleration tube which is usually located downstream from the analyzer slit. Since this entire system is elevated at positive potential, electrons which are formed by collisions in the region downstream from the negative extraction electrode cannot leak to ground. However, once the ion beam enters the axial electric field of the acceleration tube, space charge compensation is entirely eliminated. Electrons which are created in the axial field are immediately accelerated to high energies and lose their usefulness to screen the positive charges in the beam from each other. Typically, the last active electrode of the acceleration tube is negatively biased to act as an electron reflector for electrons which are produced at ground potential. The expansion of the ion beam during acceleration is a primary physical limitation to the high current performance of pre-acceleration analysis systems.

Another disturbing feature of this configuration is the variability of the optical properties of the acceleration tube when the energy is varied over a broad dynamic range. Figure 11 illustrates two configurations of the acceleration tube where attempts have been made to apply the field to obtain the best optical result. The number of elements that must be involved in the acceleration depends upon the axial gradient which can be sustained by the acceleration tube. For Figure 11a, the energy before acceleration was 25 keV and the beam was accelerated to 120 keV. The optical effects of this acceleration are evident. Clearly, the beam would have a much larger radial extent at the exit of the tube if the field had not been present. Figure 11b represents the situation where the beam is being decelerated by the application of a retarding field across a small section of the tube. These cases illustrate the strong optical properties

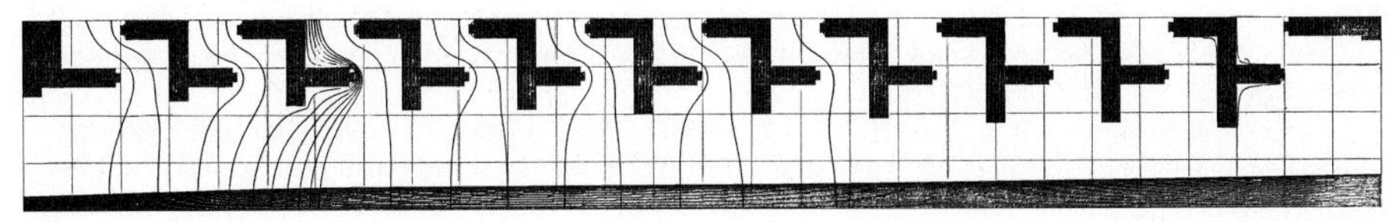

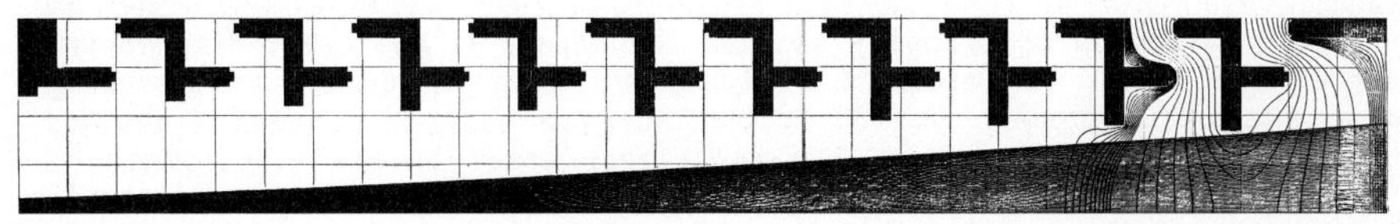

Figure 11. Space charge calculations of an acceleration tube. a. Acceleration, $E_f > E_i$. b. Deceleration, $E_f < E_i$

inherent in the acceleration process and demonstrate the need for an additional independently variable optical element to compensate for the changing optical properties as the energy is varied over a broad dynamic range. Because of beam utilization and overscanning constraints, it is undesirable to allow the beam to change size in an uncontrolled manner as the energy is changed. Therefore, an additional independently variable optical element is usually placed after the acceleration tube, such as a quadrupole doublet with the asymmetry of the quadrupole selected to offset the asymmetry inherent in the ion beam. When an electrostatic quadrupole is employed, the transverse electric fields eliminate the electrons required for space charge compensation in the beam. Under most conditions the beam reaches its maximum size in the quadrupole and this is very often the limiting optical element of the system. The operation of these two optical elements represents the major physical limitation to the beam current capability of pre-acceleration analysis systems. The task of providing higher beam currents through this type of equipment is concentrated on these two optical elements.

5. Scanning

Turner [2] recently reviewed various beam scanning techniques. His criteria for scan systems are: that they must provide an adequate number of beam passes across the wafer to provide a uniform dopant distribution, that the scanning rate of the beam at the wafer surface be uniform (or controlled by the current measured on the wafer), and that there be a reasonable beam utilization. The various beam scanning techniques employ a combination of electric fields, magnetic fields and mechanical displacement in the two dimensions X and Y. The major advantage of mechanical displacement and magnetic fields is that they do not interfere with the space charge compensation of the ion beam by low energy electrons which is a disadvantage of transverse electric field scanning systems. These effects can be minimized because the ion beam is typically large in the electric field scanner plates and the beam has been accelerated to its full energy so that space charge forces will be minimized. In addition, electron reflectors can be installed at either end of the scanner plates so that the positive scanning plates will not act as a sink to pump electrons out of the beam. If these precautions are taken, considerably higher beam currents than had previously been believed can be scanned effectively by this technique.

The frequency of scanning systems is limited by stored energy considerations. These limitations are related to the energy stored in the plate capacity of electric field systems, in the gap of magnetic field systems, and in the inertia of mechanical systems. For all scanning systems, the two orthogonal directions in motion are scanned at very different frequencies and are typically different by one or two orders of magnitude. This is done to insure the beam spot overlaps many times in the slow direction of scanning so that the dopant is uniformly distributed across the wafer. In electric field systems, one frequency is typically at 1 kHz and the other is 100 Hz. Disc-type batch end station designs obtain the high frequency by the rotational speed of the disc, which is typically 16 Hz. This implies that the slow direction of scanning should be of order between 0.1 and 1 Hz. For these frequencies, both magnetic field scanning and mechanical displacement have proven to be acceptable methods of scanning. In both cases, the scanning rate is preprogrammed to minimize effects caused by the finite diameter of the disc, and the beam motion in the slow direction is determined by the measured beam current incident on the disc or in a sampling Faraday cup. All of these methods have produced good uniformity of dopant across the wafer with minimal short period scanning [2] [15] [18]. Good uniformities can be obtained across relatively large scan dimensions. For example, a hybrid magnetic-mechanical system has been shown to achieve uniformities to significantly better than are required by most process applications while scanning across a dual row of 100 mm diameter wafers mounted on a 720 mm diameter disc as shown in Figure 12 [25].

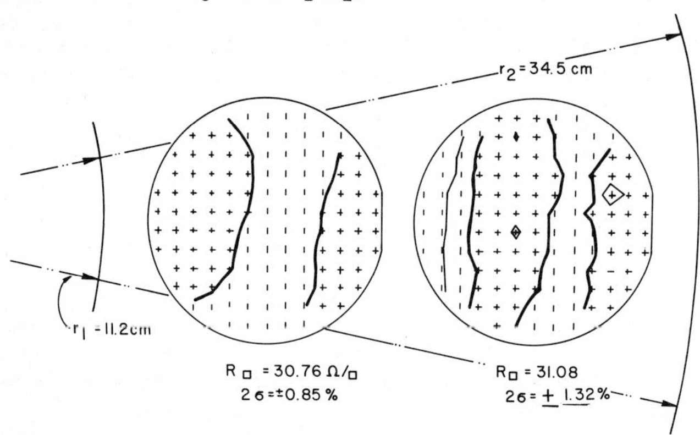

Figure 12. Dose uniformity data. Dose uniformity (contours 1%) for 80 keV, 10 mA, 75 As^+, 5×10^{15} across a dual row of 100 mm ø wafers in a hybrid scan batch system

Each of these scanning techniques requires a minimum implant time to achieve dose uniformity. In the case of electric field systems, the minimum implant time is established by the need to be able to interrupt the scan midway across the wafer while not measurably affecting the uniformity. This is necessary because the scan generator and dose control are not coupled. The slow frequency scan is typically 100 Hz and in five seconds the wafer would have received 500 passes so the dose/pass is 0.2% which is well within the desired uniformity limit. This does not seem to be a serious constraint on the performance of electric field scanning systems. For disc-type scanning systems, the slow frequency can be as low as 0.1 Hz and the minimum implant time will therefore be one cycle or ten seconds. The only requirement is that the scan rate be adjusted such that the desired dose can be achieved in one complete cycle. The minimum implant time per wafer is insignificant for batch systems and does not represent an important physical limitation.

Scanning systems can produce dopant reproducibilities and uniformities which are in the range of 2 sigma less than 2%. With careful setup and control, dose reproducibility and uniformity values of 2 sigma approximately equal to 1% have been observed. For special applications, dose uniformities of 2 sigma approximately equal to 0.2% may be obtainable although these have not been demonstrated, and there is a significant question as to how they could be measured. Performance of modern scanning systems does not represent a significant limitation to the dose uniformity that can be obtained, and the major physical limitation of scanning systems is the deleterious effect that scanning can have on beam size.

Turner has compared the beam utilization obtainable with different scanning systems [2]. The size and shape of the ion beam at the wafer scanning plane will dominate the beam utilization. When a round scan pattern is employed, it is interesting that the beam utilization for a two-dimensional electric field scanner exceeds that of most other systems, if the beam size in the scanning plane is less than 2 cm. Beam utilization is clearly an important parameter as it will affect implant time directly when the implant is beam current limited.

One of the major simplifications of ion implantation applications to semiconductors is that the workpiece (i.e. the wafer) is a regular, flat and well-controlled surface. Beam scanning across irregular objects is more difficult. Severe complications sometimes occur when scanning complex solids as may be encountered in metallurgical applications. Custom fixturing and scanning for each individual application may be the most significant limitation to the application of implantation to these technologies.

6. Rate-Dependent Effects

Three significant rate-dependent effects can be identified in semiconductor implantation which are related to the stopping of the ions in the wafer. The first is the loss of kinetic energy when the ions are stopped which increases the temperature of the wafer. The second is related to the evolution of gas into the vacuum system from the radiation damage caused by the energy deposited in the photoresist mask. The third is related to the build up of charge which results from ions being implanted into insulating layers.

6.1 Wafer Heating

In Figure 13 the temperature of a wafer is shown as a function of doping level. In this case the only cooling mechanism is radiation. The dashed line represents the temperature the wafer would achieve if the incident energy were being absorbed by the heat capacity of the wafer. A steady-state condition can be reached where the final equilibrium temperature is a function of the bombarding beam power. For beam powers equal to 0.1 W/cm^2, photoresist could probably not be applied at doping levels above 3×10^{14} $atoms/cm^2$.

The concept of beam sharing has been proposed by Turner [2] to effectively increase the scanned area by a factor of 2 for photoresist

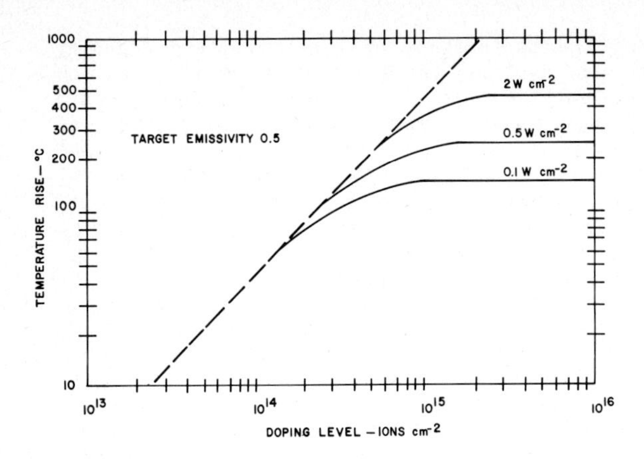

Figure 13. Temperature as a function of dose. Illustrating the effect of radiation cooling with beam power

applications. In this scheme, sequential implant segments are performed alternately on a dual end station system where the individual segment time is selected to be of order less than the thermal time constant of the wafer and cooling system.

Active cooling methods have been successfully applied to remove heat from the wafer, the earliest of which was contact cooling where the wafer was pressed against a pliable substrate. Better cooling was obtained by King and Rose [26] by using gas cooling to remove heat from the wafer to the substrate. Recently Holden [27] has invented a new scheme which combines the best of both methods. The wafer is held over a carefully contoured substrate and the inevitable voids are filled by air. Temperature measurements as a function of time are shown in Figure 14 [28]. In order to examine higher power densities, it was necessary to reduce the wafer size to 3" because of power limitations in the beam itself. Photoresist test patterns using Shipley AZ1370 have been shown to remain dimensionally stable up to doses of 5 x 10^{15} p^+/cm^2 at the extreme conditions of 180 keV, and 3 mA scanned across 51.9 cm^2 which is a power density in excess of 10 W/cm^2. These preliminary results do not imply that viable production processes can be designed around these extreme conditions using presently available hardware, but these observations do suggest that wafer heating will not be a limiting physical constraint to the next generation of serial process ion implantation systems. With the ever increasing trend towards larger wafer sizes and the beam sharing concept, it will be possible to avoid temperature-induced damage to photoresist up to quite high beam powers in serial process systems.

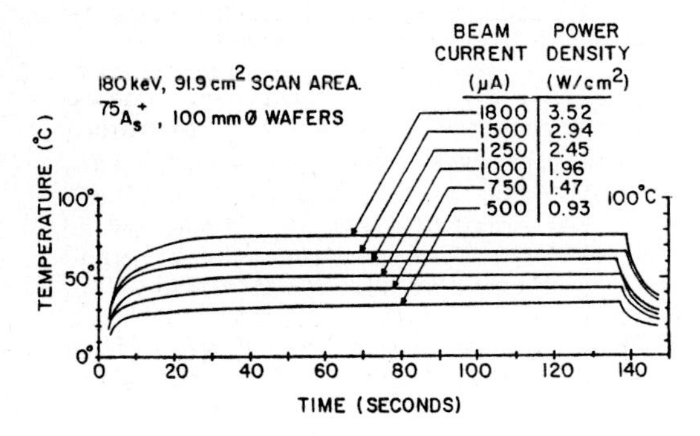

Figure 14. Temperature as a function of time. Wafer heating for air and contact cooling at various beam powers

6.2 Photoresist Outgassing

When photoresist is used to mask the wafer, energetic ions are stopped entirely in the photoresist and contribute their energy to the nuclei and electrons of the photoresist molecules. The resulting radiation damage releases large quantities of gas into the vacuum system. For properly prebaked photoresist, the major pressure excursion occurs up to a dose of 1×10^{15} atoms/cm^2 as is illustrated in Figure 15 [29]. It is likely that this gas evolution is not a thermal effect because the time constant for wafer heating as shown in Figure 14 is of the order of 10 seconds, and the outgassing pressure burst peaks approximately one second after the implant begins. Even with careful differential pumping, beam line pressures of this magnitude can affect dose reproducibility. As a simple expedient, production processes often implant photoresist wafers in two stages, the first being performed at lower beam powers up to 1×10^{15} atoms/cm^2 to minimize the outgassing peak and then the bulk of the implant proceeds at full beam power. If the beam power is reduced to 10% of its maximum value, and the dose for this initial implant is 10% of the desired dose, then throughput in wafers/hour is half of what could be obtained if the implant could proceed uninterrupted at full power. Clearly, this photoresist outgassing is a fundamental limitation to the application of high beam powers and must be addressed if higher currents are to be successfully utilized with photoresist.

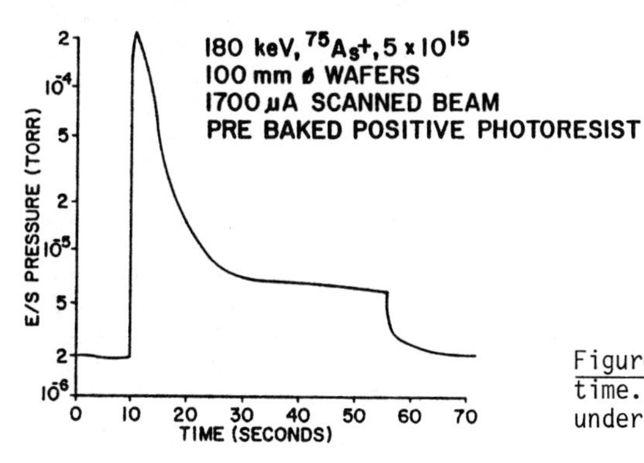

Figure 15. Pressure as a function of time. Gas evolution from photoresist under ion beam bombardment

6.3 Oxide Charging

When high current density ion beams are used to dope semiconductor devices to high doses, the arrival rate of charge often exceeds the rate at which it can be neutralized by the redistribution of mobile carriers. The result is that quite high voltages can build up on isolated elements of the device. Hofer [30] pointed out that at the implant stage of the process, low resistance connections are often made by conducting layers which are placed over insulating layers of significantly different thicknesses. This is equivalent to charging two parallel connected capacitors with a constant current source where the voltage rating of the smaller capacitor (as determined by the insulator thickness) may be an order of magnitude smaller than that of the large capacitor. Catastrophic failures of the insulating layers are often observed which are seen to depend upon the details of the device geometries which determine the field enhancement factors that create regions of high electrical stress. When high dose implantations were being originally investigated a few years ago, these changing effects were shown to depend on the current density and the scan rate of that current across the wafer. Introduction of the disc-type batch process systems reduced the magnitude of this effect as the wafers are scanned at rates between one and two orders of magnitude higher than had been common in previous systems. Therefore, the usable beam currents could be increased in rough proportion to the increase in scan velocity.

Active methods to reduce beam charging have been employed which use an electron shower to provide adequate charge compensation for the implanted ions [15]. Turner has designed a system which uses secondary electrons as a source of carriers [16]. These secondary electrons are created by bombarding the Faraday walls in a controlled manner with an intense low energy beam of primary electrons which are accelerated from an electron gun mounted at Faraday potential. These systems are now coming into routine use in production applications, and the problems of device charging should not represent a physical restriction to the increase in the beam current of either serial or batch implanter systems.

7. Conclusions

Most of the physical limitations of ion implantation equipment covered in this discussion have concerned the ability to implant semiconductor wafers in high doses at high wafer throughputs. Although wafer throughput is the leading term in the economic equation that must be balanced for a successful commercial process, the semiconductor industry is interested in their final product, i.e. good devices produced per manufacturing period. Several of the physical limitations that were discussed such as dose reproducibility, dose uniformity, photoresist integrity and device charging are directly related to the device yield question. As device ground rules have continued to shrink, this yield factor becomes dominated by particulate contamination. As the wafer size increases, the value added represented by each wafer is futher increased. These economic factors will combine to place stringent requirements on ion implanter systems to maximize yield and reduce wafer damage.

Gravity fed wafer handling systems (where the wafers are subjected to significant relative motion with respect to the wafer handler) will inevitably produce particulates which result from wafer damage. Although there are over 600 of these systems employed in semiconductor fabrication today, future trends towards VLSI and larger wafer sizes will require new approaches to wafer handling to minimize relative motion between the wafer and the handler and thereby minimize wafer damage and particulate production.

Another aspect of particulate contamination has been discussed by Marsh and von Burg [31], where the implanter is isolated from a clean room aisle and remote implanter controls are provided. An important feature of this design is that all maintenance can be performed outside the clean room area. This concept will be extended to automated wafer or cassette handling and automated operation of the implanter. When these features are incorporated in wafer fabrication lines of the future, the operator will be excluded from the clean room aisle as much as possible to further reduce particulates. In addition, automated monitoring and setup of the implanter will minimize operator errors which presently are a source of a yield loss. There will be a significant effort over the next few years to improve wafer handling and system automation to address these issues.

Wegmann [1] opened the Plenary session of the Third Conference with a figure that showed targeted beam current as a function of time. This has been updated for new developments which have occurred as illustrated in

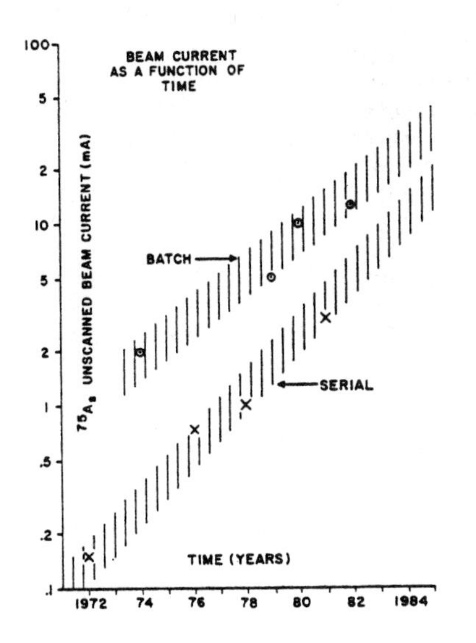

Figure 16. Some beam current projections for serial and batch process ion implanter systems

Figure 16. Batch process and serial process systems have been separated to better illustrate the trend for each of these configurations. The data points represent the achievable unscanned arsenic beam currents shown for the year in which the equipment was introduced. Surprisingly good regression lines can be fitted to these few data points and the goodness of fit would probably lead to erroneous conclusions about what is possible in the future. Consequently the regression line is shown as the lower limit of the shaded areas, as the long awaited recovery in the semiconductor industry will undoubtedly spark aggressive developments of the technology by the equipment manufacturers. The trend here confirms the conclusions of Figure 6: That more is to be gained by increasing the current capability of the serial process machines than for present day batch machines. Developments in the current available from serial process machines will probably cause the currents of batch process machines to increase as well to maintain their economic advantage for high dose implants.

The subject matter of this paper should serve as a caution to those who would too readily believe in the projections of Figure 16. Several significant constraints still remain to be resolved before these projections can be realized. Ion implantation in semiconductors is rapidly becoming a mature technology and it is not unlikely that the rate of development of this technology will begin to slow down.

For other applications of ion implantations such as insulating layers and metallurgy, the higher dose requirements will drive the technology. Significant changes will probably be necessary in system configurations to accommodate the very much higher currents and specialized workpiece handling that will be required for these applications. The remarkable growth which has been seen in the application of implantation to the semiconductor industry over the last ten years may well not be able to be easily duplicated in other industries.

Acknowledgements

Several people on the Extrion staff contributed material and ideas for this paper and their support is gratefully acknowledged. A special thanks

is due to P. Davis and P. Mansfield for preparation of the manuscript.
References are always a difficult subject in a review paper and apologies are undoubtedly due to some colleagues whose detailed work on the broad range of subjects covered could not be cited because of space limitations.

References

[1] L. Wegmann, Nucl. Instr. and Meth. 189 (1981) 1-6
[2] N.L. Turner, These Proceedings
[3] J.H. Freeman, D.J. Chivers, G.A. Gard, G.W. Hinder, B.J. Smith and J. Stephens, Ion Implantation in Semiconductors, ed., S. Namba, Plenum, NY 1975, p.555
[4] M.I. Current, D.S. Perloff and L.S. Gutai, These Proceedings.
[5] D.M. Jamba, Nucl. Instr. and Meth. 189 (1981) 253-263
[6] R.B. Fair and W.G. Meyer, Bell Laboratories, Reading, PA. To be published
[7] R.B. Liebert and D.F. Downey, Varian/Extrion, Gloucester, MA. To be published
[8] K. Itoh, N. Horino, M. Kanegae and T. Tsuchimoto, Electrochem. Soc. Ext. Abstracts No. 114 (1979) p.316
[9] R.G. Wilson and G.R. Brewer, Ion Beams, Krieger Publishing Co., Huntington, NY, 1979
[10] C.J. Russo, D.F. Downey, S.C. Holden and R.T. Fulks, These Proceedings
[11] S. Namba; Nucl. Instr. and Meth. 189 (1981) 175-182
[12] D.K. Sadana, J. Washburn, M. Strathman, M. Current and M. Maenpaa; Inst. Phys. Conf. Ser. No. 60 (1981) p.453
[13] H.M. Bird, J.H. Jackson, B. Weissman and N. Williams; J. Vac. Sci. Tech. 15 (1978) 1070
[14] J.G. McCallum, G.I. Robertson, A.F. Rodde, B. Weissman and N. Williams; ibid. 1067
[15] G. Ryding and M. Farley, Nucl. Instr. and Meth. 189 (1981) 295-303
[16] N.L. Turner, Varian/Extrion, Gloucester, MA, Patent Pending
[17] N.L. Turner, Varian/Extrion, Gloucester, MA, To be published
[18] P.R. Hanley, Nucl. Instr. and Meth. 189 (1981) 227-237
[19] T.C. Smith, These Proceedings
[20] P.H. Rose, Radiation Effects, 1979, Vol. 44, pp.137-144
[21] N.L. Turner, S. Dinaro and R. Hertel, These Proceedings
[22] D. Aitken, "Ion Sources", pp.23-71 in "Ion Implantation Techniques" Editors: H. Ryssel and H. Glawischnig, Springer-Verlag, Berlin (1982)
[23] W.B. Thompson, I. Honjo and N.L. Turner, These Proceedings
[24] R.B. Liebert and B. Pedersen, Varian/Extrion, Gloucester, MA, Private Communication
[25] R.B. Liebert, Varian/Extrion, Gloucester, MA and C. Neville, Signetics Corp. Sunnyvale, CA, Private Communication
[26] M. King and P.H. Rose, Nucl. Instr. and Meth. 189 (1981) 169-173
[27] S.C. Holden, Varian/Extrion, Gloucester, MA, Patent Pending
[28] N.L. Turner and W.B. Bramhall, Varian/Extrion, Gloucester, MA, Extrion Internal Report, to be published
[29] N.L. Turner, Varian/Extrion, Gloucester, MA, and T.C. Smith, Motorola, Mesa, AZ, Private Communication
[30] G. Hofer, National Semiconductor, Salt Lake, UT, Private Communication
[31] R.L. Marsh and H. von Burg, Nucl. Instr. and Meth. 189 (1981) 187-191

A New Ion Implanter for Solar Cell Fabrication

K. Tokiguchi, H. Itoh, N. Sakudo, H. Koike, T. Warabisako, T. Saitoh, I. Kanomata, and T. Tokuyama

Central Research Laboratory, Hitachi Ltd., Higashikoigakubo 1-280, Tokyo 185, Japan

A high-current ion implanter based on a continuous wafer-processing concept has been newly developed, in order to apply the implant technique to solar-cell p-n junction formation. In this implanter, a single magnet carries out mass separation as well as ion-beam scanning, and wafers mechanically traverse the scanned-beam region only once, perpendicularly to the beam-scanning direction. The implanter provides the maximum implant current of 20mA at 30kV with the use of a coaxial microwave ion source. Wafer throughput is about 400 wafers/hr for 100mm-diameter wafers, at a 3.0×10^{15} ions/cm^2 dose. Dose non-uniformity is a standard deviation of 3% of the sheet-resistivity distribution. Energy-conversion efficiency is 13.5% with an anti-reflection coating. It is shown experimentally that the newly developed implanter is applicable to low-cost solar-cell fabrication.

1. Introduction

Ion implantation has been applied to low-cost fabrication of a solar-cell p-n junction, in conjunction with laser or electron-beam annealing [1],[2]. To apply the implant technique to solar-cell fabrication economically, wafer throughput must be as high as possible, in order to lower the junction-formation cost.

However, the throughput of a conventional high-current ion implanter is limited to about 200 wafers/hr, at the required dose level for solar-cell fabrication [3]. This is because the wafer-exchange operation is carried out with the chamber kept under atmospheric pressure. Therefore, in order to obtain a satisfactory solar-cell implanter, a high-speed wafer processor and a high-current ion source must be developed.

In solar-cell implantation, problems regarding ion purity and dose uniformity are less critical than in conventional applications. Therefore, optimization of implant techniques for the required dose uniformity and ion purity could also be carried out to lower the machine cost [4].

This paper describes a newly developed solar-cell implanter, which consists of a coaxial microwave ion source, a magnet for mass separation and beam scanning, and a continuous high-speed wafer-processor chamber. Several implant characteristics are studied in detail.

2. Solar-cell Ion Implanter

The schematic diagram of a new solar-cell ion implanter is shown in Fig.1. This is composed of a coaxial microwave ion source, a magnet for mass separation and beam scanning, and an implant processor chamber.

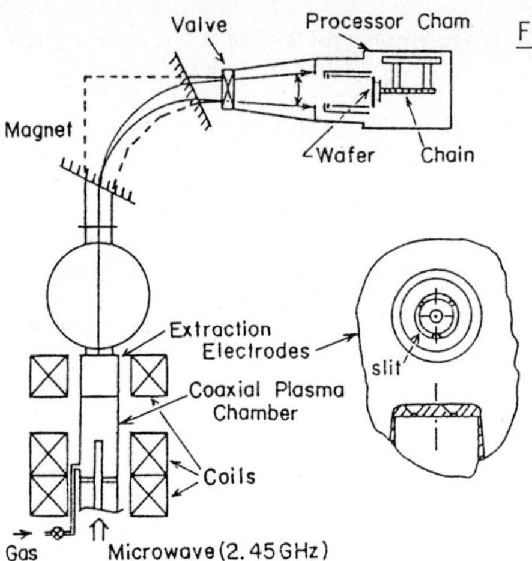

Fig.1. Schematic diagram of a new solar-cell implanter

2.1 Coaxial Microwave Ion Source

In Fig.1, a microwave discharge(2.45GHz) takes place in the plasma chamber at low pressure between 0.1 and 0.01Pa. An axial magnetic field with an intensity greater than that of the electron cyclotron resonance is imposed over the entire plasma chamber. The microwave discharge under the off-resonance condition continuously produces high-density and high-temperature plasma($n_e=10^{11}\sim10^{12}$ e/cm^3, T_e=4∼6eV), which is suitable for obtaining high-current beams of singly charged ion species [5],[6].

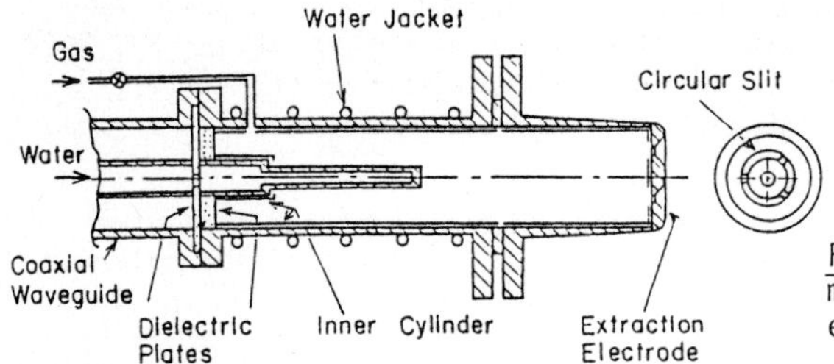

Fig.2. Structure of a coaxial microwave plasma chamber and extraction electrodes

Structures of the plasma chamber and extraction electrodes used in this implanter are shown in Fig.2. Microwave power is introduced into the discharge chamber through a coaxial waveguide and vacuum-sealing dielectric plates. Phosphine(PH_3) with a purity of 99.9% is introduced into the source through a leak valve as a working gas.

In order to extract ion beams from a uniform plasma region efficiently, new three-stage extraction electrodes, each of which has a 2mm-wide circular slit of 30mm diameter, are employed in this implanter. A mass-analyzed P^+ implant current of 20mA is obtained at 30kV with the source shown in Fig.2.

2.2 Mass Separation and Beam Scanning Magnet

In Fig.1, a single magnet carries out mass separation and ion-beam scanning at the same time. The deflection angle of the magnet is 90°and the beam radius in the magnetic sector is 30cm. This magnet consists of a laminated yoke and two pairs of coils. One pair is supplied with a 50Hz sinusoidal wave current to produce a beam scanning field. The other is supplied with direct current to produce the static field for mass separation. As a result, the total magnetic flux density B can be expressed as:

$$B = B_0(1+\frac{B'}{B_0}\sin\omega t) , \qquad (1)$$

where B_0 and B' are the static and maximum scanning magnetic flux densities, respectively. Some other ions, such as H^+, H_2^+, H_3^+, PH^+, PH_2^+, PH_3^+, and P_2^+, may be implanted into a wafer together with the P^+ ions. However, as shown in a previous report, PH^+, PH_2^+, and PH_3^+ ions do not affect the energy-conversion efficiency of a solar cell [7].

On the other hand, even small amounts of H^+, H_2^+, and H_3^+ ions do decrease this efficiency, when the implant energy is so high that the peak position of the defect distribution caused by H^+, H_2^+, and H_3^+ ion implantation approximately coincides with the p-n junction depth. Furthermore, P_2^+ implantation should be avoided to obtain the correct P^+ dose. Therefore, the magnetic-flux-density ratio, $a(=B'/B_0)$, is limited to less than 20% in this implanter [8].

2.3 Wafer-processor Chamber

A side view of the processor chamber is schematically shown in Fig.3. This is composed of a moving chain, two wafer-transport assemblies, and an implant beam-current detection system.

In Fig.3, two wafer-transport assemblies can operate continuously, taking wafers in and out of the evacuated platen chamber one by one. When the wafer is introduced into the upper platen, the platen rises up and the wafer falls onto the moving chain. The chain leans at 7°to avoid a channeling

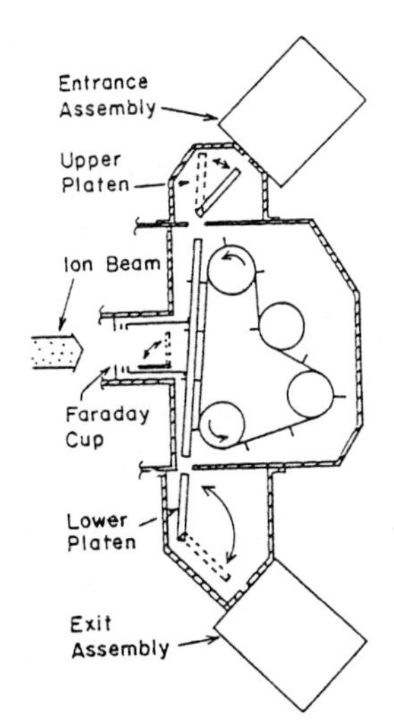

Fig.3. Schematic diagram showing the side view of the continuous wafer-processor chamber

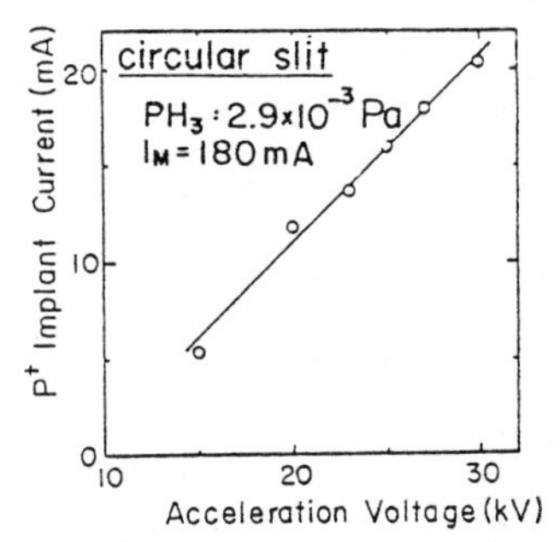

Fig.4. Relationship between the implant P^+ current and the acceleration voltage. Microwave power is about 400W

implantation of the wafer. Wafers traverse the scanned-ion beam region only once, perpendicularly to the beam-scanning direction. At the point where the chain turns around the wheel, the implanted wafer falls into the lower platen. Then, the wafers are taken out through the exit-transport assembly. The P^+ ion dose is controlled by varying the chain speed.

A Faraday cup with an effective area of 116 cm^2 is placed in front of the moving chain. The Faraday cup contains a movable plate, which is used for the implant-beam adjustment prior to implantation, and is then moved out of the path of the beam during implantation.

Implant operation is carried out automatically, using a microprocessor controller. Under the usual implant conditions, the implant time per wafer is about ten seconds, and the time required for a wafer to pass from the entrance assembly to the exit is about 1 minute.

3. Experimental Results

3.1 Ion-beam Extraction

The relationship between implant current and acceleration voltage is shown in Fig.4. Circular-slit extraction electrodes, shown in Fig.2, are used in this experiment. In Fig.4, the implant-beam current includes small amounts of PH^+, PH_2^+, and PH_3^+ ions, amounting to a few percent of P^+ ions. Results show that the implant current increases with the acceleration voltage, and the maximum implant current is 20mA at 30kV.

3.2 Dose Uniformity and Solar-cell Characteristics

The uniformities and the efficiencies of 100mm-diameter wafers were investigated under the usual implant conditions for solar-cell fabrication.

Implant energy and dose were 15keV and 3.0×10^{15} ions/cm^2, respectively.

A typical sheet-resistivity distribution is shown in Fig.5; it was measured using automatic four-point-probe equipment. The wafers were 10Ω-cm p-type silicon with a $\langle 100 \rangle$ orientation. In this figure, the ion beam is horizontally scanned and the wafer moves downwards mechanically. An alternating coil current for producing a scanning magnetic field, I_{AC}, of 25A corresponds to a beam-scanning width of about 12cm at the wafer position. The standard deviation of the dose variation is about 3.0% in Fig.5.

The dependence of dose non-uniformity on scanning magnetic flux density, indicated by I_{AC}, is shown in Fig.6. It can be seen that dose uniformity tends to be improved by increasing the scanning field intensity.

One thousand 100mm-diameter wafers were serially and automatically implanted at I_{AC}=22.5A and V=15keV. Resistivity values of these wafers deviated within the limits of ±3.5%, which shows that the implanter has good dose reproducibility for solar-cell fabrication.

A solar cell is fabricated by annealing the implanted 100mm-diameter wafer for 30 minutes at 850°C in a dry N_2 atomosphere. Energy-conversion efficiency is typically 13.5%(J_{SC}:30.4mA/cm^2, V_{OC}:0.560, FF:0.793, 28°C), which is equal to that obtained by a conventional lower-current implanter, but with better dose uniformity.

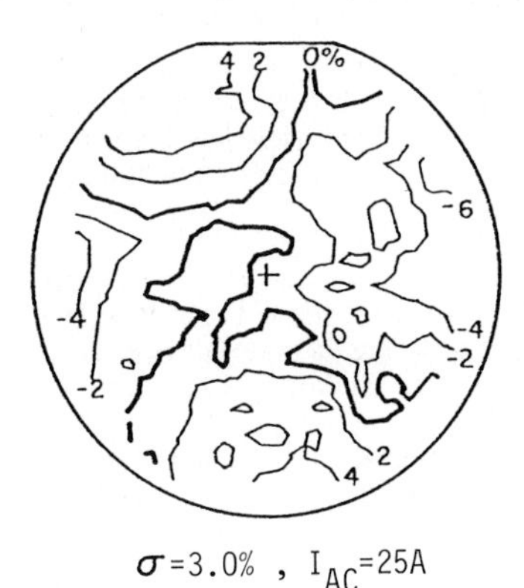

σ=3.0% , I_{AC}=25A

Fig.5. Sheet-resistivity distribution of the implanted 100mm-diameter wafer. Deviation from the average resistivity is shown in percentage

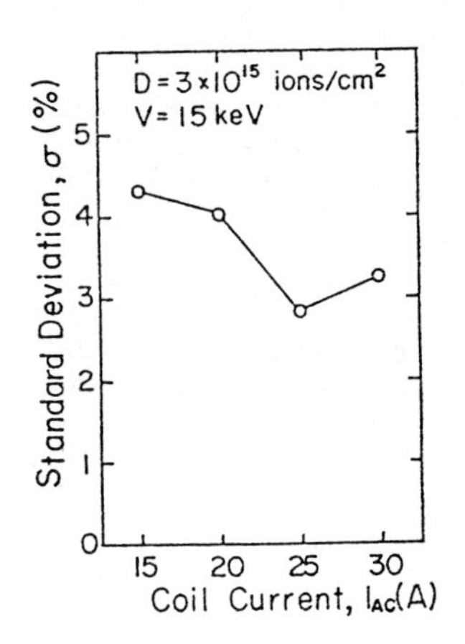

Fig.6. Dependence of dose non-uniformity on scanning-field intensity indicated by coil current, I_{AC}

In order to study the dependence of the efficiency on wafer-temperature rise, the wafer temperature during implantation was measured as a function of beam power. A wafer temperature up to 200°C was measured at an implant current of 18mA(V=27.5keV). However, the energy-conversion efficiency was found to be the same as that of lower-temperature implantation. Since the usual implant energy is 15keV with this implanter, the wafer temperature is maintained under 100°C.

3.3 Wafer Throughput

The dependence of 76mm-diameter and 100mm-diameter wafer throughput on the implant current is shown in Fig.7. The experimentally obtained throughput is proportional to the current at low current levels. However, the throughput is limited to 400 wafers/hr at a higher current. The limiting factor is the time required to transport the wafer into and out of the evacuated

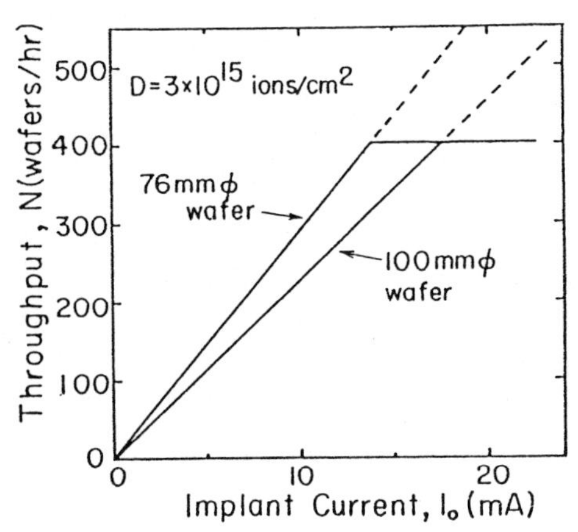

Fig.7. Dependence of wafer throughput on the implant current

chamber. If this limitation is removed, a throughput of more than 500 wafers/hr for 76mm-diameter wafers would be obtained at the implant-current level of 20mA, as shown by the dashed lines. Therefore, the development of a higher-speed transport system would be useful in improving the throughput.

4. Discussion and Conclusion

It is apparent that the utilization of triangular magnetic beam scanning is preferable for good dose uniformity and for decreasing the beam overscan, and that dose uniformity in the direction perpendicular to beam scanning would be improved by increasing the frequency. However, at higher frequency, the realization of a triangular beam-scanning field becomes increasingly difficult, because of the high inductance of the electromagnet. Therefore, commercially available 50Hz sinusoidal current is applied in this implanter to lower the machine cost.

It is shown in section 3.2 that a few percent of dose non-uniformity is allowable in solar-cell fabrication. This indicates that the triangular beam-scanning frequency can be lowered to about 8Hz. A magnetic field with a triangular wave form can be easily obtained at 8Hz. Adoption of triangular beam scanning and a dual-row wafer-transport system will double the wafer-transport speed and decrease the effective beam overscan to under half of the present value. Therefore, a throughput of more than 1000 wafers/hr will be obtained by the use of this combination.

In conclusion, it has been experimentally confirmed that the new solar-cell implanter provides sufficient implant current and dose uniformity for low-cost solar-cell fabrication. The solar cell thus produces a high-energy-conversion efficiency. The present maximum throughput is about 400 wafers/hr. The limitation is due to the wafer-transport speed in the exit assembly. A further improvement of the wafer-transport system will result in a throughput increase of over 1000 wafers/hr, at the present implant-current level.

Acknowledgements

This work is being carried out under contract with the Agency of Industrial Science and Technology, MITI, as a part of the national R&D "Sunshine Project" programme.

The authors are grateful to Dr. O. Okada of the Hitachi Central Research Laboratory for his suggestions regarding triangular magnetic beam scanning. In addition, they would like to thank Mr. S.Kamejima and Mr. T.Habu for their valuable suggestions and discussions concerning implanter improvement.

References

1. H.Goldman et al.: Proc. of 14th IEEE Photovoltaic Specialist Conf., California, 923(1980)
2. M.D.Sirkis et al.: Proc. of 15th IEEE Photovoltaic Specialist Conf., Kissimmee, Florida(1981)
3. G.Ryding: Nucl. Instr. and Meth. 189, 239(1981)
4. J.C.Muller et al.: Nucl. Instr. and Meth. 189, 205(1981)
5. K.Tokiguchi et al.: J. Vac. Sci. Technol. 17, 1247(1981)
6. N.Sakudo et al.: Rev. Sci. Instrum. 48, 762(1977)
7. H.Itoh et al.: Jpn. J. Appl. Phys. 20, suppl. 20-2, 39(1981)
8. K.Tokiguchi et al.: Rev. Sci. Instrum. 52, 1110(1981)

SURIM - A Westinghouse Surface Implantation Machine

M.D. Nahemow, R.E. Fromson, R. Kossowsky, and J.L. Pack

Westinghouse Elec. Co., R&D Center, Beulah Rd.,
Pittsburgh, PA 15235, USA

This paper describes the design of, and initial operating experience with, an ion implantation system at the Research and Development Center of the Westinghouse Electric Corporation. The ion beam energy can be varied from 30 KeV to 185 KeV at currents up to 10 ma. The beam optics can vary the spot size at the target from <1 cm^2 to 100 cm^2. The beam can be direct or analyzed. The final lens is after the analyzer and before the post accelerator. The system is currently using a gas source. The ion-source power supplies floating at the high voltage are optically coupled to the controls at ground. The chamber is 1 meter in diameter. A large Rootes blower backing the diffusion pump facilitates fast pump-down of the chamber. A microprocessor-based numerical control system moves a table in the chamber with x, y, and θ motions to program the tool through the beam to provide the desired average flux and dose. By folding the beam profile with the geometry of the tools being implanted, the numerical control system can be programmed to optimize the use of the beam. With many of the tools and dies that are of interest to implant the shapes are complex and only some surfaces are to be implanted. As a result a good control algorithm is worth an order of magnitude in beam current. Provisions are made to cool the tool holders and monitor the temperature during implantation.

The SURIM facility was built to serve the dual role of batch tool implantation facility and flexible R&D system. The facility now has a 1 ma 100 KeV unanalyzed beam of argon or nitrogen. The beam is variable from 1 cm^2 to 10 cm^2. The beam is stable for several hours of continuous operation at a time. We are in the process of developing tool handlers and control algorithms for a wide range of tools. We now have about a 6 month's backlog of tools to implant with the present configuration before upgrading the system. The upgrade being developed includes a 185 KeV 10 ma beam, modified optics to increase the beam size from a maximum of 10 cm^2 to 100 cm^2 and mass analysis.

An important choice being studied is the optimum beam size. Curved objects rotated in a large beam present a problem due to low-angle sputtering. If a sphere is rotated in a beam larger than the sphere, the angular dependence of the sputtering will increase the net sputter yield by a factor of at least 5 over a flat plate. If the beam is small compared to the sphere and the sphere is rotated fast to give the same average flux, the sputtering will be reduced by a factor of 5 to the flat plate value. However, the metallurgical differences for the same dose and average flux at different peak fluxes has yet to be determined.

Figure 1 shows the system with the pressure tanks removed. From right to left are shown the vacuum valves, diffusion pump, viewing port and the

Figure 1.
Bare system in shielded room

rack which houses the magnet, arc, extraction and first and second lens power supplies. The rack is surrounded at the base by a voltage grading ring below which is the lower flange plate of the pressure tank. From top to bottom are shown the ion source, H.V. insulator and main vacuum vessel. Figure 2 shows the fully assembled system. On the left is the black tank containing the supply rack. At the top is the silver tank containing the source and H.V. insulator.

Figure 3 shows the control panel for the system. At the extreme left is the shielded test room containing the system. The rack on the left contains from top to bottom secondary electron collector and suppressor supplies, primary isolation transformer, H.V. supply, filament control, the six controls and 12 meters optically coupled through the fiber optics system to the power supplies in the pressure tank shown in Figure 1. The right rack contains the interlock and vacuum control systems and the microprocessor that controls the positioning table. The optical receiver and the numerical control were originally very sensitive to sparking in the H.V. column, but are now immune to all but extreme flashovers.

Figure 4 shows an argon beam focused to 1 cm^2. The beam shown is 110 KV 3 ma.

Figure 5 shows the numerical controlled table with the x-y-θ stepping motors. The tables move at speeds to several hundreds of inches per minute or 1000 rpm, under full computer control. The water manifolds which cool the motors and the tables are not installed yet in this picture. Figures 6 and 7 are partially machined jigs to manipulate tools in the ion beam. For the jig in Figure 8 the x-y control positions the proper spindle in the beam and the θ control rotates the cutter. The next tool is then positioned in the beam finally returning to the first tool

Figure 2. System with pressure tanks

Figure 3. SURIM control panel

and going around again. The control is programmed to implant all the proper cutting edges at the right average flux for the required total dose. The jig in Figure 7 positions the table so that the beam is centered on the overlap at the center of the 4 blades while they rotate so that the cutting face is implanted. A small faraday cup in the center samples the beam.

Figure 4. Argon beam focused to 1 cm^2

Figure 5. Front view of x-y-θ motion table in the vacuum chamber

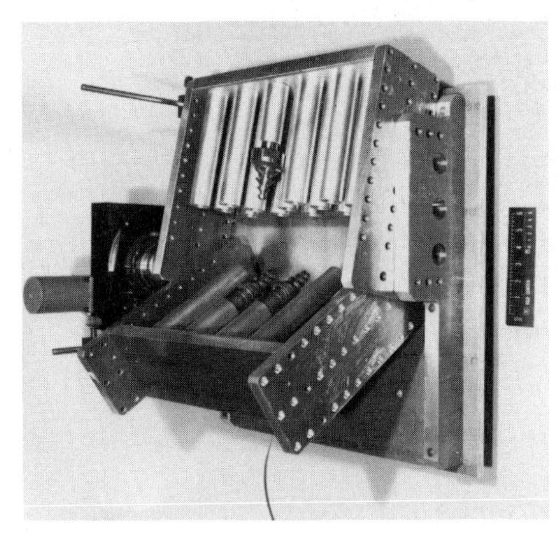

Figure 6. Mock up of cutting tool spindle system controlled by θ axis

Figure 7. Mock up of slitting knife jig

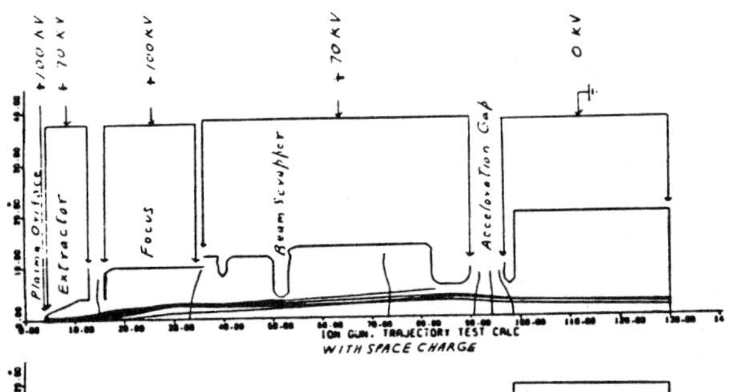

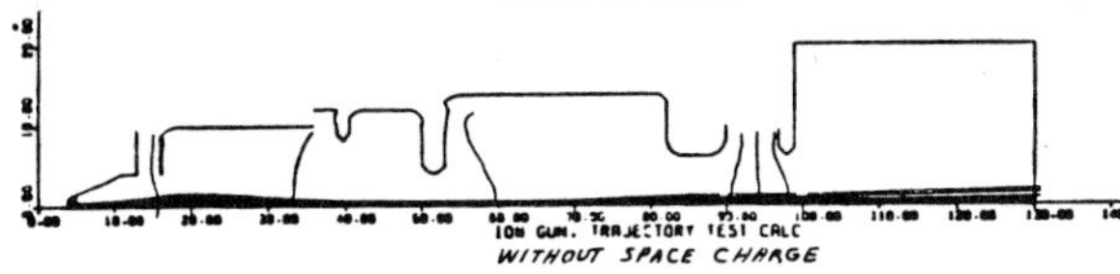

Figure 8. Output of transport code for the (W) SURIM system

Another part of the program is to study the shapeing of the beam. In Figure 8 two ray traces reproduced by a particle transport code are shown. The top figure shows the ray trace for the SURIM system with a 1 ma 100 KeV beam and the second lens turned off. The second trace shows the beam neglecting the self-field of the beam. This shows that space charge cannot be neglected in the design of transport systems above 1 ma.

We wish to acknowledge the invaluable technical assistance of K. R. Waldorf without whom this system might never have worked.

A New Research Implanter at the University of Surrey

P.L.F. Hemment, J.E. Mynard, E. Pãsztor*, C.J. Richmond, and K.G. Stephens

Department of Electronic and Electrical Engineering, University of Surrey, Guildford, Surrey, England

Abstract: A new 400 keV Research Implanter at the University of Surrey is described. The beam is extracted from a Freeman type source at 40 kV, analysed by a Lintott Separator magnet with adjustable pole pieces which match the beam to the ion optics of a cylindrical electrostatic lens/ accelerator system. Electrostatic elements further transport the beam and incorporate two neutral particle traps and electrostatic beam scanning over a maximum area of 100mm x 100mm. Beam diagnostics include calorimeters for current and power density determinations and facilities for IR wafer temperature and beam purity measurements during implantation. Samples are loaded through an air lock using a UHV compatible transporter which includes provisions for sample cooling or heating.

1. Introduction

Research into the uses of ion beams commenced at the University of Surrey more than 15 years ago. During this period three particle accelerators have been built, the two most important being a 500 keV Heavy Ion Implanter and a 2 MeV machine based upon an HVEC Van de Graaff. Both of these machines have been in daily use for 12 years; each is used for about 1500 hrs/annum and less than 10% of the possible running time is necessary for servicing and maintenance. About 18 ion species are regularly run on the implanter with a 4 week cycle time for the most common species which are Se^{+}_{78}, O^{+}_{32}, Ar^{+}_{40}, B^{+}_{11} and As^{+}_{75}. The Van de Graaff is regularly used for light ion irradiation and for surface analysis using Rutherford backscattering (RBS) or Proton-induced X-ray excitation (PIXE). The latter facility is described in reference (1).

The work at the University is funded by internal research projects, industrial customers and by the U.K. Science and Engineering Research Council, which supports the Ion Implantation Facility to enable research groups in other U.K. universities to have direct access to the comprehensive ion beam annealing and surface analysis facilities. The special feature required of a university facility is that is should be flexible in its operation and be able to provide a wide range of ion species over a large energy range. The demand for our implanter has been great and a few years ago it became clear that a new machine was required.

The decision was made to base the new machine on components used in the Lintott Implanter, since many of these components were already available within the laboratory, including a Freeman type ion source. The Freeman

*permanent address: Central Research Institute for Physics, Budapest, Hungary

source, with its many variants gives great flexibility in generating high currents of all ion species of interest. Also the yield of multi-charges species is sufficiently high to enable useful beam currents to be generated and this effectively increases the energy range of the machine. The source is also suitable for O^+, Be^+, Si^+, Fe^+ ions and refractory and noble metal ions, all of which are very difficult to generate in our existing implanter with its Nielson type ion source.

An important part of the design specification was that excellent control of dose and dose uniformity should be achieved and that the target chamber (end station) should accept samples of irregular size up to and including 125mm Si wafers and that sample cooling and heating should be available. Also the target chamber has to be enclosed in a clean area, suitable for wafer processing.

2. Description of Accelerator System

2.1 Design Features

The following decisions were taken with regard to the design of the new machine.

1. The beam to be extracted from a Freeman type ion source at 40 kV, analysed and then fast accelerated to a maximum of 400 keV (single charge).

2. Beam shaping to be included to match the source emittance to the ion optics of a cylindrical electrostatic lens/acceleration system.

3. Electrostatic beam scanning to be used to provide the flexibility of working with samples of various geometry and the ability to include sample heating or cooling.

4. Two target chambers to be installed to meet the diverse requirements of users. One chamber would be a UHV system, with an electron beam evaporator for deposition of ultra pure thin films whereas the second chamber would be used for implants into semiconductor samples, of various geometries with a maximum diameter of 125mm. Only this latter chamber is discussed in this paper.

5. The semiconductor target chamber should contain: a Faraday cup for accurate measurement of charge, a calorimeter to measure total power, an X-ray detector and an infra-red thermometer to measure the temperature of samples.

6. The samples to be loaded through an air lock using a transporter.

7. Use of telemetry to control and monitor instrumentation in the high voltage terminal.

2.2 Ion Source, Extraction and Magnet System

This part of the accelerator is very similar to existing Lintott Series III implanters, with the flexibility of being able to interchange the Series III ion source with a modified high temperature source using a graphite chamber or a sputter mode source. Also, recently one of us developed a source using an indirectly heated cathode with the extraction slit reduced to 22mm.

Extraction takes place at 40 kV and a standard Lintott Separator Magnet, with adjustable pole pieces, analyses the beam which then enters the post acceleration stage.

Components within the HT terminal are controlled using an analog/digital IR telemetry system which provides a total of 48 channels for read-out and control.

2.3 Post Acceleration and Beam Transport

A 500 kV homogenous field tube has been in use on another implanter for over 12 years. This tube was designed by P.T. Cracknell(2) in conjunction with Megavolt Ltd. It consists of 24 gaps each of width 49mm. The maximum voltage per stage for this machine is thus 20.8 kV and the voltage divide takes a current of 1 mA and the power rating per gap is 20.8W.

Calculations, supported by measurements, enable the pole face angles of the magnet to be set to match the beam to the optics of this tube to give an acceptable beam diameter of 10-15mm at the deflection and scanning plates.

Electrostatic deflection is used to switch the beam between the two beam lines which are mounted at -22° and $+5^{o}$ to the axis of the accelerator tube. The electrodes are mounted on a moveable plate inside a large vacuum chamber which acts as a pumping manifold for the accelerator tube. Two pairs of electrodes are attached to the plate and the set required to give either the -22° or $+5^{o}$ deflection is selected by pivoting the plate in the horizontal plane. This design gives the advantage of having specially designed electrodes for each of the two beam lines, whilst the asymmetry in the deflection system enables a large angular separation of the beam lines to be achieved whilst keeping beam aberations at an acceptable level. The switch also removes neutrals from the beam. A water-cooled dump tank (a graphite Faraday cup) also is included in this chamber, in the straight through position, to help in beam alignment and setting up. The beam, which then emerges from the deflection chamber into the target chamber, passes through a water-cooled graphite or silicon aperture.

2.4 Beam Scanning

The semiconductor beam line is a self-contained system which is designed to accept an approximately parallel beam with a circular cross-section of about 10mm. The ion beam enters this section through a pneumatically operated gate valve and a wedge-shaped vacuum coupling which displaces the beam line through an angle of 3° to the beam axis. By this means it is possible to include a second trap for neutral particles. A differential pumping aperture is fitted at the entrance to this section and good pumping efficiency is achieved by using rectangular vacuum chambers with large cross-sectional areas. Components within the vacuum chamber may be adjusted or removed with ease through large ports in the top of the chambers.

Dose uniformity is achieved using electrostatic beam scanning with a raster pattern covering a maximum area of 125mmx125mm at a machine voltage of 340 kV. In order to achieve a dose uniformity of better than ± 1% a high voltage power supply has been designed which uses digital techniques to shape the wave form of the voltage applied to the scan electrodes. By this means a correction may be made for the cosine dependence of the current density in the plane of the sample. The x and y scan frequencies will be crystal controlled, the actual values will be defined after the complete system has been assembled and the stray capacitance is known. A d.c. voltage off-set is built into the x (horizontal) unit and this, in conjunction with the 3° wedge at the entrance to the chamber, enables a second neutral trap to be affected.

2.5 Target Chamber

Figure 1 is a schematic diagram of the components within the target chamber. The area to be implanted is defined by an aperture (A) with the sample (B) mounted on a plate which acts as the base of a large Faraday cup (C) (40 cm deep x 12 cm wide). The sample, which is inclined at 10° to the beam axis, may be of an irregular shape but not larger than 125mm diameter and no thicker than 10mm. The maximum area which may be implanted is a circle of 100mm diameter but smaller areas may be selected by fitting alternative aperture plates. Four small Faraday cups are placed symmetrically around the aperture and serve as monitors of the beam scanning. Correct alignment of the beam, to affect a neutral trap, may be achieved by using a fifth Faraday cup (D), which is on the geometric axis of the beam. When the appropriate dc bias is applied to the x scan plates, the beam will be deflected through about 3° onto the sample.

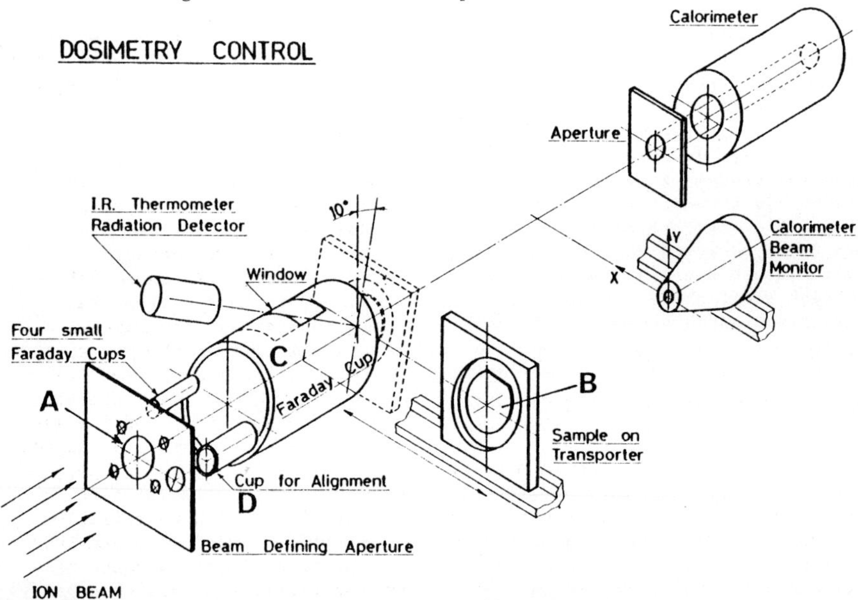

Fig.1. A schematic drawing of the components within the target chamber. A - beam defining aperture, B - sample on a mounting plate, C - Faraday cup for dosimetry and D - Faraday cup for beam alignment

The Faraday cup (C) is integral with a liquid nitrogen reservoir, for cryopumping, and it also includes a remotely operated window so that the sample may be inspected during implantation, as shown in the figure. In particular, this shutter enables infra-red measurements to be made of the sample temperature and will also permit X-ray or particle detectors to be used for dosimetry(3).

Sample loading will be carried out inside a lamina flow workbench, with the individual wafers being mounted on plates and fitted into a cassette within a separate vacuum chamber. The plates will then be transported, in turn, through an air lock and into the position for implantation. Both the cassette and transporter are UHV compatible. Sample plates are available for standard 50, 75, 100 and 125mm wafers and also irregular III-V semiconductor wafers. Hot implants will be possible up to 200°C, using resistive heating, or for particular geometries up to 600°C, using beam heating. Sample cooling is possible using a further set of plates which may be coupled to a liquid freon reservoir.

The vacuum chambers and sample transporter have been manufactured by Vacuum Generators Ltd., Hastings, Sussex.

2.6 Dosimetry

Experience gained from our present implanters confirms that errors in the incident dose and dose uniformity may occur and pass unnoticed. It is highly desirable to avoid this and in order to do so, some novel features have been included in the design of this machine.

The most obvious means of achieving efficient charge collection is to incorporate the sample in a large Faraday cup. The method of doing so has been described above. A second approach is to include methods of determining the dose which do not rely upon charge collection. This is achieved by the use of a calorimeter(4) mounted behind the sample as shown in Fig.1. The instrument will be used to calibrate the current integrater just prior to implantation. A dummy sample will be used with an aperture of known size, which will permit part of the scanned ion beam to pass through the target chamber and enter the calorimeter. The instrument gives a direct reading of the absolute beam power with a resolution of 1 in 10^4 and a sensitivity to detect a 10 mW (50 keV, 0.2 μA) beam with ± 1% accuracy. The calorimeter has been designed and built within the department and tested on our implanters. Unfortunately, the calorimeter does not have adequate sensitivity to detect the low beam currents used for the lowest dose implants of, say 10^{10}-10^{12} ions/cm^2. In these cases the technique described by Lurio and Ziegler(3) will be used in which the ion induced X-rays emitted from the target are counted using an end window gas flow detector. The sample will be viewed from the front through the window in the top of the large Faraday cup.

As this implanter uses electrostatic beam scanning, it is necessary to align the beam and to set the scan parameters before commencing an implant. The dose uniformity may be predicted from the profile of the current or power density across the scanned beam. Therefore, prior to implantation the current density in the plane of the target is sampled, using a mounting plate with a matrix of nine Faraday cups. During the implantation the current density in the plane of the beam defining aperture is continuously monitored using the four small Faraday cups shown in Fig.2 and the signals from these will be compared with preset limits. On occasions when more detailed information is required about the scan uniformity, it will be possible to use a calorimeter/Faraday cup beam monitor(4) shown schematically in Fig.2. The sensing head of this unit may be driven horizontally or vertically through the electrostatically scanned beam and will sample the current and power density with a spatial resolution, typically, of 1 to 3mm. The signals can be processed to give profiles of the current and power density and also the distribution of high energy neutral particles

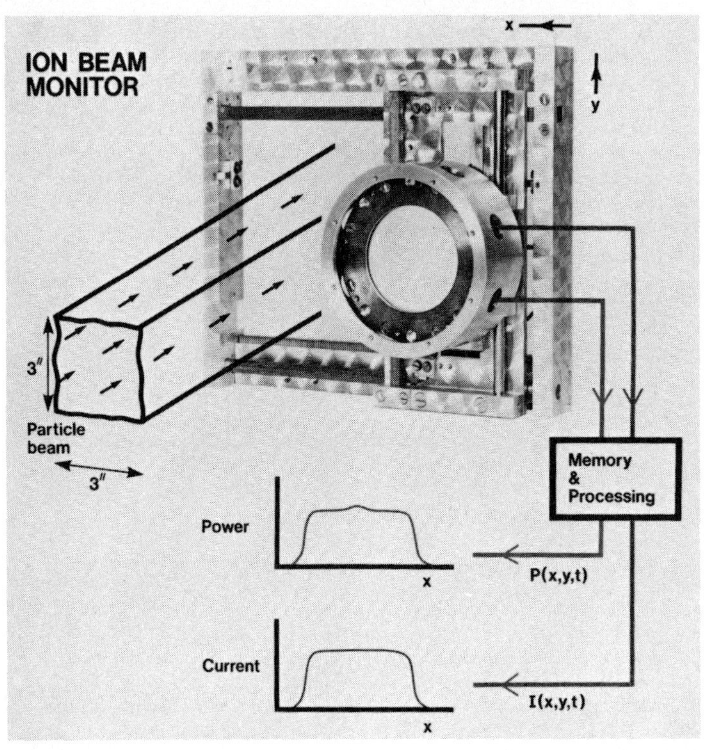

Fig.2 Schematic of the prototype beam monitor, with a calorimeter/Faraday cup for power and current density measurements across the electrostatically scanned beam

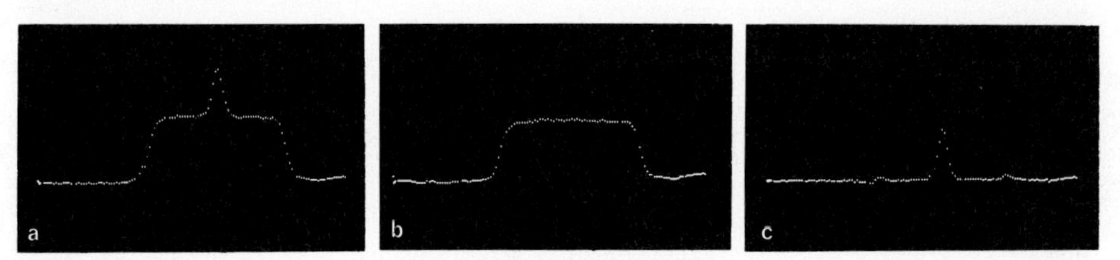

Fig.3 (a) Energy density, (b) current and (c) neutral beam profiles of an electrostatically scanned 200 keV Ar^+ beam measured at a line pressure of $1x10^{-5}$ torr (N_2) using the prototype beam monitor on a low current implanter

within the ion beam. Figure 3 shows experimental profiles plotted whilst using the instrument on the 500 keV implanter.

Finally, an absolute measurement of the retained dose will be possible for certain combinations of ion and substrate, using the Rutherford back-scatter facility within our own laboratory(1).

The sample transporter and beam diagnostic equipment incorporates stepper motor and pneumatic drives and the whole system is designed, eventually, to be under computer control.

3. Calculations and Measurements of the Extracted Beam

To achieve a proper beam at the target, ion-optical calculations were carried out. The optical system of the machine consists of the following parts: ion source with its extraction system, analysing magnet with adjustable pole faces, homogenous-field accelerator tube and the field-free beam lines at earth potential but including electrostatic bending and scanning plates. The calculations showed that for a maximum beam diameter of 15mm at the target, the beam radius and half-angle at the sources should be r_{oxmax} = 0.15mm, r'_{oxmax} = 8 mRad in the x-z plane, and r_{oymax} = 10mm, r'_{oymax} = 1.8 mRad in the y-z plane, (where z is the beam axis and x the horizontal axis). The emittance calculated using these parameters can be seen in Fig.4. The formation of the emittances along the beam path (at the most important places) also are shown in the figure.

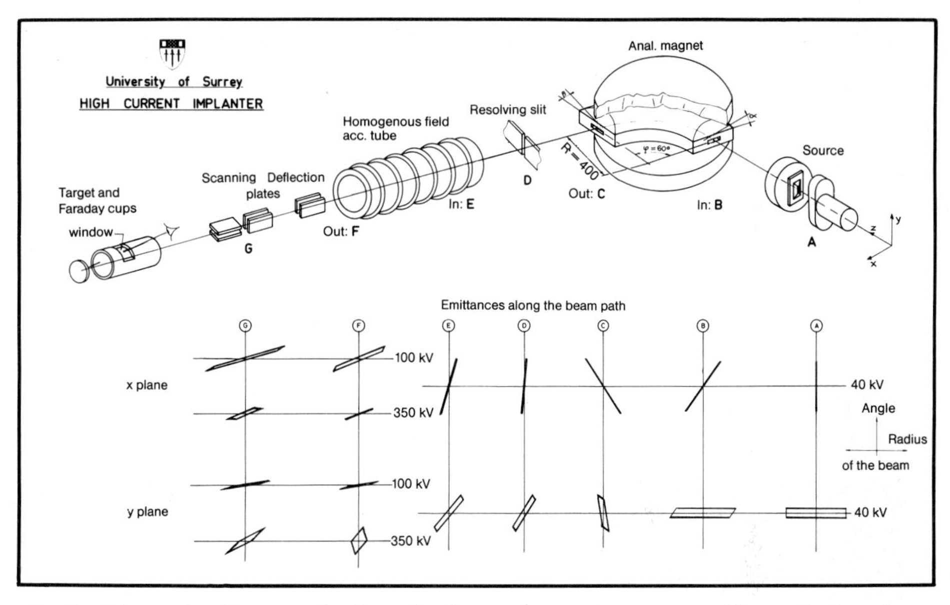

Fig.4. Schematic diagram showing the beam transport system. The calculated beam emittance at critical positions is shown in the lower part of the figure

Efforts were made to measure the emittances at the source. Unfortunately, no absolutely reliable data could be obtained because the plastic foil used to measure the size and angle of the elementary beams was too sensitive, not only to the ions but to the heat radiated by the cathode. But the whole picture suggests that the beam size and angle should be very similar to that mentioned above.

The emittance measurements indicated that the source cathode deeply influences and perhaps changes the emittance during its lifetime. A considerable loss of the cathode material was observed: the original 2.0mm diameter of the cathode became 1.7 and 1.5mm after 15.5 and 20 hours, respectively. The cathode also was distorted taking on a concave shape with 1.4 to 2.5mm deep bending. This bent shape establishes a similar concave emitting surface of the discharge, forming a converging beam instead of the expected parallel or slightly diverging one. Fortunately, the extraction system of the source can be moved along the z axis making it possible for the operator to compensate the changes of the beam shape and angle.

4. Summary of Present State of the Commissioning of the Machine

The measurements of the source emittance, reported above, have been made on the actual implanter. This experimental programme has served as a test of the vacuum system and also has permitted realistic checks to be made of the IR telemetry system. The system works well and is insensitive to noise and spikes on the mains supply and has good immunity from rf noise within the laboratory.

A 40 KeV beam has been analysed and a 1mA beam of Ar^+ shows the expected beam shape. The target chamber is now under vacuum and, as all capital equipment is available, it is anticipated that a beam will shortly be transported into the target chamber.

Acknowledgements

The authors are pleased to acknowledge the work of F.S. Zhou in designing and building part of the telemetry system and C. Knowles for assistance in the assembly and testing of the instrumentation. This work is supported largely by the U.K. Science and Engineering Council.

References

1 P.L.F. Hemment, E. Maydell-Ondrusz and K.G. Stephens: - this conference.

2 P.J. Cracknell, M. Gettings and K.G. Stephens: Nucl. Instr and Methods, *92*, 465, 1971.

3 A. Lurio and J.E. Ziegler: Appl. Phys. Letts., *31*, 482, 1977.

4 P.L.F. Hemment: Low Energy Ion Beams I, Inst. of Phys. Conf. Ser. *38*, 117, 1977.

5. E. Pasztor, L. Kiralyhidi and P. Riedl: Report of the Central Res. Inst. for Physics, Budapest. KFKI-1977-96.

Radio Frequency Ion Accelerator

N.J. Barrett

Department of Electronic and Electrical Engineering, University of Surrey, Guildford, Surrey GU2 5XH, England

Abstract A pilot project to acclerate helium and argon ions was successfully completed (in July 1981) using a radio frequency voltage applied alternately to a series of linear drift tubes. The r.f. power supply was self-oscillating which made the system very simple to run and in general its compact design makes it very economical to build for a range of non-relativistic ions.

1. Introduction

The original r.f. accelerator was a 1.3 MeV machine developed by Sloan and Lawrence(1) in 1931 which was designed for use in the field of high energy particle physics. This accelerator was the forerunner of today's r.f. accelerators which mainly accelerate protons or electrons with little emphasis on heavy ions(2)(3). It now seems appropriate to look at the role of the r.f. accelerator at energies below 1 MeV suitable for most ion implantation applications.

2. Experimental Equipment

A d.c. power supply was used to extract a beam of singly charged ions from an ion source. The ions were then focussed and passed into the r.f. section which consisted of an eight-gap linear drift tube construction. Alternate tubes were linked together with one set connected to the inner of a copper quarter wave co-axial line and the other set, including the first and last tubes, were at earth potential (see Fig.1).

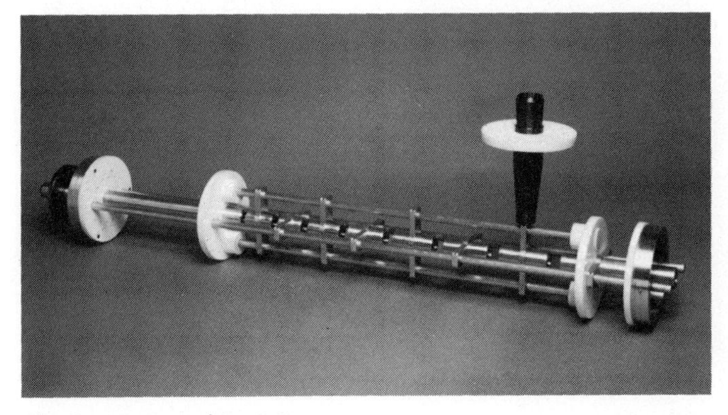

Fig.1. R.F. Drift Tubes

A capacitative probe at the open circuited end of the quarter wave co-axial line was used for feedback to provide self-oscillation. The accelerator was operated at the resonant frequency of the quarter wave line. To change frequency it was necessary to adjust the length of the line. Consequently the transmitter's tapping point into the line had to be repositioned for an optimum impedance match(4) and the length of the feedback cable changed to give the correct phase at the transmitter. This method produced a very stable and clean sine wave on the drift tubes.

Energy variations were achieved by controlling the peak r.f. voltage and the resonant frequency of the quarter wave line. For ion energies greater than 400 keV, more drift tube sections could be added, limiting the peak r.f. voltage to 50 kV which is an optimal value. The ions were accelerated in synchronism with the applied electric field between the drift tubes. The ions then passed through an energy analyser formed by two parallel curved plates with a mean radius of 0.5m. One plate was earthed and the second had a voltage applied to it producing a transverse electric field between them. The mean energy of the ion beam was calculated from equation(1)below.

$$\text{Voltage on plate in kV} = 0.6 \times \text{Mean energy of beam in keV} . \qquad (1)$$

After passing through the energy analyser the beam struck an isolated metal plate where the current was deduced from the voltage measured across a high resistance between the plate and earth potential. The current could be read down to 1 nA which was essential for monitoring the current while adjusting the focussing voltage, the r.f. voltage and the energy analyser (see Fig.2).

Fig.2. R.F. Accelerator

A 1 kW Redifon G341 transmitter was used for the r.f. power supply which was matched into the copper quarter wave co-axial line near the short circuited end(5). The small co-axial cable from the capacitive probe, was taken straight to the transmitter's power amplifier bypassing the wideband amplifier which produced harmonics detrimental to the final output power. The output from the transmitter went to a tapping point which could be moved one metre along the inner of the quarter wave line which gave extra flexibility to the matching network in the transmitter.

2.1 Beam Characteristics

Impurity ions in the beam will also be accelerated but in most cases they will have energies significantly lower than the required ions. Thus the energy analyser can separate these impurities assuming they have a different e/m ratio from the required ion. By increasing the number of gaps the energy of the impurities will be reduced even further. With a d.c. accelerator all the singly charged ions appear, in theory, with more or less the same energy, but the impurity ions will have a different momentum, and consequently can be deflected away from the required ions by a magnetic field.

The ions tend to bunch around a particular phase of the r.f. cycle, i.e. the phase stable position. For example, ions which enter the r.f. cycle with a phase spread of 55° may exit the final gap with a phase spread of 25°. There is only one phase stable position when the r.f. accelerator is correctly synchronised with the initial ion beam (see graphs 3 and 4). However more than one current peak at different energies can occur when the r.f. voltage is not correctly adjusted.

The bunching of the ions is an inherent characteristic of a r.f. accelerator. An ion which is slightly ahead of the phase stable position will be accelerated by a smaller electric field whereas an ion entering a gap behind the phase stable position will experience a larger electric field and so catch up.

A computer programme was written in BASIC assuming no field penetration. Some of the theoretical predictions from this programme are shown in graphs 1-4. The energy of an ion beam with optimum accelerator conditions can be theoretically predicted by the programme within a few per cent. However at voltages below the optimum conditions a far higher energy distribution appeared than predicted. An explanation of this is that the energy gain is higher near the edges of the tubes rather than at the centre of the drift tubes due to field penetration. In order to predict these higher ion energies using the programme, the tube voltage must be about 10% more than expected. At optimum conditions this effect is not seen as the maximum energy is reached and any ions experiencing a larger electric field near the edge of the tubes will not gain higher final energies.

A programme was run to take account of field penetration. The non-linear field was divided up into sections and assumed to be linear within these sections. The fields within the gaps were very approximate and more calculations will have to be carried out to obtain precise results. The programme did predict that at optimum acceleration conditions 7% more volts are required on the tubes compared with a linear voltage drop across each gap and also the current would be about 18% less.

There are four main variables which are related to each other:

m	the mass of the ion to be accelerated
V_{dc}	the d.c. extraction voltage
V_{pk}	the peak r.f. voltage
f	the resonant frequency of the line .

The relationships between these variables are dependent upon the dimensions of the drift tubes and the gaps between them. To achieve optimum accelerating conditions the following equations were used:

$$V_{dc} = \alpha \times \frac{m}{\text{mass of the He ion}} \times f^2 \qquad (2)$$

$$V_{pk} = \beta \times V_{dc} \qquad (3)$$

$$\text{maximum energy (eV) of ion beam at optimum conditions} = (8.35 \pm 0.07) \times V_{dc} \qquad (4)$$

The value obtained for α after a series of tests was $1.07 \pm 0.02 \times 10^{-10}$ $V \cdot s^2$. The accelerator was designed with a value of $\beta = 1$, however as previously shown β was theoretically calculated to be between 1.07 and 1.1 due to field penetration.

The theoretical results showed that with no field penetration $\beta = 1$ to obtain maximum energy at optimum conditions. For maximum currents $\beta = 1.02$. This variation was too small to confirm experimentally. With β increasing from 0 to 0.7, which is below the optimum conditions and V_{dc} set for optimum conditions, the beam energy will increase slowly as shown in section A of Figs. 3 and 4. As more r.f. voltage was applied to the drift tubes, i.e. β was increased, the energy of the beam increased very quickly as shown in

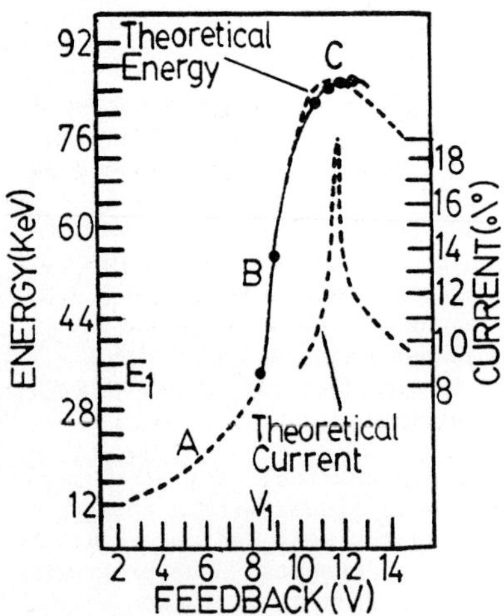

Fig. 3. Beam energy as a function of feedback voltage for He^+ at a frequency of 9.8 MHz and initial energy of 10.2 keV

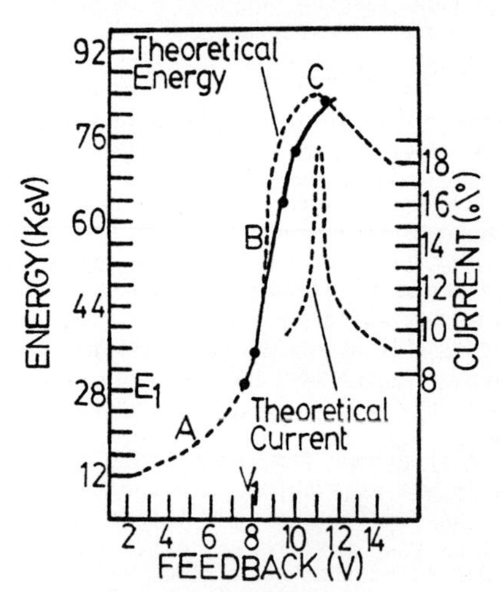

Fig. 4. Beam energy as a function of feedback voltage for Ar^+ at a frequency of 3.08 MHz and initial energy of 10.1 keV

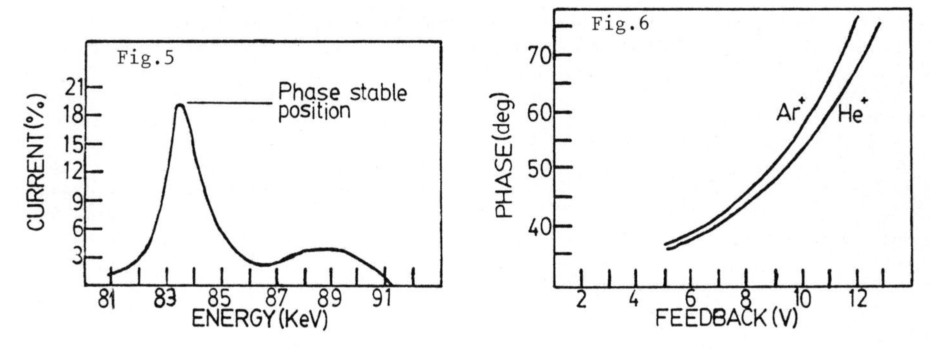

Fig.5. Theoretical beam current while scanning the energy analyser

Fig. 6. Change in the phase stable position with increasing feedback

section B. The beam energy reached a maximum at C and decreased as β increased. The same was true for the theoretical current which is shown as a percentage of the initial beam current. However it will be noted that when β = 0, the current will be 100% as the beam will be monoenergetic with all the beam passing through the energy analyser. At C, the r.f. voltage is large enough to keep the ions in synchronisation with the oscillating electric field.

In Figs. 3 ,4 and 5 the theoretical curves have been plotted against the feedback voltage to the transmitter when in self-oscillation. The feedback voltage which produced the lowest beam energy in the experimental results (E_1) was used to convert the theoretical r.f. voltage for the theoretical energy E_1 into the measured feedback voltage (V_1). Assuming that the feedback voltage was proportional to the r.f. voltage on the drift tubes the rest of the theoretical results were plotted.

3. Experimental Method

The gas line was pumped out by fully opening the needle valve which controlled the gas flow over a tungsten filament in the ion source. It was then closed and the chosen gas was allowed to fill the line. The drift tube region was pumped down to 10^{-5}m bars.

At first the r.f. voltage was not activated and a 25 keV beam was set up using the d.c. power supply only. It was not possible to operate the energy analyser with energies below 25 keV. The r.f. voltage was then turned on coupling energy into the beam with a feedback voltage of about 6V. The voltage supply for the energy analyser was kept the same as V_{dc}, was decreased until the beam current dropped to 1 nA at which point the r.f. voltage was increased. This operation was carried out until V_{dc} was decreased to its optimum value as in equation (2). After this the peak r.f. voltage (V_{pk}) was increased and monitored by the feedback until the optimum conditions were reached. Also the energy analyser was adjusted to find the energy at which the maximum current occurred each time V_{pk} was increased.

4. Results

Many experimental runs were carried out changing the d.c. extraction voltage at the same time as the r.f. voltage. These results have been omitted as there were too many variables to make a useful interpretation of the results. During this time a 100 keV helium beam was obtained but with very low current, clearly indicating that the optimum conditions had not been reached. The best results were obtained with a 10.2 keV helium beam which was accelerated to 86 keV using a frequency of 9.8 MHz and a 10.1 keV argon beam accelerated to 83.5 keV with a frequency of 3.08 MHz; beam currents were 0.07 μA and 0.05 μA respectively(‡). Table 1 shows the increase in energy as the feedback voltage was increased.

Table 1: Energy of ion beams as the feedback voltage was increased

feedback in V(9.8 MHz)	Energy of He^+ ions in keV
0	10.2
8.5 ±0.1	34.7 ±0.7
9.1 ±0.1	54.0 ±1.0
10.8 ±0.1	81.7 ±1.5
11.6 ±0.1	84.2 ±1.5
12.0 ±0.1	84.8 ±1.5
12.4 ±0.1	85.4 ±1.5
12.5 ±0.1	86.0 ±1.5
12.7 ±0.1	85.3 ±1.5

feedback in V(3.08 MHz	Energy of Ar^+ ions in keV
0	10.1
7.6 ±0.05	30.0 ±0.7
8.1 ±0.1	36.0 ±0.7
9.4 ±0.1	66.1 ±1.0
10.1 ±0.1	73.0 ±1.5
11.5 ±0.1	83.5 ±1.5

4.1 Discussion of Results

A major reason for the low beam energy was discovered after the project had finished. One of the P.T.F.E. insulators had an electrical breakdown due to a sharp edge on a support rod located in P.T.F.E. which had been overlooked. Passed experience indicates that the problem initially occurred between 20 and 30kV which indicates an energy up to three times larger may have been possible.

The voltage used to produce the initial energy for a beam was too low to extract large currents from the ion source. The current would increase dramatically from the source if larger voltages could be used. By increasing the voltage from 10 kV to 40 kV the current would be 25 times greater. However, the d.c. voltage cannot be chosen independently from the peak r.f. voltage and there was insufficient range on the latter to allow a d.c. voltage of 40 kV. Current losses are also due to the energy analyser only accepting a 3% energy spread as ions outside this energy window will collide with the curved plates of the energy analyser.

It was expected that because argon ionises very well the final current would be much higher than the helium current. This was not the case as the r.f. voltage was below the optimum conditions. The lower voltage on the drift tubes was a result of not having the correct matching conditions while accelerating argon. This was purely due to a supply problem as there was not enough copper tubing left or time to adjust to the correct impedance. It was noted that the current increased dramatically as the peak energy was approached.

The difference between the theoretical and experimental results (graphs 1 and 2) was caused by the fact that once the meter reading aerial current

‡ The effect of secondary electrons has been allowed for.

reached a value of 9.5 the transmitter became non-linear. This caused the feedback to be non-linear with respect to the r.f. voltage on the drift tubes. With the impedance mismatch in the argon case this was emphasised even more when compared with the theoretical results.

With the time and equipment available it was not possible to make continuous measurements of the beam current but near the optimum conditions it was observed that a small variation in voltage on the energy analyser reduced the current considerably. (Theoretically shown in Fig. 5). It was also found that the extraction voltage was critical. For example, in one particular run by reducing this voltage by 3% to bring it closer to the optimum conditions, the current doubled. It is important to point out that each time the extraction voltage on the r.f. tubes was changed the focussing voltage had to be adjusted as well as the energy analyser.

5. Quarter Wave Line Considerations

The quarter wave line approach was chosen because of its high quali y factor and low cost. However with higher powered oscillators the short circuit of the line may have to be cooled as in these experiments the temperature rose to 60°C.

With the quarter wave line used there were basically three sections; the first was the length between the accelerator and the tapping point slide (see Fig.2), the second was the tapping point slide and the third was the length which ends in a short circuit. There are two problems involved; changing the total length of the line and then fitting the tapping point slide into the line near the correct impedance.

The quarter wave line has many electrical properties in its favour. The problem is changing the length of the line quickly but with a suitable design it should be possible. For appearance and ease of operation an LC network could replace the quarter wave line but this would be more expensive and the power efficiency of the system would go down.

The drift tubes are part of the resonant circuit and so act as an extension of the co-axial line causing a phase shift along the accelerator. This results in a different peak voltage on each drift tube. This will not affect the output energy greatly as the phase stable position will change to compensate for the variation in voltage but the beam current will drop. If the phase change along the drift tube is extreme there are several possible solutions. One is to connect the co-axial line to the centre position of the accelerator but with a long accelerator there will still be a phase shift from the centre to either end. A loading coil would help the situation whereby inductance is used to change the phase of the r.f. voltate. Accelerators with more than thirty gaps may require two or more r.f. power supplies excited by one master oscillator. Finally the co-axial line could be split into several equal lengths connected along the accelerator producing the same phase at each point.

6. Focussing

It is anticipated that there will be space charge problems(6) occurring below the predicted current due to the high instaneous current produced by bunching. With high beam currents care must be taken with focusing. The gaps between the drift tubes have focussing properties. With a constant voltage the gap will focus the beam. In the first half of the gap there are radial forces towards the centre axis and in the second half there are equal forces away from the axis. However as the time to transverse the second half is shorter than the first half the beam is focused. This effect decreases with increasing energy and when considering an r.f. voltage the overall effect tends to be defocussing, as the defocussing radial forces in the second half of the gap are larger than the focussing effects in the first half.

Focussing is improved if the accelerator is designed to run very close to the peak of the r.f. cycle. This would however tend to reduce the effect of bunching. With a short accelerator there should be no problem focusing before and after the r.f. section. With more than 10 drift tubes it may be beneficial to provide focussing in the drift tube region. A simple method would be to divide the longer earthed tubes into saddle-field lenses(7)(8). Care must be taken as this method will change the phase of the ion bunch with respect to the r.f. voltages. This however could be an advantage when considering the change in the peak r.f. voltage along the accelerator.

A possible method is to replace the drift tubes by quadrupole lenses(9) and superimpose the r.f. voltage on top of the d.c. voltages so as to focus the beam continuously. This structure may be necessary if beam currents greater than 200 μA are required, with large energies.

7. Conclusions

The pilot project has shown good agreement between experimental results and computer simulations which should give confidence for future designs. A possible important application is the ability to add extra energy to existing ion beams. If, for example, a 400 keV increase in energy were needed, a 2m long section, which would include focussing facilities, would have to be incorporated into the existing system. As the accelerator uses r.f. voltages, high static voltages are avoided and furthermore the design also allows the ion source to have a very low extraction voltage. In addition, the specimen target chamber can be at earth potential and as low peak voltages are used the size of insulators are smaller than for a d.c. accelerator of the same energy. The overall size of the r.f. accelerator gives the opportunity to use a small vacuum system.

One disadvantage of this design is the loss of current due to the partial use of the r.f. cycle. Theoretically, when field penetration in the drift tubes is taken into account, the efficiency of the accelerator (the ratio of beam current at the target to that from the ion source) is 14.9% for a 3% energy variation in the beam and 20% for a 5% energy variation. The efficiency of the system could be improved by careful design but the limit for most applications would be 25% when a small energy distribution is required. Methods have been considered which would bunch the ions before the r.f. section which may increase the efficiency to 75%.

In principle the r.f. accelerator is very efficient at producing high beam energies whereas the d.c. accelerator is ideal for large beam currents. For example, the r.f. accelerator appears to be commercially viable when compared with a d.c. machine, for energies above 400 keV with current beams up to 150 μA. If currents of 500 μA are required then the r.f. machine may be viable at 600 keV. Obviously the cost is dependent on who constructs the accelerator and the particular application for which it is built, so the estimates are only notional.

Heavy ion accelerators are used in many fields. For example, inducing nuclear reactions where the energy required must be at least equal to the height of the Coulomb barrier between the two reaction elements. When considering uranium the energy required would be a minimum of 6 MeV. Such an accelerator would have approximately 62 gaps, a 100 kV peak r.f. voltage and have a 12 metre long r.f. section.

The results from this feasibility study indicate that there is room for exploration of the machine in the future. With the construction of a 1 MeV r.f. accelerator it would be possible to compare it with Van der Graaff technology and at the same time have a low cost heavy ion accelerator not generally available to the scientific and industrial communities.

Acknowledgements

This project was initiated by the late Professor D.R. Chick and it is to him that primary acknowledgement must be made. The constant support and encouragement which has been received from Professor C.W. Miller who collaborated with Professor Chick on the original idea is gratefully acknowledged.

Acknowledgement must also be made of the financial help received from the Paul Instrument Fund Committee of the Royal Society who made this programme of work possible and to Sir Charles Oatley representing the Committee who expressed continued interest in the project.

Thanks must be expressed also to Professor K.G. Stephens who undertook to be responsible for the project after the death of Professor Chick.

Interest in the project has been expressed by a number of colleagues in the Department and the Department of Physics at the City University. A great deal of practical advice has been given by J.C. Sunderland. In addition, help and advice has come from Q.V. Davis. Continual support has been forthcoming from the staff of the Accelerator Laboratory and the Electrical Engineering Workshop.

The loan of a transmitter from Rediffusion Radio Systems Ltd. through Professor Miller is also acknowledged.

References

1. D. Sloan, E. Lawrence: Phys. Rev. *38*, 2021 (1931).
2. G. Nassibian, J. Bennett, D. Broadbent, S. Devons, R. Hoisington, V. Miller: Rev. Sci. Instr. *32*, 1316 (1961).
3. J. Slattery, D. Becker, B. Hamermesh, N. Roy: Rev. Sci. Instr. *44* (1973).
4. J. Groszkowski: *Frequency of Self-Oscillations* (Polish Scientific Publishers, 1964) p.315.
5. T. Moreno: *Microwave Transmission Design Data*, (McGraw Hill, 1948).
6. C.W. Miller: *Ion Accelerator Report* (May 1977).
7. O. Klemperer, M. Barnett: *Electron Optics* (Cambridge University Press, 1971), p.82.
8. E. Harting, F. Read: *Electrostatic Lenses* (Elsevier Scientific Publishing Company, 1976).
9. G. Nagy, M. Szilagyi: *Introduction to the Theory of Space Charge Optics* (MacMillan Press Ltd. 1974) p.389.

Part II

Ion Sources

Performance of the Bethge-Baumann Ion Source with Radio Frequency Operation

H.F. le Roux and A.G.K. Lutsch

Research Unit for Solid State Electronics, Department of Electrical Engineering, Rand Afrikaans University, P.O. Box 524, Johannesburg 2000, Republic of South Africa

1. Introduction

High energy ions are required for the direct implantation (i.e. without subsequent drive-in diffusion) of the emitter, base and buried layer of bipolar transistors[1]. These rather shallow structures ($\simeq 1\ \mu m$) are required for high frequency operation. Direct implantation eliminates the need for epitaxial growth which is difficult to implement for such thin layers.

Two paths are open for obtaining high energy ($\geqslant$1MeV) ions, namely the use of an ion accelerator with the necessary energy capability or employing an ion source with reasonable yield of multiple charged ions. In order to achieve penetration (R_p) to the order of $1\mu m$, both alternatives should be investigated. We will, however, concentrate on the latter, less expensive alternative.

The requirements for such an ion source would be:

(i) A relatively high beam current for double (and possibly triple) charged ions in order to maintain reasonable implantation times.

(ii) A relatively high ratio of double charged to single charged ion current for maintaining a low level of contamination of the implantation equipment, and particularly the mass separator.

(iii) Longer operation times without special attention, since the ion source of most accelarators is situated at a high potential which in turn complicates recharging and/or rebuilding of the source. This problem is even worse in van de Graaff accelerators.

The source according to Bethge and Baumann[2] fulfills a number of the abovementioned requirements, and therefore provides an interesting basis for further development.

Improved performance of the Bethge-Baumann source could possibly be achieved by means of pulse operation. The results thus far are however not very encouraging[2,3], perhaps due to impedance matching problems; see below.

Operation with a radio frequency source however, appears to hold more promise for the following reasons:

(a) The probability for exciting multiple charged ions should be high at all frequencies between say 10MHz and 100MHz.

(b) Radio frequency sputtering takes place at lower gas pressures and consequently the contamination level is reduced.

One of the practical problems is the matching of the radio frequency source impedance (usually 50 ohms) to the input impedance presented by the sputter electrodes of the ion source. One of the basic difficulties encountered is the fact that this impedance changes considerably with the advent of a plasma in the ion source. Ideally a continuous matching system, by means of which proper matching can constantly be achieved, should be used. It is also worth mentioning that the source impedance during plasma conditions is also affected (albeit to a lesser extent) by the applied d.c. magnetic field within the source. The source used, is shown in Fig. 1, where (1) refers to 9S20K stainless steel and (2) to 1.4571 stainless steel.

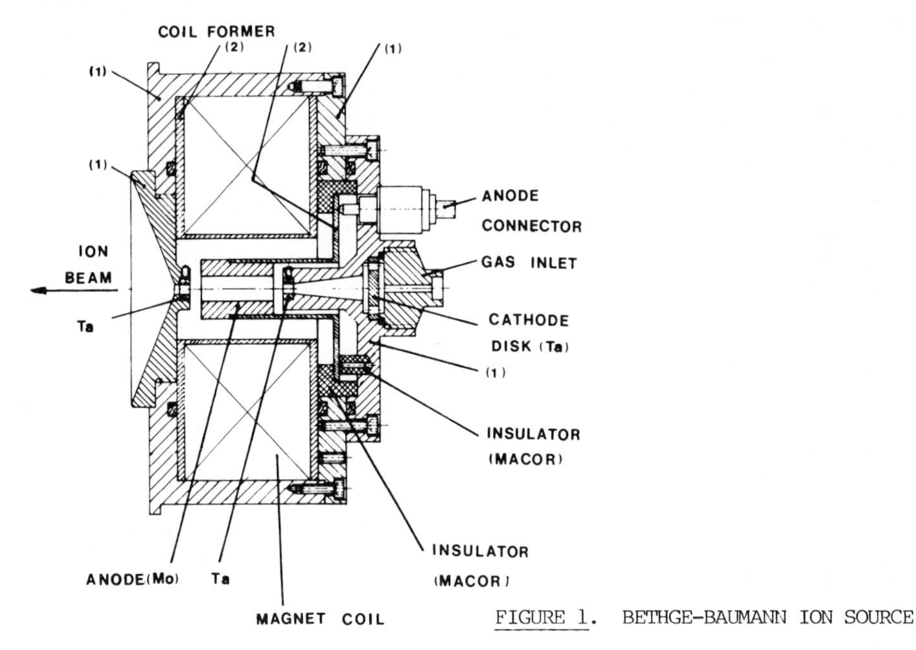

FIGURE 1. BETHGE-BAUMANN ION SOURCE

2. Experiments

A radio frequency generator with an output impedance of 50Ω and a maximum power output of 200 W was coupled via a Π-type matching network (two parallel capacitors with a series inductor) to the source electrode. In order to initiate a plasma, the matching network was first detuned; in order to achieve a high output voltage the gas inlet valve was set for a comparatively high gas flow and the source magnetic field was set to a high value.

Instantaneous ion generation was observed on the standard beam profile monitor, although the generating conditions were far from optimised. The matching network was tuned for maximum power transfer (i.e. max forward power combined with minimum reflected power). Furthermore the gas pressure was reduced whilst the source magnetic field was maintained. Under these conditions, using an extraction potential of 20 kV, without any further acceleration, a max beam current of 1 μA for Ar^+ was observed. At the same time the beam current for Ar^{++} was observed to be approximately 12% of the above value. An appreciably lower gas pressure was observed on the vacuum gauge in the proximity of the source, indicating that the plasma, as expected, is maintained at a lower gas pressure of argon than required when operating the source from d.c. power.

However, a compromise must be made between impedance match (and consequently operation stability) and more favourable excitation of multiple charged ion, which occurs at a relatively high radio frequency voltage, which favours inner shell excitation.

3. Conclusions

As expected, the relative yield of double charged ions of this source becomes higher when excited with radio frequency power while at the same time a plasma is maintained at a lower pressure of source gas.

Further work has to be undertaken in order to prove that the absolute yield of the ion source is indeed higher with radio frequency operation as opposed to d.c. operation. To achieve this an accelerating potential will have to be applied in order to operate the source under standard implantation conditions. It is also assumed that the electron optics of our implanter is not yet optimum. It is also necessary to evaluate the performance of this source for other source materials that are of interest for semiconductor technology.

Acknowledgments

The authors would like to thank the following persons and/or organisations for making this project possible.

(i) K. Bethge and H. Baumann for making their basic design available to us, and for valuable discussions.

(ii) The Research Grants Division of both the CSIR and the RAU for the funding of the project.

(iii) The mechanical workshop of the RAU, and in particular H.H. Nieuwoudt for the actual machining of all the source components.

References

1. H. Baumann, K. Bethge, W. Fuss, E.F. Krimmel, R. Langfeld, A.G.K. Lutsch, H. Runge, S. Witkowski: "Laser and Electron Beam Annealing of Buried Layers produced by MeV Ion Implantation", Proceedings of the Symposium on Laser and Electron beam processing of electronic materials, Vol 80-1, The Electrochemical Society, Inc, P.O. Box 2071, Princeton NJ, pp 152-160.
2. H. Baumann and K. Bethge: "The Frankfurt PIG Ion Source", Nuclear Instruments and Methods 189, 107 (1981)
3. P.D. Townsend, J.C. Kelly, N.E.W. Hartley: "Ion implantation, sputtering and their application", Academic Press, 1976, pp 164ff.

Emittance Measurements on an Indirectly Heated Heavy-Ion Source

E. Pásztor and L. Királyhidi

Central Research Institute of Physics, P.O. Box 49,
H-1525 Budapest, Hungary

1. Introduction

Heavy ion sources with indirectly heated cathode are preferred in many cases because of their long lifetime and because of the ease with which the extracted ion current can be stabilised. But the stability of the beam is only one of the important parameters; the uniformity of the dose implanted into the wafers strictly depends on the shape of the ion beam as well. The shape of the beam, i.e. its radius and angle on the target, is a function of the same parameters at the source. This function can be characterised by the emittance of the beam.

From the point of view of stable work with an implanter no change at all of the parameters would be a desired optimum, but that is physically impossible. Apart from the natural changes occurring during the life of the source, there is the deliberate adjusting of the extracting voltage, of the pressure, etc., all of which affect the emittance of the source and so can also affect the implanted dose. It seemed to be very useful to investigate the effects of such changes of the different source parameters on the emittance since, for example, serious troubles caused by an overfocused beam can be avoided by having some knowledge regarding the emittance.

2. General Effects

It is obvious that an ion source having not a circular but slit extracting geometry has different emittances in the "x" plane (defined by the shorter size of the slit) and in the "y" plane (defined by the longer size of the slit) [1]. Emittance measurements carried out after changing many parameters of the source have - quite unexpectedly - shown that there is no substantial change of emittance in the "x" plane. This emittance seems to be defined by the geometry of the source-extraction system and is only slightly affected by the other source parameters. So, having a well-constructed geometry suitable for providing the required beam on the target, no variation of the beam radius and angle should be expected using the source with various parameters. On the other hand, there are serious alterations in the "y" plane. In view of this, our efforts were concentrated on measuring the effects in the "y". In the following, all results, remarks, figures, etc. refer to the emittance in the "y" plane.

An indirectly heated ion source has different modes of working. The different modes mean substantially different extracted currents. Such modes can be generated by changing the source pressure as well as the magnetic field [2]. All the following remarks regarding the effect of the pressure should be understood in one of the possible modes; in other words, the effect of pressure on the emittance can be observed in so far as the working mode of the source does not change, in another mode the whole trend begins again (for details, see later).

The third general feature of our results is that all the observed effects on the emittance were more characteristic using higher extracted currents. This means that with high currents any variation of the source parameters should be carried out with great care.

Finally, our experience is that all of the effects on the emittance are somehow linked with the shape of the emitting surface of the discharge. In certain cases, e.g. in the case of the effect of the extracting voltage, this link is obvious; in other cases, such as pressure or magnetic field, the influence is not so direct, but very probable.

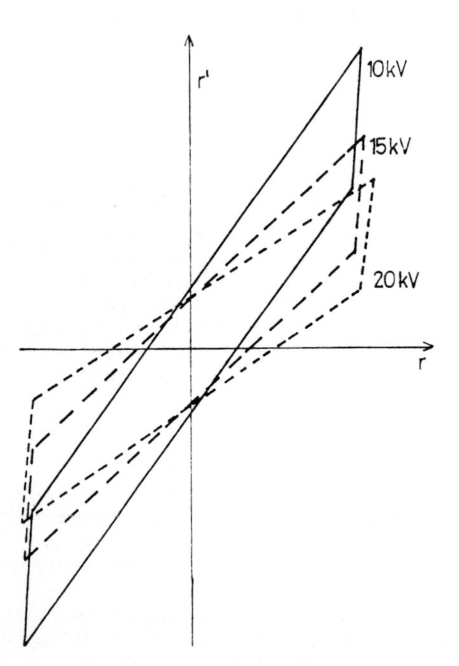

Fig. 1. Effect of the extracting voltage on the emittance

3. Effect of Extracting Voltage

Using different gaseous materials such as N, Ar, CO_2, no effect could be measured on the emittance. There is possibly some slight change in the case of solids, this will be reproted in the future. With gases, increasing the extracting voltage, e.g. in order to increase the ion current, one may expect some decrease of the area of the emittance diagram, according to general ion-optic rules. As can be seen in Fig. 1, the source works in accordance with the general rules, the emittance decreases with increasing extracting voltage. But, it should be underlined, this decrease is due to the decrease of the beam angle not to the beam radius. The probable cause of the phenomenon is the longer radius of the emitting surface of the discharge with higher extracting voltages. (Using too high voltage, one can just extract the plasma through the slit, thereby producing a diverging beam instead of a converging one.)

Because the extracting voltage has a significant effect on the emittance, it is highly recommended that the same extracting voltage always be used. The requirement to produce different currents can be fulfilled by changing other parameters, primarily by correctly controlling the arc current.

4. Effect of Gas Pressure

If the pressure in the source is increased, a similar decrease in the beam angle can be observed, as was seen with increasing extracting voltage (Fig. 2). However, if the pressure exceeds a certain value, the source pops into another working mode where the previously "high" pressure means a relatively low one, so the earlier small angle suddenly increases and the whole process starts again. That is why the operator has to be very careful when increasing the pressure to obtain a higher current. It can happen that the previously well-focused beam, sometimes just as the required higher current is achieved, suddenly defocuses and causes breakdowns, sparks, increasing secondary current with higher radiation level, etc.

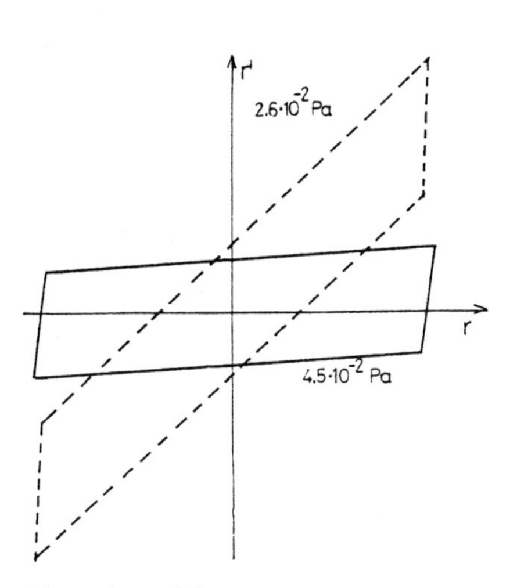

Fig. 2. Effect of the gas pressure on the emittance

5. Effect of Magnetic Field

As opposed to the case of the extracting voltage and gas pressure, the lower magnetic field generates a smaller beam angle, i.e. decreasing the magnetic field leads to a decreasing beam angle (Fig. 3).

Of course, the magnetic field - as does the pressure or the extracting voltage - influences the yield of the source. This indicates that it is a complex and complicated task to find an appropriate set of paramters for a reliably working ion source, even if one has a well-stabilised, easy working source such as the indirectly heated arc-discharge-type ion source.

6. Summary

Measurements were carried out on an indirectly heated heavy ion source using different materials to be ionised and different working parameters (gas pressure, extracting voltage, etc.). There is practically no effect when changing the source parameters in the "x" plane, but increasing extracting voltage and

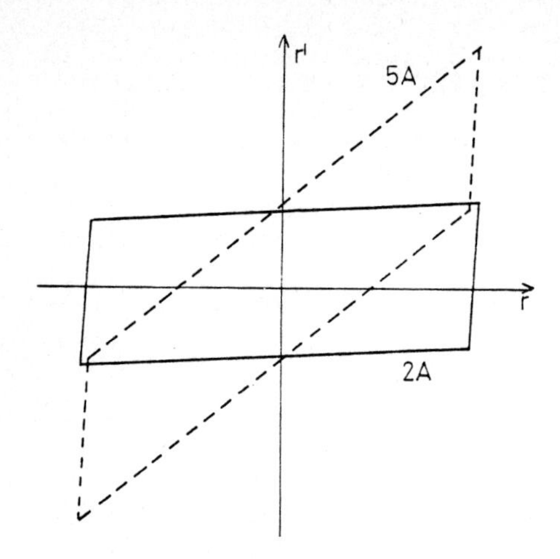

Fig. 3. Effect of the magnetic field on the emittance

gas pressure result in a decreasing beam angle in the "y" plane; the same is true if the magnetic field is decreased.

References

[1] E. Pásztor, L. Királyhidi, P. Riedl, KFKI Report No 96 1977
[2] E. Pásztor, Low Energy Ion Beams, 1980, Conf. Series of Inst. of Phys. No 54, p.345

A High-Brightness Duoplasmatron Ion Source*

R. Keller

GSI, Gesellschaft für Schwerionenforschung mbH, Postfach 110541,
D-6100 Darmstadt, Fed. Rep. of Germany

Abstract

Ion-beam lithography relies on high-brightness beams up to the 100 μA range. For such intensities, the well-known Duoplasmatron ion source is a good choice as it offers high efficiency and easy operation with many gases. The usually applied technique of beam formation, however, cannot succeed in producing highly brilliant beams.

In this study, the GSI Duoplasmatron for multiply charged heavy ions was modified according to the rules of high-current ion-beam generation. The anode-outlet bore is now placed far from the magnetic-field maximum, allowing for an "inner expansion" of the dense plasma column. A very precisely self-aligning accel/decel extraction system is directly attached with its insulator to the anode flange.

Several gases have been used in this source; the top result for argon at 15 keV beam energy was a 105 μA ion current with an emittance of 2.8 mm mrad and a normalized brightness of 16 A/(mm mrad)^2.

1. Introduction

For ion-beam lithography and similar techniques, beams of medium currents but high optical quality are essential [1]. When judging ion sources that produce such beams, it is somewhat complicated to compare the results obtained with different ion species. Therefore, in the following, some basic quantities will be defined that describe the most important parameters of ion beams in a general way.

Many of these definitions are frequently used with high-current ion sources, and the main features of the extraction system presented here are also adopted from these sources. Starting from the required values of various beam parameters, and considering the results with high-current sources, the choice of a Duoplasmatron as ion source to produce the type of beams in question will then appear quite convincing.

2. Definitions of Beam Parameters

High-brightness beam currents of different ion species generally scale as [2]:

* This study was funded by NTG Nukleartechnik, D - 6462 Hailer, Fed. Rep. of Germany.

$$I_{tr} \propto \frac{S^2 \cdot U^{3/2}}{(1+aS^2)\cdot(\zeta/A)^{1/2}} \quad (1)$$

where I_{tr}: transported ion current; S: aspect ratio of the extraction system, S=r/d with r: radius of outlet aperture and d: extraction gap width; U: extraction voltage; A: atomic mass number; ζ: charge state; a: dimensionless parameter, depending on desired beam quality; $a \sim 3$.

Because of equation (1), we define as "normalized transported current" the quantity $I_{tr,n} = I_{tr} \cdot \sqrt{A/\zeta}$; its dimension (mA) is put into brackets in the following, to avoid confusion with absolute currents. The charge state ζ is 1 for the beams treated here, and thus ζ will be omitted from now on.

The beam quality is described by the value of the (absolute) emittance ε, which is defined as the area A_E taken by all the particle trajectories in the two-dimensional phase space, divided by π: $\varepsilon = A_E/\pi$. For a diverging beam in the plane of its waist, the emittance is simply calculated as product of the waist radius r and the divergence angle α_0 of the trajectories crossing the axis, at least as long as the emittance figure can be described by an ellipse, which is fulfilled in most of the cases.

The acceptance of a beam transport system is the maximum emittance a beam can have that still passes the system without losses.

The normalized emittance ε_n is defined as $\varepsilon_n = \beta \cdot \gamma \cdot \varepsilon$, where $\beta = v_i/c$; c: velocity of light in vacuum; v_i: ion velocity; $\gamma = (1-\beta^2)^{-1/2}$. One can derive from Liouville's theorem that the normalized emittance is a constant, independent of the beam energy.

The term "brightness" relates the beam current to the emittance. The frequently used term "normalized brightness" B_n will here be referred to as "emittance-normalized brightness" $B_{\varepsilon n} = I_{tr}/\varepsilon_n^2$. Much more useful to compare sources, however, is the "current-normalized brightness" B_{cn}, here defined as $B_{cn} = I_{tr,n}/\varepsilon^2$. The reason is that for a given beam-transport system, currents of different ion species delivered from the same source should scale as $1/\sqrt{A}$ within the same acceptance, that is, with identical absolute emittance ε. This holds as long as physical effects within the source plasma, such as different ion temperatures or collective motions, are not dominant.

3. Required Beam-Parameter Values

The following derivation will be conducted for an argon beam, extracted at 30 kV, and $I_{tr,n}$ - 1 (mA) is the value of reference for a medium normalized current.

From high-current sources, it is known that top values of the emittance-normalized brightness reach 10 A/(mm mrad)^2 [3]. This brightness value implies that at an absolute current $I_{tr} = 1/\sqrt{40}$ mA = 158 μA, the normalized emittance must be $\varepsilon_n = 4 \cdot 10^{-3}$ mm mrad, or the absolute emittance ε = 3.1 mm mrad.

If we now look at the usual high-current extraction, out of either a typical high-current source or the classical Duoplasmatron with expansion cup, beam-divergence angles of 20 mrad are already a very good result. This means, however, that the beam-waist diameter must be smaller than 0.31 mm; and finally, knowing that this waist diameter is about one-half the diameter of the emitting aperture [4], the latter is limited to 0.6 mm.

When choosing a source to meet these requirements, one must further observe the fact that the plasma density necessary to match the extraction conditions increases inversely to the outlet aperture [2]. As an example, a 110 mA/cm^2 ion-current density was sufficient to yield 55 mA Ar^+ from a high-current source [5]; while in this study, nearly 800 mA/cm^2 only produced a 1 mA beam, of which 100 µA were of high quality. Therefore, it seems extremely difficult to obtain the desired high-brightness beams from the rather diluted plasmas of high-current sources, or within a Duoplasmatron expansion cup.

The source presented in this study is a Duoplasmatron, the anode of which is shifted away from the maximum magnetic field; this configuration causes the plasma to expand somewhat in front of the outlet aperture. The so-called inner expansion assures a more homogeneous plasma over the whole aperture cross section, but does not reduce the plasma density in the outlet plane too much. The advantage of the Duoplasmatron is that it has to yield the plasma density which would match the extraction conditions at the outlet plane only for a column diameter of a few mm, while the high-current sources or expansion cups are usually several cm wide. This small size effectively reduces the total discharge power necessary for narrow outlet apertures, which would become prohibitive for wider plasma columns.

4. Source Design

The well-established GSI Duoplasmatron for multiply charged ions [6] has been used as the main body of the new source. Its anode and extraction system, however, have been completely changed, compared to the former design; see Fig.1. In an enlarged sketch of the essential parts, Fig.2, one sees that the outlet plane is now situated in a region of lower magnetic field, while the source for multiply charged ions has this plane exactly at the maximum of the magnetic field (so-called B_{max} anode).

A minimum wall thickness of 0.3 mm is sufficient for the anode to withstand the discharge power. The outlet angle on the anode bore has been made 67° against the axis, though 45° seems to yield better results with high-current sources [7]. The explanation is that the anode flange is also shaped with an angle of 67°, which facilitates the design of the extractor electrodes; further, it is quite difficult to machine the phase angle of 45° over the minute total length of 0.05 mm (about 0.1 times the anode bore diameter); and last but not least, our own computer simulations of high-current extraction systems have shown that the transported current obtained with the 67° angle is only 5% less than the value with 45°.

The anode bore was 0.4 mm wide in all cases. This aperture size probably produces a beam-waist radius of 0.1 mm, but in the emittance calculations, see Table 1, the value of 0.125 mm has been assumed to give a security margin. The value 0.4 mm, compared to 0.6 mentioned in the preceding section, was chosen since the higher plasma density rendered necessary by the smaller outlet hole in the case of hydrogen favors the share of atomic atomic ions H_1^+ as apposed to molecular ions $H_{2,3}^+$. The current reduction, on the other hand, seemed to be tolerable.

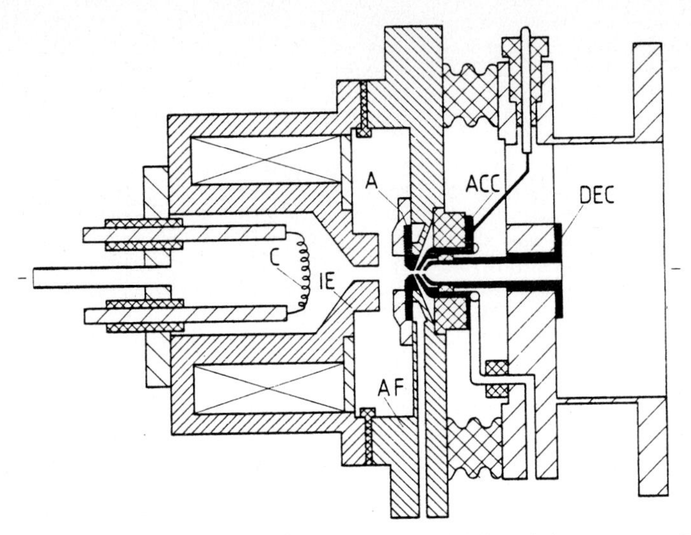

Fig. 1. Cross-sectional view of the high-brightness Duoplasmatron.
C: tantalum filament cathode, IE: intermediate electrode, A: anode, AF: anode flange, ACC: accel-extractor (negative-biased), DEC: decel-extractor (grounded). The extraction electrodes are directly cooled and directly aligned to the anode axis by two inner insulators

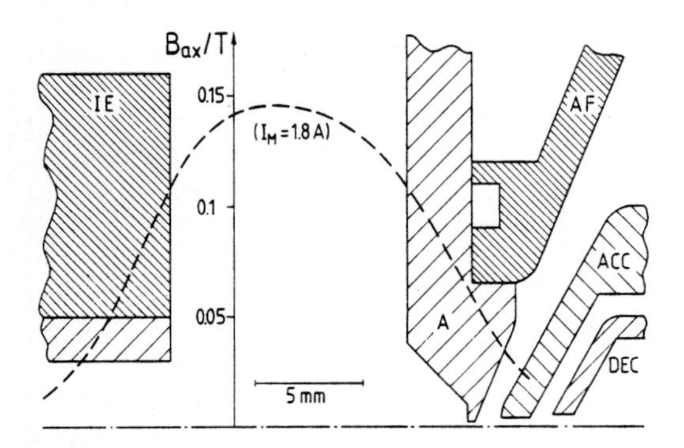

Fig. 2. Detailed sketch of the central source region (half section).
The slope of the axial component of the magnetic flux density B_{ax} is indicated by the broken line. The curve is obtained at 1.8 A coil current.
IE: intermediate electrode (ferromagnetic) with titanium insert, A: anode, AF: anode flange (ferromagnetic), ACC: accel-extractor, DEC: decel-extractor

Generally, the brightest beams are produced when the extractor-hole diameters are typically 3/4 the diameter of the outlet hole. In the present case, even with an extractor-bore diameter equal to the outlet diameter, the power load on the accel extractor was too high and led to erosion of this electrode. Therefore, the extractor bores were enlarged to 0.8 mm, compared to 0.4 mm for the outlet hole. This brought a drop of 10% in beam brightness, but also a great reduction of the sparking rate.

Under certain high power conditions, the decel electrode suffered from too high a thermal load. Thus, its diameter was once more increased, to 1.1 mm. The influence of the decel-bore diameter on the beam quality, on the other hand, is very weak, considering the relatively low electric fields involved.

The ferromagnetic intermediate electrode of the source had a bore of 10 mm diameter, and a titanium tube with 4 mm inner diameter was pressed into it in order to reduce the discharge-current requirement. With N, He and H, however, ignition was nearly impossible, and consequently the bore in the titanium tube was increased to 7 mm. The best hydrogen results were obtained with a purely ferromagnetic intermediate electrode, having a 6 mm bore.

5. Results

All measurements have been done on the high-current test stand of GSI, equipped with several screened Faraday cups. Aperture diameters and distances between the cups used and the source are listed in Table 1. At 2.6 m distance from the source, one emittance measurement has been made with a hydrogen beam focused by a magnetic triplet. Mass analysis was obtained by using a 90^{0} double-focusing magnet with a 30 mm cup at 4.2 m from the source.

Table 1. Measured and Derived Results

Ion species	I_{tr} (μA)	ε (mm mrad)	$10^3 \cdot \varepsilon_n$ (mm mrad)	$B_{\varepsilon n}$	d_{FC} (m)	D_{FC} (mm)	$I_{tr,n}$ (μA)	$10^5 \cdot B_{cn}$
Ar^+	100	2.8	2.5	16	1	45	632	8.06
Ne^+	150	2.8	3.5	12	1	45	674	8.60
N^+	200	2.8	4.2	11	1	45	748	9.54
He^+	350	2.8	7.9	5.6	1	45	700	8.93
$H^+_{1,2,3}$ †	443	2.8	12.1	3.0	1	45	581	7.41
$H^+_{1,2,3}$ ††	1250	5.7	24	2.2	0.49	30	1672	5.15
H^+_1	520	3.1 †††	17.5	1.7	4.2	30	520	5.41

†: Species share for $H_1^+/H_2^+/H_3^+$: 50/28/22%,with effective mass $\bar{A}$ = 1.72. ††: Species share 46/29/25%, with $\bar{A}$ = 1.79. †††: The emittance value given is calculated as $\varepsilon = \sqrt{\varepsilon_v \cdot \varepsilon_h}$ from the two measured emittances: vertical ε_v = 2.55 mm mrad and horizontal ε_h = 3.75 mm mrad; the difference between both is due to the nonuniform acceptance of the focusing triplet in both planes. d_{FC}: Distance between source and Faraday cup: beam freely drifting except for d_{FC} = 4.2 m. D_{FC}: Diameter of Faraday cup. The other symbols are explained in section 2. $B_{\varepsilon n}$ and B_{cn} are given in A/(mm mrad)^2.

The total ion current has never been directly measured, but from the power supply load, one can see that it amounts to about 7 mA in the case of hydrogen, taking into account that the high electron-screening voltage inhibits all the electrons from streaming back to the source and thus participating in the load current. The current and brightness values given below thus apply to the collimated part of the beam only, passed into the different Faraday cups.

The beam energy was always 15 keV, with a negative voltage of 2.5 kV applied to the accel extractor. After conditioning the extraction system, no sparking occured at these voltages for more than 30 min.

The share of doubly charged ions was largest with argon, and was always below 4% particles. It can be further reduced if one accepts slightly lower current values than shown here, since then the matching plasma density can be reached at higher gas pressure and lower discharge power.

As mentioned in section 2, the current-normalized brightnesses are expected to be constant in the first order, rather than the emittance-normalized brightnesses usually found in the literature. The first five lines of Table 1 demonstrate that this assumption is valid, allowing for a maximum deviation of 13% from the mean value $B = 8.51 \cdot 10^{-5}$ A/(mm mrad)^2. The last two lines of the table show B_{cn} values similar among themselves, but somewhat different from the former mean value, because the experimental conditions were changed. These significant deviations indicate that the total beam has an inhomogeneous radial-density profile, in accordance with general experience.

The best brightness values obtained up to now with high-current sources are: $B_{\varepsilon n} = 9.5$ A/(mm mrad)^2 with 13 mA absolute xenon-ion current from a DuoPIGatron [8], giving $B_{cn} = 5.66 \cdot 10^{-5}$ A/(mm mrad)^2, and $B_{\varepsilon n} = 16.1$ A/(mm mrad)^2 with 16 mA argon current from a reflex-discharge ion source with five-electrode extraction [9], giving $B_{cn} = 2.7 \cdot 10^{-4}$ A/(mm mrad)^2. The GSI Duoplasmatron with B_{max} anode and 16 mm expansion cup [6] yielded 12 mA Ar with $B_{\varepsilon n} = 0.063$ A/(mm mrad)^2 and $B_{cn} = 8.4 \cdot 10^{-7}$ A/(mm mrad)^2.

Acknowledgements

The kind permission of the GSI to conduct this study, and especially the supporting interest of Dr. N. Angert, are thankfully acknowledged.

References

1. G. Dearnaley, J.H. Freeman, R.S. Nelson, J. Stephen: Ion Implantation (North Holland Publ. Comp., Amsterdam, 1973), p. 275
2. J.R. Coupland, T.S. Green, D.P. Hammond, A.C. Riviere: Rev. Sci. Instr. 44, 1258 (1973)
3. R. Keller: Symposium on Accelerator Aspects of Heavy Ion Fusion, GSI-82-8, Darmstadt (1982)
4. W.S. Cooper et al.: Nucl. Fusion 12, 263 (1972)
5. R. Keller: Nucl. Instr. Meth. 189, 97 (1981)
6. R. Keller: Radiation Effects 44, 201 (1979)
7. Y. Ohara, S. Matsuda, H. Shirakata, S. Tanaka: Japn. J. Appl. Phys. 17, 432 (1978)
8. M.R. Shubaly: Inst. Phys. Conf. Ser. 54 (Bristol, 1980), p. 333
9. R. Keller, P. Spädtke, K. Hofmann: this conference

Optimization of a Single-Aperture Extraction System for High-Current Ion Sources

R. Keller, P. Spädtke, and K. Hofmann[†]

GSI, Gesellschaft für Schwerionenforschung mbH, Postfach 110541,
D-6100 Darmstadt, Fed. Rep. of Germany

Abstract

Single-aperture extraction offers much higher beam brightness compared to multiaperture systems, but the attainable ion current is limited by geometrical restrictions. Insertion of a "puller" electrode into the extraction gap then permits the use of a larger aperture with correspondingly higher current, and without deteriorating beam quality. Additionally, in our system, the electron-screening electrode is enclosed between two ground electrodes, assuring high operational reliability.

The optimization of this five-electrode system was performed both by experiments and by calculations, using the computer code AXCEL, version GSI. Theoretical and experimental dependences of beam quality from various parameters coincide very closely.

The top result at 50 keV beam energy was 38.5 mA of Ar^+ ion current, with an absolute emittance of 42 mm mrad and an emittance-normalized brightness of 8 A/(mm mrad)^2.

1. Introduction

This study is concerned with high-current singly charged argon-ion beams of maximum brightness. It was motivated by the GSI activities in the field of heavy-ion fusion, where beams of typically 50 mA are required [9]. Such beams are usually obtained by multiaperture extraction systems; with these, however, one must accept a considerable loss in brightness, compared to a single-aperture system.

Therefore, the question arises of to what current limits a single-aperture system can be improved. By combining computer simulations of the extraction process using the code AXCEL [1], version GSI [2], and experiments with the high-current ion source ELSIRE [3], we tried to give an answer to this. The results are of interest not only for fusion accelerators but also for high-current ion-beam facilities.

2. Theoretical Considerations

Before going into detail, some formal definitions and laws regarding the beam quality will be given.

[†]Fachhochschule Wiesbaden, Fed. Rep. of Germany

More than the entire extracted beam current, I, its transportable fraction, I_{tr}, is of importance. The value of I_{tr} is determined by the (absolute) beam emittance: ε: $\varepsilon = A_E/\pi$, where A_E is the area of the beam trajectories within the two-dimensional phase space. Generally, two phase-space diagrams have to be considered, for two orthogonal transverse directions. In our case, however, cylindrical symmetry can always be supposed; and therefore, one emittance figure taken in one radial direction is sufficient.

In the plane of a beam waist, its emittance is calculated as the product of waist radius r_0 and divergence angle α_0 of those trajectories that cross the axis of symmetry: $\varepsilon = r_0 \cdot \alpha_0$, at least if the emittance figure is an ellipse, which is normally fulfilled.

The acceptance of a beam line is defined as the maximum emittance a beam can have that is still passed through the system without losses. Complex beam-transport systems have different acceptances for the two transverse directions, even if the original beam is perfectly symmetrical.

The normalized emittance is defined as $\varepsilon_n = \beta \cdot \gamma \cdot \varepsilon$, where $\beta = v_i/c$; v_i: ion velocity; c: vacuum light velocity; $\gamma = (1 - \beta^2)^{-1/2}$. ε_n is an invariant for beam-energy changes.

The quantity "brightness" relates the transported current to the beam emittance; here, the "emittance-normalized brightness" will be used: $B_{\varepsilon n} = I_{tr}/\varepsilon_n^2$, often simply called "brightness", B or B_n. The above-mentioned difference in brightness between beams of equal current, obtained from either single- or multiaperture extraction systems, is demonstrated in Fig.1. For actually measured beams, Fig. 2 shows the same effect, though the currents were not exactly equal.

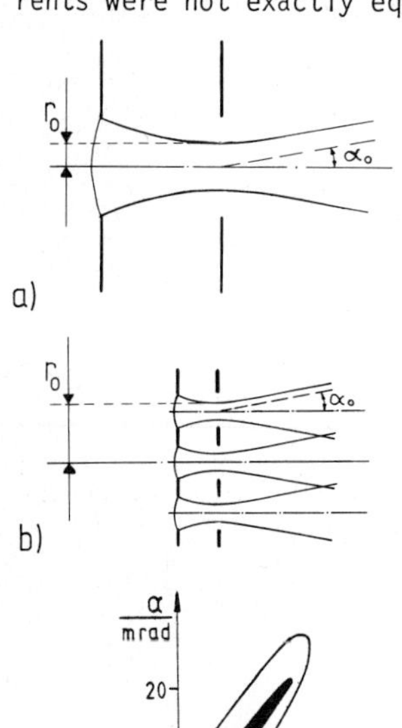

Fig. 1. Comparison between single-aperture a), and multiaperture b), extraction. Both systems have the same emitting area, assuming seven apertures for b). The effective beam waist radius r_0, which for equal divergence-half-angle α_0 determines the emittance, is much smaller for the single-aperture system. In this example, the resulting ratio of both radii leads to a brightness gain of a factor of 6.6 in favor of the single-aperture system

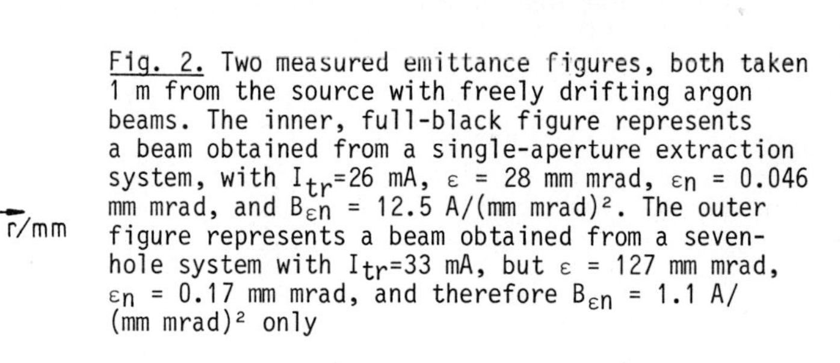

Fig. 2. Two measured emittance figures, both taken 1 m from the source with freely drifting argon beams. The inner, full-black figure represents a beam obtained from a single-aperture extraction system, with I_{tr}=26 mA, ε = 28 mm mrad, ε_n = 0.046 mm mrad, and $B_{\varepsilon n}$ = 12.5 A/(mm mrad)². The outer figure represents a beam obtained from a seven-hole system with I_{tr}=33 mA, but ε = 127 mm mrad, ε_n = 0.17 mm mrad, and therefore $B_{\varepsilon n}$ = 1.1 A/(mm mrad)² only

The formation of high-brightness ion beams in a single-extraction aperture has been extensively treated in the past, both theoretically and experimentally [4]. The developed theory combines the space-charge limit for a stable ion flow (Child/Langmuir law) with the optical-lens action of the extraction apertures. As a result, the currents of extracted low-divergence ion beams should scale as:

$$I^{theor} \propto S^2 \cdot \frac{U^{3/2}}{(A/\zeta)^{1/2}} , \qquad (1)$$

while experimentally, the actually-transported high-brightness beam currents were found scaling as:

$$I_{tr}^{exp} \propto \frac{S^2}{1 + a\,S^2} \cdot \frac{U^{3/2}}{(A/\zeta)^{1/2}} , \qquad (2)$$

with S: aspect ratio $S = r/d$; r: outlet-aperture radius; d: extraction-gap width; U: extraction voltage; A: atomic-mass number; ζ: ion-charge state; a: "aberration factor": dimensionless fitting parameter, $a \sim 3$ for conventional accel/decel systems and an acceptance angle of 22 mrad.

According to Eq. (2), the aspect ratio of usual systems should not exceed the limit $S \sim 0.4$, as for higher values the gain in transported ion current is quite low. Only systems with refined outlet-aperture contours [5], [6] arrive at values of $S \sim 0.6$ without losing beam quality. This suggests that the deviation of Eq. (2) from (1) is due to aberration effects within the extraction aperture which are not treated in the theoretical model.

Still higher aspect ratios, $S \sim 1$, can be used by introducing an additional "puller" electrode into the extraction gap [7], as with this, the aberrations can also be corrected by changing the electrical potentials applied, and not only by refining the outlet contours.

In our study, we optimized such an extraction system, varying outlet size and contours as well as the voltage ratio of the two gaps, and in all cases looking for the matching ion-current density.

One aspect of Eq. (2) has not yet been considered in the discussion above; that is, the voltage dependence of the beam currents.

Due to the effect of breakdown discharges, the high voltage across a gap cannot be raised infinitely. In the ion-source-related literature, two empirical laws for the breakdown voltage $\hat{U}$ are published: the classical $\hat{U} \propto d^{1/2}$ law [4], here written in the form:

$$\hat{U} / kV = 19\,(d / mm)^{1/2} \qquad (3)$$

and a linear law [8] :

$$\hat{U} / kV = 10\, d/mm. \qquad (4)$$

Several existing or proposed systems range between these two limits; see Fig. 3. A long time ago, a formula had been derived for RF accelerators that also covers d.c. voltages [10]. This Kilpatrick law is originally written in the implicit form:

$$W\,E^2 \exp(-\,1.7 \cdot 10^5 / E) = 1.8 \cdot 10^{14} \qquad (5)$$

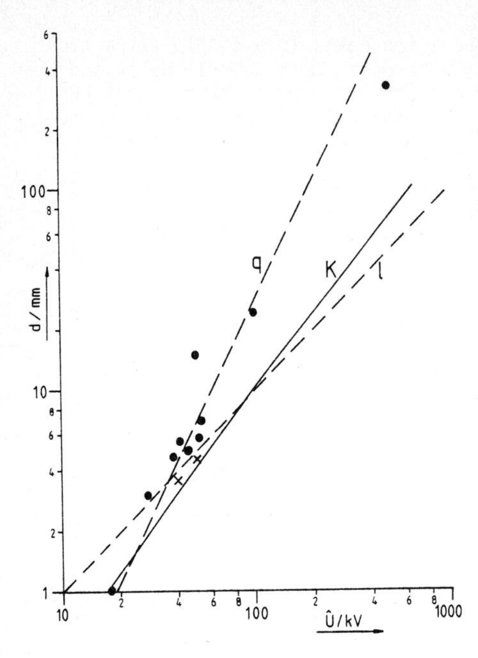

Fig. 3. Breakdown laws for extraction gaps. Û: breakdown voltage, d: gap width, q: quadratic law, K: Kilpatrick d.c. law, l: linear law. The filled circles indicate the limits d(Û) for existing or proposed systems, listed in [9]; the crosses show the limits for two widths of our second gap

with W: ion-energy limit (eV) and E: gap field-strength (V/cm). For this report, Eq. (5) has been numerically evaluated and plotted in the form $d = f(\hat{U})$.

In fact, Eq. (5) gives the best overall fit to the marked experimental points, keeping in mind that the true limit must never be exceeded.

3. Mechanical Design

A simplified cross section of our system is shown in Fig. 4. We adopted design criteria developed for a spark-resistant high-current accelerating column [11]. The main flanges, made from stainless steel, are water-cooled; the insulators made from polyimide. The source outlet and the first two extractor plates are easy to exchange and made from molybdenum; the other two electrodes are machined as entire pieces from stainless steel.

A more detailed view of the electrodes, together with typical applied potentials, is given in Fig. 5. The electron-screening electrode is enclosed between two grounded electrodes because, with this arrangement, high-voltage sparks in the extraction gaps do not affect the screening electrode or its power supply; therefore, the reliability of the whole system is much enhanced [12].

The positions of the source outlet and puller plates are freely adjustable to the axis of the other three electrodes, which are directly aligned among themselves by the close-fitting insulators. Screening and second ground electrodes are not cooled, but no sign of overheating was ever seen during the experiments.

The gap widths can be adjusted by inserting or taking away distance rings between the two extractor flanges and the electrode-support

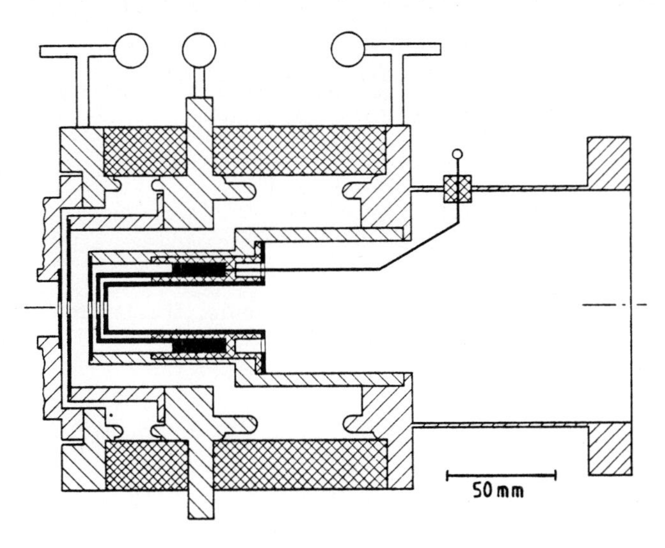

Fig. 4. Simplified cross section of the extraction system. The ion source is thought to be at the left, ending in the outlet plate (first full black line from the left). The beam is extracted to the right. Insulators are cross-shaded

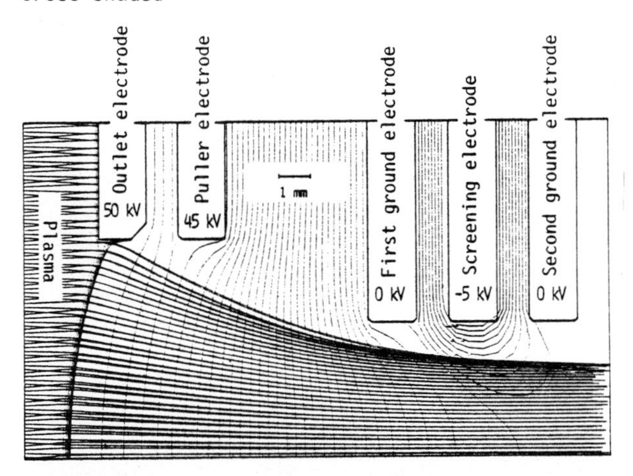

Fig. 5. Electrode configuration of the system with applied electrical potentials. The ion trajectories and equipotentials within the gaps are calculated by AXCEL-GSI

tubes; the rings are not shown in Fig. 4. During this study, the gaps were fixed to 1 mm (first gap) and 4.5 mm (second gap), allowing the full 50 kV of the high-voltage supply to be applied to the second gap alone, leaving the puller on source potential, whenever desired.

In a preliminary selection by computer calculations, two outlet-aperture contours were chosen to perform the main optimization. The first one, "Ohara", is rather robust and promises good mechanical and thermal stability [13]; see Fig. 6. The second one bases on a double-angle design

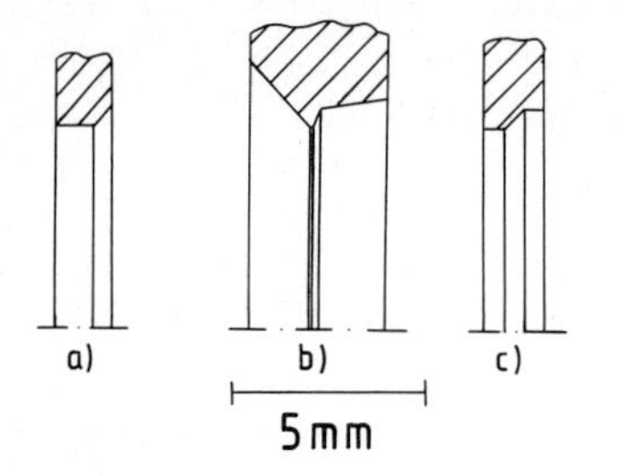

Fig. 6. Contours given to the apertures of the source-outlet electrodes.
a): Ohara, b): Shubaly,
c): Hofmann/Keller/Spädtke (HKS)

[14]. Since its fabrication would have required special tools, the design was simplified in another series of computer runs; and only this "HKS" contour was really tried, besides the Ohara contour.

4. Strategy of the Optimization

The essential feature of the code AXCEL is that it can adjust the position and shape of the ion-emitting plasma meniscus in iterations, converging to a self-consistent solution of the coupled Poisson and Vlassov equations. The plasma-physical background of the meniscus formation is derived from a one-dimensional theory [15].

The GSI version of the code gives the calculated equipotential curves, particle trajectories, and the resulting emittance figure at the last ground-electrode plane in a detailed plot, as well as the percentage of transported current within a chosen acceptance angle, which was taken as 20 mrad in this study.

For single-parameter variations, the last iteration of the preceding run is used as the first iteration of the next one, to speed up the convergence. Space-charge compensation by electrons can be simulated in the code, from the plane of the screening electrode onwards in the downstream direction of the beam.

An example of emittance plots is given in Fig. 7. One should note that for practical purposes, as a measure of the emittance, the envelope

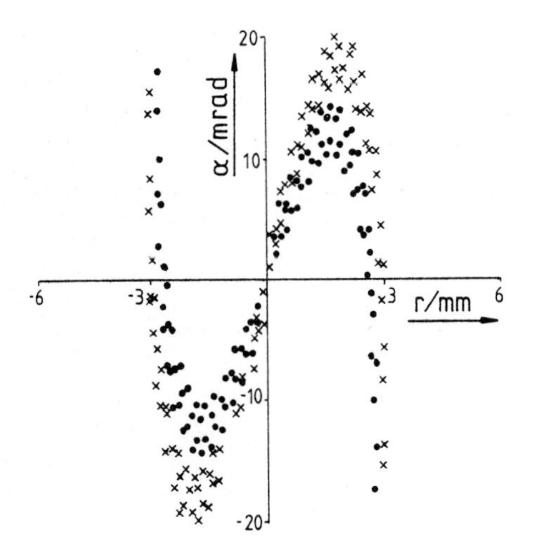

Fig. 7. Calculated emittance plots for beams of different current density j, all other parameters held constant. Points outside of ± 20 mrad are not shown. The crosses represent a well-matched beam (j = 28 mA/cm²), while the filled circles indicate that the density of this other beam (j=26 mA/cm²) is too low. Transported currents: 29.5 mA (79.6% of the total extracted beam) for the crosses and 26 mA (75.3%) for the circles. Extraction system: Ohara contour, apertures 13/15/8/8/8 mm from source-outlet to second grounded electrode; voltages +50/+45/-6 kV at outled, puller, and screening elecrodes

ellipse is taken for such beams rather than the area really covered by trajectories, since it is prohibitive and without sense to construct beam lines with an acceptance closely matching these S-shaped figures.

Therefore, the absolute emittance values in this example both amount to 3 mm · 20 mrad; consequently, the emittance-normalized brightness values are 3.1 $A/(mm\ mrad)^2$ for the well-matched beam, and 2.7 $A/(mm\ mrad)^2$ for the other one.

The computer optimization of the system was conducted in the following way. Starting from a certain configuration, one geometrical parameter was systematically changed; and for each of its values, the ion-current density and voltage ratio between the two extraction gaps were varied, until the relative maximum of the transported beam current was found.

In parallel, the experiments gave good indications of what density and voltage-ratio values to start with. On the computer, then, the effects of new outlet-electrode contours could be predicted more easily before actually cutting the electrodes.

As to the trajectory picture (Fig. 5.): in optimizing a system, one tries to reduce the convergence angle of the outer trajectories when the inner ones are already laminar. This is done by flattening out the strong curvature of the outer zones of the equipotentials, increasing the current density, or shaping the outlet contour in a different way. If one goes too far with this procedure, however, the inner trajectories become divergent and the transported current decreases again.

5. Experimental Results

The experiments were performed on a special high-current test stand. All results shown here were measured by a Faraday cup at 1 m distance from the source, with a 45 mm Ø aperture, and by a mechanical emittance-measurement device (pepper pot and Kapton foil to detect the beamlet size and position).

The source was pulsed in all cases at 10% duty factor, 50 Hz. Whenever the obtained ion-current pulses were not uniform in time due to dynamic effects in the source plasma, the maximum value was recorded, since the study was oriented towards the demonstration of beam-transport possibilities rather than the production of beams for a user. Up to an outlet aperture of 10 mm Ø, the transported current pulses were uniform.

One example of an experimental optimization is given in Fig. 8. The maximum transported current is obtained with a 6 mm Ø aperture when the puller electrode has a 8 mm Ø bore. Note that the optimum voltage ratio U_1/U_2 shifts from 0.1 to 0.0 with increasing puller aperture. This means that the aberration-correcting action of the widest puller aperture could also have been obtained by using a considerably thicker outlet plate, shaped accordingly. This arrangement does not yield the absolute maximum current, however.

The most important experimental result is shown in Fig. 9. The HKS contour always yields slightly higher currents than the Ohara contour, but the difference is nearly negligible. The continuous curve in Fig. 9. is a fit to all experimental points together, in terms of Eq. (2). It obeys the following relationship:

$$I_{tr}^{exp} = 5.65 \cdot 10^{-8} \cdot \frac{S^2}{1 + 1.7\,S^2} \cdot \frac{U^{3/2}}{\sqrt{40}} \left[A \cdot V^{-3/2}\right] . \quad (6)$$

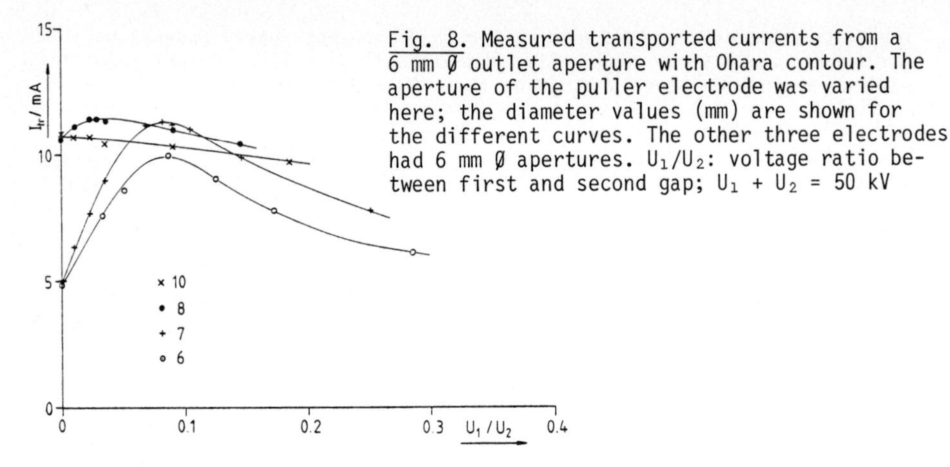

Fig. 8. Measured transported currents from a 6 mm Ø outlet aperture with Ohara contour. The aperture of the puller electrode was varied here; the diameter values (mm) are shown for the different curves. The other three electrodes had 6 mm Ø apertures. U_1/U_2: voltage ratio between first and second gap; $U_1 + U_2 = 50$ kV

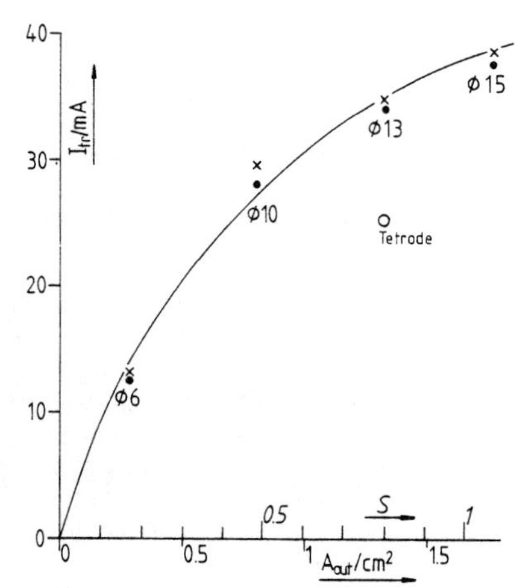

Fig. 9. Measured transported currents at optimum extraction-system parameters, depending on the outlet-aperture area A_{out} (lower scale) and the aspect ratio S (outlet-aperture radius vs distance between outlet and first ground electrode). Crosses: HKS contour; filled circles: Ohara contour; continuous curve: see text (sect. 5, para. 4). The open circle marks the maximum current obtained with a 13 mm Ø Ohara contour after the puller electrode was removed from the system

Thus, our data confirm the validity of a current-scaling law of the type of Eq. (2), but the parameter a amounts to only 1.7 here; this is about half the value given in Ref. [4].

The reduction of the "aberration factor" a, compared to conventional extraction systems, is the numerically expressed benefit brought by our two-gap extraction system. In fact, a control measurement with a four-electrode configuration, where the puller electrode was absent, demonstrated that the correcting action of this electrode is indeed responsible for the enhanced transported-beam current yielded by the five-electrode system.

It should be emphasized that our system has one electrode more than comparable systems used elsewhere, since the screening electrode is enclosed between two ground electrodes rather than being in front of a single ground electrode. Thus, our pentode compares to usual tetrodes; and our four-electrode system, used in the control measurement mentioned, corresponds to a conventional accel/decel system with three electrodes.

Beam parameters for which emittance measurements have been made are listed in Table 1. It is seen that the Ohara contour produces somewhat

Table 1. Beam-quality parameters for different system configurations. The symbols are explained in the text above

I_{tr}/mA	ε_n/mm mrad	$B_{\varepsilon n}$/ A/(mm mrad)^2	U_1/kV	U_2/kV	System configuration
16	0.031	16.1	3.0	47.0	Ohara Ø 10/10/6/6/6
26	0.047	11.8	0.15	49.85	Ohara Ø 10/10/6/6/6
29.5	0.061	7.8	0.15	49.85	HKS Ø 10/10/6/6/6
11.4	0.054	3.8	0.15	49.85	Ohara Ø 6/ 8/6/6/6
12	0.060	3.3	0.15	49.85	HKS Ø 6/ 6/6/6/6
36	0.067	8.0	0.15	49.85	Ohara Ø 15/15/10/10/10
33	0.17	1.11	-	33.4	7-apert. triode Ø 4, gap 5 mm, Ohara

brighter beams than the HKS contour, even if the currents are lower, due to the smaller emittance values. This systematic trend may be exploited, depending on whether highest brightness values or highest currents are desired, by further improving the Ohara contour towards the former goal, or the HKS contour towards the latter one. In our study, we were oriented more towards the high-current goal.

In the last line of Table 1, beam parameters are shown that were obtained from the identical ion source ELSIRE, but using a seven-hole accel/decel system. At even less current than yielded by the pentode, the brightness of this system is lower by a factor of 8 than the pentode brightness.

The overall top current result with the pentode was 38.5 mA Ar^+ at 5.9/44.1 kV, from a Ø 15/15/10/10/10 mm configuration with HKS contour. Its brightness should amount to 8 A/(mm mrad)^2, corresponding to the value in the sixth line of Table 1.

The best heavy-ion-beam brightness value published up to now has been $B_{\varepsilon n}$ = 9.5 A/(mm mrad)^2, for a 13 mA, 32 kV xenon beam from a triode extraction system [14]. To compare these two results obtained for different ion species, one should make use of the current-normalized brightness $B_{cn} = I_{tr}\sqrt{A}/\varepsilon^2$ [16]. In this scale, the triode system arrives at
$B_{cn}^{tri} = 5.7 \cdot 10^{-5}$ A/(mm mrad)^2, while our system yields
$B_{cn}^{pent} = 1.3 \cdot 10^{-4}$ A/(mm mrad)^2.

Acknowledgements

Parts of this study are taken from the graduate thesis of K. Hofmann at the Fachhochschule Wiesbaden. Thanks are due to Dr. U. Wolfangel, who supervised this thesis and gave valuable technological suggestions.
We further wish to thank K. Leible, F. Schäffer, and R. Vrtal for technical assistance.

References

1. E.F. Jaeger, J.C. Whitson: ORNL-TM-4990, Oak Ridge (1975)

2. P. Spädtke: to be published (GSI Darmstadt)

3. R. Keller: Nucl. Instr. Meth. 189, 97 (1981)

4. J.R. Coupland, T.S. Green, D.P. Hammond, A.C. Riviere: Rev. Sci. Instr. 44, 1258 (1973)

5. M.R. Shubaly, R.W. Hamm: IEEE Trans. Nucl. Sci. NS-28, 1316 (1981)

6. B. Piosczyk: KFK 3180 B, Karlsruhe, p. 83 (1981)

7. E. Thompson: Inst. Phys. Conf. Ser. 38 (Bristol 1978), p. 236

8. T.S. Green: Inst. Phys. Conf. Ser. 54 (Bristol 1980), p. 271

9. R. Keller: Symp. on Accelerator Aspects of Heavy Ion Fusion, GSI-82-8, Darmstadt (1982)

10. W.D. Kilpatrick: Rev. Sci. Instr. 28, 824 (1957)

11. J.D. Hepburn, M.R. Shubaly, J. Ungrin: Inst. Phys. Conf. Ser. 54 (Bristol 1980), p. 158

12. E.A. Meyer, D.D. Armstrong, J.D. Schneider: IEEE Trans. Nucl. Sci. NS-28, 2687 (1981)

13. Y. Ohara, S. Matsuda, H. Shirakata, S. Tanaka: Japn. J. Appl. Phys. 17, 432 (1978)

14. M.R. Shubaly: Inst. Phys. Conf. Ser. 54 (Bristol 1980), p. 333

15. S.A. Self: Phys. of Fluids 6, 1962 (1963)

16. R. Keller: "A High-Brightness Duoplasmatron Ion Source", this conference

Development of a High-Current Ion Source for Non-Volatile Elements

R. Keller, F. Nöhmayer, and P. Spädtke

GSI, Gesellschaft für Schwerionenforschung mbH, Postfach 110541,
D-6100 Darmstadt, Fed. Rep. of Germany

Abstract

A high-current ion source for non-volatile elements, HORDIS (HOt Reflex Discharge Ion Source), has been constructed and tested with calcium and bismuth. HORDIS was derived from the GSI high-current source for gases, ELSIRE, conserving its discharge geometry, magnetic multipole field, and exchangeable single or multiple aperture extraction system.

In order to process metals or other non-volatile elements, HORDIS is equipped with an evaporator oven, and its interior parts run hot due to cathode heating and discharge power. By properly tailoring the heat conduction of the suspending structures according to the expected heat load, the temperature of the inner source parts is maintained above the oven temperature, and thus virtually no condensation takes place within the source.

The discharge can be burnt in a pure vapor atmosphere without auxiliary gas after a heating-up period. Actually, any feeding material can be used the vapour pressure of which exceeds 2 mb at 1200° C.

1. Introduction

The knowledge and applications of high-current ($I_n \equiv I \cdot \sqrt{A} \geq 100$ mA, A: atomic mass number), high-brightness ion beams have much increased in the last ten years. Up to now, however, only gaseous elements or mercury could be processed in high-current plasma ion sources, while the interest in the field of accelerators as well as ion-beam treatment of materials seems mostly to be directed towards non-volatile elements, chiefly metals.

In this paper, we present a new high-current, high-brightness ion source called HORDIS, capable of processing a wide range of non-volatile elements. HORDIS yields ion beams with round or rectangular cross-sections, depending on the extraction system employed. The first results obtained indicate that $100/\sqrt{A}$ mA beam current may be largely exceeded.

2. Operating Principle of the Source

The source was designed to have three almost completely separate functional sections: a furnace chamber for particle generation, a discharge chamber with a magnetic multipole field for the ionization, and an extraction unit allowing the installation of various extraction systems: with single or multiple apertures, circular holes or slits, and three- or multi-electrode systems. During the source operation, the inner source parts run hot and their temperature exceeds the furnace temperature. Thus, condensation of the vapour generated in the furnace is completely avoided.

The discharge chamber design is based on the high-current reflex discharge ion source for noble gases, ELSIRE [1]. However, the anode consists of two coaxial tubes (Fig. 1), the inner one forms the confining wall for the plasma and runs hot while the outer one, the original anode of ELSIRE, serves only as a support for the 12 cobalt/samarium permanent magnets and is well cooled.

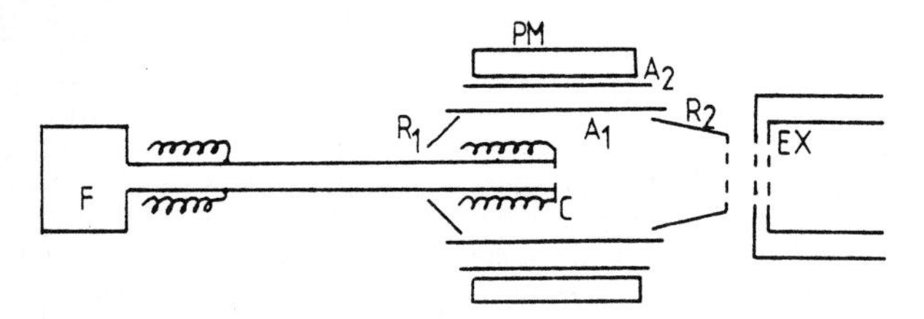

Fig. 1. Schematic view of the source. A_1: inner (hot) anode tube. A_2: outer (cold) anode tube. PM: permanent magnets. R_1: reflector on cathode side. R_2: reflector on extractor side, bearing the source outlet plate. C: cathode. F: furnace. EX: extraction system

The thermionic cathode, with generally six tantalum filaments as emitters, is inserted through one of the two reflector electrodes into the discharge chamber. The furnace is heated by another set of filaments, generally eight, made of tungsten wire. The vapour diffuses from the furnace through the inner cathode conductor into the discharge chamber. The opposite reflector carries the source outlet plate which can have varying geometries of extraction apertures.

3. Mechanical Design

The mechanical design for a reliable source of this type is quite complicated for the simple reason that the inner source parts are hotter by 1000 to 2000 K than the cooled outer parts. This temperature difference causes high stresses on the mounting structures and large expansion motions. On the other hand, the position of the outlet plate with respect to the extraction axis must be fixed with a maximum deviation of 0.02 mm, and other pieces must at least not contact each other during the source operation, though the free gaps between them are narrow in order to avoid vapour losses.

The most dangerous effect would be that a flat, ring-shaped plate, heated up at its inner surface, tilts as the large expansion of the inner parts causes a mechanical instability (Fig. 2a). This effect is avoided by giving such supporting plates a conical cross-sectional shape (Fig. 2b).

Any resulting axial motion is partially compensated by this double cone, since both parts move in opposite axial directions, conserving the mechanical stability. This principle has been adopted, wherever possible, for all mounting structures (Fig. 3).

There was no space left in the source to fabricate the plates that hold the hot anode tube with conical shapes as well. Here, the length of the

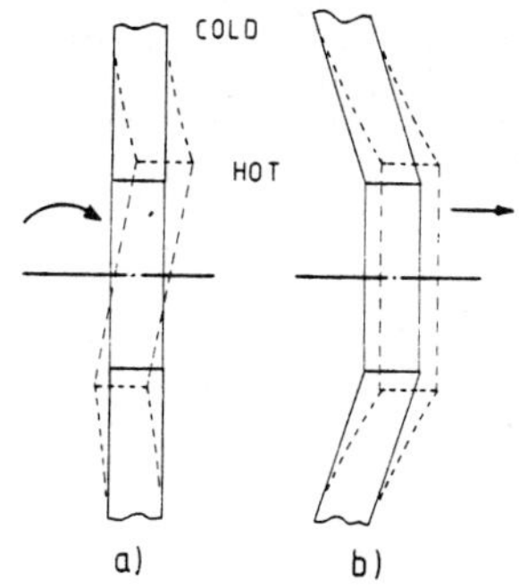

Fig. 2. Expansion of ring-shaped plates under a high-temperature gradient. a: flat plate. b: conical plate. The arrows indicate the direction of the resulting motion

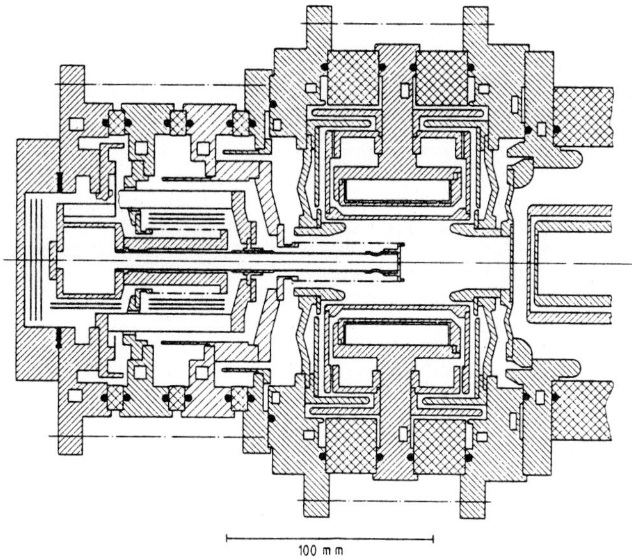

Fig. 3. Overall view of the source design. Several viewing planes have been projected into the design plane to give a complete picture in one figure

anode tube is slightly greater than the thicknesses of the anode flange and the two supporting rings together, which hold these plates at their outer border. By assembling these pieces, the plates are axially pressed at their inner borders and, being thin enough, they receive a very slight conical deformation which is already sufficient to avoid the possible tilt effect mentioned above.

All the insulators are well protected against condensing vapour by cool metal rings which, in the case of the anode, form a labyrinth. Cooled plates between anode and reflector electrodes help to reflect the thermal radiation between their hot suspension plates, and thus decouple the influence of varying powers on their temperature. The furnace is surrounded and backed by sets of heat shields, made from 0.1 mm tantalum foils.

The permanent magnets which produce the multipole field (Fig. 4) are directly cooled by glycol since they do not withstand exposure to water, which is employed as the coolant for the other source components.

Fig. 4. Cross-section of the calculated magnetic multipole field line pattern. The position of the hot anode wall is shown by the full circle

The most difficult portion of the design concerns the temperature control of the various components. It is accomplished by tailoring the suspending structures with regard to heat conduction, considering cross-sections, varying specific conductivity, and lengths. Radiation, however, also takes part in the power balance, and its influence is quite difficult to calculate since neither the exact temperatures nor the surface quality and actual absorption coefficients are known. Therefore, utmost flexibility has been provided for, and whenever a certain component should take on too low or too high a temperature, corrections can be made by replacing the suspensions by thinner or thicker ones, by reducing or increasing the number of supporting rods, or by choosing different materials: titanium instead of molybdenum or copper instead of stainless steel, depending on the direction of the desired temperature change. The insertion of additional heat shields is also a useful means of obtaining higher temperatures when necessary.

The temperatures of all critical points are measured by thermocouples inserted through the outer flanges. Auxiliary gases recommended for the start of the operation can also be fed into the source through the anode flange.

The furnace heating filaments do not touch the furnace wall directly, but are suspended around a thick molybdenum tube. This tube conducts the filament power to the furnace. Through the arrangement shown in Fig. 3, the thermal expansions of filaments and conducting tube tend to compensate each other, limiting filament deformation due to heating.

The furnace charge material can be fed into the source from the rear when the two cover plates which close the furnace chamber and the furnace itself are dismounted. Grain material may also be passed through the vapour outlet holes within the inner cathode conductor when the whole furnace/cathode chamber is taken away from the discharge chamber and turned upright.

The furnace is supported by four stainless steel bolts, and these are fixed to four thin stainless steel bands which serve as elastic suspension, tolerating any residual axial shifts of the whole assembly. For high-temperature (1000° C) applications, the bolts and bands are chosen from poorly heat-conducting material. For low furnace temperatures, it may be more convenient to work with higher heat conductance, and consequently rather high heating power, because then the heat capacity of the system is not so difficult to overcome for precise, fast temperature regulation.

An important feature of the extraction unit is the ease of exchangeability of the whole system, as well as the fact that the source outlet plate can be directly aligned to the extractor plates when the main source body is still removed. Mounting of the source, then, does not change the alignment once established. Usually, an accel/decel system with one or seven round holes is employed. Also, the extractor plates can easily be removed from their bearing tubes; the second (grounded) extractor is always mounted in a fixed radial position, but can be axially shifted, whereas the first one (negative potential to screen the source from beam-neutralizing electrons) can be radially aligned to the second one. The axial distance between the source outlet and the extractor plates can be varied by inserting distance rings between the holder tubes and their support flanges. The main extraction insulator holds a maximum voltage of 50 kV.

4. Source Operation

The required furnace temperature governs all operation parameters and, to a certain degree, also the choice of particular mechanical dimensions, as explained above. First experiments indicated that the temperature must be such that the vapour pressure of the charge material amounts to about 1.5 mbar. This pressure is not to be confused with the operation pressure within the discharge chamber, as the limited particle conductance of the furnace outlet pipe and the inner cathode conductor cause a substantial pressure decrease. (The inlet pressure of the gas ion source ELSIRE with quite a similar discharge configuration typically amounts to 0.1 mbar.)

In view of the vapor pressure curves [2], the following elements will be suited as charges for HORDIS:
Li, Na, Mg, Al, P, S, K, Ca, Zn, Ge, As, Se, Rb, Sr, Cd, Sn, Sb, J, Cs, Ba, Hg, Tl, Pb, and Bi.

For In, Ag, and especially Ga, modifications seem to be necessary which will allow the furnace to be operated at temperatures up to 1500° C, and other source components at correspondingly higher temperatures.

It should be kept in mind that HORDIS can always be operated with gases or vapours (BF_3, CS_2, CCl_4) if so desired as a secondary application.

The operating procedure normally followed starts by heating up the cathode step by step, in order to avoid too heavy outgassing. Then an auxiliary gas, usually argon, is let in and the discharge is ignited. In our first studies, we tried at once to produce a high share of doubly and triply charged ions of Ca or Bi. By using an extraction system with narrow holes, we had to create a very dense plasma which is best suited to generate multiply charged ions. The necessary discharge power to maintain this high plasma density, however, cannot be withstood by the source continuously. Therefore the discharge was pulsed at 10% duty factor, 50 Hz, meeting the requirements of the GSI accelerator UNILAC. The maximum mean power load for HORDIS amounts to about 4 kW. If the extraction geometry chosen has wide apertures (≥ 6 mm) and especially with elements of low ionization potential (in general all metals) requiring low discharge power only, the d.c. oper-

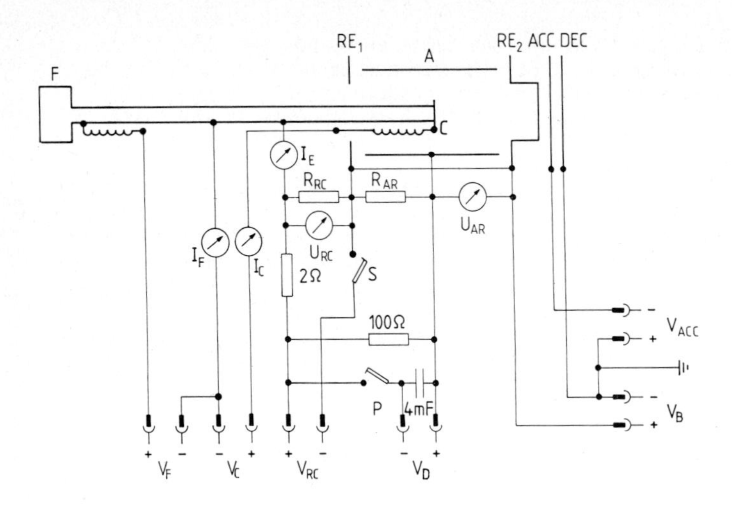

Fig. 5. Electrical circuit. Three connecting modes are possible:
a) R_{AR} = 1 kΩ and R_{RC} = ∞ and S open
b) R_{AR} = 100 Ω and R_{RC} = 10 Ω and S open
c) R_{AR} = R_{RC} = ∞ and S closed. Only in this case is a power supply to yield V_{RC} necessary. If the outer bolts which keep the source main body together are insulated, a hybrid mode may also be applied: a) or b) to the reflector on the cathode side and c) to the reflector on the extractor side, bearing the source outlet plate. In this way, the potential of the outlet plate can be adjusted to the extraction conditions independently of the discharge parameters

ation mode may be used as well. For example, 10 mA Ar^+ ions could be extracted at 47 kV from a single Ø 6 mm aperture with a discharge power below 2.4 kW.

For the electrical circuit, see Fig. 5.

When the anode temperature has reached a value above the desired furnace temperature, the furnace itself can be heated. When the desired furnace temperature is approached, the auxiliary gas supply is slowly closed, and can finally be shut off completely. The discharge then burns on the pure charge material vapour. Thus, vapour condensation during the heating-up phase is avoided.

The behaviour of the source running on pure metal vapour does not exhibit any difference from that of the gas source ELSIRE. The furnace temperature only replaces the gas pressure as one of the operation parameters, besides discharge power and cathode heating power.

At the end of an operation period, the starting procedure is repeated in reverse order.

5. Results

The results are given in Table 1. The ion-beam currents were measured in a doubly screened Faraday cup, Ø 45 mm wide and 1 m distant from the source.

Table 1. Measured source and ion beam parameters.

El	I_D/A	U_{AC}/V	P_C/kW	P_F/kW	T_F/°C	P_F/mbar	U_B/kV	f_2/%	f_3/%	I_B/mA
Ca	200	50	1.66	1.40	840	2.0	21	20	-	6
Bi	140	75	1.23	2.32	990	1.6	31	28	6.5	8

El: furnace charge element. I_D: discharge current. U_{AC}: discharge voltage. P_C: cathode heating power. P_F: furnace heating power. T_F: furnace temperature. P_F:vapour pressure of the charge element at temperature T_F. U_B: ion beam voltage. $f_{2,3}$: proportion of doubly/triply charged particles within the ion beam. I_B: transported ion-beam current. During these measurements, no auxiliary gas was present in the source

For both ion species, the extraction system had seven round apertures of Ø 2.5 mm each; its first gap was 3.1 mm long. While running with calcium, the source parameters were not optimized by far for the highest transported ion current.

These preliminary tests already gave a normalized current value $I_n \equiv I_B \cdot \sqrt{A}$ of I_n = 116 (mA). Considering that there are no important differences between the gas sources ELSIRE and HORDIS, one can anticipate that for optimized singly charged ion beams, normalized currents of $I_n \sim 500$ (mA) should easily be reached. The best result with ELSIRE [1] was 112 mA of argon ions from a slit extraction system, amounting to I_n = 708 (mA).

Emittances were not measured during these first experiments. A maximum value can be estimated, however, from the geometrical dimensions: a radius of r = 5 mm at the beam waist and the acceptance half angle of α_0 = 22.5 mrad lead to ε = 112.5 mm mrad emittance (area of the emittance figure divided by π) for both beams, or normalized emittances $\varepsilon_n = \beta \cdot \gamma \cdot \varepsilon$ of 0.063 mm mrad for Bi and 0.12 for Ca. The normalized brightness values, $B_n = I_B/\varepsilon_n^2$, amount to B_n = 2.0 A/(mm mrad)^2 for Bi and B_n = 0.42 for Ca.

A rather typical result obtained with ELSIRE for Ar at 30 kV, using a seven-aperture (Ø 3 mm each) outlet plate, was 55 mA, I_n = 348 (mA), with ε = 232 mm mrad, ε_n = 0.20 mm mrad and B_n = 1.0 A/(mm mrad)^2.

Acknowledgements

The authors would like to acknowledge the skillful and accurate assistance of F. Schäffer in preparing mechanical components of the source and the test stand. Thanks are further due to R. Vrtal for the maintenance of power supplies and electronic equipment.

References

1. R. Keller: Nucl. Instr. Meth. 189, 97 (1981)

2. C.J. Smithells: Metals Reference Book - 1967 (Butterworths, London)

The Use of Computers for Designing and Testing Ion Beam Systems

W.B. Thompson*, I. Honjo, and N. Turner

Varian Associates, Extrion Division, Box 1226,
Gloucester, MA 01930, USA

Abstract

The optimization and design of ion implantation equipment may be accomplished with computer modeling. The beam extraction simulation program SNOW [1], which produces space charge dependent solution of the Poisson and Lorentz equations in the plasma-sheath and extraction region of a typical ion source is described. The phase space diagrams and beam profiles predicted by SNOW are compared with experimental measurements. A computerized measurement system capable of measuring and plotting beam profiles, emittance and source brightness is used. The dependence of the system's phase space on geometry, plasma electron temperature, ion mass and plasma density is analyzed. Application of advanced computer models to ion beam equipment of the future are proposed.

1. Introduction

Ion beam systems for semiconductor applications are increasing in sophistication. In order to obtain efficient beam transmission throughout large ranges of currents and energies in these systems a complete knowledge of the entire ion beam trace space is necessary. We have computerized an emittance measurement system to provide beam profiles, current density maps, and 'trace space' diagrams for a wide variety of charged particle sources under diverse operating conditions. In addition to diagnosing source behavior this beam analysis system (BEAST) can be useful for empirical studies of the behavior of such optical elements as analyzing magnets, accelerating tubes, quadrupoles, and einzel lenses.

In order to further reduce the system design time an ion source simulation program SNOW has been adapted to produce trace space information in BEAST's format. We will discuss how the ion source data base of BEAST can be used as a reference with which to judge the success of SNOW designed ion source hardware.

2. Computerized Beam Analysis Using BEAST

2.1 Mathematical Foundations

For a Hamiltonian ensemble of charged particles several useful quantities may be defined which allow the designer to forecast beam current density and dimensions throughout the beam line. In

---

* Present address.Varian/Lithography Products Division

the notation of Lejeune and Aubert[2] the first of these quantities, emittance, may be related to the classical Hamiltonian transverse phase space parameters, momenta, P_x and P_y, and position x and y by the following equation:

$$x' = dx/dz = P_x/(m_o c\beta\gamma) = P_x/P_z$$
$$y' = dy/dz = P_y/(m_o c\beta\gamma) = P_y/P_z$$
$$P_z = m_o c\ \beta\ \gamma$$
$$dV_4 = dx dy dx' dy'$$
$$V_4 = \int dx dy dx' dy'$$

with the transverse hyperemittance being,

$$E_4 = V_4/\ \pi^2$$

and the X and Y emittances being,

$$E_x = (^1/\pi) \iint dx.dx' = A_x/\pi$$
$$Ey = (^1/\pi) \iint dy.dy' = A_y/\pi \qquad \text{where}$$
$$V_4 = A_x\ A_y\ /2\ .$$

The four n-dimensional coordinate space comprised of X, Y, X´, and Y´, for a n-particle ensemble is often referred to as 'trace space'. Since it is this energy-dependent particle density distribution which is easiest to deal with experimentally, our future discussions of 'trace space' will assume the above definitions. The average current density per unit trace space is often referred to as brightness and defined as

$$B = I/V_4 = 2I/(\pi^2 E_x E_y).$$

Figure 1 shows the current envelope of a typical field free ion beam and the corresponding Y emittance contour at the left, center, and right-hand beam cross sections. From a single arbitrary emittance contour alone one can determine from data accumulated in the divergent portion of the beam the location of

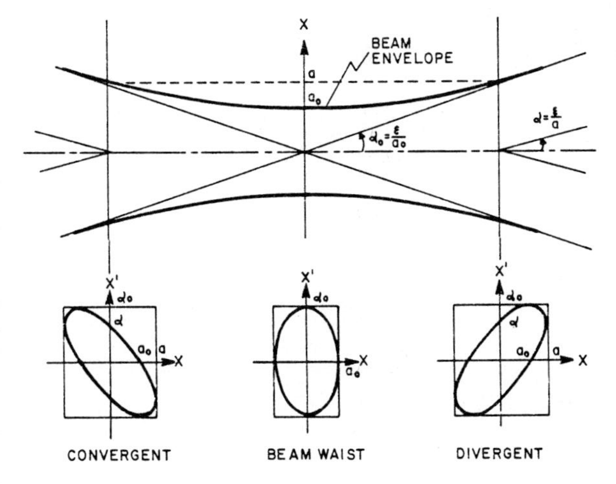

$\mathcal{E} = a_o \cdot \alpha_o =$ CONSTANT

$B = \dfrac{2I}{\pi^2 \varepsilon_x \varepsilon_Y}$

Figure 1. Typical beam envelope and the position dependence of its emittance diagrams

the beam waist as well as the beam dimension and divergence at that waist. Thus from X and Y field free emittance diagrams it is possible to determine the drifted beam dimensions at all other positions within this field-free region.

2.2 BEAST Hardware and Measurement Results

Figure 2 shows schematically the Faraday cup and the four motorized slits used to measure the trace space of a Freeman ion source similar to that shown in Figure 3. An HP 9845 desk top computer controls the slit motion, makes current measurements and reduces the data to produce beam profiles emittance information and brightness values (Figure 4).

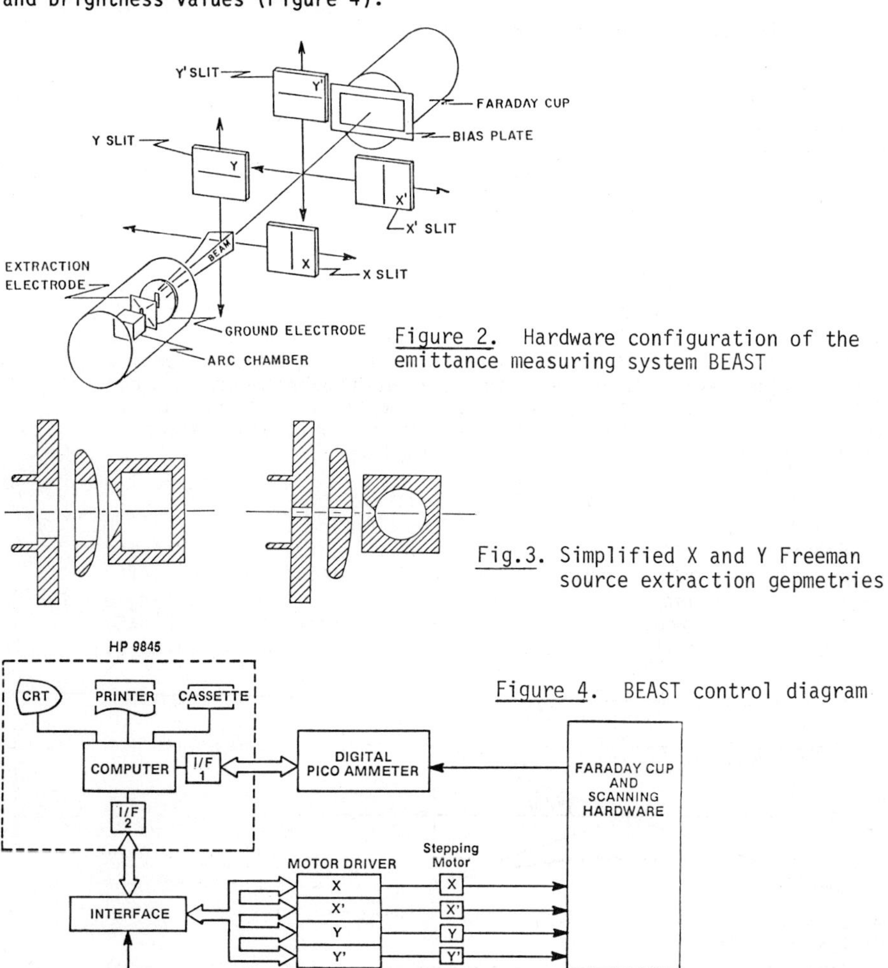

Figure 2. Hardware configuration of the emittance measuring system BEAST

Fig.3. Simplified X and Y Freeman source extraction gepmetries

Figure 4. BEAST control diagram

The flow charts of the Programs PROFIL and EMITTN are given in Figures 5 and 6. Figures 7 and 8 depict representative 'PROFIL' current density maps taken 60 cm's downstream from our Freeman source. Figures 9, 10, and 11 show the plots generated by EMITTN

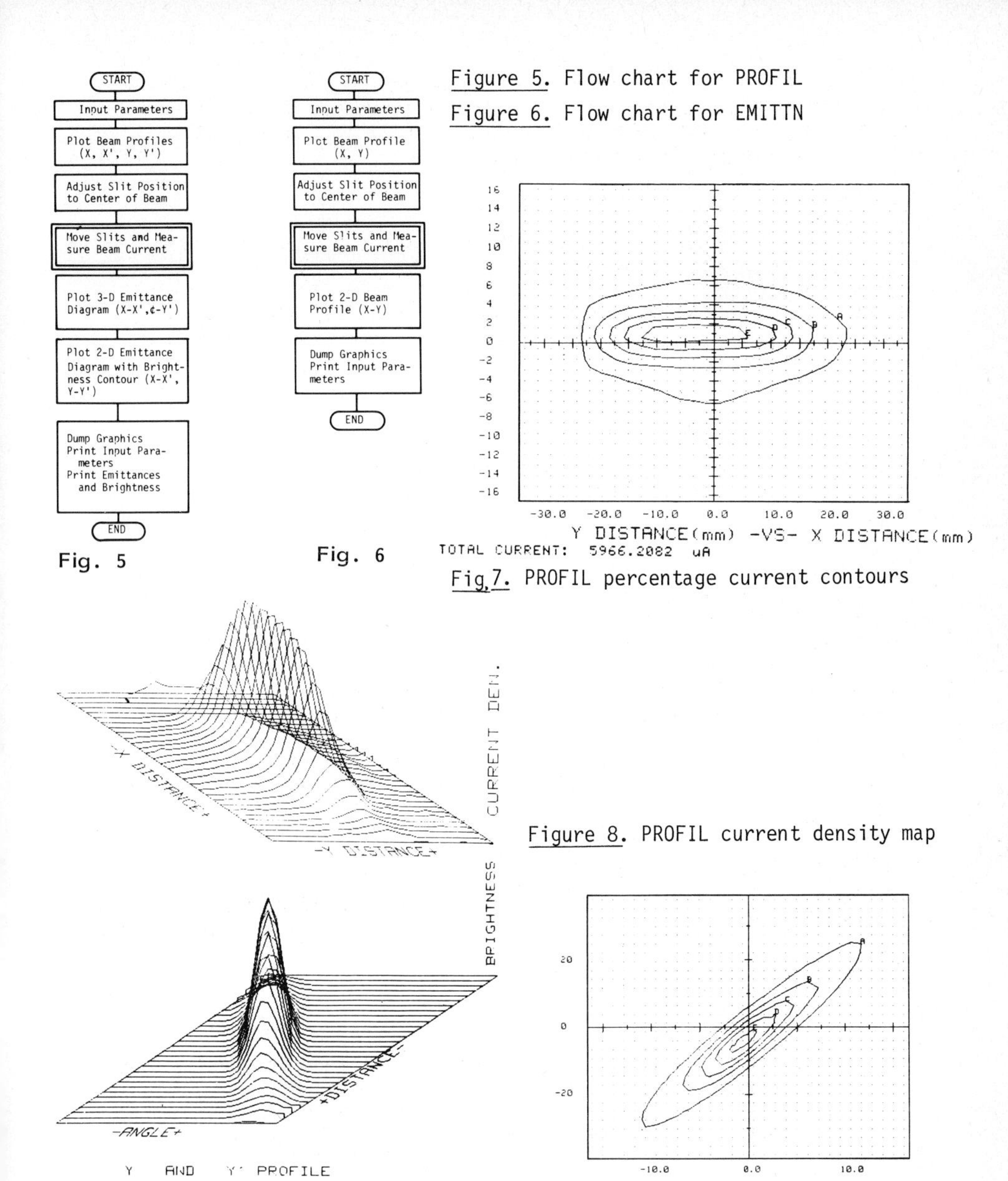

Fig. 5

Fig. 6

Figure 5. Flow chart for PROFIL

Figure 6. Flow chart for EMITTN

Fig.7. PROFIL percentage current contours

Figure 8. PROFIL current density map

Figure 9. EMITTN brightness map

Figure 10. EMITTN measured Y emittance diagram

to give the researcher a graphic representation of the X and Y emittance diagrams.

The Programs PROFIL and EMITTN have proved extremely helpful during the studies of brightness dependence on source parameters and geometries. We have improved analyzed beam currents in one model implanter by a factor of four using these programs alone and have made major modifications to our analyzing magnets and quadrupoles based on the information obtained with EMITTN.

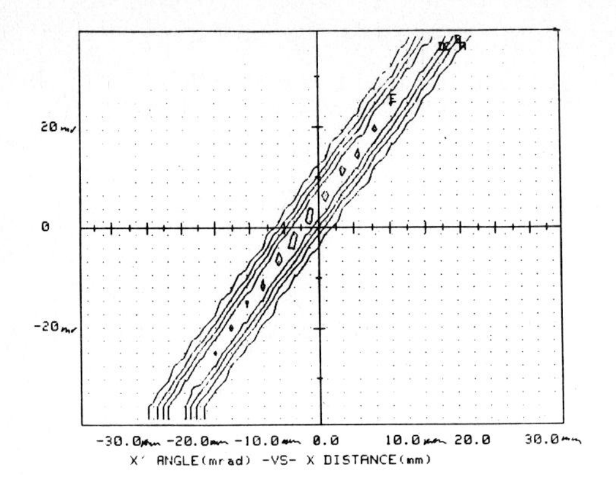

Figure 11. EMITTN measured X emittance diagram

3. Ion Source Simulations

As we soon discovered with EMITTN that there were large trace space variations with changes in source conditions, and geometry, our first improvement in the standard Freeman source [3] used on Varian's Model DF-4 implanter was a geometric one indicated by EMITTN measurements and experimental results on an actual implanter. It became clear, however, that a mathematic model of the source extraction region was necessary to evaluate all of the source configurations of interest without actually constructing the hardware for each iteration.

Numerous theoretical studies on ion beam extraction optics have been done. They all essentially conclude that for plasma sources the extraction region plasma boundary (or meniscus) changes curvature with plasma density. This variation of meniscus curvature moves the virtual object position and alters the beam divergence for subsequent optical elements. In our medium current implanter the ion beam is analyzed by a 90 degrees magnet just down stream of the source. Thus an accurate knowledge of the object positional variation and beam divergence is necessary to determine the magnet's acceptance and image quality.

We have examined theoretically the relationship between beam divergence and plasma density to anticipate what limitations extremely high brightness sources might have.

3.1 Dependance of Beam Divergence on Space Charge Effects

The Child-Langmuir space charge limited current density for a diode consisting of two infinite planes is given by:

$$J = (4/9)\varepsilon_0 (2q/M)^{1/2} (V^{3/2}/d^2)$$

for a diode voltage V of separation d and ions of mass M and charge q. For the special cases of a cylindrical geometry the space charge limited current is given by the Langmuir-Blodgett formula

$$I = (8\pi/9)\varepsilon_0 (2q/M)^{1/2} (V^{3/2}/\beta^2 r_a)\ell \quad \text{where}$$

$$\beta = \gamma - 2\gamma^2/5 + 11\gamma^3/120 + \ldots$$

$$\gamma = \ln (r_a/r_c)$$

r_a = anode radius

r_c = cathode radius

and ℓ = cylinder length.

For a spherically symmetric geometry this expression reduces to

$$I = (16\pi/9)\varepsilon_0 (2q/M)^{1/2}(V^{3/2})/\alpha^2$$

for $\alpha = \gamma - 0.3\gamma^2 + 0.075\gamma^3 + \ldots$

and $\gamma = \ln(r_a/r_c)$.

The divergence angle ω is related to the perveance for each of these cases by, in the cylindrical geometry

$$\omega \simeq (4/15)\ (a/d)\ (1 - (9/4)\ (P/P_c))$$

and in the spherical geometry

$$\omega \simeq (7/6)\ (a/d)\ (1 - (15/7)\ (P/P_c))$$

with ω = the divergence angle
a = the plasma aperture width
d = the distance between the plasma boundary and the cathode
P = the beam perveance
= $(m)^{1/2}\ (I/V^{3/2})$
P_c = the perveance at the Child-Langmuir limit .

These relationships assume that the plasma surface is either a rectangular slab between the cylinder walls or a tube between two concentric spheres. In actuality, however, the beams tend toward fans and cones respectively for the cylindrical and spherical cases and finite electrode thicknesses further perturb the idealized potential distributions. This variation of ideal potential can produce a lens effect and significantly alter ω.

The analysis of the Langmuir-Blodgett formulae obviously represent an over simplification of the real situation in an electrode configuration similar to Figures 3 and 4. Whealton[4] has discussed the impact of these perturbations on the convergence conditions of any numerical approximation to an ion extraction region.

Three methods of iterations to the complete solution of Poisson's equation

$$\nabla^2 V = -\rho/\varepsilon_0$$

in the plasma extraction region are possible. The first assumes that the trajectories initiate on a surface in the aperture where the electric field is taken to be zero and that the free electrons do not influence this region. The second approach initializes the ion trajectories on equipotentials at the plasma sheath and includes the influence of electron space charge. The approximate sheath position potential at the plasma surface, and initial ion velocities are approximately established by a solution to the collisionless one-dimensional sheath problem.

The third method used by the program SNOW for our simulations solves Poisson's equation within the plasma sheath assuming some ion and electron density distributions. With this approach the position and potential of the sheath surface are made consistent with the extra-plasma mesh potentials.

3.2 Ion Extraction Simulation with SNOW

Figure 12 shows the basic flow chart and formulae used in the program SNOW. As input to SNOW one specifies the plasma parameters of ion temperature, electron temperature, and ion density; electrode geometries; electrode potentials; and ion species. Poisson's equation is then solved by the method of finite differences on a mesh with the method of successive under-relaxation. In the plasma region the charge density 'source' term ρ also contains the electron density contribution assumed to be a Boltzmann distribution.

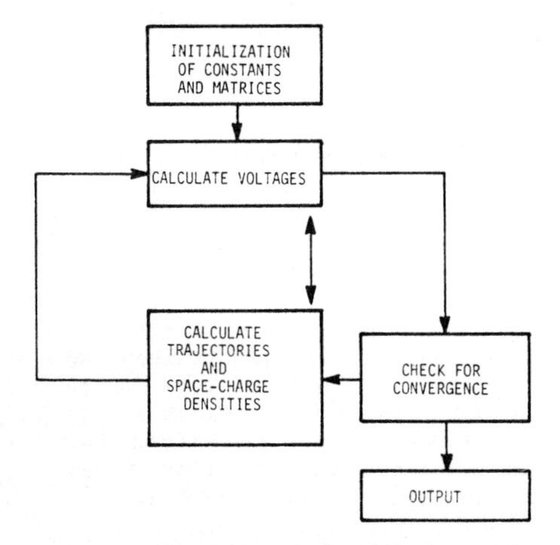

Figure 12. SNOW flow chart

Ions are injected into the plasma starting plane at shallow selectable angles and velocities. The trajectories of these ions are continuously calculated toward the exit plane at the edge of the simulation region with the assumption that within each mesh section the ions follow a parabolic trajectory due to the constant electric field in that section. The charge modification due to the ion trajectories is determined and the mesh potentials modified accordingly.

This process is iterated until there is no change in either the mesh potentials or trajectories and the solutions are self-consistent.

Upon completion SNOW outputs the following:

A. The Equipotential Distributions
B. The Ion Beam Trajectories
C. Current Density Profiles at the Exit Plane
D. Emittance Diagrams With Current Contours .

3.3 SNOW Results

Typical results for a SNOW run are shown in Figure 14. Figures 13 and 14 show the comparison of SNOW (Figure 14) and BEAST (Figure 13) profiles. The forecast profile variations with beam current of SNOW match our experimental results very well.

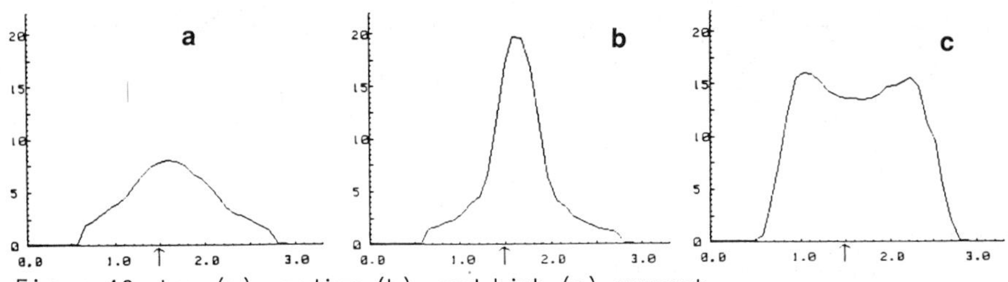

Figure 13. Low (a), medium (b), and high (c) current PROFIL measured beam profiles

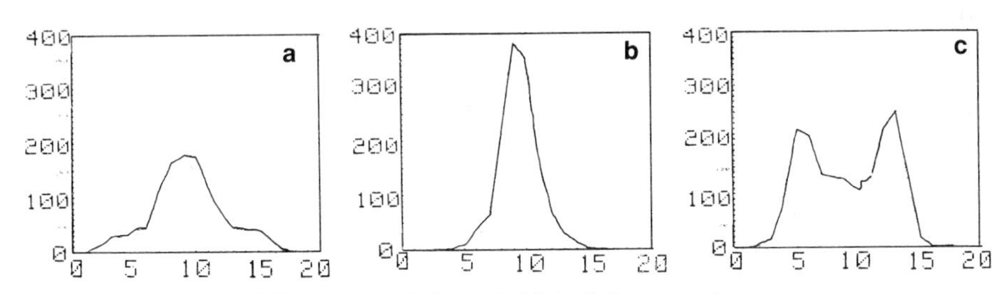

Figure 14. Low (a), medium (b), and high (c) current SNOW forecast profiles

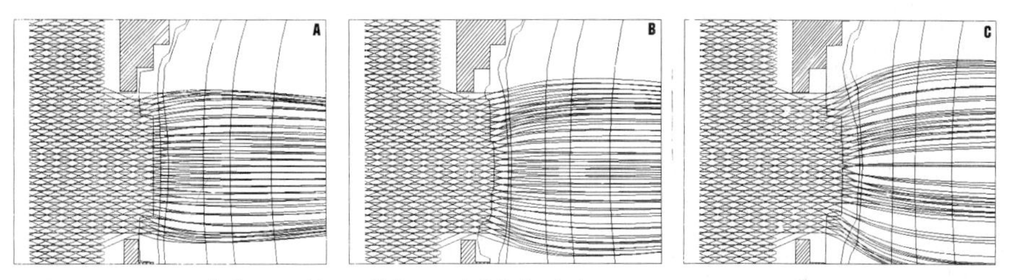

Figure 15. Low (a), medium (b), and high (c) current plasma sheaths

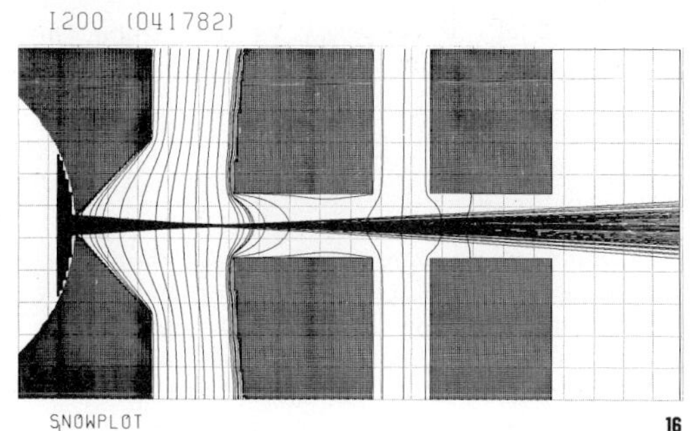

Figure 16. SNOW equipotentials and trajectories

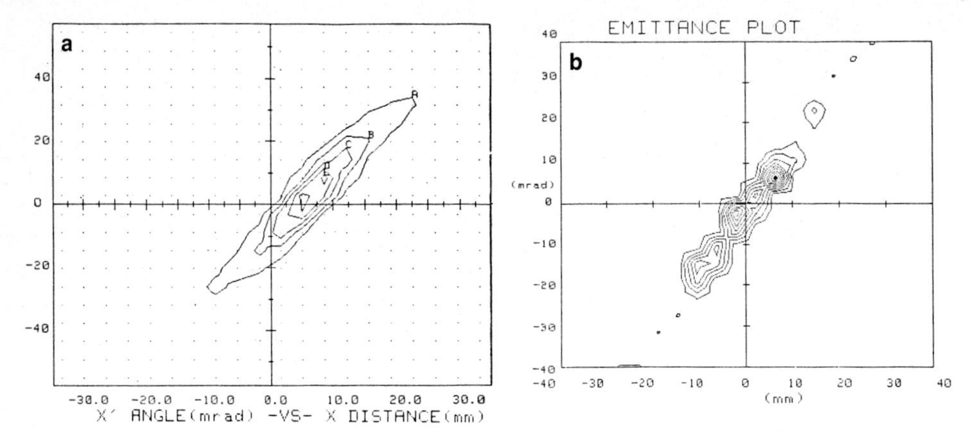

Figure 17. Emittance predicted by SNOW (a) and BEAST (b)

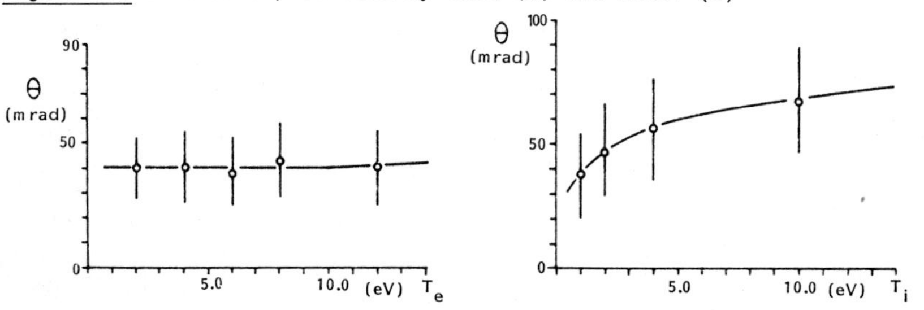

Figure 18. Divergence vs, electron temperature according to SNOW

Figure 19. Divergence vs ion temperature according to SNOW

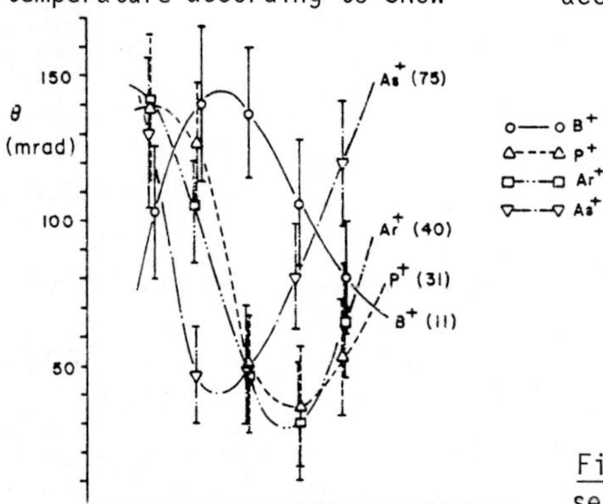

Figure 20. Divergence vs perveance for several ion species

Figure 15 shows the corresponding plasma sheath region for each case. These graphically depict the influence of the plasma sheath on beam profile. As we mentioned earlier, these variations have a profound effect on the design parameters of subsequent optical elements especially the analyzing magnets entrance gap and angle. Figure 16 is a representative SNOW plot of equipotentials and trajectories.

Figure 17 shows a comparison of SNOW and BEAST emittance diagrams. The ability of SNOW to produce trace space diagrams makes it especially useful in system design.

We show in Figures 18, 19, and 20 the dependence of beam divergence on such parameters as ion temperature, electron temperature, and ion mass. As can be seen, the electron temperatures directly have very little effect on divergence. As a confirmation of this prediction, we made a Langmuir probe study of the electron temperature and the parameters which influenced the electron temperature. It was evident from our variation of those source conditions which did effect electron temperature (i.e. source magnetic field, source pressure etc.) that these indeed, in themselves, did not influence the beam divergence. The one area where the beam divergence was found to be extremely sensitive was the arc chamber exit geometries.

3.4 New Design of Arc Chamber

We show in Figure 22 three types of arc chamber exit geometry we modified. The divergence angle variations with normalized beam perveance of each arc chamber were calculated by SNOW and they are shown in Figure 21. As can be seen, No. 1 arc chamber gives small divergence angle in low perveance (i.e. in low current), but quickly it becomes a wide angle as beam current increases. No. 3 arc chamber is about the same as standard one. No. 2, however, gives a smaller divergence angle in the high current mode compared with the standard.

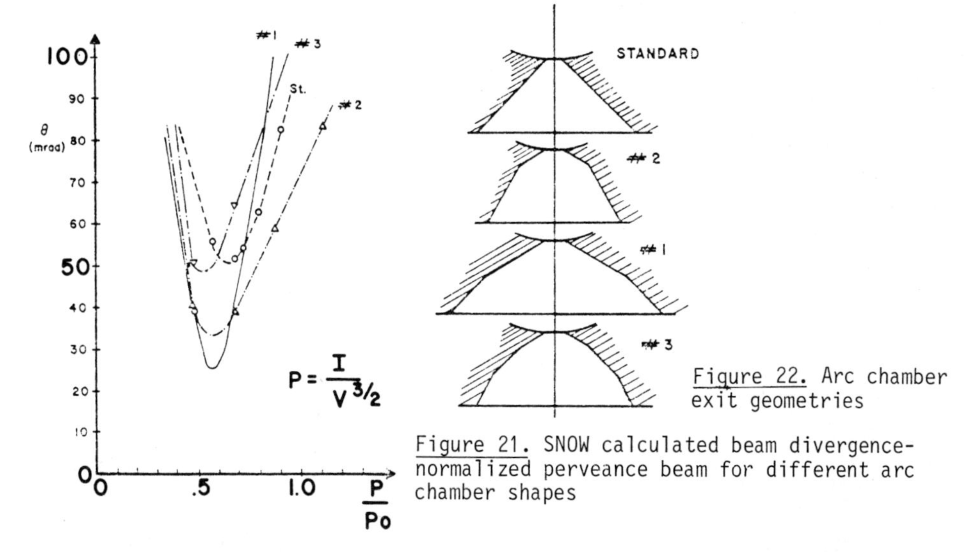

Figure 21. SNOW calculated beam divergence-normalized perveance beam for different arc chamber shapes

Figure 22. Arc chamber exit geometries

We examined these three types of arc chamber by BEAST. Measured divergence angles are shown in Figure 23. Although the smallest angles of each case are slightly different from SNOW's results, the trends of No. 1 and No. 3 arc chamber are well correlated and No. 2 keeps a small divergence angle in even high-current mode as predicted by SNOW.

This small angle in high current mode is because the big opening geometry in vicinity of arc chamber slit makes it easy to

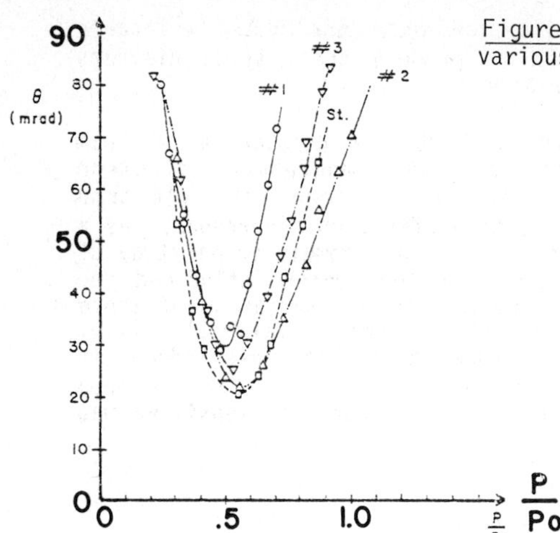

Figure 23. Measured divergence angles for various arc chambers arc chamber shapes

extract more beam and steep angle following big opening focuses outgoing-beam to the center axis.

We also mounted No. 2 arc chamber in our medium current ion implantation system. Testing of No. 2 arc chamber produced spot sizes at the target which were 50% smaller for identical source operating conditions.

4. Conclusion

There is no doubt that computers will play an ever increasing role in the design of all charged particle systems of the future. We have shown how with PROFIL, EMITTN, and BEAST they may be used for ion source testing and optics evaluation.

We have presented results of an ion source computer model which reliably forecasts the actual performance of the ion source and which gives the designer the ability to "test hardware" with only a change of an input datafile. Nevertheless, we feel that these accomplishments represent only the beginning of the field of computer aided ion beam system design; yet to come are the optimization algorithms for which the designer needs only input the system specifications and which in turn produce a complete optical layout.

Acknowledgements

The authors wish to acknowledge Peter Hanley and Roger Bastide for their contributions and support of the computer aided equipment discussed in this paper.

1. Boers, J.E.: SNOW - A Digital Computer Program for the Simulation of Ion Beam Devices: Sandia National Laboratories: Albuquerque, New Mexico: 1980
2. Lejeune, L. and Aubert, J.: Emittance and Brightness: Definitions and Measurements; in Advances in Electronics and Electron Physics edited by A. Septier: Academic Press: New York: 1980
3. Freeman J. H.: Nucl. Instr. and Methods 22 (1963) p. 306
4. Whealton, J.H.: Nucl. Instr. and Methods 189 (1981) p.55

Multipole Ion Source for Ion Implantation and Isotope Separation

J.H. Keller

IBM, East Fishill Fac., Dept. 52 G, Bldg. 300-40E,
Hopewell Junction, NY 12533, USA

A multipole or magnetic cusp type ion source was designed for application as a source for ion implantation and electromagnetic isotope separation. The source has a single slit extractor. The multipole field was created by a combination of rare-earth cobalt magnets with iron yoke and pole structure. The magnetic structure is freon cooled and surrounds a graphite arc chamber. We tested 4, 6, and 10-pole configurations.

These configurations were such that a virtual pole was formed at the extraction aperture. The combination of cooled magnetic structure and graphite chamber allows operation of the source at high gas temperatures of approximately 500 to 1000°C. These temperatures arise from operating at extracted current densities above 15mA/cm^2 of arsenic. The source was generally operated in the mode where the graphite arc chamber acted as the anode and the extraction slit was at or near the cathode potential. Thus, the anode included all but one pole face. This mode showed easy starting conditions.

The source was tested with argon, boron trifluoride and arsenic vapor. A comparison to a Bernas-type ion source with identical filament structure showed a greater than 5 times improvement in gas efficiency for normal operating conditions and similar arc currents. The source also exhibited higher current and voltage capability.

1. Introduction

In ion implantation and the related fields of electromagnetic isotope separation, "EMIS," one would like an ion source which has high gas efficiency, high arc efficiency, low noise, and an extractor which allows the beam to be mass analyzed. The high gas efficiency reduces charge exchange losses in the beam between the ion source and the target. It allows one to extract at larger voltages or higher currents. It also can reduce buildup of condensable gases such as arsenic, and thus reduce machine maintenance. High arc efficiency allows one to operate at lower arc current and thus obtain longer filament lifetime. A quiescent or lower noise plasma allows for extraction of larger beam current and produces beams with better space charge neutralization.

In the field of EMIS, one generally wants mass resolution greater than M/ΔM = 200. Thus, a single slit extractor is used. In ion implantation, somewhat lower mass resolution can be tolerated, say as low as 75 or even 30. Thus, one can use a wider multiaperture source extraction area, with a width of about two centimeters. However, most systems today use only a single slit or circular aperture.

Presently, there are three types of high-current ion-implantation sources in use. These are: 1) the arc type, 2) the Freeman type and 3) the microwave type. The arc type includes calutrons [1],Bernas [2] and related sources [3]. This type of source uses a magnetic field for confining the primary electrons as they traverse between the filament and the anode, and the ion beam is extracted transversely to the magnetic field.

Normally, the largest loss of the primary electrons, in an arc-type system, is to anode surfaces which are perpendicular to the magnetic field. If these end surfaces are held at the cathode potential, the gas and arc efficiency are increased, but the source becomes noisy. Likewise, if the magnetic field is increased above a certain amount in an attempt to increase confinement, the source becomes noisy.

The Freeman [4] source contains a coaxial filament and magnetic field with transverse extraction and end plates which reflect the primary electrons. To the author's knowledge, this source in its present stage of development [5, 6] has twice the gas efficiency of the arc source for similar filament conditions.

Microwave sources use microwave energy to excite the electrons in the source. These sources can have very high gas efficiency but can also have a large amount of plasma noise. However, N. Sakudo et al. [7] have obtained good beam current from this type of source.

In recent years, another type of source, which has been shown to have very good plasma and beam properties, is the multipole or magnetic cusp source. This source has been used in the fields of ion-beam sputtering [8], ion propulsion [9] and neutral beam injection for fusion [10].

The next sections will discuss: multipole sources, the design of a small multipole source for ion implementation, experimental results obtained using this source and conclusions.

2. Multipole Sources

Magnetic multipole sources are generally large sources which contain a large volume where the magnetic field is low, normally less than 30 gauss. This region is partially surrounded by a magnetic multipole which confines the primary electrons, and thus increases their path length before they escape to the anode. The cusp-shaped field produces a stable plasma configuration [11] and quiescent plasma [12].

In the literature, two different multipole/anode configurations are described. Both have line magnetic cusps. One configuration has anodes between the magnetic poles, and the second has an anode which includes the magnetic poles. An attempt will be made to compare the advantages and the disadvantages of these two configurations.

The configuration with the anodes between the poles has been investigated by Kaufman [8]. If the integral of B xdl between the plasma and the anodes is large enough, the primary electrons are turned around before they reach the anodes. Thus, in this configuration, the primary electrons must diffuse across the magnetic field (Bohm diffusion) to reach the anodes. Kaufman [13] has found that this configuration gives confinement of the primary electrons when the integral of B x dl is approximately 75×10^{-6} Teslameters.

If the anode area is made too small or confinement too large in this configuration, the plasma potential becomes negative and possibly unstable [13]. Also, as the confinement is increased, the plasma becomes difficult to start. Thus, this configuration has the advantage of giving confinement of the primary electrons at a relatively low magnetic field. But normally the magnetic field is not large enough to significantly increase the confinement of the plasma beyond its inertial confinement.

In another configuration the anode includes the area of the magnetic poles, and a large field strength in the order of 1 kilogauss is used. In this configuration, both the primaries and also the plasma to some extent are confined. This confinement increases with increased magnetic-field strength at the poles [14]. For a given strength ($B \simeq 2KG$) of permanent magnets, Leang, Samec and Lamm [15] found an optimum spacing between cusps of 8cm.

The primary electron-loss rates for these two configurations can be compared using simple theory. In the anode configuration which excludes the poles, the current to the anode is given [13] by:

$$I_a = A\ e\ D_B\ dn/dx$$

and after some manipulation

$$I_a = A\ KT_e N_e / 13 \int_{anode}^{\infty} B\ dx \tag{1}$$

where I_a is the anode current, A is the effective anode area which includes all the area between the poles, D_B is the Bohm diffusion coefficient, K is Boltzmann's constant, T_e and N_e are the primary electron temperature and density, respectively, and B is the magnetic field.

For the anode configuration with includes the poles there is an additional loss through the poles. From Hershkowitz et al.[14], the loss area is twice the electron gyroradius r_e times the total pole lengths L. Thus:

$$I_p = 2 r_e L e \frac{N_e}{4} v_e \quad ,$$

where v_e is the average electron velocity and L is the anode area divided by the spacing S between cusps. Substitution for r_e, L and v_e gives

$$I_p = 2.5\ A\ N_e\ K\ T_e /\ S\ B \tag{2}$$

the total anode current I_a for this configuration is the sum of Eqs. (1) and (2).

Thus, the losses between poles and at the poles are functionally very similar, and the two configurations can be compared. If both configurations were designed with the same anode area A and ratio of I_a/Ne, then they should have the same primary electron confinement. However, the latter would have a larger magnetic field, and have the advantage of providing more confinement of the plasma.

3. Multipole Source for Ion Implantation

In designing a multipole source for ion implantation or EMIS, there are several conditions one should try to achieve:

1) A low magnetic field region (<30 gauss), which is surrounded by

2) a relatively small number of high strength magnetic poles, i.e., small relative to the volume enclosed. These two conditions maximize the confinement time, and they became more difficult to satisfy in a smaller source.

3) A small or least narrow source to maximize the arc efficiency, since normally only a single slit extractor is used.

4) The plasma density, and thus the magnetic field at the extraction slit should be uniform over the length of the slit.

All of the conditions cannot be met at the same time. Considering this, the source was designed such that:

1) A weak virtual pole is produced at the extraction slit to give a uniform plasma over the length of the extraction slit.

2) The number of poles can be varied simply by changing the magnet orientations. This allows evaluations of several different compromises between low field volume, pole strength and pole number.

3) The potential of the surface where the magnetic field is low, such as the source slit, can be varied between the anode potential and a potential more negative than the cathode. This allowed us to test efficiency versus potential.

This design of the chamber and magnetic structure is shown in Figs. 1 and 2. It consists of a graphite arc chamber surrounded on five sides by a molybdenum heat-shield box which in turn is surrounded by the multipole magnet structure. The magnet structure is cooled by freon-cooled copper plates which are screwed to the magnet yoke and pole pieces.

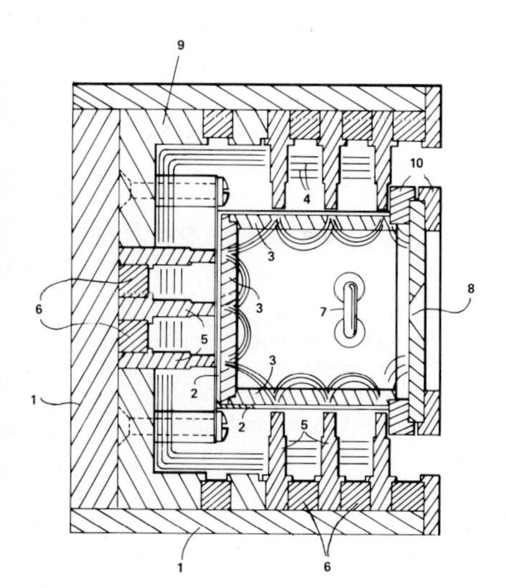

Figure 1. Multipole source, XZ section, with copper cooling plates 1, molybdenum heat shield box 2, graphite anode 3, heat shields 4, pole pieces 5, magnets 6, "U" shaped filament 7, extraction slit 8, magnet yoke 9 and insulator 10

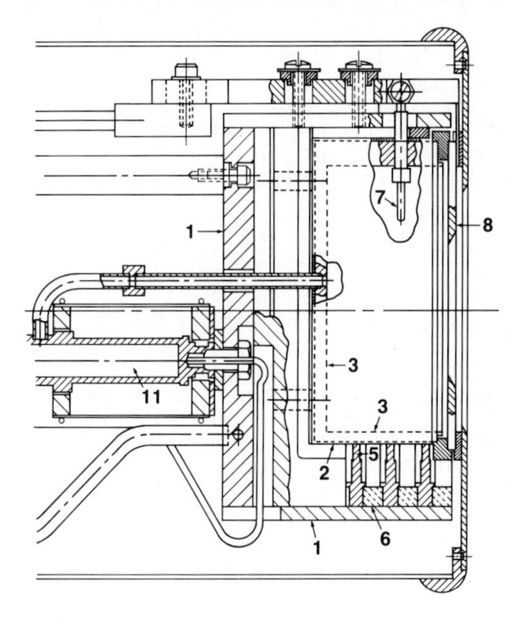

Figure 2. Multipole source, YZ section, also showing oven 11

The magnetic structure consists of nine iron pole pieces and rare-earth cobalt magnets. Since the structure produces a weak virtual pole at the extraction slit, the extracted ions do not have to cross the confining magnetic field, as in the arc or Freeman-type source.

By changing the orientation of the magnets, the source was run in 4-, 6- and 10-pole configurations. It was also run in a radial cusp configuration, i.e., only one cusp in the back of the source and two poles at the side of the extraction slit. The pole strengths at the graphite varied between 330 to 970 gauss, with the largest field corresponding to the quadrupole configuration. The average pole strengths at the graphite chamber were 390, 680, and 820 gauss for the decapole, hexapole, and quadrupole configurations, respectively.

Two "U"-shaped filaments were tested: one was identical to that in the Bernas-type source [16], and consisted of 2mm diameter tungsten with a 25mm emitting length.

The other had an emitting length of 140mm. The smaller filament was located at one end of the extraction slit, as shown in Fig. 2. The longer filament surrounded the extraction slit.

4. Experimental Results

The source described in Section 3 was run on argon, BF_3, and arsenic vapor. We describe experimental results obtained for 4-, 6-, and 10-poles configurations. The results for the quadrupole and argon are compared to a Bernas-type arc source which we use in an ion implanter [16].

Some of the physical processes involved in the source, as well as Langmuir probe data, are given by Cope and Keller [17]. Briefly the Langmuir probe data show two distributions of electrons, primaries with $T_e \simeq 16eV$ and secondaries with $T_e \simeq 5eV$, for an arc voltage of 50 volts.

For simplicity, we have expressed the results in terms of the pressure P at the diffusion pump with pumps the source chamber. A pressure of 1×10^{-5} torr is equivalent to a mass flow of 70 mA. The corresponding source pressure depends on the source temperature and the area of the extraction aperture: for a temperature of 500°C and $1 cm^2$, it is estimated to be a factor of 70 larger than the diffusion pump pressure.

4.1 Source Comparison

Figure 3 shows a plot of arc efficiency, i.e., extracted current I_{ex} divided by the arc current I_{arc} versus pressure P, for both the Bernas-type source and the quadrupole source. For the normal operating range of the sources, i.e., near the lower pressure limit for a given extracted current, the multipole source operates at one-fifth to one-sixth of the Bernas pressure. Alternately, for the same pressure, the multipole arc efficiency is two to three times greater. This data is for identical "U"-shaped filaments. For arsenic vapor, the multipole source has at least twice the gas efficiency, and probably five times as much.

The same data is plotted as I_{arc}/I_{ex} vs. P^{-1} in Fig. 4. In this plot, the inverse slope of the curve is proportional to the primary electron confinement time. The estimate was 350 nsec.

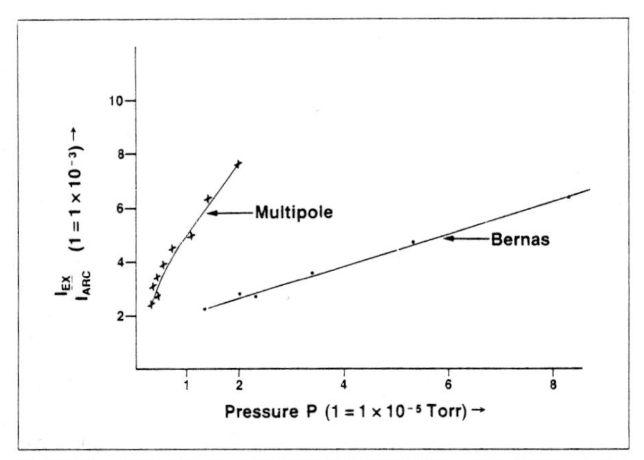

Figure 3. Source comparison I_{ex}/I_{arc} vs, pressure P

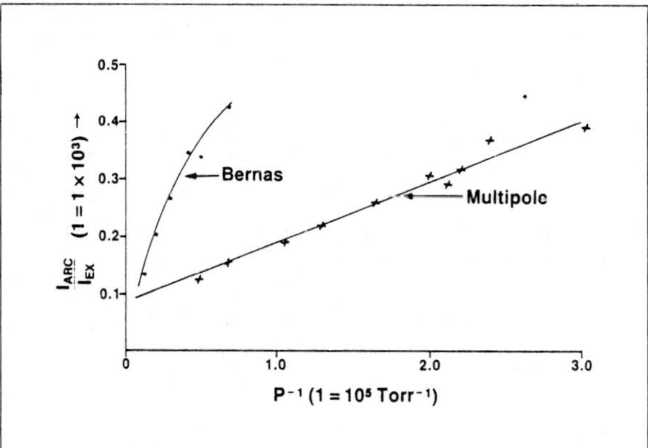

Figure 4. Source comparison I_{arc}/I_{ex} vs. inverse pressure P^{-1}

4.2 Filament Effects

For both sources, operated near their respective low-pressure limits, the maximum arc and extraction currents are a strong function of pressure. This effect was also found by Chavet and Bernas [2]. From discussions with W. W. Hicks [18], it is believed that this effect is due to a space charge limit of the electrons emitted from the filament. If this is the case then increasing the emitting length of the filament should reduce the effect. Indeed, a longer filament with a length of 14cm compared to 2.5cm eliminated the effect, i.e., above the turn-on pressure, the arc current was limited only by filament power and gas flow. However, the longer filament appears to produce more arc-current capability than was needed while also producing more heat flow to the source. This additional heat reduces the gas density for a given mass flow. A single straight filament, similar to a Freeman filament, would have an emitting length of about 7cm and would appear to be near optimum with respect to source-efficiency considerations. A straight filament can also be centered behind the extraction slit in a region of a lower magnetic field.

4.3 Pole Configuration

Figure 5 shows a comparison of the quadrupole, hexapole, and decapole configurations for argon. The quadrupole and hexapole gave similar results although the quadrupole was slightly better.

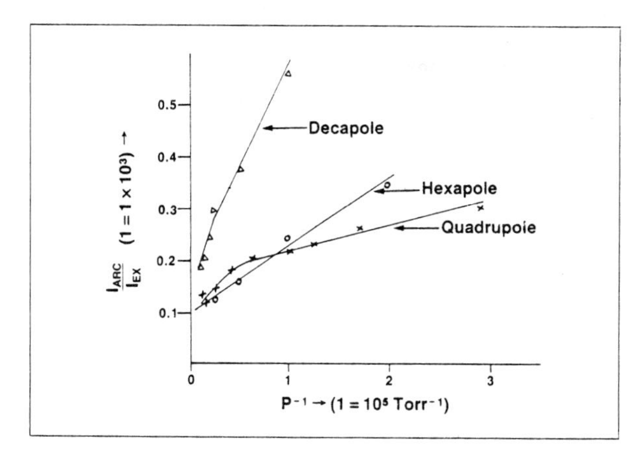

Figure 5. Comparison of quadrupole, hexapole and decapole configurations

The decapole results are not conclusive, since measurements of the magnetic field show a residual field of 36 gauss in the center of the source restricting the electrons to the region near the filament. This configuration should have at least two field-free regions. Thus, primary electrons produced at the filament could diffuse the length of the slit. This defect was not discovered soon enough to correct it.

The source was also tested in the radial cusp configuration. The problem described for the decapole, however, is magnified in this configuration, and results have not been presented.

For the quadrupole and hexapole, the plasma voltage was about 6 volts positive. This indicated that the anode area was more than adequate for these designs and could be reduced or, alternately, the field could be increased by using magnets with a larger cross-sectional area than the 6.35 x 6.35mm which was used.

4.4 Slit Potential

Varying the slit potential between the floating potential and 30 volts more negative than the cathode potential had less than 10% effect on the extracted beam currents. However, varying the potential from the floating potential to the anode potential decreased both the extracted current and the arc current, for a fixed filament power. This effect increased near the anode potential. The floating potential was near the cathode potential for low source pressure, and increased as the pressure was increased.

4.5 Gas Efficiency

The gas efficiency for argon with a quadrupole configuration was 42% for the smaller filament and an arc voltage of 50 volts. For the longer filament we achieved 55% gas efficiency and were limited by a 5 amp arc supply. The source conditions for the 55% were I_{arc} = 5.0A V_{arc} = 50v, I_{ex} = 17.5 mA and P = 4.5 x 10^{-6} torr which is equivalent to 32 mA of flow.

4.6 BF_3

BF_3 was only tested for the quadrupole configuration. For a 2.5 x 40mm slit and 8 mA extracted current the boron peak was only 15% of the BF_2 peak. For a 1 x 40mm slit, the boron peak was 30 to 50% of the BF_2. This data shows that the boron peak is improved when the ratio of plasma volume to extraction area is increased. Thus, it is expected that the hexapole configuration would give very good boron current, and that a corrected decapole may even be optimal. This is because the volume of the low magnetic-field region increases as the number of poles increases.

4.7 Current and Voltage Capability

The multipole source also appears to have higher voltage and current capabilities. We ran 23 mA of argon at 40 kV, and 8 mA at 100 kV. The latter was limited only by the high voltage supply-current capability and the pump on the test stand.

5. Conclusions

We have successfully designed a small multipole source for a high-current ion implantation system or electromagnetic isotope separation. For normal operating conditions, this source has five times the gas efficiency of the Bernas-type source. For the same pressure, it has twice the arc efficiency for the same filament. The optimum emission length for a 2mm diameter tungsten filament is greater than 25 mm.

The quadrupole configuration was found to be the best pole configuration for argon. However, for BF_3, the hexpole or decapole configuration should be better because they produce larger plasma volumes for a fixed arc chamber size.

Argon gas efficiency up to 55% at 17.5 mA/cm^2 was obtained, and the source performed well at both high extraction current densities and high extraction voltages.

Acknowledgements

The author would like to acknowledge D. B. Cope, who did most of the experimental work; W. W. Hicks, C. M. McKenna and A. E. Dosio, for their help in the source design; and J. R. Winnard for his support of the project.

References

1 Separation of Isotopes in Calutron Units, H. W. Savage, ed., Nuclear Energy Series (1951)

2 I. Chavet and R. Bernas, Nucl. Instr. and Meth. 51, 77 (1967)

3 E. Pasztor, Rad. Eff. 44, 121 (1979)

4 J. H. Freeman, G. A. Gard and W. Temple, AERE Report 6758 (1971)

5 D. Aitken, Rad. Eff. 44, 159 (1976)

6 G. Ryding, this conference

7 N. Sakudo, K. Tokiguchi, H. Koike and I. Kanomata, Rev. Sci. Instrum. 49 940 (1978)

8 H. R. Haufman, NASA Contract Report CR-1345 (1975)

9 R. D. Moore, AIAA Paper No. 69-520 (1969)

10 K. N. Leung, R. D. Collier, L. B. Marchall, T. N. Gallaher, W. H. Ingham, R. E. Kribel, and G. R. Raylor, Rev. Sci. Instrum 49, 321 (1978)

11 G. Schmidt, Physics of High Temperature Plasma, Academic Press, New York (1979) p. 133

12 R. Limpaecher and K. R. MacKenzie, Rev. Sci. Instrum 44, 726 (1973)

13 H. R. Kaufman, NASA Contract Report CR-159527, (1978)

14 N. Hershkowitz, K. N. Leung and T. Romesser, Phys. Review Letters 35, 277 (1975)

15 K. N. Leung, T. K. Samec and A. Lamm, Phys. Letters 51, 490 (1975)

16 J. H. Keller, C. M. McKenna, J. R. Winnard, W. W. Hicks and E. Hoffman, Rad. Eff. 44, 195 (1979)

17 D. B. Cope and J. H. Keller, to be published

18 W. W. Hicks (personal communication)

An Ion Source for Semiconductor Implantation

A. Latuszyński and D. Maczka
Institute of Physics, M. Curie-Sklodowska University, Lublin, Poland
Yu.V. Yushkievich
Joint Institute for Nuclear Research, Dubna, USSR

Abstract

An ion source is described which can produce ions of species possessing various chemical and physical properties. A limited review of the source characteristics is also given.

1. Introduction

The results obtained in a semiconductor-implantation process depend substantially on the ion-source construction as well as its operating conditions. In the published literature, there is a very large number of articles on ion sources designed for implantation purposes. Nevertheless, all problems of generating the required ion beams have not yet been solved, and efforts for improving existing sources and developing new constructions are continuing [1,2].

The present work concerns a new ion source which consists of a hollow-cathode source [3] and a thermo-ionization source [4]. The source can produce ions of species having various chemical and physical properties, including non-volatile elements.

In the following, a description of the source construction and a short review of its characteristics are given. A simple theoretical model of the source operation is also developed.

2. Ion-Source Construction

Diagrams of the ion source and the electrical supply systems are presented in Fig. 1. The basic component of the source is a 40-mm long discharge chamber W made of tantalum. In the discharge, it plays the role of the anode. The chamber is heated by bombardment of electrons from the filament K. When the chamber reaches a suitable temperature, its internal surface serves as the emitter of the electrons initiating the discharge. Between the chamber and the anode A, a voltage difference above the threshold for ionization is applied, so that the electrons are able to ionize atoms of the feed material which is introduced into the chamber. The generated ions are extracted through the opening E (Ø ~ 0.5 mm), and are then formed into the ion beam.

The source can be used to produce ions of gaseous as well as solid elements. In the latter case, the sample to be ionized is put into the evaporator I, from which the vapor enters the source chamber W through the tube T. The evaporator I is warmed by heat produced during operation of the source. The temperature of the evaporator can be changed by regulating its position relative to the source chamber. The controllable temperature range of the source evaporator lies between 500-2000 K.

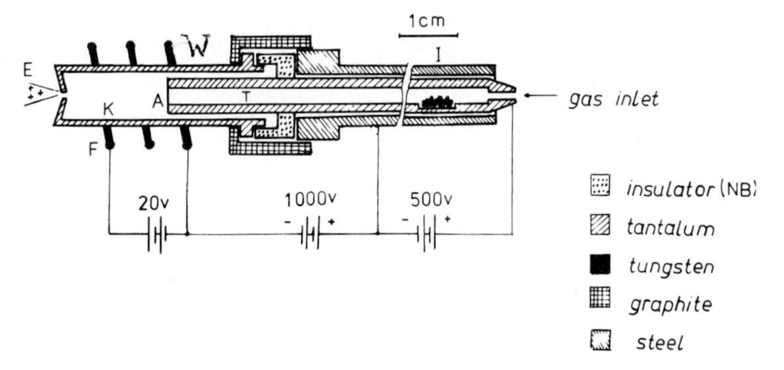

Fig. 1. Schematic diagram of the ion source. K - cathode, A - anode, F - filament, E - extraction opening, I - evaporator, W - discharge chamber

The ion source in question may also be used as a surface ionization source. This mode of source operation enables an efficient production of ion beams in the case of several elements, especially those with a relatively low ionization potential. In such cases, the anode A receives the chamber potential, and the ionization of the feed material results from collisions of atoms with the hot inner walls of the chamber.

3. Atom Ionization in the Ion Source

3.1 Plasma Ion Source

The electrons emitted by the hot walls ionize the gas which fills the discharge chamber. A minimum gas pressure p_{min} is required to maintain a stable discharge. When $p > p_{min}$, a stable plasma is created and is screened from the chamber by the double sheath of the space charge. Within this sheath, almost all of the discharge voltage is located. For constructional reasons, the electrons can oscillate in the plasma region until they lose their kinetic energy as a result of collisions with atoms.

Let us assume that the plasma region is identical with the discharge chamber, and that the extraction of the ions does not disturb the discharge. Let it also be assumed that N denotes the number of atoms which enter the plasma column within a given time unit. The rate of ion generation is then given by:

$$\frac{dn^+}{dt} = N\,P\ , \tag{1}$$

where P is the probability of creating a positive particle in the discharge

$$P = 1 - e^{-n_e \kappa t}\ . \tag{2}$$

In Eq.(2), n_e is the electron concentration in the plasma, and t is the period of time the atoms stay in the plasma column. The rate constant κ is defined in terms of the electron velocity distribution $f(v_e)$ and the velocity-dependent cross-section $\sigma(v_e)$ as follows:

$$\kappa = \int v_e f(v_e)\ \sigma(v_e) dv\ . \tag{3}$$

Let us suppose that the atom velocity distribution is Maxwellian. In such a case, the solution of Eq.(1), for the geometry of our ion source, can be formulated as follows:

$$\frac{dn^+}{dt} = \frac{3}{2} \pi r b n_o \left(\frac{kT_o}{m} \right)^{1/2} R \alpha \qquad (4)$$

where

$$R = 2 r n_e \kappa \left(\frac{m}{2kT_g} \right)^{1/2} . \qquad (5)$$

In the above equations, r and b are the radius and the length of the plasma column, respectively, n is the concentration of the feed-material atoms, T_g is the source temperature, m is the mass of an atom, and α is the integral expression concerning the atom-ionization conditions in the plasma column.

In order to calculate the density of the ions in the plasma, let us assume that there prevails a state of thermodynamic equilibrium, i.e. the ion losses are equal to the number of ions created in the entire volume of the discharge column. There are many processes leading to the destruction of the singly charged ions in the source, e.g. diffusion, recombination, ionization to a higher charge state, etc. However, it has been suggested that the ion losses can be attributed mainly to their diffusion towards the hot cathode, or towards the parts of the ion source which are at the cathode potential [5]. With regard to this, the ion-destruction rate is given by the formula:

$$- \frac{dn^+}{dt} = \frac{\pi r(r + 2b)}{4} n^+ \left(\frac{kT_e}{m} \right)^{1/2} . \qquad (6)$$

Making use of Eqs. (4) and (6), we are able to estimate the ion current emitted by the ion source:

$$I^+ = \frac{3r}{r + 2b} n_o n_e e \kappa \alpha S_M \qquad (7)$$

where S denotes the area of the plasma meniscus at the ion source extraction opening.

A second important parameter of the ion source, the source efficiency, may be expressed as follows:

$$\eta = \left(\frac{2 \pi m}{kT_g} \right)^{1/2} \frac{I^+}{e n_o S_o} , \qquad (8)$$

where S_o is the area of the extraction opening of the source.

In general, a correct evaluation of Eqs. (7) and (8), defining the basic features of the ion source, is a problem because certain parameters of the discharge plasma (e.g. κ) are very often not known, or because there are considerable difficulties with the measurements of others (e.g. S_M). This being the case, we can only give a qualitative description of the ion characteristics.

Figure 2 shows an example of Au^+ ion-current density as a function of the discharge voltage. A pronounced deviation of the curves from the well-known characteristics of the σ-ionization cross-section versus the electron energy proves that the ion-generation process is affected not only by collisions

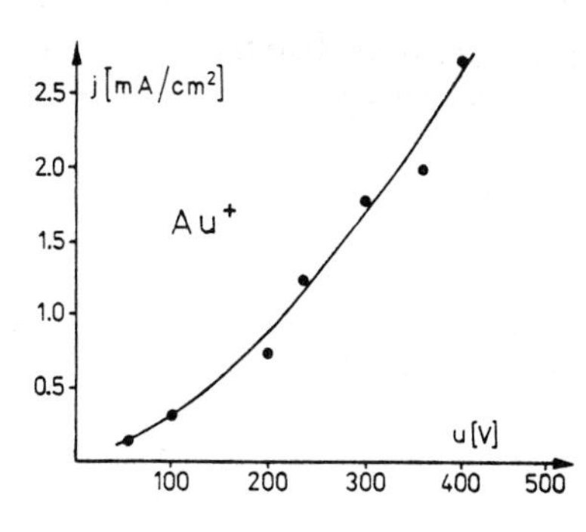

Fig. 2. Ion-current density as a function of discharge voltage

of atoms with primary electrons, but also by collisions with secondary ones. It should be pointed out that only in this case does the rate constant κ have its maximum at a higher discharge voltage than the σ cross-section.

The dependence of the Xe^+ ion current on the pressure in the source chamber is illustrated in Fig. 3. According to Eq. (7), this dependence should be linear, which is observed within the limits of experimental error. These functions have another characteristic for multiply charged ion currents: the ion current decreases with an increase in pressure, which is to be attributed to ion losses as a result of the charge-exchange process (Fig. 4).

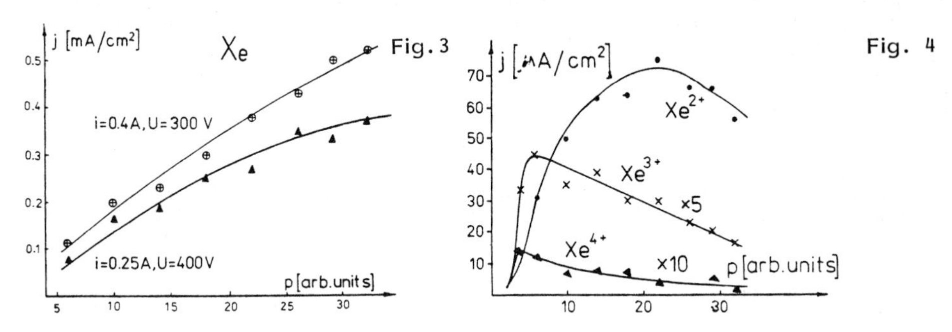

Fig. 3. Dependence of Xe^+ ion current on pressure in the source chamber

Fig. 4. Multiply charged Xe ion current as a function of pressure in the source chamber

3.2 Thermoionization Ion Source

Figure 5 shows the distribution of the temperature along the ion source. From this figure, it follows that temperatures in the 1500-2000°C region are reached quite easily. The curves concern the case where the arrangement works as a thermoionization ion source, i.e. no discharge in the chamber takes place.

Due to the high temperature of the source, it is possible to generate ions as a result of collisions of atoms with the hot inner walls of the chamber. A similar type of ion source was developed in the 1970's by Bayer et al. [4] and Johnson et al. [6]. Experimental and theoretical investigations of the processes taking place in the source have been carried out by several

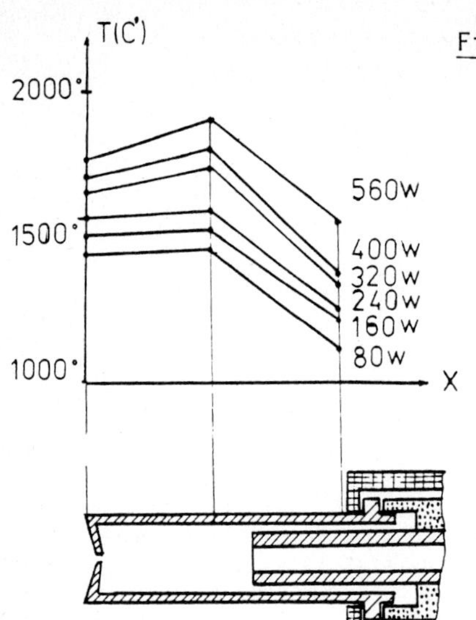

Fig. 5. Temperature distribution along the ion source

groups [7,8]. These have indicated that the ion current and source efficiency strongly depend on the source temperature and the ionization potential V of the element in question. In a series of investigations, it has been found that the ion-current density emitted by an ion source is:

$$j^{+} = \frac{AT^{2}}{\alpha} \sqrt{\frac{m}{M}} \exp \frac{V_{i}^{x}}{kT} , \qquad (9)$$

where $V^{x} = V_{i} - kT \cdot \ln A$ is the corrected value of the first ionization potential V, involving the ratio A of the statistical weights of ionic and atomic states of particles, T is the temperature, and k is the Boltzmann constant.

Figures 6a and 7a illustrate the typical dependence of In^{+} and Tm^{+} ion currents on the power of the electron current bombarding the chamber. In a first approximation, we can state that the values of the curves agree with the formula.

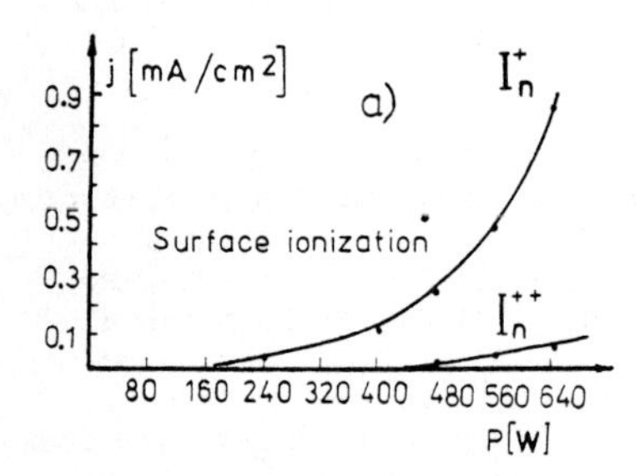

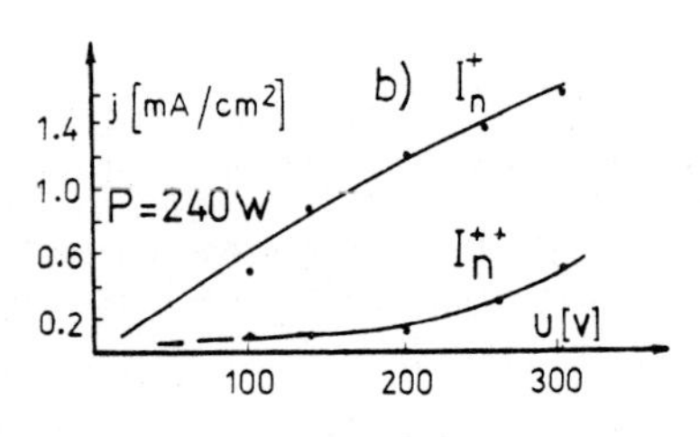

Fig. 6. a) In^{+} ion-current density as a function of the electron-current power bombarding the chamber.
b) In^{+} ion-current density as a function of the discharge voltage (P = 240 W)

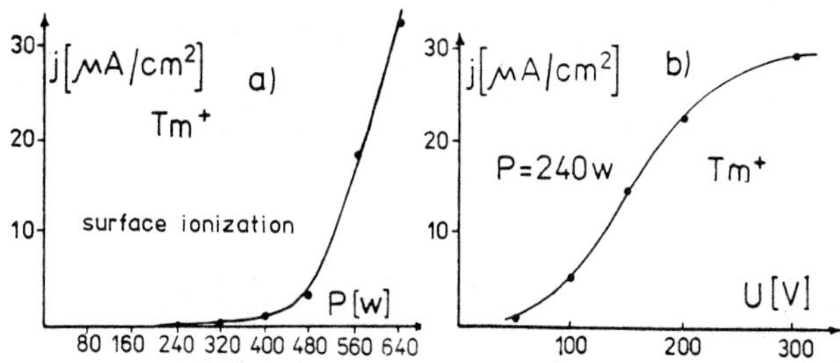

Fig. 7. a) Tm^+ ion-current density as a function of the electron-current power bombarding the chamber.
b) Tm^+ ion-current density as a function of the discharge voltage (P = 240 W)

Generally, the obtained ion-current densities for most elements reached several hundred microamperes per cm^2. However, these ion-current densities may be considerably increased when the discharge is burning in the chamber. From Figs. 6b and 7b, it follows that (for In^+ and Tm^+) this mode of source operation is more useful, and that the ion currents emitted by the source increase substantially.

A contrary effect, however, was observed for several elements, especially for species having an especially low ionization potential, e.g. Na, K. For these elements, the ion currents decreased when the discharge was initiated in the source.

4. Conclusion

The new ion source described above has been used for the past few years at the Laboratory of Nuclear Problems, JINR (Dubna), and at the Institute of Physics, M.C. Sklodowska University (Lublin), for semiconductor implantation, ion bombardment of solid surfaces, and nuclear-spectroscopy purposes.

The list of ions which have been produced in the source includes such elements as Au, B, Al, He, Xe, Ne, Kr, Li, Ga, Cu, In, Ta, Hg, Pb, Mo, Tm, Nd and Pr. The authors would like to point out that the generation of such a wide variety of ion species having diverse chemical and physical properties was possible due to the construction of the source, which offers for the operator the possibility of choosing the more effective method for atom ionization: that of electron impacts in the discharge plasma, or that of surface ionization.

Regarding the most important characteristics of the source, the relatively low consumption of electric power should be noted. In particular cases, e.g. in the production of ions from gaseous species, the operator can completely eliminate the electron bombardment. Under these conditions, the ion source consumes only about 20 W (50 V, 0.4 A). This mode of operation is very useful for long-term implantation, and from this point of view, the ion source under consideration is recommended for implanters of industrial or semi-industrial types.

A simple theoretical model of the source's operation has also been given above. The expressions obtained for the ion current and the source efficiency, even though very approximate, illustrate the manner in which I^+ and η are affected by changes in the ion-source parameters.

References

1. Proc. of the Third Intern. Conf. on Ion Implantation: Equipment and Techniques, Kingston, Canada, Nucl. Instr. and Meth. 189 (1981)
2. Proc. of the 10th Intern. Conf. on EMIS, Zinal, Nucl. Instr. and Meth. 186 (1981)
3. G. Sidenius, Proc. Intern. Conf. on Electromagnetic Isotope Separators, Marburg, Fed. Rep. Germany (1970), p. 423
4. G. Beyer, E. Herrmann, A. Piotrowski, V.I. Raiko, and H.Tyroff, Nucl. Instr. and Meth. 96, 437 (1971)
5. J. Koch, R.H.V.M. Dawton, M.L. Smith, and W. Walcher, Electromagnetic Isotope Separators and Applications of Electromagnetically Enriched Isotopes (North-Holland, Amsterdam, 1958)
6. P.G. Johnson, A. Bolson, and C.M. Henderson, Nucl. Instr. and Meth. 106, 83 (1973)
7. A. Latuszynski and V.I. Raiko, Nucl. Instr. and Meth. 125, 61 (1975)
8. V.P. Afanasiev, V.A. Obukhov, and V.I. Raiko, Report JINR (Dubna), P6-/0031 (1976)

Part III

Implanter Subsystems

High Throughput Wafer Handling System for Serial Process Ion Implantation

S. Dinaro, R. Hertel, and N. Turner
Varian/Extrion Division, Box 1226, Gloucester, MA 01930, USA

Wafer handling has been a key issue in the acceptance of ion implantation equipment as a production tool. Some early ion implantation equipment processed one wafer at a time, by automatically moving wafers mounted on metal wafer holders in and out of the target position from specially designed cassettes. Further equipment developments which eliminated the need for mounting wafers on holders, allowed automatic handling and implantation of wafers directly from standard industrial cassettes.
This paper reviews the features and capabilities of wafer handlers for serial process implantation and describes a recently developed vertical wafer handling system, capable of very high throughput with improved wafer handling techniques.

1. History

Early serial process (one wafer at a time) ion implantation systems of the 1970's, implanted wafers mounted on metal holders. Two different systems such as this are shown in figures 1a and 1b.

Each wafer was required to be hand loaded by an operator using tweezers. Although this technique had some advantages in the ability to

Figure 1. Early wafer handling systems for serial wafer implantation
1a. Extrion carousel end station

1b. Extrion 30/25C end station

process odd shapes or broken pieces, it often resulted in wafer damage or particulates due to handling.

In the mid 1970's, fully automated wafer handlers which loaded wafers automatically into vacuum, directly from industrial cassette carriers were developed [1,2] by Accelerator Inc., and Extrion. This represented a major step forward in semiconductor processing and eliminated much of the handling previously required. Figure 2 shows a diagram of wafer movement, through a wafer handler designed to unload and reload from wafer cassettes.

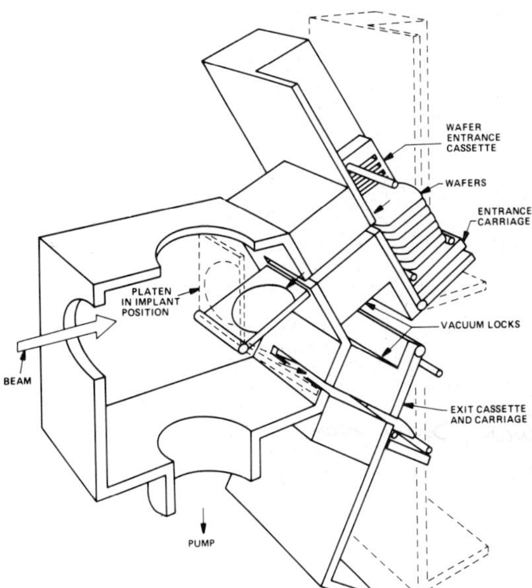

Figure 2. Wayflow Processing Station. Capable of processing up to 275 wafers per hour directly from industrial cassettes

This type of system allows wafers to slide from cassettes into a vacuum lock, and after evacuation, into the target position. After implantation, the wafer slides into the exit lock, is vented, and slides back into an empty receiving cassette. This type of wafer handling system moves wafers principally by gravity, sliding them down guides or concave surfaces, and stopping them against metal or plastic bumpers.

Although these types of systems are simple, they inherently can generate particles scraped off of the wafer surface during sliding or stopping, since there is relative motion between the wafer and its surroundings. Dust and particles generated by wafer scratches and bumping can end up on the front surface of wafers and during implantation, causing unimplanted areas and resulting in device defects. Figure 3 shows a typical scratch as a result of this wafer being passed through this type of wafer handler.

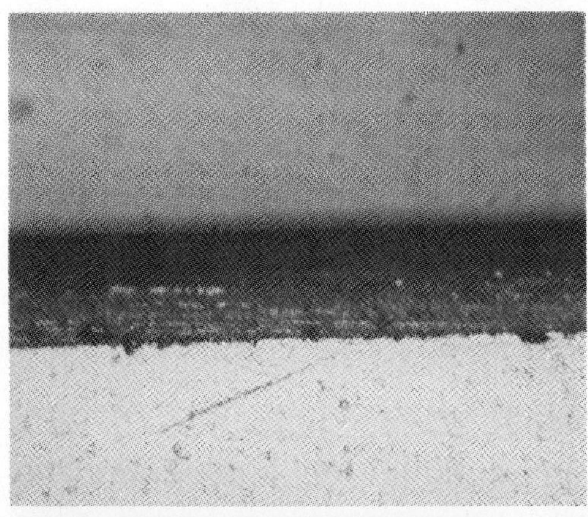

Figure 3. Wafer scratch near edge after 5 cycles through a wafer handling system which moves wafers by sliding

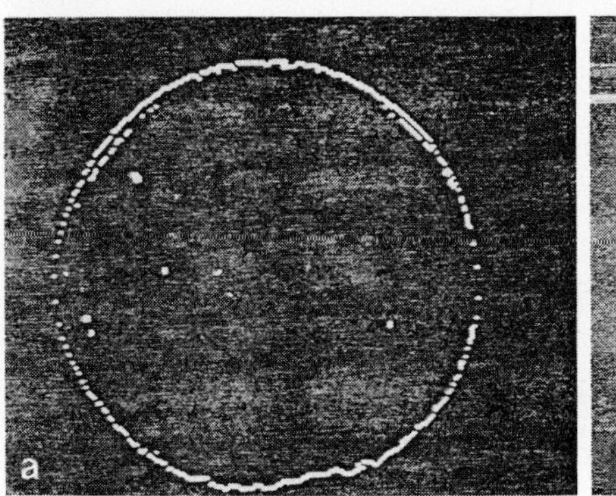

Figure 4. Particles counted [3] on a wafer after one pass through an unclean wafer handling system 4a.Wafer particulates $>1\ \mu m$ before cycling 4b. Wafer particulates $>1\ \mu m$ after 1 cycle through the processing station.

Tencor, Surface scan

Figure 4 is the resulting particulates deposited on a wafer passed through a particularly dirty system only once.

2. Wafer Handling

In order to minimize particulate contamination such as this, one must design a system of wafer handling which provides:

1) clean air environment for wafers being processed
2) minimize relative motion between wafer and its surroundings; no sliding or bumping
3) minimize wafer travel distance.

2.1 Clean Air Environment

The high performance wafer handling system described in this paper is designed to meet particulate requirements for VLSI technology, the Varian/Extrion Model 350 D. The wafer handling portion of the machine is separated from the rest of the machine with a gasketed sheet metal enclosure. A Class 100 laminar air flow hood is provided which covers the entire wafer handler (see figure 5).Air exhaust fans are provided under the wafer handler which provide a slight negative pressure in the machine base and exhaust the air out of the clean room environment. A dust cover is provided, with its own air intake and removal of any possible particulates generated from the platen assembly wafer.The exhaust fans in the base prevent contamination from backstreaming from the lower mechanisms up onto wafers being processed. Exhaust provided to the wafer handler mechanism prevents the wafer lift assembly from contaminating the wafers.

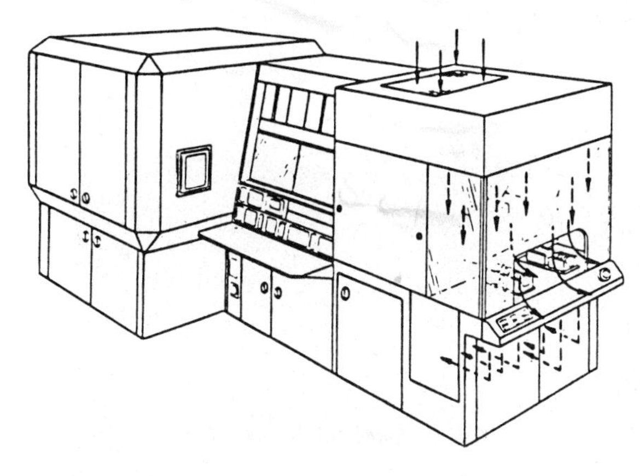

Figure 5. Varian Extrion Model 350D with separate wafer handling compartment

2.2 Wafer Motion

In order to provide the wafer motion without relative motion to eliminate scratching and particulates, vertical and horizontal wafer handling systems were evaluated. The vertical wafer handling system was selected based on the following advantages:

1) since wafers to be processed rest vertically in their cassettes, the wafer center is always known, which eliminates the need for a separate centering station
2) wafer motion is minimized since wafers are implanted in the vertical position

3) there are no wafers stacked above the wafers to be implanted, which can cause air turbulance and possible contamination
4) plastic SEMI standard cassettes may be used, thus eliminating the need to dump transfer to special machine cassettes
5) wafers are maintained in their respective slots throughout the process .

2.3 Wafer Loading

The wafer cycle starts with loading up to 100 wafers in four cassette carriers. The wafers are then positioned over a vertical wafer pick after the flats are automatically aligned to the bottom. Wafers are then edge handled by the pick moving through the cassette (see figure 6). A wafer exchange is then performed between the pick and a vacuum chuck. The pick is lowered, the wafer is mechanically clamped to the platen. See Figure 7.

Figure 6. Vertical wafer handling from a standard industrial cassette

2.4 Results

Test results of this system have demonstrated:

1) no edge or backside damage as a result of wafer handling after transferring a new wafer 100 times
2) 150,000 exchanges of the same wafer were performed between the wafer pick and the vacuum chuck with no failures
3) 750,000 wafer exchanges of 50 wafers between the pick and a cassette indexing system.

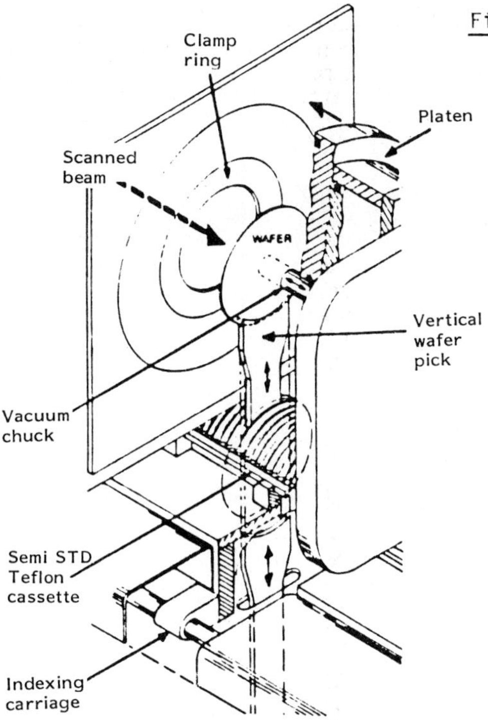

Figure 7. Wafer motion is minimized in the 350 D wafer handler

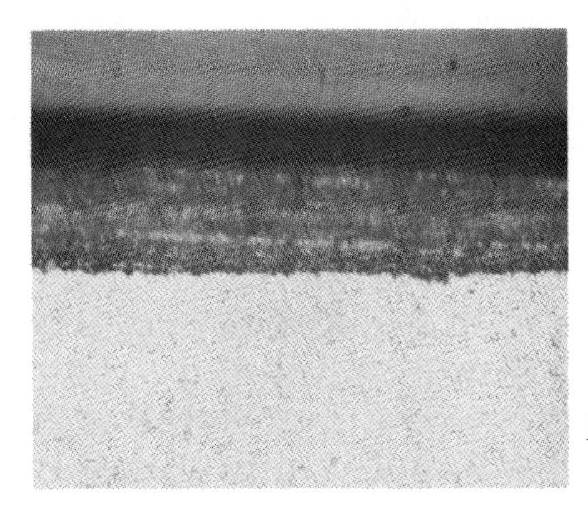

Figure 8 Wafer passed through the 350 D wafer handler 10 times, no scratches were found

3. Throughput

The 350 D is designed with high throughput performance in mind. A key to high throughput is high beam utilization. When wafer handling is serial to implanting, the beam must be off the wafer for extended periods of time. This is the case with any implant systems utilizing a single processing station. This new system utilizes a dual target

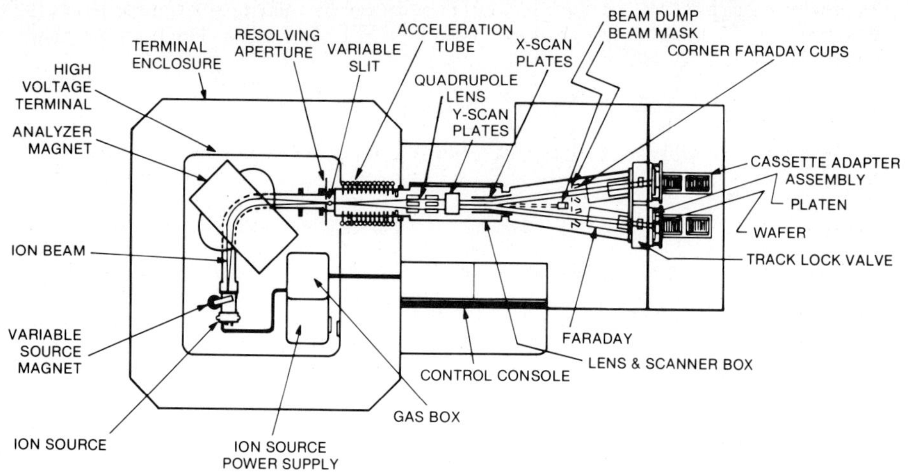

Figure 9. Ion implantation system using electrostatic deflection and dual target positions

chamber, which houses two ground masks, beam set up flags, and faraday cages, see figure 9.

Dual processing chambers allow implanting one wafer while the other wafer is exchanged. The only time the ion beam is not being utilized is during the vacuum recovery time, which represents about 2.0 seconds in a 9.7 second cycle. This technique provides beam utilization of >75%, which allows a throughput of 350 wafers per hour.

3.1 Wafer Cassette Speeds

In order to maintain the high level of throughput, we must unload and load wafers in 7.7 seconds and execute vacuum recovery in <2.0 seconds. Cassette carriages are moving at linear speeds of approximate 45 inches per minute. Wafer cassettes are reliably and accurately indexed in .25 seconds. On a test stand, 750,000 wafers were transferred from a moving cassette to the vertical pick. The wafer pick gently engages with the wafers then accelerates and decellerates at the top of the stroke using sinusoidal motion. The machine has the capacity to load 25, 50, 75, or 100 wafers.

Operator loading of cassettes into any processing system is a function of the total number of cassettes per load at a processing rate. Table 1 shows the operator attention interval required for various cassette loads at a machine throughput rate of 350 wafers/hour.

Table 1. Operator attention interval for systems with 1,2, or 4 cassettes (25 wafers/cassette) at a processing rate of 350 wafers/hour

Cassettes @ 25 wafers/cassette	Operator Loads/Hr	Operator Intervals
1	14	4.25 min
2	7	8.50 min
4	3.5	17.14 min

In order to minimize operator attention intervals, this system was designed to accommodate 4 standard full cassettes, and no empty cassettes are required.

3.2 Vacuum Performance

In order to achieve throughput design goals, vacuum recovery from atmosphere to $5x10^{-6}$ torr for implanting must occur in 2.3 seconds. In order to achieve this high level of performance, several stringent design tasks were required. End station isolation valves have been designed to move 8 inches in 0.5 seconds with a design life of 1,000,000 cycles. The first prototype valve has performed 1,500,000 cycles with linear speeds of 8 inches, in 0.5 seconds without a failure. Special attention was given to minimizing the volume of the lock and quick clean pump down of the locks. The locks are roughed from atmospheric pressure to 250 microns through two stages of volume expansion (see figure 10).

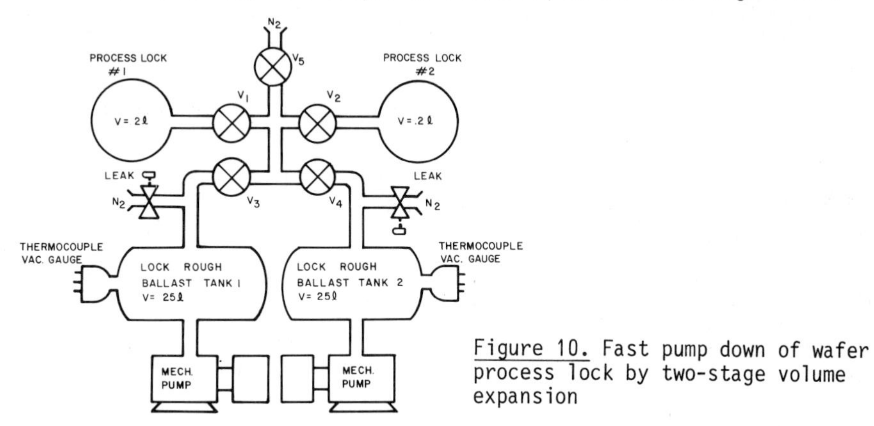

Figure 10. Fast pump down of wafer process lock by two-stage volume expansion

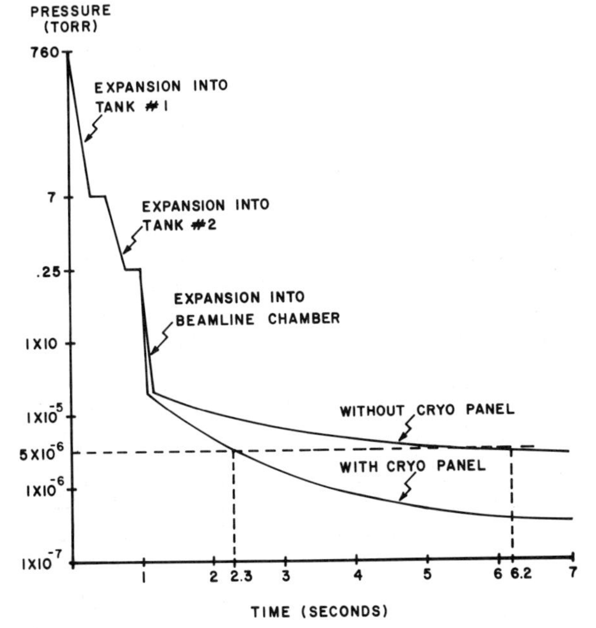

Figure 11. Vacuum pressure vs. time for fast evacuation of wafers to be processed in the 350 D wafer handler system

Two lock ballast tanks, each 25 liters in volume, are maintained at rough vacuum levels by 7 CFM mechanical pumps. The lock volume is roughed from atmospheric pressure to 250 microns in approximately one second using this two-staged volume expansion technique. After quick lock pumping by volume expansion, the 25 liter tanks may be again roughed to 150 microns easily within the allowable 9 seconds by a conventional 75 cfm mechanical pump. The third stage volume expansion occurs when the end station isolation valve opens. The beam line pressure instantly rises to 8×10^{-5} torr when this occurs, and is reduced to 5×10^{-6} torr in 1.3 seconds (see figure 11).

Since each cycle opens the lock to atmosphere, special attention to water vapor pumping was provided by an integral faraday LN_2 cryo panel. Vacuum recovery testing with and without cryo panels indicate the following results:

Time to reach 5×10^{-6}Torr	Without Cryo Panel	With Cryo Panel
seconds	3.2	1.3

A summary of the implant and exchange cycle is shown in figure 12.

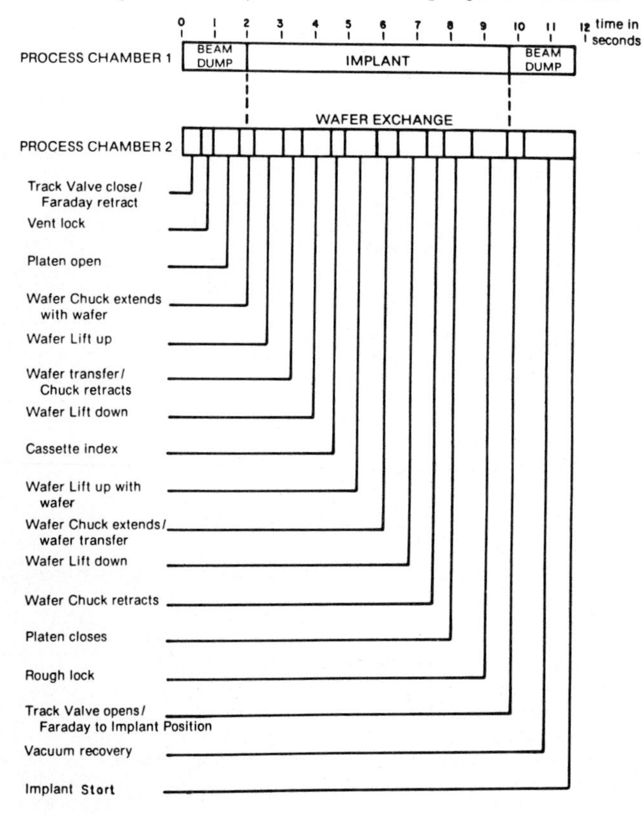

Figure 12. Wafer implant and exchange cycle of the 350 D Ion Implantation System

4. Wafer Cooling

Wafer cooling is a critical requirement for medium to high dose implantation with high wafer throughput of photoresist masked wafers, whose melting point is in the region of 120° C. The following chart describes the cooling requirements for an ion implanter with a scanned beam current of 1.5 ma at 200 keV.

Wafer Size	Implant Area (cm^2)	Beam Power Density ($Watts/cm^2$)
3"	52	5.8
100 mm	92	3.3
125 mm	136	2.2
150 mm	190	1.6

Wafer cooling techniques have been developed, and will be reported at this conference, which provide thermal conductivity coefficients [5] H/A=50 to 80 milliwatts/°C/cm^2 for 3" and 100 mm diameters wafers. Wafer temperatures have been maintained below 120° C for beam power densities of 5W/cm^2 [4].

5. Dosimetry

Accurate dose measurement is provided by a deep faraday with a depth to width ratio of > 10, see figure 13.

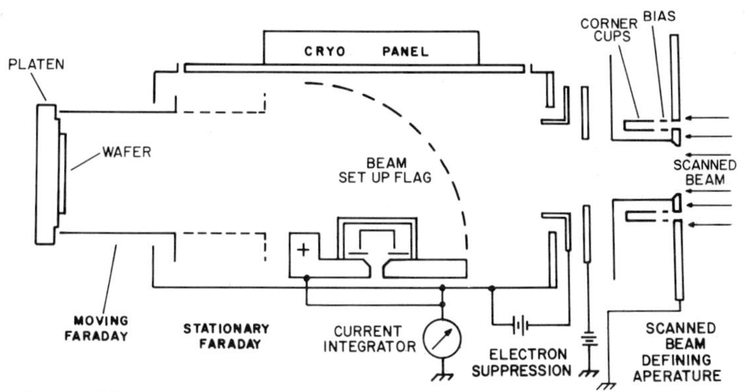

Figure 13. Schematic of a deep faraday system with integral cryo panel

One section of the faraday is movable to allow the process lock isolation valve to seal the lock. Motion for the movable faraday section is provided by the isolation valve stroke. Two secondary electron suppression plates are arranged so as to properly repel secondary electrons without dose error [6]. A beam set up flag for focussing and beam spot size adjustment is provided. A beam defining aperture with corner cups allows on line dose uniformity measurement and/or corner cup integration of dose.

6.0 Operating Modes

The wafer process controller utilizes a microprocesser allowing flexibility in selecting operating modes. The implant operating modes include:

1) alternate end station cycling (normal mode)
2) simultaneous end station cycling (beam share mode)
3) independent end station cycling
4) test cycling modes .

Table 2. Summary of implanter operating modes

	DESCRIPTION	ADVANTAGES
IMPLANT	ALTERNATE E.S. CYCLE	MAXIMUM THROUGHPUT
MODES	SIMULTANEOUS E.S. CYCLE	REDUCED AVERAGE
(SEE NOTE 1)	E.S. # 1 ONLY	BEAM POWER DENSITY
	E.S. # 2 ONLY	
TEST	ATMOSPHERE/VACUUM CYCLING	EXERCISE WAFER
MODES	OF WAFERS	HANDLER
MANUAL MODES	ALL FUNCTIONS OF END STATION	MAINTENANCE

Note 1. A wafer flat orientation option is available on all implant modes.

7. Summary

The 350 D VLSI™ wafer handling system processes wafers reliably with positive edge handling. Unlike many existing designs, gentle wafer motion with no sliding drastically reduces particulate contaminates. The dual end stations can operate independently or synchronously for maximum beam utilization. The system is designed to handle wafer sizes of 2" to 150mm from standard teflon casssettes.

Vacuum system performance is enhanced with the unique two-stage design. These technical advances contribute to creating an implantation system with throughput rates of up to 350 wafers per hour.

In order to produce higher die yield of VLSI circuits utilizing micron or sub-micron geometry, the 350 D performs the critical step of ion implantation, using a wafer handling system specifically designed to reduce particulate contamination.

Acknowledgements

The authors also would like to thank the many participants in the design of this system for their hard work and inventive ideas and concepts. A special thanks to Fred Turner and Marty Hutchinson of Varian, Thin Film Vacuum Division, for their pioneer development of vertical wafer handling.

References

1. Varian/Extrion - Wayflow Processing Station
2. Accelerators, Inc. - Wafermatic
3. Tencor - Surf Scan
4. N. Turner, B. Bramhall - To be published
5. R.D. Parry, J. Vac Sci Technology 13 (1976) 622
6. D. Jamba, Rev. Sci. Instruments, 49 (1978) 634

Comparison of Beam Scanning Systems

N. Turner
Varian/Extrion Division, Box 1226, Gloucester, MA 01930, USA

ABSTRACT

Present day ion implanters provide uniform distribution of energetic ions into target materials, utilizing one or two of the basic beam scanning techniques; electrostatic, magnetic, and mechanical. Each beam scanning technique has physical limits and characteristics which affect its successful use in an ion implanter for semiconductor processing. This paper reviews the features and limits of each beam scanning technique. X-Y beam scanning systems using magnetic and electrostatic deflection are described. The ability for electrostatic X-Y scanning of μ perv.*, is reviewed and results reported.

1. Introduction

Most ion implantation systems in use today are applied to the doping of semiconductor material. Since doping applications vary in dose typically from 10^{10} to 10^{16} ions cm^{-2}, beam current requirements ranging from 20 na to 20 ma are required to meet production throughputs commonly required for semiconductor production [1].

Uniform doping of semiconductors, typically with σ <1%, have been provided by a variety of scanning techniques, which are:

- electrostatic (time varying tranverse electric fields)
- magnetic
- mechanical
- hybrid (combination of any two of the above).

The success of application of these implanters to a particular doping process may be determined by the limits of its scanning technique. The purpose of this paper is to review and compare these techniques.

2. History of Scan Techniques

Electrostatic scanning employed in most early ion implanter systems provided high speed scanning, 25 $\times 10^3$ cm s^{-1}, of the ion beam over the target surface. These early systems scanned beam currents which were typically less than 1 ma. For higher current ion beams greater than 1

* Perveance is defined as $P = (M/Q)^{1/2}(I)\,(E)^{-3/2}$

where M is the mass number, I is the beam current in amps, Q is the charge number, E is the beam energy in Kev.

ma, at lower energies such as 50 Kev, beam expansion due to space charge caused insufficient beam utilization, and thus has limited the use of this scan technique in high current, low energy systems. Capability of a present day implanter [3] will be measured and results reported.

With the development of high dose implanters, whose ion beam currents are in excess of 5 ma, magnetic or mechanical scanning have been successfully employed. Most double mechanical scanning systems which have been built to date contain one axis of scanning with a slow scan rate of 2 to 5 cm s^{-1}, (0.1 HZ), and a fast scan speed of 2.5 x 10^3cm s^{-1} (13 HZ). Their application to low dose implantation is limited by beam current measurement (dosimetry) and scan pattern.

Hybrid scan systems, combining one axis of mechanical scan with one of electrostatic were developed early by Accelerators, GCA, and Balzers. More recently, Varian/Extrion introduced a hybrid system combining magnetic beam scanning and mechanically scanned targets mounted on disks, each in its own target chamber [4].

3. General Requirements for any Scan Systems

Any scan system employed in an ion implant system must provide:

1. A scanning pattern which places enough beam passes with overlap over the target so as to provide a uniform doping distribution.

2. Uniform scanning rate of the beam at the target surface.

3. Reasonable beam utilization, typically >40%.

Other factors which must be considered in successfully applying a scan technique to ion implantation are:

a. wafer heating
b. dose accuracy
c. vacuum performance (throughput)
d. auto loading .

4. Review of Various Scan Techniques

The following figures are schematics of the various scanning techniques employed in commercial ion implanters, and a summary of their general advantages and disadvantages is reviewed.

4.1 Ion Beam Scanning Using Electrostatic Deflection Plates

An X-Y beam scanning system using electrostatic deflection is shown in figure 1. Although developed early in ion implantation, [5] recent improvements have extended the use of this technique to higher dose applications. Most ion implanters used in semiconductor manufacturing today utilize this beam scanning technique.

4.2 Mechanical Scanning

Mechanical scanning of targets through a stationary beam has been done several ways, and has been reported by Rose [6] and Ryding [7] and Kranik [8].

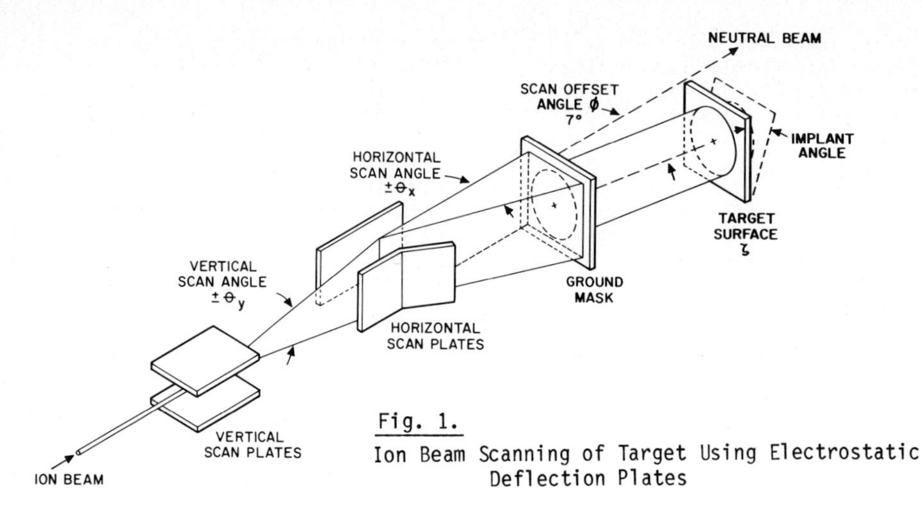

Fig. 1.

Ion Beam Scanning of Target Using Electrostatic Deflection Plates

Advantages	Disadvantages
Fast scan speed	Variation in beam angle of incidence due to scan angle
Faster minimum implant time	Poor beam utilization for high current, low energy beams
Low cost	Wafer heating at high energy/high current
High throughput capability	
Easily autoloaded	
Serial processing of wafers	

4.2.1 The Ferris wheel scanner incorporated two axis mechanical scanning[9]. The scanning was done by rotary motion providing the fast scan along with the 4-bar parallel linkage to maintain a constant angle of incidence with the beam. The entire mechanism translated horizontally forming the slow scan direction.

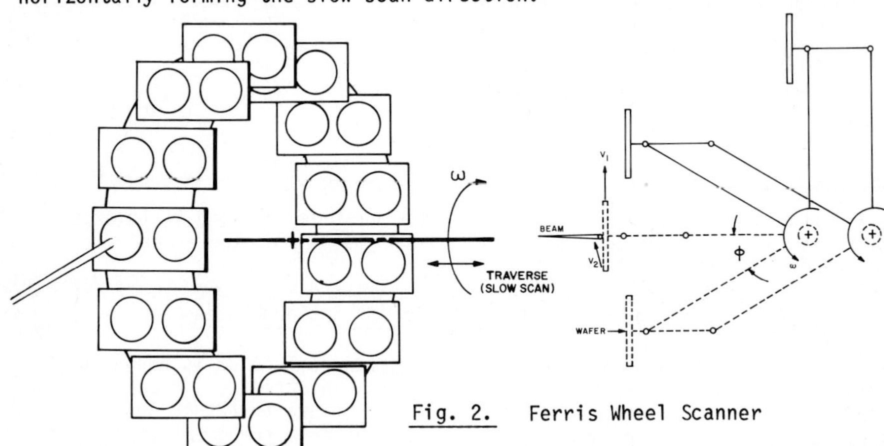

Fig. 2. Ferris Wheel Scanner

Advantages	Disadvantages
Suitable for high current beams	Scan velocity error ($V_2 > V_1$)
Constant angle of incidence	Difficult to cool targets
	Not easily autoloaded
	Lower throughput capability
	Large vacuum chamber
	Slow scan speeds <100 rpm (1.7HZ)

4.2.2 The Lintott carousel or racetrack system was developed in the early 70's at Lintott Engineering. In this concept scanned wafers mounted on metal plates pass at a constant velocity through the ion beam in the horizontal fast scan direction, while the entire mechanism is slowly raised, by a common single drive shaft. The helical scan pattern is fixed.

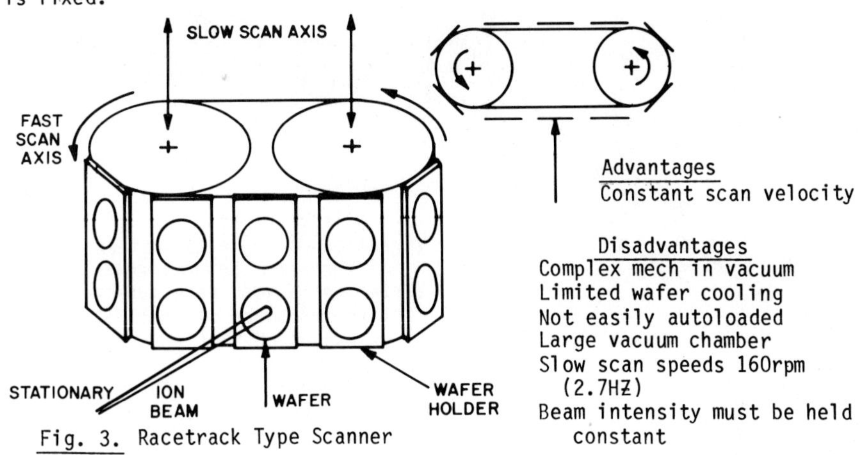

Fig. 3. Racetrack Type Scanner

Advantages

Constant scan velocity

Disadvantages

Complex mech in vacuum
Limited wafer cooling
Not easily autoloaded
Large vacuum chamber
Slow scan speeds 160rpm (2.7HZ)
Beam intensity must be held constant

4.2.3 The spinning and translating disk system for mechanically scanning wafers thru a stationary beam is shown in Figure 4. This scanning technique has several advantages over other all mechanically scanned systems and has been used in several ion implant systems since 1974 [11].

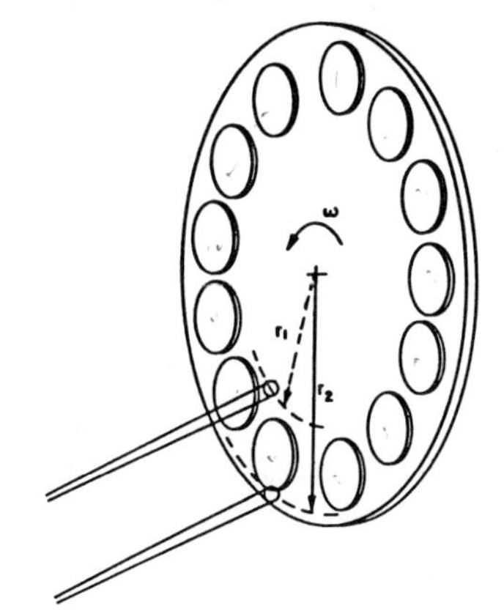

Advantages

Simpler mechanism
Smaller vacuum chamber
Autoloading possible

Disadvantages

Requires some compensation to maintain uniform scan rate since $V \propto r\,\omega$

Fig. 4. Translating/Rotating Disk

4.3 Hybrid Scanning Techniques

4.3.1 The carousel hybrid scan system combines electrostatic scanning with mechanical rotation. [12] Wafers mounted on the outside perimeter of a faceted drum provide the slow scan axis, while the beam is scanned across the wafer diameters vertically using electrostatic deflection.

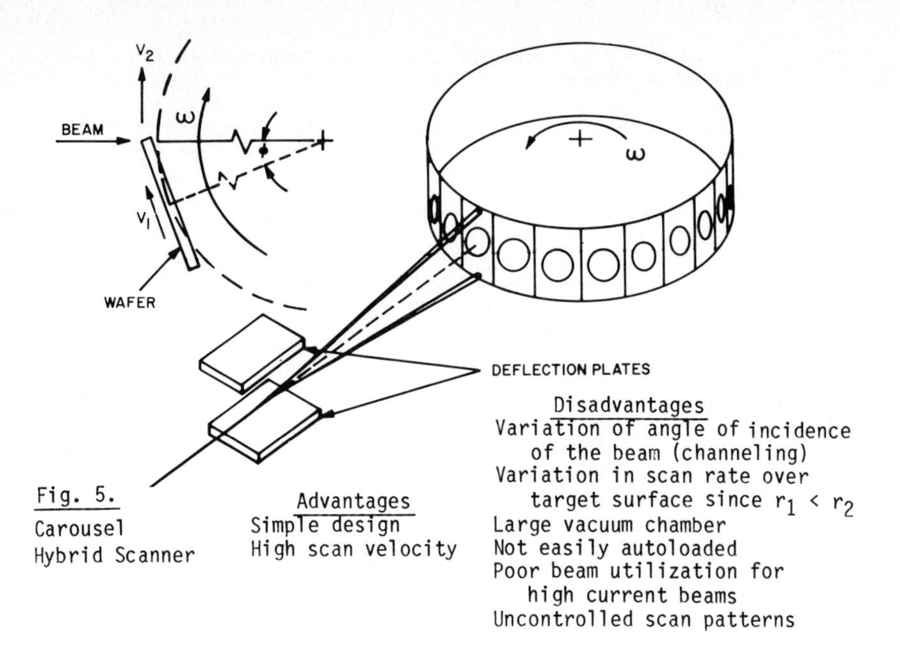

Fig. 5. Carousel Hybrid Scanner

Advantages
- Simple design
- High scan velocity

Disadvantages
- Variation of angle of incidence of the beam (channeling)
- Variation in scan rate over target surface since $r_1 < r_2$
- Large vacuum chamber
- Not easily autoloaded
- Poor beam utilization for high current beams
- Uncontrolled scan patterns

4.3.2 Another combination of electrostatic scanning and mechanical rotation is utilized in the Balzers implanter [13]. In this system, wafers mounted on plates are inserted onto the inner perimeter of a large drum oriented in the vertical plane. Horizontal beam scanning and beam offset angle forming a neutral trap are provided by electrostatic scanning plates.

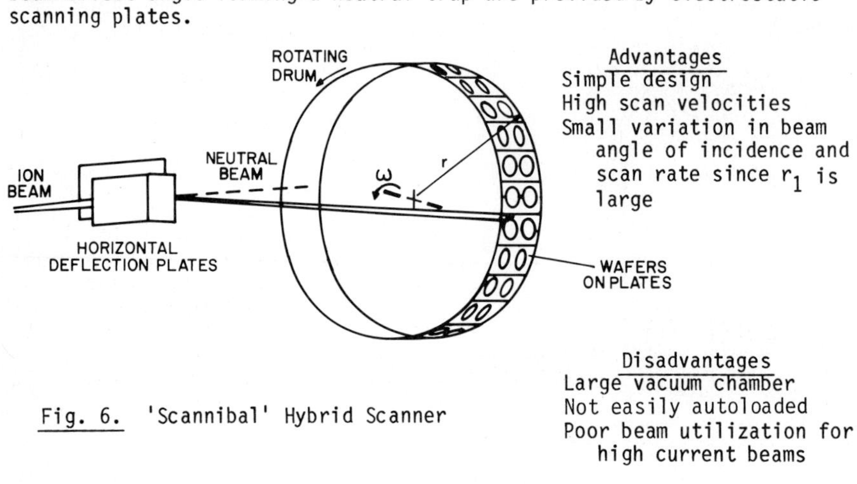

Advantages
- Simple design
- High scan velocities
- Small variation in beam angle of incidence and scan rate since r_1 is large

Disadvantages
- Large vacuum chamber
- Not easily autoloaded
- Poor beam utilization for high current beams

Fig. 6. 'Scannibal' Hybrid Scanner

4.3.3 Magnetic beam scanning with mechanical target scanning on rotating disks are used in the Extrion 80-10. Parallel scan correction is applied to maintain constant beam angle of incidence with the targets. Dual disks arranged with a common scanning and angle correcting magnets are used to provide improved throughput [14].

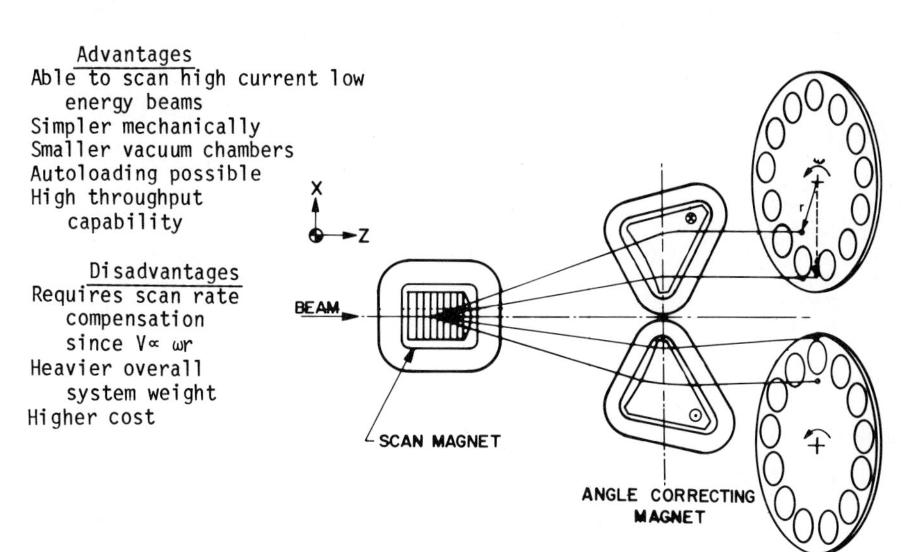

Fig. 7. Hybrid Magnetic-Mechanical Scan

4.4 Other Scan Techniques

Although nothing written could be found in the literature, a novel hybrid system utilizing ion beam extraction energy modulation and the fixed magnetic field of the analyzer to attain beam scanning in one axis, was reported to have been built at Harwell [15].

Scanning in the other axis was done mechanically by mounting the targets on a rotating faceted drum, see Fig. 8.

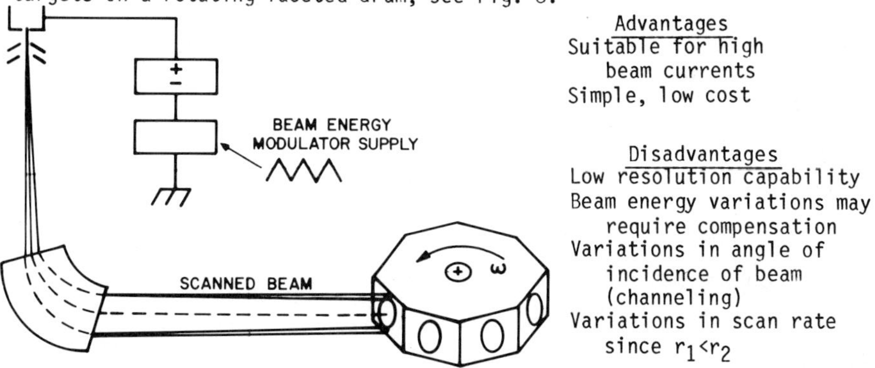

Fig. 8. Beam Scanning By Energy Modulation

5. Features of Electrostatic Scanners

Electrostatic deflection systems were extensively developed for use in cathode ray tubes and detailed design considerations for electrostatic deflection systems are given in the literature [2,5]. In applying an electrostatic deflection technique to ion implantation, these design considerations must be applied in to achieve the general requirements for uniform scanning.

5.1 Factors Limiting Uniformity of Implant

A review of factors limiting uniformity of implant with symmetrically driven electrostatic scanning plates such as those of Fig. 1, are summarized:

1) Misalignment - beam to scanner plates
2) Beam noise/hash
3) Beam spot size - variation
4) Scan angle - center to edge
5) Offset scan - neutral trap
6) Wafer tilt - implant angle
7) Scan pattern .

The notation used is:

Δ = fractional change in dose between the center to the edge of the wafer,

σ = standard deviation of dose distribution .

5.1.1) Misalignment: Misalignment of the beam center through the deflection plate gap by an amount of $1/4$ the gap distance may result in uniformity variation of $2\sigma = 0.75\%$, J.H. Keller [16].

5.1.2) Beam noise: Beam noise causing a variation in beam intensity during scanning could cause variations in dose if a small number of passes of the beam across the wafer are made. In a typical electrostatic scan system, even the shortest implants <10 seconds, are done with greater than 10,000 passes of the beam. Tests done to prove beam noise tends to average was demonstrated by D.S. Perloff et al. [17].

5.1.3) Beam spot size: If we assume a spot size of a $1/4$ wafer radius and allow a 50% variation in spot size, the non-uniformity produced is only $\Delta = 0.8\%$; and if this variation is symmetrical about the wafer center, then the spot size variation produces a dose variation of only $2\sigma = 0.6\%$. Beam burns done at the center and edge of wafers show that the spot size variations are not large, typically <10%.

5.1.4) Scan angle: The test implants given in this paper were done on a medium current implanter [3] with scan angles; for a 100mm wafer of:

$$\theta_x = \pm 2.0^\circ \qquad \theta_y = \pm 1.8^\circ .$$

Dose variations, due to this angle, are given by $\Delta = 1/\cos^2\theta$

$$\Delta = 0.12 \text{ and } 0.1\% \text{ respectively .}$$

5.1.5) Offset scan: In most implanters, a neutral beam trap is provided by offsetting the beam line in one axis. This offset causes the distance travelled by the beam to be shorter at the maximum deflected beam and longer for the minimum deflected beam. For the implanter used, Model DF-3000, the beam and target are offset 7° in the horizontal axis. The non-uniformity introduced by this offset is given by:

$$\Delta_x = -2 \tan \theta_x \tan \phi$$

where θ_x is scan angle and ϕ is offset angle

$$\Delta_x = 0.0086 \; , \; 2\Delta_x = 1.72\% .$$

5.1.6) Implant angle: When the wafer is tilted (in our case, about the vertical axis) non-uniformity of dose for a common angle of 7° for a 100 mm wafer is given by:

$$\Delta_y = -2 \tan \theta_y \tan \zeta$$

where θ_y is scan angle and ζ is the implant angle

$$\Delta_x = 0.0077 \; , \; 2\Delta_x = 1.54 \; \% \, .$$

This effect is not small, and should be compensated for optimum uniformity [18].

A summary of the scanning systems geometric factors and their effect of dose uniformity is:

Table 1. Summary of dose variations for typical X-Y scan system with 7° offset and target orientation angle.

	Worst Case Dose Variation	Typical Dose Variation
Misaligment	Δ =0.75%	0.25%
Beam Noise	0.1	0
Beam Size	0.6	0.2
Scan Angle	0.12	0.1
Scan Offset Angle (Neutral Trap)	2Δ =1.72	1.72
Implant Angle (7°)	2Δ =1.54	1.54

5.2 Scan Patterns

In order to achieve uniformity of implanted dose, careful design consideration must be given to the beam scan pattern.

Fig. 9 shows two types of beam scan patterns which might be used to uniformly scan an ion beam over a single circular target.

Fig 9a. Raster Type Scan Pattern

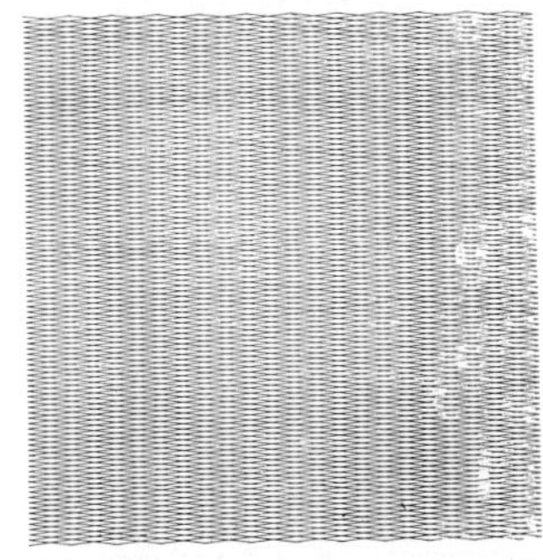

Fig 9b. Lissajous Type Scan Pattern Frequency Ratio 200/23

Scan pattern uniformity is determined principally by the distance between the scan lines d, and beam spot size w , in the direction of the slowest scan [19]. These calculations have been done by Rogers [20], and Glawischnig [19] and others, and the relationship for uniformity is given as a ratio of distance between scan lines d to beam dimension w for a Gaussian beam, see Fig. 10.

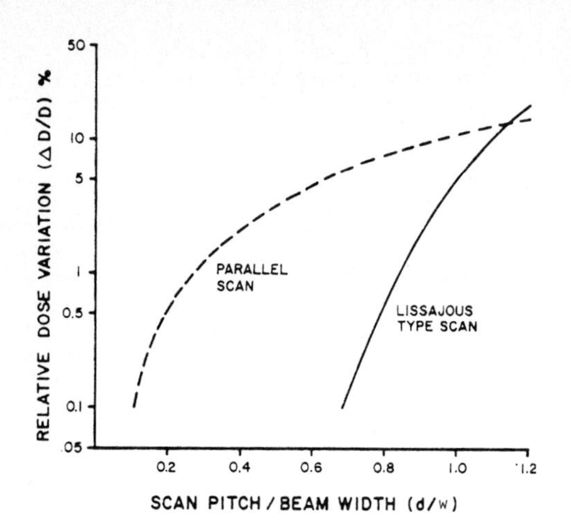

Fig. 10. Ratio of Scan Pitch/Beam Width, d/w and the Resulting Uniformity For A Gaussian Beam

From Fig. 10, higher uniformity can be obtained by minimizing the scan pitch (d). Since most scan patterns are essentially a locked Lissajous type, one technique for decreasing scan pitch is to introduce a shift in pattern position one direction several times by a small amount to minimize beam pattern retracing [21].

A schematic of a scan pattern generator which provides pattern interlacing, is shown in schematic of figure 11. This system moves the scan patterns of figure 9b, in the vertical direction 1/8 of the scan pitch approximately every scan field. After 8 pattern shifts or interlaces, the scan field retraces it first field.

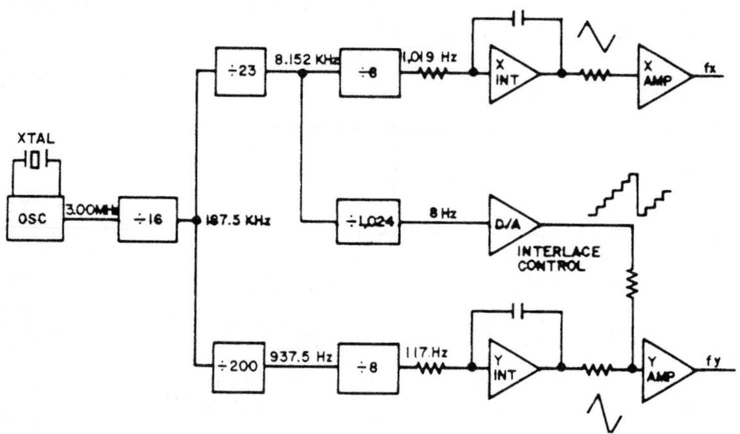

Fig. 11. Schematic of A Scan Pattern Generator With Interlacing

5.3 Scan Rate Compensation

Since dose variations due to geometric effects and target orientation, shown in Table 1 for a typical electrostatic scanned system, are not small (>1%), schemes for compensating the scan rate based on the beam position on the target have been devised [18], See Fig. 12.

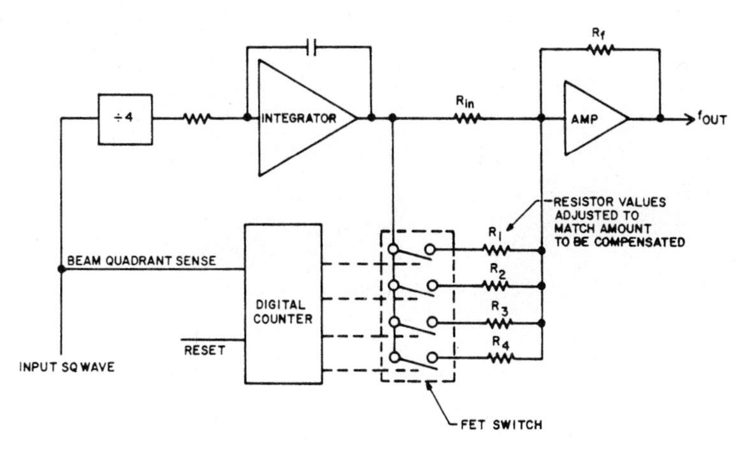

Fig. 12. Schematic of A Technique For Changing Scan Rate Based On Beam Position, In 4 Areas

This compensation scheme allows four different scan voltage rates dv/dt during one sweep of the beam. Scan rate is set by resistor values switched in and out digitally according to beam position.

Another scheme using scan rate controlled by a high speed D/A converter whose output is determined by values stored in digital memory is shown in Fig. 13. This scheme offers a precise method of tailoring scan waveform so as to compensate for repetitive system non-linearity.

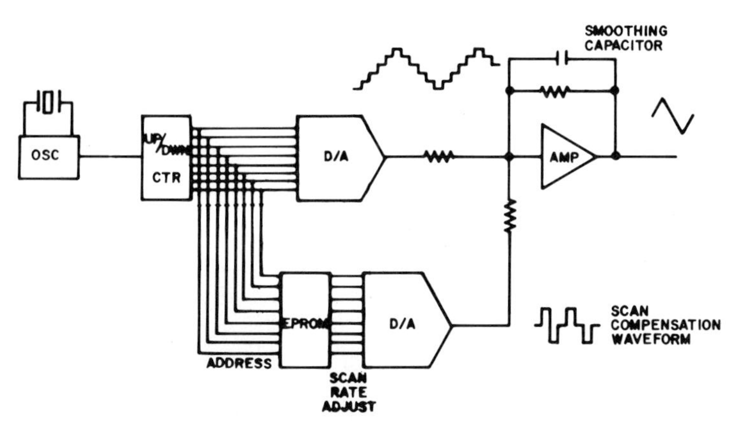

Fig. 13. Technique for Programmable Scan Rate Based On Beam Position

5.4 Space Charge Compensation

In order for any scan system to be efficient, maintaining a reasonable beam spot size (<5 cm) is important for adequate beam utilization. In order to reduce space charge effects due to electron removal from outside the scanner plates, by positive potential deflection plates, electrostatic or magnetic fields can be placed near both ends of a pair of deflection plates [22]. Fig. 14 shows a scanner deflection plate assembly used in a common electrostatically scanned ion implanter.

Fig. 14. X-Y Scanner Deflection Plates

This scanner assembly uses electron gates biased at -2 Kv. Beam defocusing due to space charge effects are thus confined to the scanner region. The amount of this defocusing may be calculated by [22]:

$$\frac{dy}{dz} = \frac{Ps}{4\ \varepsilon_0\ (2e/M)^{1/2}\ W}$$

where
P = beam current/$V^{3/2}$
s = length of unneutralized region
W = beam width
ε_0 = permittivity
e = charge
M = mass .

And the focal length is given by:

$$1/f = -\frac{\Delta\theta}{h} = -\frac{Ps}{2\ \varepsilon_0\ (2\ e/M)\ 1/2\ h\ W}$$

where:
h = beam width in direction of scan plate gap
θ = scan angle .

Thus, the amount of defocusing depends directly upon the length of the unneuralized region beam current, ion mass, and inversely upon the beam area.

Using the geometry of the scanner plates shown in Figure 14, the following table compares beam spot size calculations with measured results. Defocusing due to the bias of the Faraday cage was not accounted for.

Differences between calculated and measured values of beam spot size may be due to lens effects and gas collisions in the beam, which were

Table 2. Comparison of calculated beam spot size to measured sizes for various high perveance ion beams

Species	Energy (keV)	Perveance (μP)	Beam Current (ma)	Calculated Spot Dia (cm)	Measured Spot Dia Unscanned (cm)	Scanned (cm)
$^{75}As^{+}$	35	108	2.6	18.1	9.5	14
	50	68	2.8	11.8	7.0	12
	100	33	3.8	5.2	1.4	2.2
$^{31}P^{+}$	155	13	4.6	3.9	2.0	2.6

not considered in the calculation. In addition, beam dimensions in the scanner plate region were estimated.

6. Comparison of Two Different Scanning Techniques

While satisfying the criteria for uniform distribution of ions, let us compare two scan systems' ability to perform a low dose implant.

One system uses electrostatic scanning similar to figure 1 scanning a single 125 mm wafer with typical scanning frequencies of approximately 100 HZ and 1000 HZ. The other system utilizes mechanical target scanning, with 13-125 mm wafers mounted on a disk. From the graph of Fig. 10, it can be seen that the ratio of beam dimension/scan pitch dimension $d/w < 0.8$ for a Lissajous type scan system and $d/w < 0.25$ for a parallel type scan pattern similar to that produced by a slowly translating spinning disk.

Table 3. Comparison of 2 typical scan systems X-Y electrostatic and translating/rotating disk

	Electrostatic	Mechanical
Wafer Size	125 (1)	125 (13)
Scan Pattern Area (w/overscan)	225 cm^2	2,658 cm ^{2}
Slow Scan Speed	3×10^3cm/s	2.5 cm/s
Fast Scan Speed (typical)	30×10^3cm/s	3×10^3cm/s
Slow Scan Distance	15 cm	15 cm
Fast Scan Distance	15 cm	130cm,r min =20.7 cm 224cm,r max =35.7 cm

6.1 Minimum Implant Time Per Various Beam Diameter

Using the two systems of table 3, the following comparison of minimum implant time per wafer necessary to achieve uniformity of $\sigma < 1\%$ for various beam spot sizes is shown in table 4.

6.2 Comparison of Beam Utilization

During this comparison let us compare two disks: one single row of wafers and one dual row with two types of X-Y scanning of a single wafer.

In order to insure uniform implantation of wafers adequate beam overscan of wafers must be assured. The amount of overscan required

Table 4. Minimum implant time per wafer as a function of beam diameter for typical X-Y electrostatic and translating/rotating disk scanning systems

	Electrostatic X-Y		Mechanical	
Min. Beam Dimensions In The Slow Scan Direction w in mm	Min. No. of Scan Lines For X-Y Scan d/w = 0.8	Time Per Wafer in secs	Min. No. of Scan Lines on A Row of Wafers d/w = 0.25	Time Per Wafer in secs
.1	1,875	.94	6,000	30.8
.5	375	.19	1,200	6.2
1.0	186	.09	600	3.1
3.0	63	.03	200	1.0
5.0	38	.02	120	0.6 (A)
10.0	19	.01	60	0.5 (B)

(A) Under this spot size condition, the mechanical system is limited by the fast scan speed of 900 rpm. i.e.: 15 scan lines/sec x .6 secs/wafer x 13 wafers = 117 lines.

(B) Under this spot size condition, the mechanical system is limited by the slow scan speed of 2.5 cm/sec, in order to cover one scan pattern equal to 150mm - 1-125 mm wafer plus overscan. i.e.: Minimum time is 15.0 cm - 2.5 cm/sec - 13 wafers = 0.46 secs/wafer.

must therefore be equal to or greater than the size of the beam in the scan direction.

Improved beam utilization may be provided by maintaining smaller beam spot sizes. In the case of serial process implanters with x,y scanning, round scan patterns and masks minimize the amount of beam lost in overscan.

Beam utilization may be defined as the total wafer area compared with the total implant area.

Beam current for high dose implanters is usually specified as the total available beam current, and beam utilization is not mentioned. Beam current for serial process implanters is usually specified as the usable beam portion which is incident on the wafer called "scanned beam current".

For the disk-type batch process, we will assume 25-100 mm wafers mounted in both a single row and dual row with nominal separation and a circular beam diameter. For the serial type implanter, a beam defining aperture of 7.37 cm which is typical for a 100 mm wafer is used, and both round and square scanning patterns are calculated. See Fig. 15.

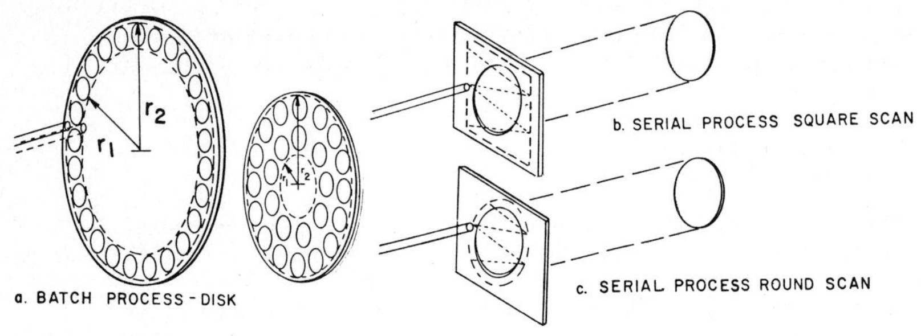

Fig.15. Comparison of Beam Utilization for Two Types of Scan Systems

The following data was used to calculate beam utilization.

Mechanical Scan Single row, 25 wafer disk 25-100mm wafer disk - 44 cm mean radius. Total wafer area = 1,962.5 cm^2. Beam size is in the direction of disk radius.

Mechanical Scan Dual row, 25 wafer disk 25-100mm wafer disk - 22.9 cm mean radius. Total wafer area = 1,962.5 cm^2. Beam size is in the direction of disk radius.

X-Y Scanning Single wafer 1 - 100 mm wafer Wafer area 78.54 cm^2 Implant area at round mask of 7.36 cm diameter, 42.5 cm^2.

Fig. 16 shows the comparison of total beam current utilization for the three scan techniques described in figure 15. For large diameter beams, batch process machines utilizing disk scanning tend to be more efficient; however, for the conditions described, a serial process implanter scanning with a round scanning pattern, beam utilization is higher than batch processing for ion beams smaller than 2.0 cm in diameter.

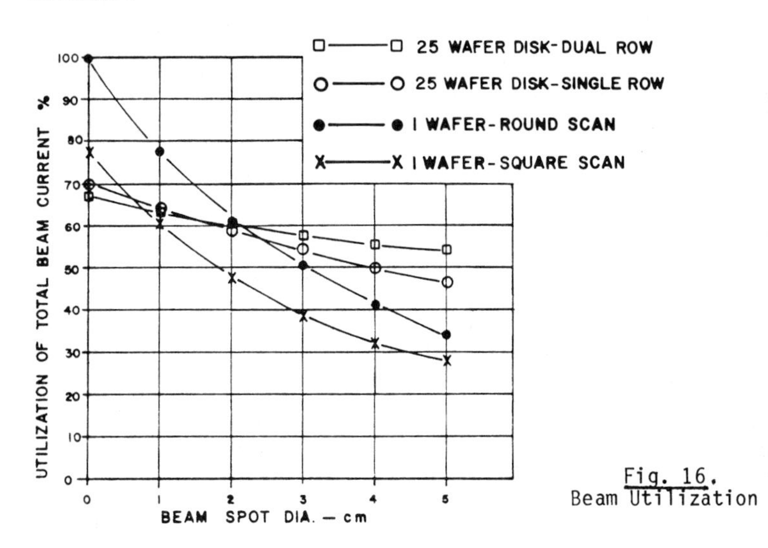

Fig. 16.
Beam Utilization

6.3 Comparison of Average and Instantaneous Power Densities

Since in any ion implant system the entire beam passes over the wafer during implantation, the ion beam power density and rate of scan or instantaneous beam power density may affect silicon lattice damage and mask material.

As a basis for comparison let us use typical parameters for both types of scanning systems, shown in table 5.

Its interesting to note from this scanning systems comparison that:

1) Due to slower scanning rates of mechanical scanners, very high instantaneous power densities over times like 1 millisecond are seen.

Table 5. Comparison of average and instantaneous beam power densities for a typical X-Y electrostatic scan and a mechanical translating disk system

	Electrostatic (square scan)	Mechanical Translating Disk
Wafer Size	125mm(1)	125mm (13 single row)
Peak Beam Current	5ma	10ma
Beam Energy	200Kev	100Kev
Peak Beam Power	1Kw	1Kw
Beam Spot Size	2.5cm dia	2.5cm width
Fast Beam Scan Rate	$20 \times 10^3 cm\ s^{-1}$	$2 \times 10^3 cm\ s^{-1}$
Slow Beam Scan Rate (typ)	$2.0 \times 10^3 cm\ s^{-1}$	$2.5 cm\ s^{-1}$
Total implant area	$136\ cm^2$	$2,657\ cm^2$
Average beam power density	$3.16 w/cm^2$	$0.38 w/cm^2$
Implant area after 1 sec (typ)	$136\ cm^2$	$462.6 cm^2$
Average beam power density/ scanned area after 1 sec	$3.16\ w/cm^{-2}$	$2.16 wcm^{-2}$
Implant area after 1 msec	$65\ cm^2$	$5 cm^2$
Instantaneous (1 msec) power density	$15.4\ w/cm^2$	$200\ w/cm^2$

2) If the slow scan speed is not maintained near its maximum for high power beams, beam power densities over a 10 second period can become near equal to that of single wafer scanning.

3) Some form of wafer cooling is required for both systems in order to maintain wafer temperatures below 100° C.

7. Improvements in X-Y Scanning

In higher dose implantation, maintaining beam utilization is important for economic reasons. In X-Y systems utilizing electrostatic scan, particularly at energies of less 50 Kev, beam utilization is maintained >40% for beams with perveance of up to 20 μ perv., see table 2.

7.1 Beam Space Charge Expansions

If proper electron traps are used, beam expansion is confined to the region between the suppression rings at the ends of the scan plate deflectors, see Fig. 14.

Beam expansion or defocussing effect have been compensated by utilizing a beam space charge focusing lens [23]. Zhukov et al.[24] reported the successful operation of such a lens for He and Ar ions of energies between 3 to 8 Kev and found that the focal length of the lens followed the expression

$$F = \emptyset/2U \times R/\theta$$

Where U is the lens voltage
$\emptyset$ is the particle potential difference
R is the radius of the ring electrode
θ is a value based on geometry.

It is interesting to note that neither ion mass nor ion charge appears in the equation.

An X-Y scanning system was proposed which placed the space charge lens between the X and Y scan deflector plates, a working system is not known at this time.

Magnetic scanning is employed in present day implanters for high current beams with scanning frequencies of 0.1 HZ typical. In order to apply this technique to single wafer scanning, a high frequency magnetic scan system would have to be designed. Such a system would probably require a fixed field for beam offest, and a scanning magnetic of thin lamination or ferrites for X-Y. This system would be larger due to the high flux fields required for higher mass, high energy ions, and would probably remove the main advantages of the X-Y electrostatic systems in simplicity and cost.

7.2 Dual Target Beam Scanning

Since X-Y scan systems utilizing electrostatic scanning have high scan speeds, one scan system can implant 2 targets or more, in a way to reduce wafer heating. A recently developed system [25] scans ion beams of over 3 ma in a beam sharing mode over 2 wafers. The duty cycle of scan is kept below 1 second so that the average beam power per wafer is approximately ½ the scanned beam power.

7.3 Wafer Cooling

Recent developments in wafer cooling maintain wafer temperatures < 100°C with scanned beam powers of 5W/cm^2 [26]. This wafer cooling capability combined with beam sharing over 2-100mm wafers should allow implantation of beams whose current and energy could be:

Energy	Scanned Beam Current	Total Beam Current
100 Kev	9.0 ma	18 ma
200 Kev	4.5 ma	9 ma

8. Summary

Improvements in unformity of scan have been made in X-Y electrostatic scanning, mechanical, and hybrid system to provide dose uniformity of 1σ ≤1%. Systems utilizing mechanical scanning have been improved for lower dose applications [7]. The development of the rotating disk [11] has provided a superior method of mechanically scanning a batch of wafers. In addition, the ability to automatically load the wafers, on and off the disk, insures wide acceptance of this technique in production facilities.

Some work already done indicates improvements in X-Y electrostatic scanning could result in significant improvements in the ability to scan higher perveance beams. This coupled with improved wafer cooling could result in an implant system of high productivity for most semiconductor implant requirements.

9. Acknowledgements

The author would like to thank those who have contributed to publishing their work on scanning systems, especially J. Keller, J. Kranik, G. Ryding. Also R. Kalbfus for beam measurements, and P. Mansfield, J. Padre, for typing and graphics.

References

1. R.G. Wilson and G.R. Brewer, Ion Beams With Application to Ion Implantation. N.Y. Wiley 1973.
2. P. Grivet, Electron Optics, Academic Press, N.Y. 1965.
3. Varian/Extrion, Model DF-3000 Ion Implanter
4. Varian/Extrion, Model 80-10 Ion Implanter
5. L. Frenkel, J. Res. N.B.S. C eng. Instr, 64C No.2, 1960
6. P.H. Rose, Radiation Effects, Vol 44. pp.137-144, 1979
7. G. Ryding, Nuclear Instr. and Methods, 189, pp.239-251, 1981
8. J.R. Kranik, Radiation Effects, Vol 44. pp.81-92, 1979
9. Extrion, Model 200-1000 Ion Implanter
10. A.I.T., Series III, Ion Implanter
11. G.I. Robertson, J. Electrochem, Soc., Solid State Science & Technology 796, June 1975.
12. Accelerators, Inc., Ion Implanter
13. Balzers, Inc. Scannibal Ion Implanter
14. P.R. Hanley, Nuclear Instruments and Methods, 189, pp.227-237, 1981
15. G. Ryding, private communication
16. J. Keller, Radiation Effects, Vol.44, pp. 71-80, Gordan & Breach Science Publishers, 1979
17. D.S. Perloff, F.E. Wahl and J.T. Kere, Proc. 7th Int. Conference on Electron and Ion Beam Science and Technology, Princeton, N.J., 1976
18. N. Turner, Nuclear Instruments and Methods 189, pp.311-318, 1981
19. H. Glawischnig et al., Nuclear Instruments and Methods 189, pp.291-294, 1981
20. E. Rogers, Nuclear Instruments and Methods 189, pp.305-310, 1981
21. N. Turner, U.S. Patent No. 4,283,631
22. J. Keller, Nuclear Instruments and Methods 139, pp.41-45, 1976
23. R. Booth, H.W. LeFevre, Nuclear Instruments and Methods, 151, pp.143-147, 1978
24. V.V. Zhukov, A.I. Morozov, G.1/a Shehepkin, ZHETP Pis Red 9, 1969 24; JETP Litt 9 (1969) 14
25. R. Booth, H.W. LeFevre, Nuclear Instruments and Methods, 151, pp.143-147, 1978
26. P. Hanley, proceedings from this conference

A Low-Internal-Resistance and High-Precision High-Voltage Power Supply

J. Wu, H. Ma, and B. Ren

Hebei Semiconductor Research Institute, P.O. Box 179,
Shijiazhuang, Hebei, China

Abstract

In this paper, a low-internal-resistance and high-precision high-voltage power supply for an ion implanter is described. The high-frequency voltage-doubling form is used, and there is a double-arm precision-voltage divider. In order to restrict the discharge current and surge voltage caused by high-voltage sparking and to decrease the output-voltage ripple, a high-value resistor is added in the output terminal of the high-voltage power supply. The output characteristics of the power supply cannot be deteriorated, and the internal resistance is decreased by taking special compensation measures.

1. Outline and Principles of the Power Supply [1, 3, 5]

The power supply is a preaccelerating power supply used in a high-energy ion implanter. The main demands are as follows: output voltage -80kV (fixed point), max. output current 5mA, low ripple, low drift over long time periods, and high stability. We selected the method of d.c. conversion and indirect adjustment. A schematic diagram of the electrical principle is shown in Fig. 1.

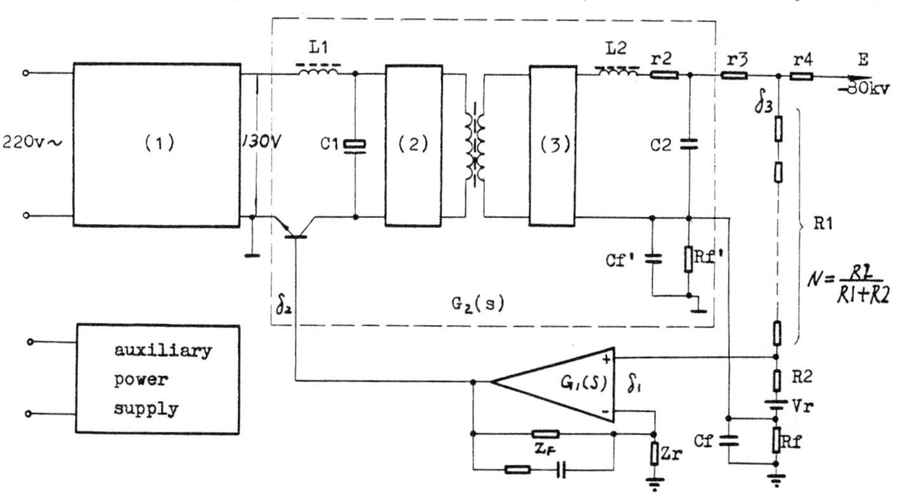

Fig. 1. Schematic diagram of the -80 kV power supply of high precision and low internal reststance. (1): transformer and rectifier; filter, over-current protection, constant voltage in series control, (2): improved SCR parallel converter, (3): voltage-doubling rectifier

The high-voltage closed-loop feedback-control system is a finite difference-adjusting system. Its output voltage may be approximately expressed by the following formula:

$$E = \frac{1}{N} V_R + \delta_1 + \frac{\delta_2}{G_1(S)} + \frac{\delta_3}{G_1(S)G_2(S)} = \frac{1}{N} V_R \qquad (1)$$

where E is the output voltage (V), V_R the standard voltage (V), N the voltage dividing ratio, δ the equivalent noise, G the gain, G_1, δ_1 the values of the integrated operational amplifier, and G_2, δ_2 the values of the section between adjusting transistor and conversion circuit.

This formula having been analyzed, a very useful conclusion for the design of the power supply can be drawn; i.e., the output voltage E depends mainly on V_R/N. If E is constant, the higher V_R becomes, the greater is N. In order for the power supply to achieve a constant output, if N is large, either δ_1 and δ_2 are made large, or G_1 and G_2 are made small. In order to make E steady, the voltage divider and reference voltage must possess the properties of high stability, low noise, and low drift; there must also be a good amplifier with definite amplification, a stable low-voltage d.c. power supply, and a well-designed and fine-adjusted conversion circuit.

2. Main Parts and their Features

2.1 Precision Double-Arm Voltage Divider [1, 2, 3]

In order to obtain precision voltage dividing and sampling, we have given attention to the following points: First, a high-performance wire-wound resistor, model RX9-20, is used as the voltage-dividing resistor. Second, a reasonable electrical-field design is used. In order to decrease or avoid sparking and leakage from the high-potential parts as much as possible, a double-arm voltage-dividing structure is used, as shown in Fig. 2.

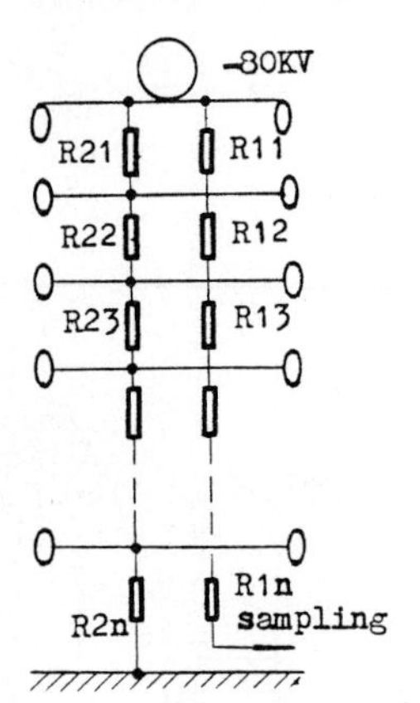

Fig. 2. Double-armed voltage divider

The voltage divider is divided into n sections. The electrical potential of the metal shield in each section is controlled by high-voltage metal film resistors, R_{21} - R_{2n}. The precision resistors in the sampling circuit, R_{11} - R_{1n}, are distributed in these shielding cases in a screw shape. The design considerations are as follows: the precision resistors are always located in the equipotential space of the equigradient field formed by the voltage-dividing action of the R_{2n} branch loop. The sparking and leakage from the high-potential section to surrounding objects are caused by the R_{21} - R_{2n} branch loop. There is little sparking in the R_{11}-R_{1n} branch loop. Thus, the precision of voltage dividing is ensured. A further point is that the voltage divider must have a good temperature stability, and its insulating supports must be stable. Therefore, we used oil-immersed insulation and selected a low sampling current (160 μA). The measured temperature rise of the voltage divider was 0.8 °C over 2h. A higher sampling current helps to decrease the effects of sparking, leakage, and output impedance of the voltage divider. However, it will increase power dissipation and temperature rise, and cause the temperature characteristics of the system to deteriorate. As a final point, the voltage divider and sampling output should have a good electrical and magnetic shielding.

2.2 High Constant Reference Voltage Circuit [5]

The components we used were standard Zener diodes with temperature compensation. After having made a high-temperature aging test, we selected five Zener diodes with low time drift and similar working points at zero temperature coefficient. They are used in cascade. The circuit is shown in Fig. 3. This circuit was used because it can easily achieve optimal compensation in a wide temperature range, and is also simple and reliable. The load-current output is only 160 μA. The load-current variation is so small that the output impedance does not influence the output voltage. Because the main-loop voltage, 130 V, is highly stable, external voltage fluctuation does not affect the precision. The circuit can easily produce a higher output voltage; we selected approx. 31 V for the power supply.

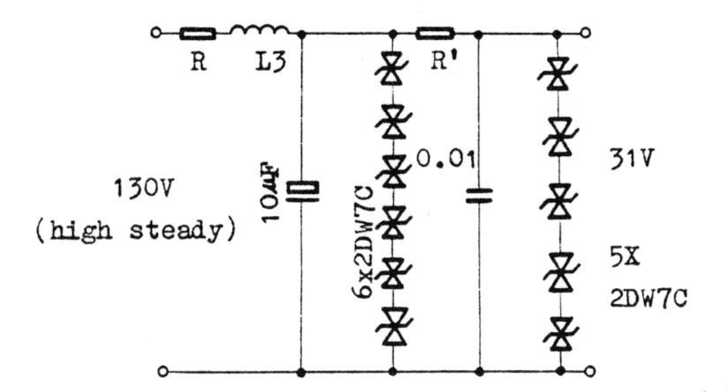

Fig. 3. Reference circuit

2.3 Amplifier [4]

The amplifier consists of a high-performance semiconductor-integrated operational-amplifier unit. The addition of the reference voltage and feedback voltage occurs at the same input. The amplifier has a high input impedance, as shown in Fig. 4. The expression for the amplifier gain is given by:

$$V_0 = \left(1+\frac{Z_F}{Z_r}\right)\left(\frac{R_1}{R_1+R_2}\cdot V_R + \frac{R_2}{R_1+R_2}\cdot E\right) + Z_F \cdot I_{0s} + \left(1+\frac{Z_F}{Z_r}\right)\cdot V_{0s} \qquad (2)$$

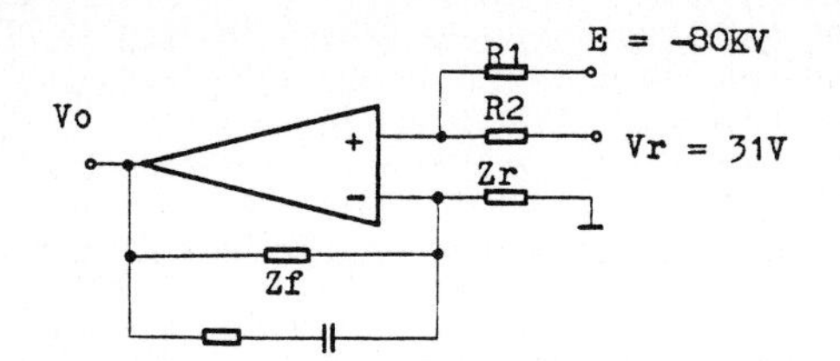

Fig. 4. Adder for reference and feedback voltage

where V_0 is the amplifier output voltage (mV), V_{0s} the input offset voltage (mV), I_{0s} the input offset current (μA), and Z_F the feedback resistance (kΩ).

To eliminate the self-excited oscillation produced by phase shift, a compensation loop for the frequency characteristic is also added.

2.4 Internal resistance [1]

The high-voltage power supply with d.c. conversion has a high internal resistance (this power supply is measured up to several MΩ). The main reasons for this high internal resistance are as follows: A) The internal resistance of the voltage-doubling circuit is directly proportional to the cubic power of the voltage-doubling series. B) There are leakage inductance, slug loss, and copper loss in the high-voltage transformer. C) There is a resonance circuit composed of the leakage inductance of the high-voltage transformer and the stray capacitance. The resonance effect is related to the amount of the high-voltage load. Thus, the ratio of the transformer varies with load. D) There are the internal resistance losses of conversion components, SCR's, and diodes, the loss of change-over components, and the loss of the L_1 C_1 filter before the converter. E) The operating condition of the converter varies with different high-voltage loads. F) Due to the step-up ratio of the transformer and the amplification of the voltage-doubling circuit, the effects caused by the above factors can expand by up to several hundred times.

High internal resistance has some benefits. Specifically, when a load sparks, discharges, or short-circuits, it will produce a higher surge current and surge voltage. The high internal resistance of the power supply, however, has a certain limiting effect on these destructive phenomena. But in many cases, it is not sufficient to rely only on the internal resistance r_1 , so that two resistors r_3 and r_4 , must be added (see Fig. 1). In order to obtain a low output ripple, the single filter must be used. It consists of inductor L_2 , resistor r_2 and capacitor C_2 , as shown in Fig. 1.

As mentioned above, the output characteristics of the high-voltage power supply will be deteriorated by the inherent internal resistance r_1 , filter resistor r_2 , and current-limiting resistors r_3 and r_4 of the power supply. That is why an increase in the load current will decrease the output voltage. The voltage drop of r_1 , r_2 and r_3 can be compensated to some extent through the high-voltage closed-loop feedback control; this compensation, however, is limited. Since an excessive compensation furthers production of self-excited oscillation, the closed-loop amplification is adjusted to an optimal value. In accordance with the amplifier-gain expression (2) as already given, it is known that the change in input offset current I_{0s} and input offset voltage V_{0s} of the amplifier will produce an unfavorable effect. For the voltage drop of V_4 , the high-voltage feedback-control system does not produce any compensation. In order to ensure that the output voltage is held constant after the change in the high-voltage load current we have taken special compensation measures (see Fig.1). Resistors R_f , $R_{f'}$, and capacitors C_f and $C_{f'}$, are added between the positive terminal and the ground of the high-voltage power supply. Thus, at the positive terminal, the a.c. component is grounded, while the d.c. component is not directly grounded. The voltage drop of $R_f \parallel R_{f'}$, produced by the high-voltage load current is below the reference voltage V_R in cascade. Obviously, this is a positive-feedback current circuit.

Assuming $R_f'' = R_f \parallel R_f' = \frac{R_f \cdot R_f'}{R_f + R_f'}$, and if the load of the high-voltage power supply belongs to the resistive load, the condition needed for the system to work stably is $N (r_1 + r_2 + r_3) \geqslant R_f''$ (N:dividing voltage ratio). However, experiments proved that the load of the power supply (ion-beam preaccelerating system) is not a resistive load, but a non-linear load; when the accelerating voltage reaches a certain value, the value of the load current will mainly depend on the operating parameters of the ion source, and does not have much to do with the value of the accelerating voltage. The characteristic curve of the load voltage and current is shown in Fig. 5. This load characteristic provides a new condition which is very beneficial to the compensation of the internal resistance, i.e., the value of R_f is not restricted by the unequation given before. The value of R_f can be greatly increased, and the gain of the positive feedback loop will still be kept below 1. The voltage drop in r_4 can also be compensated to some extent.

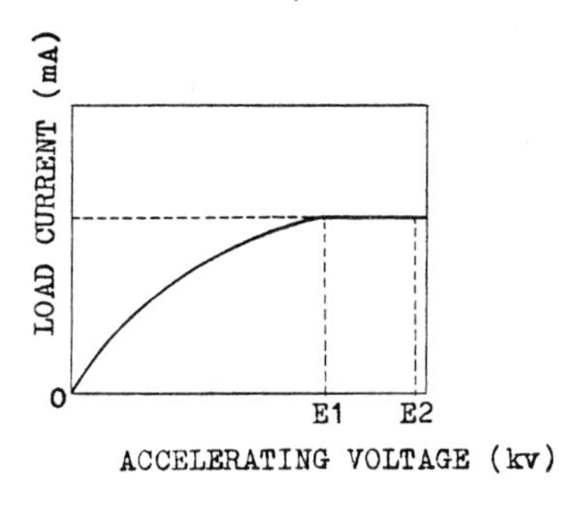

Fig. 5. The relation of the voltage and current of the accelerating system

Adjusting the internal-resistance compensation circuit is simple and convenient. Due to this compensation circuit, the power supply has variable output-resistance characteristics. There are both a very high internal resistance against transient changes, due to sparking and discharging, and a very low internal resistance against the normal slow change in the load.

3. Results

a) Output Voltage -80 kV
Max. output current 5 mA

b) Output Voltage Stabilizing Coefficient

$$S_{vs} = \frac{\Delta E/E}{\Delta v_i/v_i} \ll 10^{-4}$$

(v_i: alternating input voltage)

c) Output Voltage Drift (Including Temperature)
Drift and time drift $\Delta E/E < 1.3 \times 10^{-4}/2h$

d) Output Voltage Ripple

$V_{pp} < 5V$

e) Load Variation 0.5 mA

$\Delta E/E < 1x10^{-4}$

4. Conclusions

In the development of a high-precision high-voltage power supply, not only is careful circuit design important, but also painstaking engineering considerations. Points of special importance include reasonable layout, careful considerations of the electrical fields, voltage balance, insulation, heat sinking, as well as electrical and magnetic shielding. Although there are some limitations in low response (transition characteristic) in the power supply described, it does contain some widely useful design features.

Acknowledgements

We wish to express gratitude to the colleagues of our group for their valuable assistance, and to Mr. Zhu Ming-lian for his help in revising the paper.

References

1. Ohotsuka: D-C Steady Power Supply
2. Okamura: Power Supply Circuit, Chapter 4
3. A manual of Electrical Engineering, Chapter 3 (China) 1978
4. Qin Shi-cai and Wand Zhao-ying: The Principle and Application of the Integrated Operational Amplifier, p.73 (People's Publishing House, Tianjin), 1979
5. J.R.Nowicki: Power Supplies for Electronic Equipment, Vol.1,2

Electrostatic Switch Used for 600 kV Ion Implanter

J. Wu, S. Yan, S. Yang, and X. Deng

Hebei Semiconductor Research Institute, P.O. Box 179,
Shijiazhuang, Hebei, China

This paper describes a new electrostatic switch, used for a 600kV ion implanter. The switch has been developed on the basis of a typical electrostatic analyzer. It consists of two pairs of symmetrical electrodes, each of which has two coaxial cylindrical metal plates with mechanical moving units. Deflection of the ion beam at high energies (up to 600keV) to a sufficient angle has been achieved through the application of a low voltage by the new switch. This allows the changing of different targets, on-off beam gating and removal of neutrals.

1. Introduction

In 1981, a 600kV ion implanter with 210 AMU mass analysis capability was successfully developed (Fig. 1). It was specially designed to use three separate target chambers:

a. a system for ion beam analysis of materials

b. a fully mechanical scanning target which solves the problem of the thermal effect on targets at higher energies and beam current values. It also provides production efficiency in the batch processing of semiconductor devices.

Fig.1. The 600 kV ion implanter

c. an electrostatically scanned target for research and development use (Fig. 2).

In order to allow the ion beam to be routed to the appropriate target chamber, the implanter has been equipped with a switch. The use of various switch designs results in significant differences in economic effect, difficulties in processing and technology, and operating performance. Each of three switch designs will be discussed.

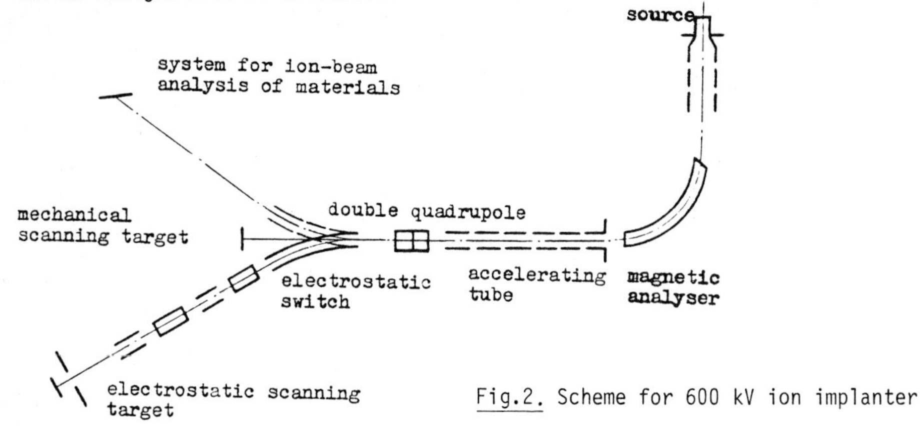

Fig.2. Scheme for 600 kV ion implanter

2. Two Traditional Types - Magnetic and Electrostatic Switches

For ease of comparison, it will be assumed that each of these switches is designed to deflect the ion beam $\pm$ 23 degrees.

It is well known that an ion beam can be deflected by a magnetic field, according to the equation:

$$\sqrt{mV_o} = \frac{B\ R\ Z_e}{144.5}$$

where m = ion mass (AMU)

V_o = accelerating voltage (V)

B = intensity of magnetic field (Gauss)

R = radius of deflection (cm)

Z_e = number of ion charge .

At V_o = 600kV, m = 210 AMU and Z_o = 1, if $\pm$ 23 degrees beam deflection is expected, the geometrical shape and size of the magnet required is indicated in Fig. 3. In this case the weight of the magnet will be 3-4 tons and the power supply will be as high as 7-8kW. Furthermore, higher precision of the power supply will be required, and the magnetic field will require adjustment with each change in ion species at constant ion energy.

Deflection of the ion beam can also be performed by an electrostatic field. However, if this field is designed in compliance with the traditional, flare-shape construction shown in Fig. 4, a very high deflection voltage will be necessary. When the acceleration voltage is 600kV, the deflection voltage must reach 154kV. This will lead to insulation problems and could result in vacuum breakdown, especially at higher beam energies.

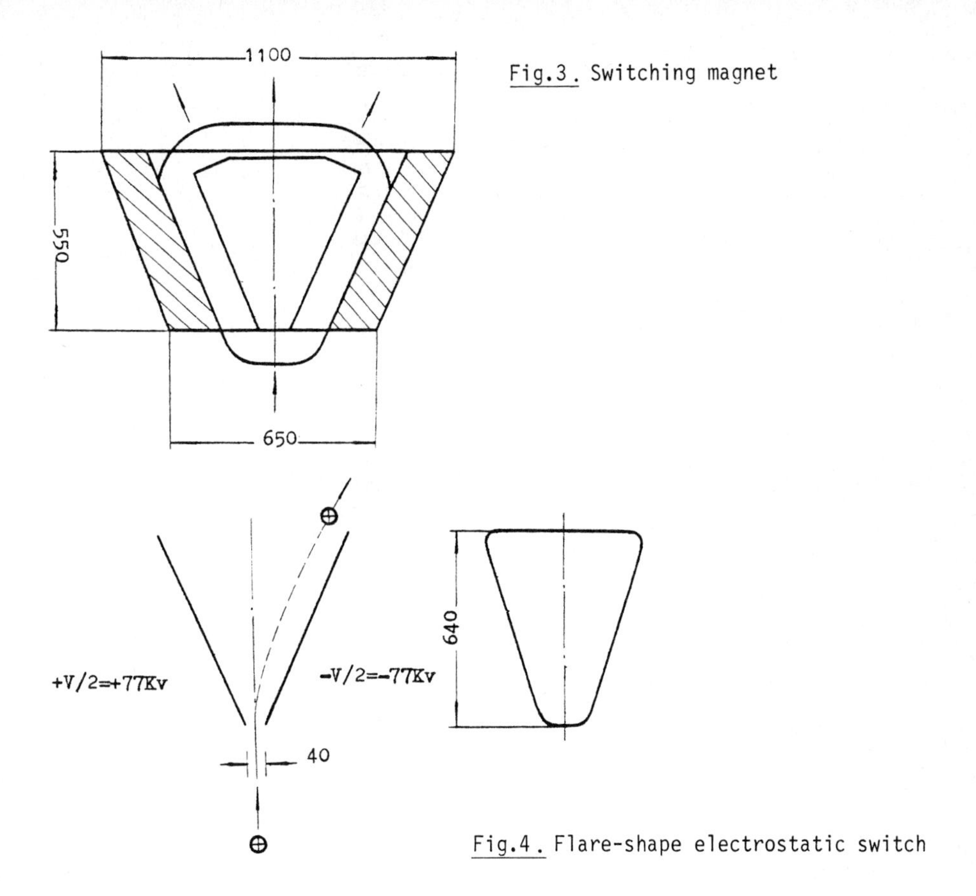

Fig.3. Switching magnet

Fig.4. Flare-shape electrostatic switch

Moreover, even if relatively large deflection plates are used at the outlet, it is difficult to insure the uniformity of the electric field and to eliminate the effect of the edge field. Thus, serious distortion of the ion beam spots would occur. For these reasons, this type of switch has been rejected for use with a high energy ion beam.

3. Modified Electrostatic Switch

3.1 Construction and Principle (1) (2)

A new type of low cost electrostatic switch has been designed on the basis of the development of a typical electrostatic analyzer used for an electrostatic accelerator (Fig. 5). The modified switch consists of two pairs of symmetrical electrodes, each of which having two co-axial, cylindrical metal plates. These electrodes are fixed by means of insulating blocks on a common flat plate under which a pair of guides are installed perpendicular to the incident direction of the ion beam. The flat plate slides over the guides and its position is adjusted by a lead screw. The lead screw has one end encapsulated by a vacuum seal and extends outside to the switch housing. The turns (or angles) of the lead screw rotation indicate the exact position of the switch electrodes.

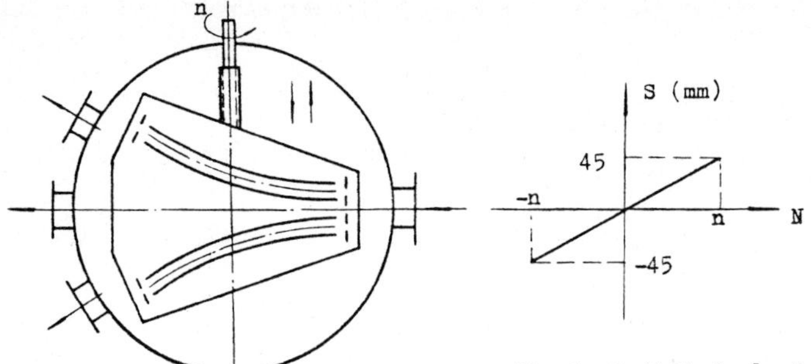

Fig.5. Modified electrostatic switch

It is obvious that when the + 1/2V deflection voltage is applied to the middle electrodes and the - 1/2V is applied to the outer electrodes, and when s = 45mm (s = the shifting position of the switch, left to right), the incident ion beam enters the left guide. Thus, the ion beam will be deflected 23 degrees to the left.

Conversely, in the case of s = -45mm, the beam will be deflected 23 degrees to the right. At s = 0 with no deflection voltages, no deflection of the ion beam will occur. Naturally, in order to remove the neutral beam, it is possible to deflect the beam 4 degrees using the deflection voltages to get the beam to the mechanically scanning target.

3.2 Calculation of Deflection Voltage and Operating Performance of the Switch (1) (3)

$$\text{Since} \quad V = \frac{2d}{Z_e R} E$$

$$\text{thus} \quad V = \frac{2d}{R} V_o \text{ at } Z_e = 1$$

where V = deflection voltage (kV)
d = distance between electrodes (cm)
Z_e = number of ion charge
R = radius of deflection (cm)
V_o = acceleration voltage (kV)
E = ion energy (keV) .

When V_o = 600kV, considering the larger section of incident beam, d = 4cm has been chosen so that the ion beam will not contact the electrodes. Now the factors to be determined are the values of V and R, which are inversely proportional to each other. In order to avoid vacuum breakdown and sparking of the switch when the 500 μA ion beam passes through it, to enable the switch to operate reliably and to keep sufficient distance between the three outlets of the switch to join the flanges, V = 30kV (at electrode voltages of + 1/2V and - 1/2V), R = 160 cm and up to 23 degrees deflection angle have been adopted. (Of course, an increase in V and a corresponding decrease in R is available). In addition, the boundary shape and size as well as the shielding slits at the outlets and inlets of the electrodes have been designed and selected to minimize the edge field effect.

The deflection voltage in the electrostatic field depends entirely on the acceleration voltage, not the mass of the ion. This allows convenient adjustment of the machine. The switch causes the neutral beam generated prior to it to be deflected away from the ion beam and can serve as a fast means of gating the ion beam on and off. Because fast on-off switching of the deflection voltages can be realized using a high voltage relay controlled by a charge integrator, the response time is as low as 10 ms.

The ion beam passing through the switch will not exceed 500 μA (in most cases, below 10 μA), the switch is installed directly behind the double-section quadrupole electrostatic lens, and the ion beam still has a larger section. It is clear that the decrease of self-neutralization effect caused by the electrostatic field of the switch should not have a markedly unfavorable influence on beam focusing.

3.3 Possibility of More Targets

As shown in Fig. 6, further improvement of the switch, such as the connection with 5-7 target chambers can be achieved. The high voltage terminals, however, are specially designed so that each electrode pair is automatically connected to the corresponding terminals as the target chambers are alternated. A special high voltage relay is used for maintaining the desirable deflection voltage polarities at all times.

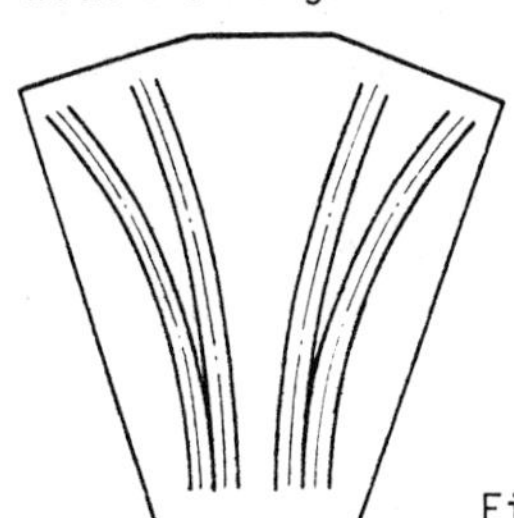

Fig.6. Scheme for the electrostatic switch with five outlets

4. Comparison of Switch Types

In order to compare the three types of switches, consult the following comparison table:

	Magnetic Switch	Flare-shape Electrostatic Switch	Modified Electrostatic Switch
Weight and Construction	large	middle	small
Price	high	lower	lowest
Power supply kW	high	lower	lowest
Price of Power Supply	high	high	lowest
Pricision Required for Power supply	high	lower	lower
Switching Speed	slowest	slower	rapid
Relation to Ion Mass	relative $B \sim \sqrt{m}$	V with no relation to m	V with no relation to m
Distortion of Beam Spot	small	great	small
Applicable Range for Ion-Beam Flow	strong or weak flow	weak flow	weak flow

5. Conclusion

The modified electrostatic switch is available for the deflection of high-energy ion beams at any mass to an angle sufficient for changing target chambers. At the same time, the switch provides a method of gating the beam on and off and eliminating the neutral beam. Both the switch and its power supply have the advantages of low cost, simple processing, fewer difficulties in technology and good operating performance. The switch is not, however, suitable for implanters using high beam currents.

References

1. Ye Ming-han and Chen Jian-pu: Electrostatic Accelerator (Science Publishing House, Peking 1965) p. 142
2. A. Septier: Focusing of Charged Particle Vol. 2
3. H. Wollnik and H. Ewald: Nucl. Instr. and Meth. 36, 93 (1965)

Automatic Wafer Handling for a Mechanically Scanned Ion Implanter

A. Armstrong, V. Benveniste, M. Farley, and G. Ryding

Eaton Corporation, Ion Implantation Division, 16 Tozer Road,
Beverly, MA 01915, USA

1. Introduction

Wafer fabrication processes which include automatic wafer removal from an input cassette, transport through the process and return to an output cassette improve process yield by reducing exposure of the wafers to damage and contamination caused by contact with a human operator. In addition, automation reduces operator stress associated with loading wafers at high repetition rates. Although automated wafer transport is available for low and medium current ion implanters which implant one wafer at a time, high-current implanters require a unique automatic transport, designed to work with batch processing and mechanical scanning. Such a transport has now been developed for the Eaton Nova NV-10 Implanter.

High-current implanters implant a batch of wafers simultaneously, allowing their high beam power (1.0 Kw) to be distributed over a number of wafers in order to avoid overheating. In the Nova NV-10, the batch of wafers is mounted on the face of a spinning disk which carries the wafers through the stationary ion beam. The characteristics of this wafer-carrying disk are listed in Table 1.

Table 1

NV-10 Wafer Disk Characteristics

1. Number of wafers:

3 inch	18
82 mm	15
100 mm	13
125 mm	10

2. Anti-channelling angle: 7 degrees standard; 0-10 degrees optional.

3. Cooled wafer pedestal: Wafer clamped to spherically curved, elastomer-coated pedestal by a centrifugally loaded, pivoted clamp. A light spring ensures clamp closure.

4. Uncooled wafer pedestal: Wafer held by centrifugal force against a pedestal inclined at 7 degrees to the plane of the disk. For this option, no clamp is required.

5. Dosimetry means: Slot through disk allows beam current measurement by off-disk faraday once each disk revolution.

Rotation of the disk provides one mechanical scan motion, the other scan being produced by moving the disk normal to its axis of rotation. In order to maximize beam utilization, the Nova implanter is equipped with two disks, exchanged automatically, so that one disk can be reloaded while the other is implanted [1]. With this configuration, all wafer loading and unloading can be performed in air using well-proven techniques for reliable and gentle wafer handling. The problems of mechanical movement and wafer handling in vacuum have been deliberately avoided.

2. Performance Objectives

Performance objectives for the AT-4 Automatic Transport system are listed in Table 2. The ability to access several input and output cassettes was specified in order to eliminate the operator's response time from the critical path affecting throughput. This aids in achieving the machine's maximum throughput and eliminates the need for constant attention by the operator. In addition, this ability enables automatic loading of "dummy" wafers to protect the elastomer-coated thermal-control wafer holders.

Table 2

AT-4 Performance Objectives

1. Wafer exchange: Onto wafer disk specified in Table 1.
2. Throughput:
   - 3 inch: 300 per hour
   - 82 mm, 100 mm : 250 per hour
   - 125 mm : 200 per hour
3. Changeover time between wafer sizes: 10 minutes.
4. Flat alignment: ± 2 degrees.
5. Cassettes accessed: 4 Input, 4 Output
6. Protection of elastomer-covered wafer holders: By automatic loading of "dummy" or scrap wafers when the supply of product wafers is insufficient to fill the disk.
7. Wafer tracking: Automatic tracking of individual wafers from input cassette position to corresponding output cassette position, maintaining lot identity.
8. Cassette type: Any SEMI-standard plastic or metal cassette designated "Automatic machine compatible".
9. Minimum generation of particulates.

3. System Configuration

The plan view of the AT-4 Automatic Transport is shown in Fig.1. All subsystems except the disk indexer and the control system are mounted on a thick aluminum plate. This plate maintains subsystem alignment and forms a barrier between the wafers above it and the major mechanical components below. The flow of wafers from input to output is indicated by the arrows:

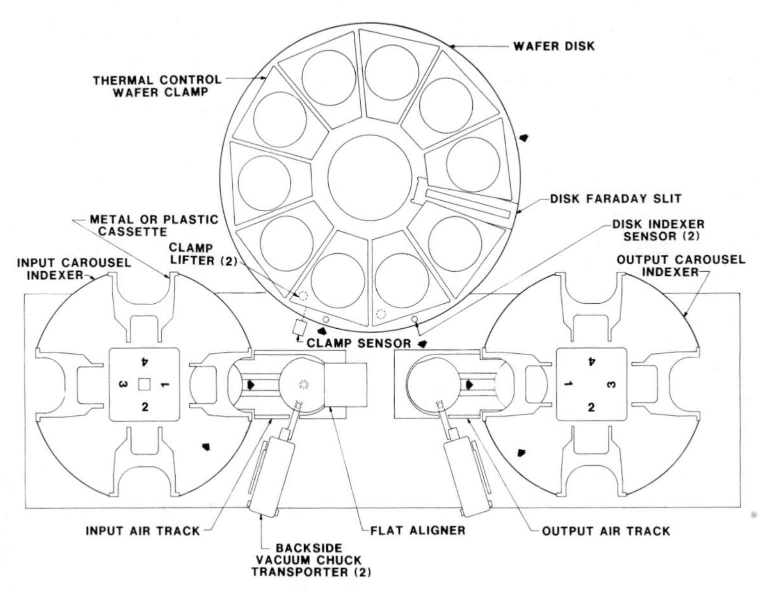

Figure 1. AT-4 System Layout

1. The input carousel indexer rotates to present one of four cassettes to the input air track;

2. As the indexer descends, a wafer is removed by the air track and conveyed to the flat aligner;

3. A backside vacuum chuck lifts the wafer and rotates it in view of optical sensors which cause the flat to be positioned toward the wafer disk;

4. Another backside vacuum chuck lifts the wafer from the flat aligner and transports it to a wafer pedestal on the wafer disk;

5. A clamp lifter, which has opened the thermal-control clamp on the wafer pedestal, lowers the clamp to secure the wafer;

6. The disk-indexer stepper motor moves the wafer disk to align the next pedestal with the output transporter;

7. Another clamp lifter lifts the thermal clamp at the output position;

8. The output vacuum chuck transporter removes the wafer to the output air track;

9. The wafer is conveyed to its cassette on the output indexer.

3.1 Disk Indexer

The wafer disk is indexed into alignment with the input and output transporters by a stepper motor driving through a worm gear reduction box. At each pedestal position, a recess in the lower surface of the disk is sensed by a pair of optical reflective sensors which control the stepper to produce an indexing accuracy of ±0.5mm without resort to mechanical indexing pawls. Pedestal position identity is determined in relation to the dosimeter slot, which is distinguished from the pedestal recesses by its greater width.

3.2 Vacuum Chuck Transporters

A vacuum chuck transporter is shown in elevation in Fig.2. The backside vacuum chuck is pivoted and actuated by a low-pressure pneumatic cylinder to permit lifting of the wafer from the air track or pedestal. The transporter is pivoted to the base plate by a four-bar linkage driven by another low-pressure pneumatic cylinder. As the transporter moves toward the pedestal, the linkage geometry causes the wafer to tilt into alignment with the anti-channelling angle of the pedestal, and enter the restricted space at the inboard side of the thermal control clamp. The lower pivot points of the four-bar linkage can be readily relocated to change wafer size or anti-channelling angle. To prevent any particulates generated in the transporter mechanism from falling onto the air tracks, the mechanism is enclosed in a box which is placed under negative pressure by a vacuum fan mounted under the main baseplate. The low operating forces are designed to minimize the possibility of wafer breakage in the event of an obstruction of the wafer's travel. In fact, no wafers have been broken by the AT-4 during testing so far (though a few have been broken by human intervention!)

3.3 Clamp Lifters

Also shown in Fig.2, the clamp lifter cylinder extends through a hole in the disk to lift the thermal control clamp. When the clamp is lowered at completion of loading, an optical sensor monitors its return to correct clamped position.

3.4 Air Tracks

Input and output air tracks convey wafers to and from their cassettes, without danger of particulate transfer from rubber belts. To minimize wafer impact, the tracks are short (0.2 m) and are equipped with polyurethane edge guides and optically sensed vacuum braking on the flat aligner vacuum chuck. Track sections can be quickly changed for different wafer sizes.

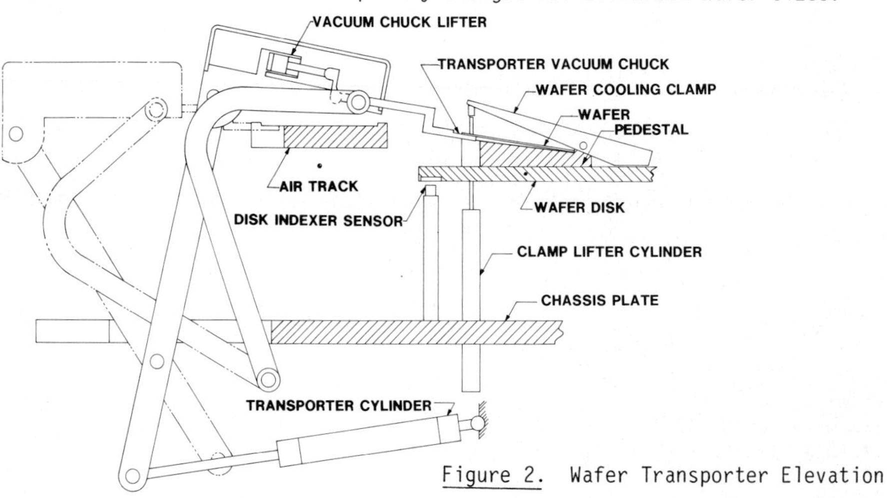

Figure 2. Wafer Transporter Elevation

3.5 Flat Aligner

The flat aligner consists of vacuum chuck and optical sensor subsystems. The vacuum chuck is mounted to a short-stroke pneumatic cylinder which lifts the wafer off the input air track for rotation by a stepper motor. During an initial revolution of the wafer, optical sensors send a series of analog light values representing the radius of the wafer for each of 200 motor steps to the microprocessor control system. From these values, the microprocessor locates the flat and rotates the wafer to place the flat toward the disk. Excess eccentricity and wafer breakage can also be detected at this point.

3.6 Carousel Indexers

The carousel indexers combine rotary indexing to each of four cassette positions with vertical indexing to each of 25 wafer positions. Rotary indexing is performed by a geneva mechanism which ensures smooth acceleration and deceleration, and is mechanically disengaged when wafer positions are being accessed vertically. A stepper-driven ball screw moves the plate supporting the four cassettes to provide vertical indexing. In order to accommodate cassettes having different dimensional tolerances, a self-calibration routine is incorporated in the control program. This routine works with a capacitive sensor mounted in the air track to detect presence of a wafer in the slot being accessed. When a wafer fails to leave (or enter) the slot indexed to the air track, the failure initiates a hunting sequence in which the indexer first moves up 0.1mm, then down 0.2mm, then up 0.3mm and so on, each time interrogating the sensor to determine the position that causes the wafer to move properly. The new position is then used as the starting point for following moves. In this way, even polypropylene cassettes with large mechanical tolerances may be utilized.

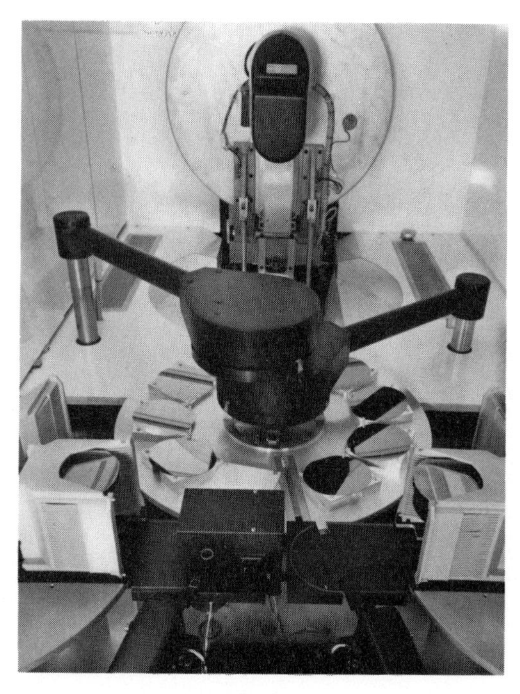

Figure 3. AT-4 System Installed

3.7 Control System

The control system of the AT-4 is based on the 16-bit TM9900 microprocessor used for end station control in the NV-10. The multi-tasking program handles sequencing, interprets operator instructions, generates diagnostic messages, tracks each wafer and monitors over 50 sensors used to verify correct operation at all points of the wafer's travel through the system.

4. Development Status

The AT-4 Automatic Transport System is presently being shipped as a standard option for the NV-10 Ion Implanter. Throughput limits, without implantation, have been measured at 309 wafers per hour for 100mm wafers and 260 wafers per hour for 125mm wafers. The system operates with the Fluoroware PA-72 series Polypropylene cassette as well as aluminum and Teflon cassettes. The installed system is shown in Fig.3.

References

1. G. Ryding and A. Armstrong, A High-Throughput Mechanically Scanned Target Chamber, Nuclear Inst. and Methods, 189 (1981) 319-325.

On-Line Control of Production Ion Implanters Using Standard Desk Computers

H. Glawischnig and K. Noack

Siemens AG, Balanstraße 73, D-8000 München 80, Fed. Rep. of Germany

Abstract

This paper describes various system requirements and gives examples for the control of high-current and medium-current implanters, using low-cost desk computers. Such a system has to prevent maladjustment or faulty set-up by the operator, as well as accomplishing on-line control of the process and its documentation. Although latest implanter models are equipped with control systems of various complexity, other presently used machines still have to be retrofitted.

1. Introduction

In modern IC production, with up to eight different implantations per wafer, computer-controlled on-line quality assurance of the implantation steps becomes a dominant factor in obtaining yield increase, since statistics show that roughly 50 % of faulty implants are caused by operator errors [1].

A few years ago, implanter set-up and adjustment was entirely done by very skilled operators, without any computer control [2,3]. The presently available machines are still set up manually in the source and beam-line sections. The microprocessor-controlled current integrator is set up manually or by a desk computer, which contains the desired recipes. The critical parameters, such as ion species, dose, energy, or uniformity, are monitored and interlocked against wrong adjustment. Printouts of the main parameters for each wafer or batch are obtainable [4,5].

The future generation of machines, however, will be able to work completely automatically. The different subsections, such as source, analyzer, high voltage, dose and wafer transport, will be regulated by individual microprocessors and controlled by a central computer, which in turn can communicate with the host computer of the factory.

This paper will describe some software considerations for on-line control, and presents examples of actually realized control systems for medium-current (MCI) and high-current (HCI) implanters, using low-cost desk computers.

2. System Demands

Depending on the application of an implanter, either in a production environment with one product only or in use for several different product families, including R&D, quite different software concepts are necessary. In the first case, an automatic set-up and control system, including bar-code readers or other wafer identification techniques, might be favored. In the second case, a less automated but more versatile system, which includes the possibility of a direct dialog for data modification, will be preferred.

To achieve sufficient flexibility, the control computer should be programmed in an easy language like BASIC or HPL, to give the user the opportunity to modify the standard software offered by the manufacturer and to create his own optimal solution.

3. Hardware

To control an originally entirely manually operated Varian DF4 MCI, Fig. 1, we chose a HP85 desk computer with 32 K-byte memory, a serial and a parallel interface. The HP85 contains a CRT, a printer, and a tape cartridge unit. The serial interface communicates with the microprocessor-controlled dose processor and receives the preset dose, the actual dose, the implantation time, uniformity tolerance and current range, relative uniformity values, and the area constant.

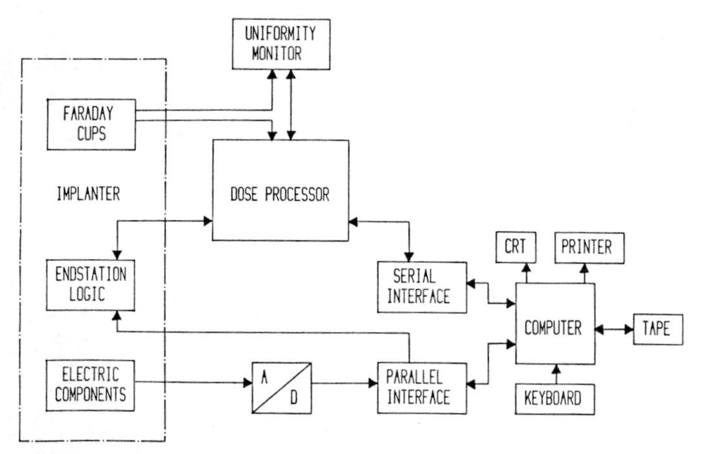

Fig. 1. Hardware-Concept of Computer-Control: The computer is a HP85 desk computer with 32 K-byte memory, the implanter is a Varian DF 4 Medium Current Implanter

The second data bus connects a parallel 32 bit interface from the computer to an A/D converter and to a series of DIP relays. The relays are used to switch the different analog inputs to the A/D converter, or to control the wafer cycling logic. The A/D converter reads the acceleration voltage, the analyzer magnet current setting, the vacuum pressure, the implantation angle, and others. To read data from the high voltage terminal, we used a light link transmission, applying pulse width modulation.

For the control of a Lintott Series III HCI, we installed a HP9825 desk computer with 32 K-byte memory, display, printer, tape cartridge, and a 40 bit parallel interface. The data transmission of the variable extraction voltage and the analyzer magnet current from the high voltage terminal was done via a modified TV-infrared transmitter receiver. The dose, number of scans, and the gas-select were hard wired. All the singnals are multiplexed and fed into the computer by the 40 bit interface.

4. Dialog-Software

One of the main efforts of the software concept was to develop a system which allows easy communication with the computer even by an operator who has no knowledge of the programming language. The program uses an autostart routine whenever a power failure occurs. By means of this routine, the program is loaded automatically from the tape, the access to the data files is enabled, the interfaces are set properly, some parts of the keyboard are disabled for unintentional inputs, and the START button of the implanter is locked. To prevent an undesired program stop, which might be caused by a communication error of the interface due to some sparks or by wrong inputs from the keyboard, several ON-ERROR routines are added. After an interface error, the interface rereads the data several times to eliminate momentary errors. In the case of false inputs, the program branches to a subroutine, tells the operator which input caused this error, and waits for a corrected new one. The whole dialog via CRT and keyboard is done in a language the operator is familiar with, preferably his native language. To prevent excessive typing, special key functions are widely used. The meaning of these functions is usually labelled on the bottom part of the CRT. In the case of real software problems, the operator can switch off the power from the computer, and this puts the whole implanter back into manual operation, thus preventing the implanter from undergoing a complete shutdown, especially during night shifts, when no software maintenance is available.

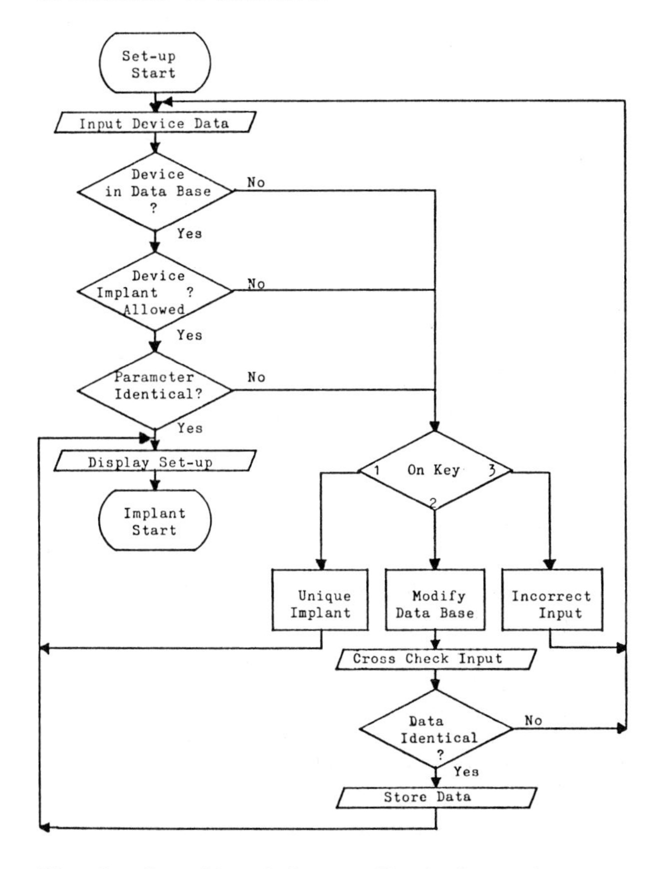

Fig. 2. Data-Base Software: The implantation data, keyed in by the operator, are compared with the data base. Differences prevent the inplantation. If the device type is new, the data base will be expanded automatically

5. Data-Base Software

A memory section, called the data base, has stored all the implant parameters for the different device types and their implantations. Besides this, there also exists a list of devices which are not allowed to be implanted on this special implanter. In a mixed production and R&D environment, the data base might contain several hundred sets of data.

To create, modify, or inspect the data base in a convenient way, an additional subroutine was written, which gives the opportunity to list or inspect individual device families or special parameters, as well as to obtain automatic alphanumerical sorting. For R&D applications with frequently changing parameters or devices, two more program segments were added. A special key function is used to override the data-base interlock function for a new single implant.

A second key is used for an automatic expansion of the data base. If a new device occurs, which is not present in the data base, it can be introduced automatically, Fig. 2. In this case, the program asks to key in the data a second time for a cross check. If the data are identical, they are stored in alpha-numerical order for future use. This new data set, which contains only a minimum of necessary data, can be expanded later during data-base inspection. Each data set contains a counter, which is activated for each individual implant. This gives the opportunity to eliminate sets which were not used over a certain period.

6. Main-Control Software

The following section describes the software for the MCI; the concept for the HCI is similar.

After the termination of a controlled implant, the next one is executed as shown in Fig. 3. First, the operator decides whether the next implant has to be executed for the same device type and the same implant step. If so, only the batch number and the number of wafers has to be typed in. If the device type is different, the program asks for the following parameters: the device type, the process code, and the most important implantation parameters such as dose, energy, ion species, batch number, and numbers of wafers. All these inputs are checked for plausibility, and senseless inputs, such as a dose of 1*10E19, are rejected. Next, the input data are compared with those in the data base, and then the program branches to one of the following four subroutines: If the data exist in the data base and are identical, a list of set-up parameters, contacting analyzer setting and beam current, are displayed to the operator. If the device type is known, but the parameters are different, the differences are displayed. Further it may be that the device type is not allowed to be implanted on this implanter; our as a fourth alternative, the device type is new. In all of these cases, the program can be branched to three alternatives by pressing a key: If there was a wrong input, it returns to the beginning. The second alternative will expand or correct the data base with the new or modified data. In the last case, the program accepts the data as a unique implant and lists the set-up parameters.

The printout of the set-up parameters for the ion-source region is rather optional. We found that the operator is usually able to adjust the source conditions by memory, according to the quality of the source.

After the operator has set up all the parameters manually, such as dose, energy, and ion species, the wafers are loaded and the start key on the com-

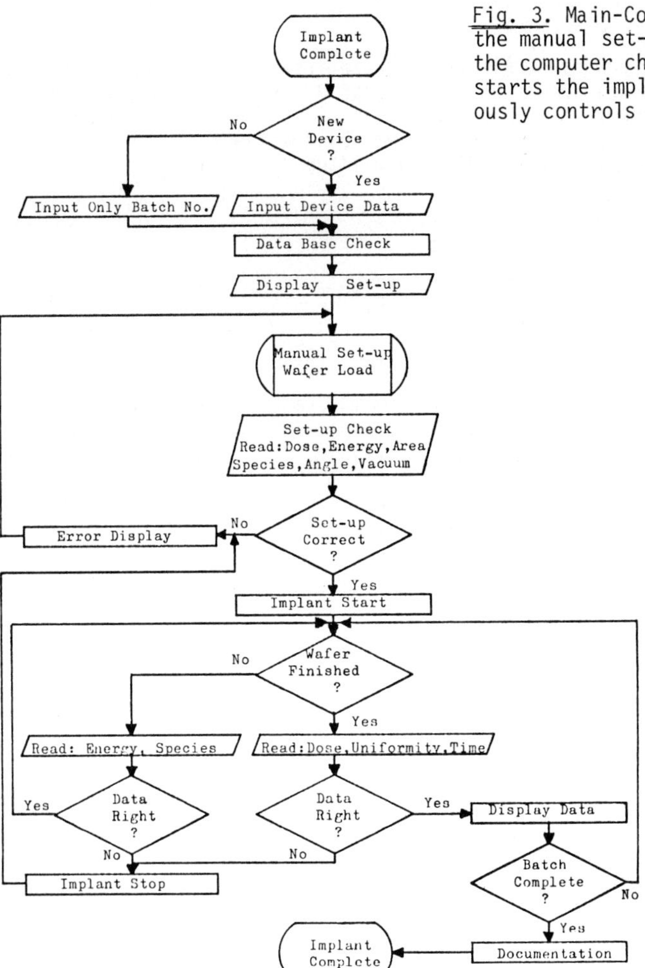

Fig. 3. Main-Control Software: After the manual set-up of the implanter, the computer checks the set-up data, starts the implantation, and continuously controls the settings

puter is pressed. The program goes to a test routine, checks the implanter set-up and the status and, if there are no errors, the implantation is started. During the implantation the computer controls on-line analyzer current, acceleration voltage, and vacuum pressure. In case of a failure, the program stops the implantation, returns to the test routing, and displays the error repetitively until the failure has been corrected:upon any machine interruption, the program is stopped. After the repair, the program can be continued from the same position where it was stopped by pressing the start key.

After every single wafer, the computer reads the current implantation data, displays them on the CRT, and stops the implantation within a few tenths of a second, if any deviation from the desired values occurs. When the batch is complete, there is a printout of all the current data, the total number of implanted wafers, and the implantation time for the whole batch. All these data are than stored in a file. Additionally, the implanter START button is blocked, and the program returns to the beginning.

7. Documentation and Statistics

A further part of the program deals with statistics. There is the possibility of printing out the total number of wafers over a certain period, selecting special device families or cost-profit centers. Since the HP 85 contains an internal timer, up-time as well as down-time observation is possible, separated into adjustment time, repair time, and maintenance time.

References

1. H. Glawischnig, Ion Implantation Techniques (Eds: H. Ryssel and H. Glawischnig), Springer p.3, 1982
2. K.O. Nielsen, Proc.Int.Conf. Applications of Ion Beams to Semiconductor Technology, (Ed. Glotin) (C.E.N. Grenoble), 1967
3. A. Wittkower, P. Rose, and G. Ryding: Solid State Technol. 18, 41 (Dec. 1975)
4. D. Aitken, Ion Implantation Techniques (Eds: H. Ryssel and H. Glawischnig), Springer p.351, 1982
5. G. Ryding, Ion Implantation Techniques (Eds: H. Ryssel and Hr. Glawischnig), Springer p.319, 1982.

A Forty-Channel Optical-Fiber Telecommunication System for Manipulation of High-Voltage Terminals in Ion Implanters

X. Chen, X. Zhang, and S. Chen

Shanghai Institute of Metallurgy, Chinese Academy of Sciences,
865 Chang Ning Road, Shanghai 200050, Hebei, China

Abstract

Basic principles and characteristics of a remote-control telemetry system for the high-voltage terminal of a 600 keV heavy-ion implanter are described. A time-sharing multichannel-signal sampling method, and high-speed V-F converters are used. All controls and signal measurements in each channel are ensured to be synchronous and capable of resisting strong interference.

1. Introduction

1.1 Brief Description

The system described here is new in some respects, although similar systems are available in both experimental and commercial ion implanters [1,2]. In this system, only three optical fibers are used to achieve remote control and telemetry for the power supplies of the high-voltage terminal. Special arrangements are provided to ensure high reliability and the capability of resisting strong interference.

1.2 Basic Principle and Characteristics

The basic principle of operation is the conversion of the signals, via infrared light-emitting diodes, to light signals, and subsequent transmission of these signals by three optical fibers to the receivers, where the light signals are detected and converted to the desired functions. The six-meter-long optical fibers can withstand a potential difference of 800 kV with leakage currents of less than 10 microamperes. In this system, multiplexed signal sampling measurement methods and high-speed V-F converters are used. Because of the large number of signals to be controlled and measured in the high-voltage terminal, and the fact that these signals are at three different potentials (namely, ion source potential, main high-voltage terminal potential, and ground potential), the maximum number of processed signals is forty.

2. Circuit Design and Main Specifications

2.1 Circuit Design

The range of each sampled voltage signal is 0 - $\pm$2V, and that of each sampled current signal is 0 - $\pm$0.2 V. All these signals are gathered in four pre-amplifier-inputs, and again in a main amplifier; then these signals are amplified to a defined full-scale signal level. The multichannel signals, under the control of forty-channel multiplexers after V-F conversion, become one-to-one correspondence time-width pulses which are directly proportional to the signal intensities. After amplification and shaping, the electrical pulses are converted to light pulses via infrared diodes.

The light signals are transmitted to ground potential via optical fibers, and are received by phototransistors. After amplification and shaping, constant-amplitude electrical pulses are obtained, with the same pulse width as the light pulses. The signals, after separation, F-V conversion, and smoothing, become D.C. signals which are directly proportional to the pulse width, and which can be displayed by ordinary meters.

A similar principle is also used for remote control of the high-voltage terminal from the control desk, situated at ground potential. The signals are converted to corresponding voltage signals, which can be used to control the operation of relays, to drive D.C. motors, to control analog circuits or to drive intermediate relays controlling the switching signals.

A block diagram of the circuit is shown in Fig. 1.

2.2 Main Specifications

1) Maximum no. of measured parameters: 40 channels, maximum no. of control parameters: 40 channels.

2) The optical fiber employed can withstand potential differences of 800 kV with leakage currents less than 10 microamperes.

3) Telemetry accuracy better than $\pm 1\%$.

4) Stability better than $\pm 0.2\%$ per hour.

5) Voltage and current signals at two different potentials can be sampled and measured simultaneously. These signals may be analog or digital, positive or negative.

6) An automatic calibration circuit is used for the multichannel-signal synchronous circuit.

7) The electronic instruments situated in the high-voltage terminal can endure the repetitive impact of surge voltages higher than 4000 volts.

3. Operating Characteristics

3.1 Method for Remote Control and Simultaneous Telemetry of Signals at Different Potentials

The signals of the main high-voltage terminal and the ion source are at different potentials with a difference of 20 - 40 kV; the conventional method is to control these signals separately. In our system, we use a sequential method; the signals at ion-source potential occupy 8 channels, and after passing through a very short optical fiber, these signals are transmitted to the main-high-voltage terminal. After being combined with another 32 channels, they are then transmitted to ground potential. Thus, the control desk can display all these signals simultaneously.

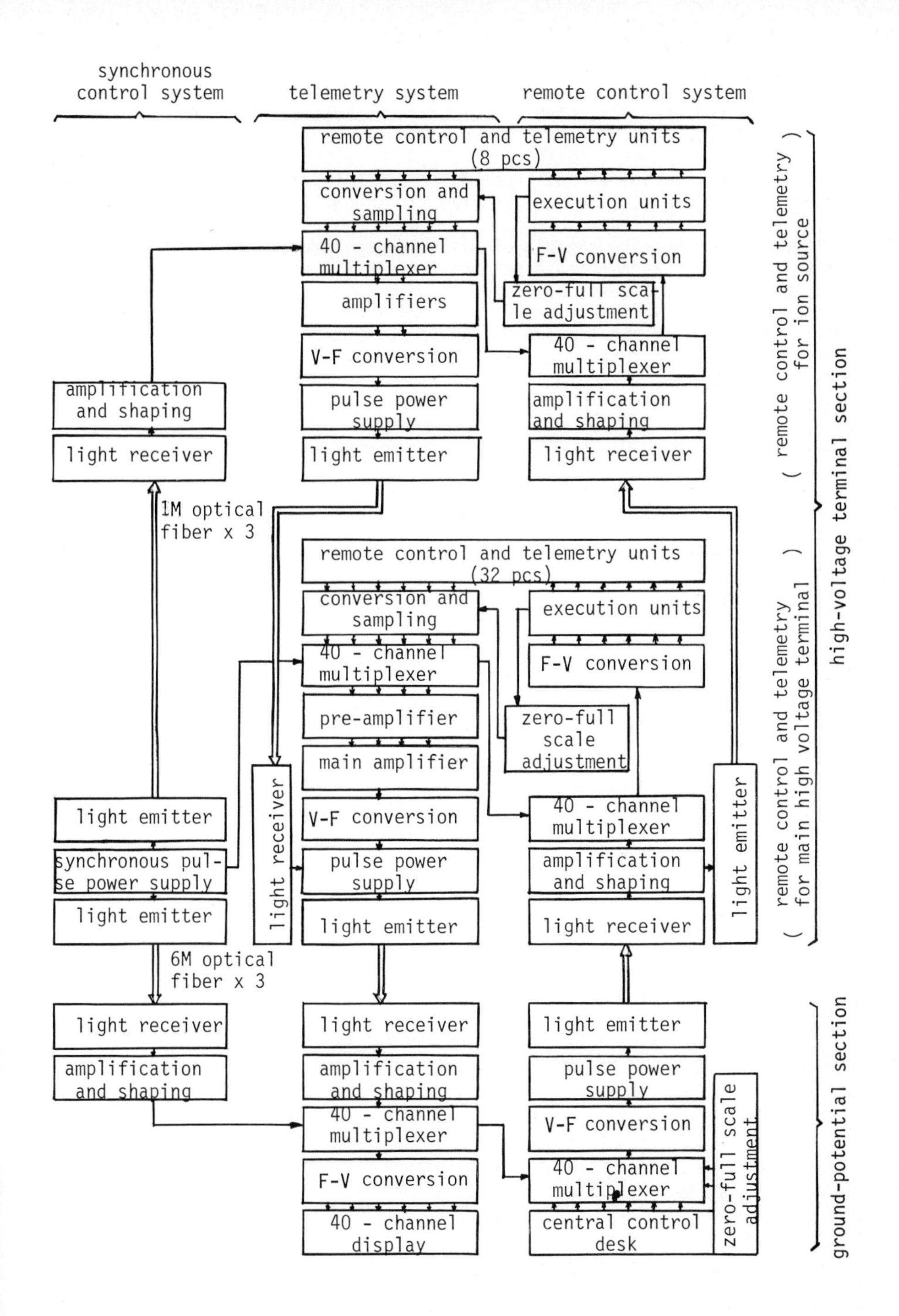

Fig.1. The block diagram of the system

3.2 Signal Synchronization

In remote-control and telemetry systems, synchronous zero restoration is important, because:

1) the signals originate at three different potentials; remote control and telemetry for these singals must be strictly synchronous.

2) the system must be capable of withstanding strong interference; if the latter is present, an automatic calibration circuit will be operated to restore the system to the normal state.

The wave forms of the synchronous and zero-restoration signals are shown in Fig. 2.

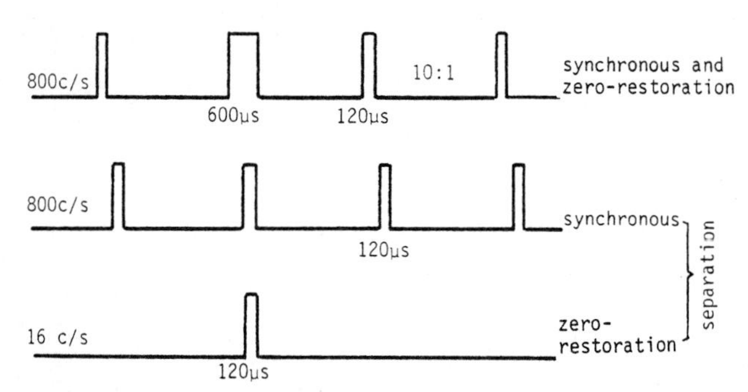

Fig. 2. Wave forms of synchronous and zero-restoration signals

3.3 Provision for Zero and Full-Scale Adjustment during Operation

For the sake of high reliability and long-time operation, this system is provided with a special method of zero and full-scale adjustment.

3.4 Protection Arrangements

Since all these electronic circuits are at high-voltage potential, strong interference, especially high-voltage breakdown, cannot be avoided. Thus, we must consider a precise circuit protection:

1) for the 40-signal input terminals and 40-control output terminals, protection circuits are provided; the protection-circuit unit is shown in Fig.3.

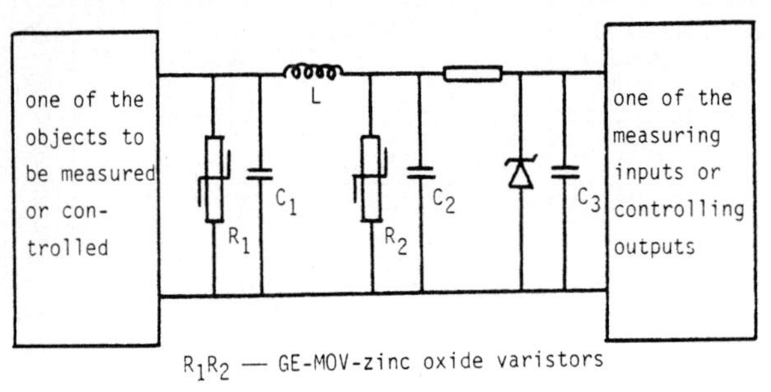

Fig. 3.
Protection-circuit unit

Thus, the instruments can withstand the repetitive impact of a 4000-volt surge-voltage, and the voltage introduced to the input terminals during high-voltage breakdown is less than 6 volts.

2) a three-layer shielded cassette on the high-voltage terminals is used, thus minimizing the interference of electric and magnetic fields.

3) all the ground lines of the 40 signals to be controlled are gathered at one point, and then connected to the ground line of the electronic instruments. Thus, interference coming from the ground line is excluded.

Acknowledgements

The authors wish to thank Associate Professor Jiang Xinyuan, Tsou Shichang, Associate Chief Engineer Jin Shiming, and also Jiang Suwei, Sang Hekang, and Shi Zhenjuan, for their helpful discussions and assistance in the preparation of this manuscript.

References

1. Danfysik Telemeter 410, Denmark.

2. "Remote Control System for 600 eV Ion Implanter". Det. Fysiske Institut, Aarhus, Universitet, Denmark.

Low-Cost Analog Signal Fiber Link with 300 kV Isolation

H. Kranz and S. Steiner

Fraunhofer-Institut für Festkörpertechnologie, Paul-Gerhardt-Allee 42,
D-8000 München 60, Fed. Rep. of Germany

Abstract

A fiber-optic data link, transmitting an analog signal over a potential difference of 300 kV, is described. Its main features are: low cost, simple and rugged design, fast fault finding, easy serviceability (on-the-spot repair), use of plastic fiber cable, and avoidance of special optical components such as expensive fiber-optic connectors.

The links are used for readout of signals and control of an ion source in the high-voltage terminal of an ion implanter. During seven months of operation, none of the 10 links in use ever failed, although the implaner was occasionally subjected to severe sparking. The cost of the material for a complete channel is under US $ 25.

1. Introduction

In high-voltage systems, it is often necessary to transmit analog signals over considerable potential barriers. With recent progress in the field of fiber optics, several new fiber-optic links have come onto the market. These systems consist of a transmitter, an optic cable, and a receiver. Unfortunately, these commercially available signal links have several disadvantages when used for the purposes mentioned above:

1. Most of them can only be used for digital signals [1, 2, 3, 4].
2. Transmitter and receiver are generally embedded [5]. Thus, if one component (diode, transistor, etc.) is damaged by sparking - as often happens in high-voltage systems - the whole device has to be discarded.
3. Most systems use glass fiber cables. To terminate these cables, special care and expensive optical connectors have to be used.
4. A complete data link is rather expensive.

2. Design of the Optical Data Link

To overcome all these problems, we have designed our own fiber-optic analog-signal transmission system. Its main features are simplicity, ruggedness, easy serviceability, and a very low price. To achieve this, we have used a plastic light guide terminated by regular BNC connectors, as well as frequency modulation of transmitted light pulses.

Figure 1 shows a diagram of the optic transmitter. The incoming signal is first fed to a low-drift operational amplifier with a floating-ground input stage (if this is required by the signal source). In the next stage, an offset is added to increase the response time of the system for low input signals. The analog signal is then converted to a proportional fre-

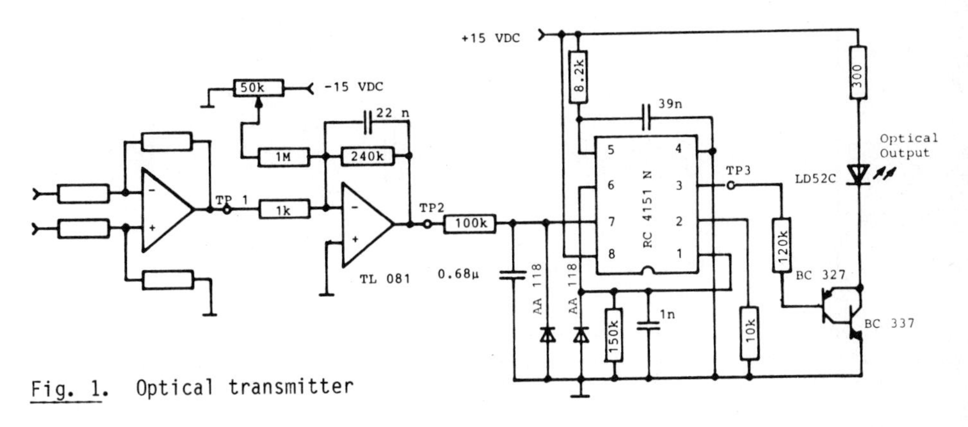

Fig. 1. Optical transmitter

quency by an integrated voltage-to-frequency converter circuit (Raytheon 4151 or equivalent).

The conversion of the analog signal to a corresponding frequency of the transmitted light pulses is a main feature of our system, since in this way, the signal to be transmitted is not affected by changes in the optical transmission (LED, optical cable, photo transistor).

The pulses are then amplified in a transistor stage, and are fed into a standard red LED. Although an infrared emitting diode would somewhat increase the efficieney of the link, a red diode has been preferred for ease of visual inspection and rapid fault finding.

Since a total of 20 signal links was needed for our system, cost reduction was a major design criterion. Therefore, we have avoided the use of expensive optical connectors. Instead, we have used regular BNC connectors for a 2.6 mm diameter cable. After removal of the center pin, these connectors fit a plastic light guide with a 2.2 mm diameter (Lumafil or equivalent).

In spite of its very high attenuation of about 1000 db/km, we have used a plastic light guide instead of a glass fiber cable because it is much easier to handle. It can be cut easily, does not require polishing at the ends, and is not brittle. An attenuation of 1000 db/km seems to be very high but for our application this is not detrimental, since this means that in the case of a cable with a length of 1 m, about 80% of the input light power is still available at the end. For a 2 m length, about 63% of the light is transmitted. In our application, signals are transmitted along a 300 kV accelerating column, through a cable of 2 m length.

The transmitted light pulses are received by a photo transistor mounted, like the LED of the transmitter, in a regular BNC connector, from which the centerpin has been removed. The resulting hole in the Teflon insulation has been enlarged to provide for a press fit of the transistor. There is no special care necessary for mounting the optical components (LED, cable, photo transistor). The link will still work if one BNC connector is disconnected and is held at a distance of about one cm from the receptacle with the LED or the photo transistor.

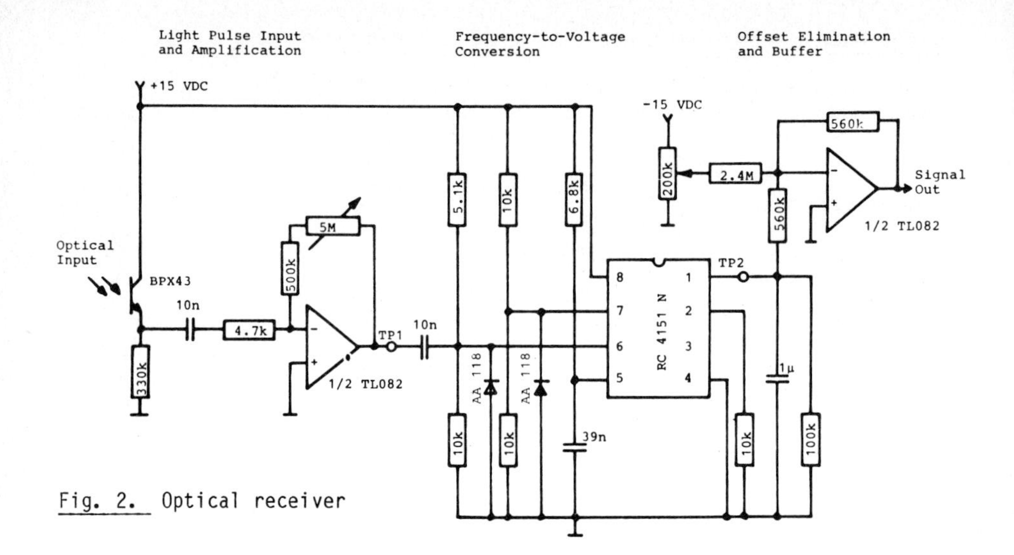

Fig. 2. Optical receiver

The electrical pulses derived from the light pulses in the photo transistor are amplified, and are then converted to the original analog signal by a converter IC identical to that used for the voltage-to-frequency conversion in the transmitter (Fig. 2). At the output of the frequency-to-voltage converter, a summing operational-amplifier stage is provided to compensate for the offset signal which is added in the transmitter for faster response of the system at low signal levels.

For a complete signal link, the cost of the components amounts to less than US$25. Although the 300 kV ion implanter is sometimes subjected to heavy sparking, none of the 10 optical signal links which were in use for more than seven months ever failed in any case.

Fig. 3. Photograph of the complete optical link

3. Conclusion

It has been shown that a rugged and simple data link (Fig. 3) for the transmission of analog signals over a potential difference of 300 kV can be built at a component cost of less than US$25 for one complete channel.

References:

1. Hewlett Packard, Company Bulletin
2. Siemens, Company Bulletin
3. Texas Instruments, Company Information
4. Burr Brown, Company Bulletin
5. Dynamic Measurements Corp., Company Bulletin

Improvements in the Vacuum System of a VDG Accelerator Used for Clean Ion Implantation

U.K. Chaturvedi, V. Shrinet, S.K. Agrawal, and A.K. Nigam

Van-de-Graaff Laboratory, Department of Physics, Banaras Hindu University, Varanasi-221005, India

Abstract

In order to obtain clean implanted surfaces free from beam-induced polymerization, and to avoid the limitations of diffusion pumps, two Varian VacIon (triode) pumps of 30 lps and 110 lps capacity were incorporated into our AN-400 Van de Graaff accelerator, replacing the diffusion pumps. The 30 lps pump is installed near the accelerating column before the switching magnet, while the larger one is fitted near the scattering chamber after the switching magnet. Although ion pumps have less throughput than cryo or diffusion pumps, the choice of VacIon pumps was made after considering all the advantages and disadvantages of the various available pumps. The average vacuum of the beam line, with the existing neoprene O-rings throughout, and without use of any cryogenic material, is found to be in the 10^{-6} torr range without the beam, which changes to the 10^{-7} torr range when the machine is loaded with the beam. Very satisfactory results are obtained with proton and deuteron beams, as these pumps have a very high pumping speed for H_2 and D_2. However, there may be some problems when one uses He^+ and other inert gaseous ions, due to the low pumping speed of ion pumps for these gases, which may be overcome by interchanging the pump positions or by using additional pumps. The beam-induced polymerization has also been reduced considerably.

1. Introduction

Since the middle of the last decade, the main role of small accelerators has changed from their main application in nuclear physics to the field of solid state physics. With this came a change in the vacuum requirements of the system. Nuclear-reaction studies, neutron-activation analysis, etc. with low-Z ion beams from small accelerators (operating at $\sim 10^{-5}$ torr do not require as clean, quick, and high a vacuum as that required in ion-implantation studies, ion-beam analysis, etc. For the acceleration of high-Z ions, a higher order of vacuum ($\leqslant 10^{-7}$ torr is essential to reduce the energy loss due to collisions with residual air molecules, and to improve focusing of the beam. Besides this, some sample-analytical techniques need a much cleaner and higher vacuum, because even a slight surface contamination, basically due to ion-beam polymerization on the implanted region, creates serious problems in surface studies. There are several surface-analytical techniques having tremendous potential, but they work only in UHV ($\leqslant 1\text{x}10^{-9}$ torr conditions. For in situ analysis of implanted samples using these techniques, UHV is essential in the scattering chamber, and can be easily obtained by differential pumping if other parts of the beam line are also at higher and cleaner vacuum. The availability of UHV pumps, hardware, systems, etc. at moderate cost have no doubt helped accelerator users tremendously.

During the last few years, several types of UHV pumps based on different physical or chemical pumping principles have been developed, with comparative costs, taking into account all factors in the long run. Thus, in order to overcome the problems of scarcity of liq.N_2 and frequent power failures, and also to have a better vacuum for ion-implantation studies, it was decided to replace the existing diffusion-pumping system of our AN400 Van de Graaff accelerator by use of a triode-type Varian VacIon pumping system. This is a more reliable, clean, efficient, and robust pumping system capable of producing a higher vacuum in the beam line and the scattering chamber, without any major changes in the elastomeric seals of the system.

2. Pumping Requirements of Accelerators

The pumping requirements of the accelerating system are quite different from those of other vacuum systems. In accelerators, one faces problems due to hazardous radiation environment, great desorption and permeation of gases from large internal surface areas and elastomeric seals, limited conductance of the beam line, limited or no bakeability of the vacuum system, required pumping speed for the unusual gases employed for acceleration, etc. The intense radiation involved with accelerators causes an increase in the gas load due to radiation-induced desorption (RID) from the material used in the system [1]. In high-energy accelerators, this problem is of a serious nature, as RID gases are released from the bulk of the material and are difficult to minimize by surface cleaning treatments. In a typical high-energy accelerator, an average radiation dose rate is $\sim 10^8$ Rad hrs^{-1}, which may increase the gas load up to 5×10^{-10}torr lps cm^{-2} for stainless steel, and nearly one order higher for Al. This is a serious constraint in the UHV pumping of accelerators. The desorbed gases are mainly H_2, CO_2, CO, and H_2O. Besides this effect, the radiation affects the pumping efficiency of the system in the long run. Due to intense radiation, Si oil is polymerized in the diffusion pump, and the elastomeric seals and ceramics are degraded in their properties [2]. In some way or another, the materials used in practically all types of vacuum pumps are affected by hard radiation in the long run.

In the vacuum system of the accelerator, the volume to internal surface area ratio is much less than that of other vacuum systems. The large internal surface area is not only due to the long beam line, but is also due to the presence of gate valves, beam viewers, quadrupole and switching magnets, etc. This large internal area is responsible for the increased gas load (desorption, permeation and degassing, etc.). Due to the long beam line having a comparatively small diameter, the effective conductance of the system is much less, which requires installation of many vacuum pumps at different sites. Collimators, etc. fitted at required places also reduce the conductance tremendously, and divide the beam line into several parts, at least from the vacuum point of view.

Intense [3] (power ~ kW) beam bombardment of the materials of the beam line, accidentally or in routine, releases adsorbed gases in large amounts due to heating, and can even melt thin sections of the materials having low melting points (Al alloys, In seals, etc.), causing catastrophical leaks [2]. This can be avoided by proper cooling of all parts subject to possible exposure to the direct beam. Beam striking of polymere materials can even burn them.

In an accelerator vacuum system, all the parts cannot be baked to a high temperature, due to various limitations, whereas a normal UHV system can be baked at suitable temperatures as a whole. Therefore, baking, the most effective desoption-reducing technique, is out of the question in the case of accelerators. While using unusual gaseous ions for acceleration, the pump installed near the ion source should have a high capacity to pump out this gas. As these uncommon gases are not present in the atmosphere, the pumps are not generally tested for them. Therefore, for such gases, a suitable and tested pump should be incorporated near the ion source.

Besides this, pumps selected for the accelerator vacuum system should also meet the following criteria:

(i) Minimum prerequisites, e.g. LN_2, cooled water, compressed air, multiphase power line, etc., for proper operating as far as possible.

(ii) Freedom from vibration and electromagnetic noise while in operation, so that other delicate equipment can work without disturbance. The pump should not have any preferential mounting, if possible.

(iii) Capability of running continuously for several years with minimum attention, without any danger of contamination of the system or reduction of the pumping speed in case of power or input breakdowns.

(iv) Easy disassembly for maintenance and repairs.

(v) Reliability; availability at short notice and at competitive cost.

3. Various Pumps and their Characteristics

In the light of the above-mentioned requirements, various characteristics of different types of modern pumps are summarized in Table I. From a comparative study of these characteristics, one can find that the triode-type ion pump is most suitable for accelerator pumping, despite its drawbacks especially while pumping H_2 and inert gases. The ion pumps have quite high speeds (up to 270% N_2 speed) for H_2 at the one extreme, and very low speeds ($\simeq$21% N_2 speed) for Ar at the other. This fact is due to the different pumping mechanism of the ion pump for hydrogen, helium, and other gases. H_2 is lighter but chemically active. Thus, it cannot sputter the Ti element of the ion pump, but reacts chemically with the surface of the Ti element and forms hydride. It even diffuses deeper into the element, which causes the cracking of the surface. This mechanism results in a higher pumping speed for H_2, but the active element surface saturates with H_2 in the long run, which reduces its pumping speed. At this stage, if the upper layer of the Ti hydride is removed, either due to thermal effects or due to sputtering by some heavier gas species, a sudden release of the diffused H_2 will take place, giving rise to hydrogen instability. Such instabilities have been observed in ion pumps after prolonged (125 hrs) pumping of pure H_2 at 2×10^{-4} torr [4]. However, such instabilities can be easily taken care of by introducing Ar or some heavier gas species into the system [5]. Due to argon's high sputtering rate, the Ti element of the pump is cleaned thoroughly, and is ready for further pumping of H_2.

In the case of He, diode-type ion pumps have only a nominal pumping speed, while triode-type pumps have up to 30% of their N_2 speed. He is neither chemically active nor heavy enough to cause sufficient sputtering. The higher speed of triode-type ion pumps having a special geometry is due to the low angle of incidence of the ionized species with respect to the Ti element plane which causes maximum sputtering. The gaseous species striking the walls of the pump are thus buried with titanium deposits. Besides this, He also diffuses into the Ti element, and can cause more instability due to its inertness. Hence, the Ti element should be cleaned from time to time, employing the same method. It may be noted here that all other pumps, except the diffusion pump and some good turbo molecular pumps, have very low speeds for

Table 1: U.H.V. Pumps and their Characteristics *)

Type of pump (operating principle) operating range (torr), and capacity available (lps N_2 at 1×10^{-6} torr)	Pumping speed for different gases at 1×10^{-6} torr (N_2:100%)	Input prerequisites	Radiation-tolerance-limiting factors	Degree of cleanness of the vacuum, type of mount	Remarks
Diffusion pump (vapor-jet momentum transfer), 10^{-2}-10^{-12}, 25-50000	H_2 : 150% He : 125% air : 100% Ar : 90% H_2O : 100% (speed of H_2 and He depends on heater wattage)	- Power (1Ø or 3Ø) - backing pump - cooled water - LN_2/other cryogenics	- Oil polymerization - Sealing elastomers	Ultraclean with DC-705 oil and LN_2-CFF system. Otherwise moderately clean. Only vertical mount.	- Oil polymerization while pumping atomic hydrogen. - Risk of non-availability of prerequisites. - Not totally vibration-free due to rotary force pump. - Remote control possible.
Turbomolecular pump (mechanical momentum transfer at very high r.p.m.), 10^{-2}-10^{-11}, 40-3500	H_2 : 10 - 105% He : 25 - 125% (depends on r.p.m. of the shaft) air : 100% Ar : 85% H_2O : 100%	- cooled water/compressed gas - power (3Ø, sometimes 1Ø) - Forevacuum pump (except ALCATEL)	- Bearing grease/oil	Ultraclean with gas or magnetic bearings. Moderately clean with grease bearings, especially at low r.p.m. Vertical mount in general; all mounts in some cases.	- Some Turbo-M pumps generate electromagnetic noise. - Pumping characteristics and cleanness vary from one type to another. - Total remote control possible.
Cryo pump (adsorption of gases on cryo-surfaces), 10^{-1}-10^{-10},	H_2 : 120% He : 20% air : 100% Ar : 80% H_2O : 400%	- Power (1Ø,3Ø) - LN_2 not compulsory	- RID of adsorbing material may cause problems	Ultraclean. Any mount except those with LN_2.	- May require periodical filling of He in case of leaks. - Periodical regeneration of the adsorbant. - Thermal loads undesirable - Total remote control is not possible.
Ion pumps Triode-type pump: (Ionization-acceleration-sputtering-ion burial or chemisorption), 10^{-3}-10^{-12}, 8-8000 Diode-type pump: (Ionization, acceleration, trapping, chemisorption), 10^{-2}-10^{-11}, 1-1000	H_2 : 200 - 270% He : 30% air : 100% Ar : 21% H_2O : 100% H_2 : 200 - 270% He : 10% air : 100% Ar : 3% (Instability) H_2O : 100%	- Power (1Ø)	- RID seldom causes problems after long pumping - Degradation of the ferrite magnet due to long irradiation	Ultraclean. Any mount.	- Can operate up to years without any attention. - Ti element needs replacement at intervals. - H_2 and rare-gas instability. - Total remote control possible.
Titanium sublimation pump (TSP) (gettering by titanium alloys deposited on cool walls), 10^{-2}-10^{-11}, 800-3500 (speed depends on exposed area and its temp.)	a At wall temp. 20°C: H_2 : 65% He : 0% air : 100% Ar : 0% H_2O : 65% b at -195°C H_2 : 100% He : 0% air : 100% Ar : 0% H_2O : 125%	- Power (1Ø) - Cooled water/LN_2	- RID seldom causes problems	Ultraclean. Any mount (except LN_2 cooled)	- Periodic sublimation is needed at $<10^{-7}$ torr. - Unable to pump light hydrocarbons, CH_4, etc. - Excellent results with ion pumps. - Total remote control possible with some modifications.

*) Data taken from technical literature provided by various manufactures of ultra-high-vacuum pumps.

He, whereas Ar is pumped out effectively by all pumps except ion and TSP pumps. Ar causes severe instability in the diode type of ion pump. The triode-type ion pump has a nominal speed (21% N_2) for Ar, and shows instability only at pressures 1×10^{-5} torr. Thus, these parameters are the important limitations in selecting the capacity of the triode-type ion pump.

In spite of these drawbacks, the ion pump is the ideal choice for the non-demountable parts of the accelerator, as it satisfies most of the criteria mentioned in the previous section. Fortunately, most of the accelerator vacuum components are non-demountable, and the vacuum improves with time on account of the continuous pumping of the system.

4. Beam-Induced Polymerization

Beam-induced polymerization at the beam spot on the target exposed for long periods to ion or electron beams is a very notorious phenomenon, generally attributed to diffusion-pump oil backstreaming. However, it is not correct to single out the diffusion-pump oil as the only source of the problem, as there are other sources also responsible for it. It has been observed that even under the very-high-vacuum conditions ($\sim 10^{-8}$ torr created by turbo-m pumps, ion-beam polymerization is not totally absent. This is a complex phenomenon, and the chemical reactions involved have not been very well studied. It is assumed that even in a vacuum of 10^{-9} torr, beam polymerization will take place in the long run, since traces of CO, CO_2, CH_4, H_2, and H_2O are always present in the system. H_2 permeates through the stainless-steel walls of the system, while CH_4 is produced by interaction [6] of these hydrogen atoms with the carbon atoms of stainless steel. CH_4 is also produced from the active Ti element of the ion pump [7], while CO & CO_2 come from the heated tungsten filaments used in the vacuum system [8]. H_2O vapors are main desorbed species [9].

It is well known that one monolayer of the gaseous species is deposited [10] on the target in $\sim 10^3$ seconds at a vacuum of $\sim 10^{-9}$ torr, and if only 1% of these deposited molecules are polymerized due to beam bombardment, it will take nearly 10^5 secs (≈ 30 hrs) to have one monolayer of the polymer on the target. Since ion-implantation time, in many cases, is quite comparable to this, it is impossible to avoid beam-induced polymerization completely, even at a vacuum of 1×10^{-9} torr. Thus, one can safely conclude that it is the composition of the residual gases that is more responsible for this polymerization. Liquid He shielding of the target is the safest method to avoid it, but this is a very complicated and costly affair.

Besides these carbonaceous gases (CO, CO_2), light hydrocarbons (etc.) and H_2O are also produced from the elastomeric O-rings due to degassing [11], and contribute to polymerization. This degassing cannot be checked effectively by replacing neoprene O-rings with Viton unless they are baked up to 150°C. However, it can be completely eliminated by the use of metallic gaskets.

Since diffusion-pump oil backstreaming is the major source of polymerization, it is not out of place to mention here the polymerization data available [12] for the widely used D.C.704 silicon oil (mol.wt.484). The polymerization rate of this oil vapor on glass substrates coated with Al film, due to low-energy electron (≈ 100 eV) bombardment, is 0.17A° sec^{-1}, with electron flux $\sim 10^{16} cm^{-2}\ sec^{-1}$ and oil-vapor flux $\sim 10^{14}$ molecules $cm^{-2} sec^{-1}$. This rate is equivalent to a vacuum of $\sim 10^{-6}$ torr with high backstreaming partial pressure, and is not negligible. It can be improved slightly with proper LN_2 trapping of the diffusion pump. Even with the very advanced Edwards

Diffstak-type diffusion pump, the rate of polymerization is reduced by only 1 or 2 orders of magnitude without the LN_2 trap. In order to avoid polymerization, turbo-m pumps have been used by many accelerator groups. However, it has been observed /13/ that in the long run, even bearing-oil backstreaming is quite sufficient to produce beam polymerization. The situation is worst with turbo-m pumps backed by untrapped rotary pumps, and only backingless turbo-m pumps with gas or magnetic bearings are totally safe from the danger of backstreaming.

5. Vacuum Requirements of the AN-400 Van de Graaff (VDG) Accelerator

In order to select the most suitable pumping system for our An-400 VDG accelerator, knowledge of the full details of the accelerator and all its vacuum requirements was essential. This accelerator is capable of accelerating singly charged particles up to an energy of 400 keV, with a maximum beam current of 150 μA for a zero-degree port. A wide range of gaseous ions can be produced in the ion source energized by a R.F. circuit through a thermo-mechanical/Pd leak from the gas bottle. The switching magnet of the accelerator deflects the beam to ± 15° ports. A schematic diagram of the accelerator is shown in Fig. 1.

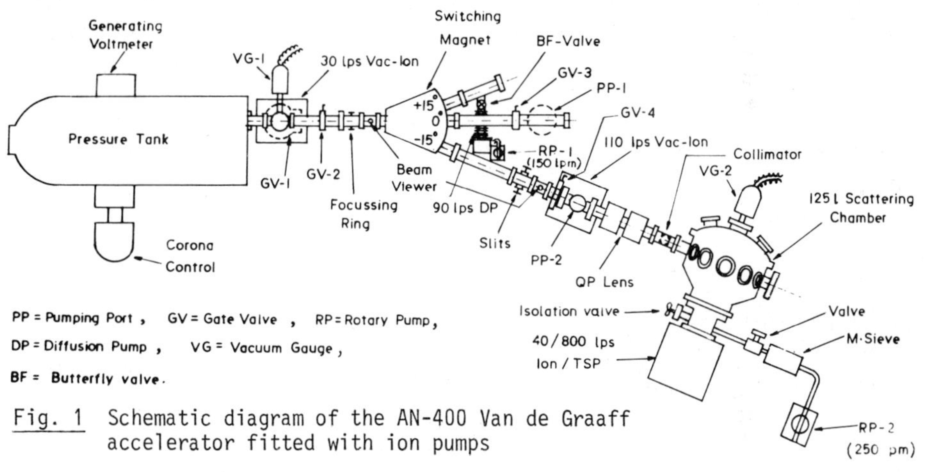

Fig. 1 Schematic diagram of the AN-400 Van de Graaff accelerator fitted with ion pumps

Unlike larger accelerators and storage rings, the internal-radiation level of the accelerator is much lower than 10^4 Rad/hr in most parts of the beam line /14/. The duty cycle of the accelerator depends on the operating load, and is generally much less than 100%. However, in considering the pumping system, a 100% duty cycle should be assumed. The beam line of 2" dia. stainless-steel tubing has a total length of 15 meters, with an internal volume of 30 liters. The internal surface area of the beam line with gate valves, view ports, slits, etc. amounts to more than 2.5 m^2. The system is sealed throughout by neoprene O-rings, numbering more than 50, with a cross-sectional dia. of 3 mm. In addition, there is one multiport 125 l volume scattering chamber pumped by a separate 40/800 lps ion/TSP pump.

The gas load of this system resulting from different sources can be calculated easily. The total gas load due to surface outgassing from the 304 stainless-steel beam line is of the order of 10^{-8} torr lps /15/, considering the surface outgassing rate as high as $\sim 10^{-12}$ torr lps cm^{-2}. The permeation of H_2 through the walls is negligible, being 3 orders of magnitude lower. However, the main sources of the gas load are the neoprene O-rings, which degas considerably in vacuum; this factor [15] amounts to 4.0×10^{-6} torr lps, if it is assumed that only a 10% area of the O-ring is exposed to the vacuum and contributes to degassing. The permeation of different gases and water vapor through these O-rings is generally lower than the degassing rate. Thus, a total gas load of $\approx 5 \times 10^{-6}$ torr lps exists in the beam line, which will require a pumping capacity $\gg 50$ lps to pump it down to 1×10^{-7} torr. However, on account of the small diameter of the beam line, its molecular-flow-conductance length (lps. cm) parameter is limited and is only 1500, which suggests the incorporation of many small pumps with a total capacity of $\gg 50$ lps at various places in the beam line.

The incorporation of many small pumps in the beam line at various places causes many additional unforeseen problems, and is hence not advisable. However, it has been found convenient to install two Varian VacIon pumps of 30 lps and 110 lps at the locations shown in Fig. 1. The 30 lps pump near the ion source is equivalent to the original Veeco 90 lps diffusion pump in respect to the actual speed available for the beam line. The 110 lps VacIon pump is attached near the scattering chamber, either to a zero-degree port, or to a -15° port, as appropriate. Both of these pumps are remotely operated by a single H.T. power supply employing a special H.T. switching arrangement.

The 30 lps ion pump attached near the ion source has a pumping capacity of 60 lps for hydrogen, but only 9 lps for He. The port connecting this pump to the beam line has a molecular conductance of 50 lps for N_2; hence, 175 lps for H_2 and 80 lps for He. Therefore, if the 110 lps ion pump is connected in place of the 30 lps ion pump, a sufficient speed for He (33 lps) can be obtained during He acceleration. This speed for He is equivalent to the original Veeco diffusion pump's effective speed for He, when attached at the same place.

6. Performance with the New Pumping System

The new pumping system, with VacIon triode pumps incorporated into the Van de Graaff accelerator, has been in operation since April of this year. Throughout the beam line, an average vacuum of $\approx 10^{-7}$ torr without beam has been obtained without use of any cryogenic material. This changes to the $\sim 10^{-6}$ torr range when the machine is fully loaded with the beam. Initially, as the 30 lps pump installed near the ion source causes a great deal of H_2 to be pumped out quickly, its vacuum reaches 2×10^{-5} torr, but this then improves to 1.5×10^{-5} torr when the machine is running smoothly at moderate beam current as high as 60-75 μA has been extracted at the zero-degree port for several hours with this vacuum system. However, with such demands upon the pump, hydrogen instability may appear, which can be eliminated easily by the methods discussed earlier. Due to the higher and cleaner vacuum, better gas control, and thereby overall better stability of the beam for both zero and -15° ports, have been obtained.

As far as the cleanness of this vacuum system is concerned, it has been observed that the beam spot is not totally free from ion-beam polymerization. The only cause of this appears to be the neoprene O-rings, as no dirty pump is employed for evacuation. The roughing of the beam line and the scattering chamber, when required, is done through a Varian molecular sieve trap. In case of prolonged power breakdowns, the original Veeco 90 lps diffusion pump, fitted at the +15° port, is used for restarting of the ion pumps. The diffusion pump is isolated from the beam line as soon as the ion pump starts. Even though our new pumping system is quite clean, the problem of beam polymerization during prolonged implantations still exists, but to only a small extent. In the case of short exposures, the ion-beam polymerization is negligible as can be seen in Fig. 2, where the boundary of the implanted (260 keV, 5.8x10 $H^+ cm^{-2} sec^{-1}$, 480 secs) and unimplanted regions is clearly seen. It can be observed that both regions have similar surface features.

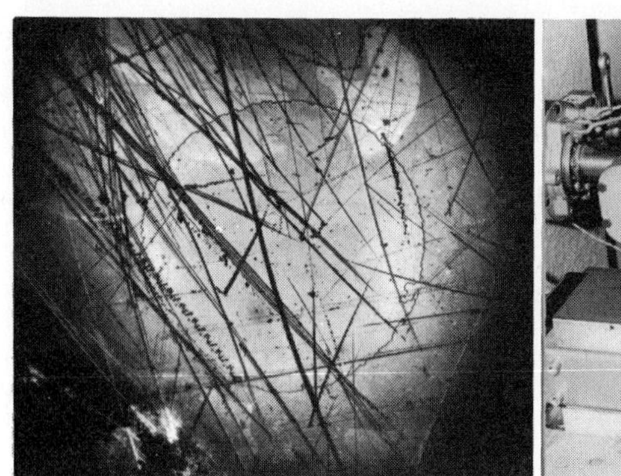

Fig. 2: A clean p^+ implanted spot on Mylar

Fig. 3: 30 lps Varian VacIon pump connected with the beam line near the pressure tank

It is not out of place to make some remarks here on the lifetime of the Ti elements of these pumps [16]. The element of the 30 lps ion pump has a lifetime of 20 khrs (nearly two years of continuous running) when used in a vacuum of $1x10^{-6}$ torr. Its lifetime, however, decreases proportionally when used at higher pressures, and remains only 2 khrs when used at $1x10^{-5}$ torr while pumping pure N_2. It should be mentioned here that the lifetime of the pump element will increase to more than 2 khrs at $1x10^{-5}$ torr when pumping H_2; being lighter, the latter causes less sputtering. After this, chemical cleaning of the ion pump and replacement of the Ti element are essential. The replacement of the element of the 30 lps ion pump has to be done by the manufacturer, whereas in the case of the 110 lps ion pump (lifetime $\approx$ 50 khrs for N_2 at $1x10^{-6}$ torr), it can be done in the laboratory.

Incorporation of a 2-100 A.M.U. R.G.A. in the scattering chamber, and development of a servo-remote-controlled L-T power supply for the TSP pump, are also being done to improve the vacuum system of our AN-400 Van de Graaff accelerator.

Acknowledgements

The authors are grateful to Prof. P.C.Sood for his keen interest in the work. They are also thankful to Mr. G.P. Mishra and N. Rajan for their assistance. They gratefully acknowledge the help in TIG welding of CFF to the beam line given by Nuclear Fuel Complex, Hyderabad. The financial assistance of UGC and DAE for this work is also gratefully acknowledged.

References

1. R. Dobrozamsky: Nucl. Instr. Meth. 118, 1 (1974).
2. J. Kaenetal: J. Vac. Sci. Technol. 6, 202 (1969).

3. J.B.A. England et al.: Technical Memorandum of the Daresbury Laboratory DL/NSF/TM-35 (Instrumentation); 20 (1978).
4. K.M. Welch: Paper presented at the 22nd National Symposium of the American Vacuum Society, Oct. 1975 (Varian Report 103, page 4).
5. S.L. Rutherford, R.L. Jepsen: Rev. Sci. Instr. 32, 1144 (1961).
6. W.R. Wheeler: Physics Today 25, 52 (Aug. 1972).
7. D.J. Santeler: J. Vac. Sci. Technol. 8, 299 (1971).
8. vg Micromass Technical Catalogue of M/s vg Gas Analysis Company (U.K.), Publication No. MJD-02-458.
9. B. Benvenuti: IEEE NS-26, 2128 (1979).
10. K.L. Chopra, in Thin Film Phenomena; McGraw Hill, N.Y., Chapt. II, p.13.
11. L. Hollond, W. Steckelmacher, J. Yarwood (eds): Vacuum Manual (E&F.N.SPON, London, 1974), Chapt. I.
12. L.E. Babcock: J. Appl. Phys. 43, 1423 (1972).
13. L. Maurice, P. Duval, G. Gorinas: J. Vac. Sci. Technol. 16, 741 (1979) and Edwards Diffstak MK2 technical catalogue, publication No. 05-B344-23-895.
14. W. Bygrave, P. Treaco, J. Lambert, in Acc. Nuclear Physics, High Voltage Engineering Corp., Burlington, Mass. U.S.A. (1970), p. 279.
15. R. Glang, R.A. Halmwood, J. A. Kurtz, in Handbook of Thin Film Technology (1970), ed. by L.I. Maissel and R. Glang, pp. 2-49 to 2-59 (McGraw Hill, N.Y.).
16. Varian Vacuum Manual (Diode and Triode VacIon pumps: Vac 2227G, 1277, Section 4), p.3.

Part IV

Special Implantation Techniques

High Temperature Implantation of Powders Using a Horizontal Ion Beam

J.P.F. Sellschop, J.F. Prins*, and U. von Wimmersperg

Nuclear Physics Research Unit, University of the Witwatersrand,
1 Jan Smuts Avenue, Johannesburg, South Africa

Abstract

An experimental arrangement is described which allows for the implantation of powders by a horizontal ion beam while simultaneously heating the powder to a high temperature.

1. Introduction

The implantation of powder targets can be advantageous in a number of applications owing to the fact that a large effective surface area may be implanted using a sample of small mass.

One of the investigations currently being carried out at our research unit is a study of the doping of diamond by ion implantation. In particular we use Mössbauer spectroscopy as well as γ - γ cascade analysis in time dependent perturbed angular correlation (PAC) to analyze the sites populated by implanted ions. Owing to the cost and problem of availability of large crystals, individual small diamonds are normally used, which limits the signal strength obtainable. Accordingly, the use of diamond powder is an attractive alternative method to increase the implanted surface to mass ratio and thus the signal strength. However, to limit radiation damage and possible graphitization of the diamond powder during implantation, heating of the target is essential.

Powder implantation has traditionally been done by bending a horizontal ion beam downwards into a continuously vibrating cup containing the powder [1] . Recently a novel technique was developed which presents a vertical powder target to a horizontal ion beam by using a rotating drum, containing the powder, which intersects the ion beam at an angle of 45° [2] . A focussed radiation heater has now been incorporated in this device to allow heating of the powder during implantation.

2. Description of Apparatus

In our case, the main requirements for hot implantation of powders were the following:

1. The heating system must not contaminate the powder grains through the release of unwanted foreign matter.

---

* On Secondment from De Beers Diamond Research Laboratory, Johannesburg.

2. The system must be adjustable to allow implantation of a variety of powdered materials.

3. Preferably, the individual grains must remain in contact with each other, when passing through the ion beam, in order to promote heat conduction between them. The latter condition minimizes severe temperature excursions which may occur in individual, thermally isolated grains under ion bombardment.

Figure 1 shows schematically a top view of the arrangement used for hot implantation of a powder target. Use is made of the "concrete mixer" shaped drum described previously [2] . The latter is rotated by a stepping motor situated outside the end station of the ion implanter, and intersects the ion beam at an angle of 45°. When the drum rotates fast enough, the powder, inside the drum, covers the drum wall owing to centrifugal action. As arranged in Fig.1, the drum rotates in a direction ensuring that the ion beam intersects the powder while it is rising against the drum wall. With the rotating speed sufficiently high, the powder covers the drum wall thickly enough to prevent sputtering of the drum material and thus undesirable contamination of the powder grains.

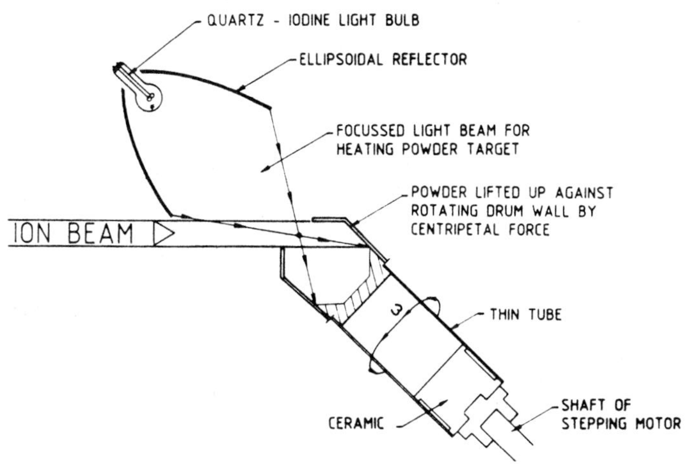

Fig.1. Top, sectional view of experimental arrangement

The stepping motor is controlled by a variable frequency pulse train pattern. By choosing the correct pulse train pattern, the drum is periodically decelerated by just enough to ensure partial collapse of the powder layer; mainly on the opposite side of the drum where the powder is moving downwards. By suitable choice of control parameters the partial collapse of the powder is enough to ensure mixing and re-orientation of the grains, but not so large as to violate condition 3 mentioned above.

Heating of the drum cavity is effected by means of a quartz-iodine projector lamp situated at one of the focal points of an ellipsoidal reflector. The reflector is located such that its second focal point lies within the drum opening through which the ion beam also enters. Consequently the light generated by the projector light bulb is focussed into the drum cavity, thereby heating this cavity and its contents. The heating of the powder thus occurs via a black body cavity containing radiation. An equilibrium temperature is reached when the incoming radiation is balanced by outgoing radiation. With a view to high thermal efficiency, the drum is insulated with respect to heat conduction and has a highly reflective outer surface.

3. Discussion

The heating action of the arrangement was tested by inserting a thermocouple into the drum cavity. In Fig.2 the equilibrium temperature measured inside the cavity is shown as a function of the power supplied to the light bulb. According to specification, the ellipsoidal reflector will deliver approximately 70% of the energy generated at the light bulb into the drum cavity. At equilibrium conditions the power delivered into the cavity should be the same as the power radiated by the drum assembly. The latter should follow Stefan's law, i.e.

$$W = \sigma e A T^4$$

where W is the power radiated
σ is Stefan's constant
e is the emissivity
A the area which radiates
and T is the absolute temperature.

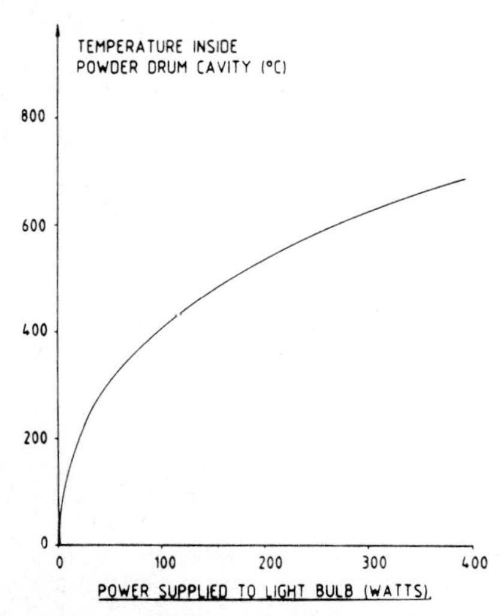

Fig.2. Temperature generated in drum containing the powder as a function of power

And indeed, by taking the logarithm of the measurements in Fig.2 and extracting the slope, a fourth power dependence of the absolute temperature is found within experimental error. Calculation of the emissivity gives a value between 0.1 and 0.2, which is fairly low.

The arrangement has been used successfully to implant powders at temperatures up to 750°C and experiments are now in progress utilizing this technique.

Acknowledgements

We would like to thank Dr. T.E. Derry and Mr.M.Rebak for helpful discussions. Mr. L. Verga and Mr. I.D. McKowen built the equipment and added useful ideas.

References

1 J.H. Freeman, W. Temple: Rad. Effects 28, 85 (1976)
2 U. von Wimmersperg, J.F. Prins, T.E. Derry: Nucl. Instrum. and Methods 197, 597 (1982).

A Technique for Implanting Dopant Distributions in Solids

J.N. McGruer, D.S. Croft*, R.B. Irwin, J.A. Rabel, J.H. Sheehan, W.J. Choyke
University of Pittsburgh, Pittsburgh, PA 15260, USA
N.J. Doyle
Westinghouse R&D Center, 1310 Beulah Road, Pittsburgh, PA 15235, USA

In many material studies, a specific distribution in depth of a dopant is required. In this paper, a method of obtaining a wide variety of distributions in depth of implants is described. The depth, measured normal to the surface, of the implanted species can be varied by changing the angle between the surface normal and the incident beam direction. A given dopant distribution can be obtained by implanting for a predetermined time or accumulated charge at each of a large number of incident beam angles. Computer programs are reported which calculate the waiting times, plot the theoretical dopant distribution, and drive a stepping motor in such a manner as to provide the desired concentration of the dopant at each depth.

1. Introduction

In many material science studies and applications, it is desirable to put a given depth distribution of a dopant into a material matrix. This is usually accomplished either by diffusion or by ion implantation. A non-Gaussian dopant distribution can be obtained from ion implantation by employing any one of three techniques: implanting through a series of thin energy degrading foils [1], changing the incident beam energy, or rotating the sample on an axis perpendicular to the incident beam direction [2], hereinafter referred to as the "Rocking Technique". In this paper, we will discuss a method of automating the rocking technique using a micro-computer.

The theory used to calculate the dwell times[1] is discussed in the next section. The hardware and the software implementations are covered in sections 3.1 and 3.2, respectively.

2. Theory

In Fig. 1, we show the geometry employed. As the angle θ between the incident ion beam and the surface normal of the sample is changed, the depth measured normal to the surface at end of range varies as $R_p \cos\theta$, where R_p is the projected range of the implanted ion. Consider three

Work supported in part by NSF grant DMR81-02968.

*Present Address: Duquesne Light Company
Beaver Valley Power Station Unit #1
Shippingport, PA 15077 USA

[1]The dwell times may be measured either in seconds or in accumulated charge (see Section 3.2).

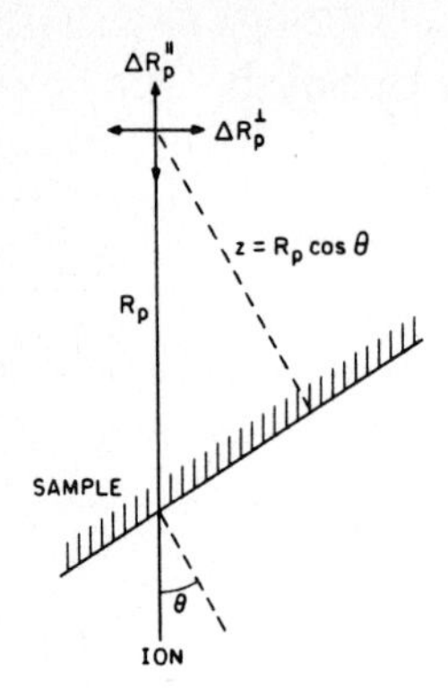

Figure 1. Implant Geometry

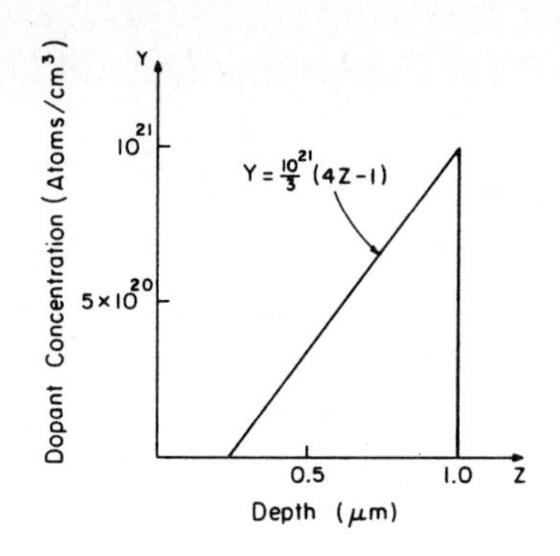

Figure 2. "Ramp" Dopant Distribution from 0.25 μm to 1.0 μm

angles: $\theta - \delta$, θ, and $\theta + \delta$, where δ is some small angle increment and $\delta < \theta < 90 - \delta$. Then in the case of a uniform dopant distribution, and number of dopant atoms/cm^2, Ψ_0, required to put the desired concentration, C_0 in atoms/cm^3, of dopant atoms into a slab of thickness ΔZ, where

$$\Delta Z = R_p\cos(\theta - \delta/2) - R_p\cos(\theta + \delta/2) \tag{1}$$

is

$$\Psi_0 = C_0\Delta Z = C_0R_p[\cos(\theta - \delta/2) - \cos(\theta + \delta/2)] \quad . \tag{2}$$

If ϕ is the ion flux through the sample surface, then from (2) the dwell time at each angle θ is

$$t(\theta) = \Psi_0/\phi = (C_0R_p/\phi)[\cos(\theta - \delta/2) - \cos(\theta + \delta/2)] \quad . \tag{3}$$

In practice, it is more convenient to measure the ion flux through a plane whose normal is the beam direction. This flux is denoted by ϕ_0. Then

$$\phi = \phi_0 \cos\theta \tag{4}$$

and substituting (4) into (3)

$$t(\theta) = \frac{C_0R_p}{\phi_0 \cos\theta} [\cos(\theta - \delta/2) - \cos(\theta + \delta/2)] \quad . \tag{5}$$

If $\Delta R_p^{\parallel}$ and $\Delta R_p^{\perp}$ are the standard deviation of the three-dimensional Gaussian distribution parallel and perpendicular to the beam, then the standard deviation, ΔR_p, measured normal to the surface is given by [3]

$$(\Delta R_p)^2 = (\Delta R_p^{\perp} \sin\theta)^2 + (\Delta R_p^{\parallel} \cos\theta)^2 \quad . \tag{6}$$

The angle increment δ must be small enough to make $R_p\delta < \Delta R_p$. This allows the tails of the individual Gaussians to overlap and smooth the dopant distribution. In deriving (2), it was assumed that all the dopant atoms implanted at angle θ remained in a slab of thickness ΔZ, (1), which would imply that $\Delta R_p << \Delta Z$. Since (5) is a slowly varying function of angle (except near $\theta = 90$), the tail of a Gaussian outside its ΔZ is compensated, to within a few percent, by the tails of the Gaussians at the adjoining angles.

If any other distribution, $f(Z)$, is desired, one simply multiplies the dwell times in (5) by the value of the desired dopant distribution, $f(R_p \cos\theta)$

$$t(\theta) = \frac{C_o R_p}{\phi} f(R_p \cos\theta) \frac{\cos(\theta - \delta/2) - \cos(\theta + \delta/2)}{\cos\theta} \quad . \tag{7}$$

For example, suppose it is desired to put a "ramp" dopant distribution in some material from 0.25 μm to 1.0 μm, Fig. 2.

$$\text{Dopant atoms/cm}^3 = \begin{cases} 0 & Z < 0.25\ \mu m \\ \frac{10^{21}}{3}(4Z-1) & 0.25\ \mu m < Z < 1.0\ \mu m \\ 0 & Z > 1.0\ \mu m \quad . \end{cases} \tag{8}$$

If $R_p = 1.0$ μm, then the dwell times are calculated using (7) with $C_o = 1.0$ and

$$f(R_p \cos\theta) = \frac{10^{21}\ \text{atoms/cm}^3}{3} (4\cos\theta - 1) \quad . \tag{9}$$

The distributions achievable are somewhat limited by ΔR_p in that very rapid changes in the desired dopant concentration will be rounded by the finite width of the Gaussians.

3. Experimental Method

The computer-controlled rocking mount and its associated hardware and software are described in subsections 3.1 and 3.2 respectively.

3.1 Apparatus/Equipment

The experimental set-up consists of a DEC LSI-11/23 microcomputer, a stepping motor and its control circuitry and an encoder wheel and sensors, see Fig. 3. The sample holder, Fig. 3a, and the sample, Fig. 3b, are the only components that are in the vacuum system. The sample can be mounted with the axis of rotation on its front surface. The power deposited in the sample by the incident beam is removed by conduction through a flexible copper braid, Fig. 3c, which is connected to an oil-cooled copper block, Fig. 3d. The sample is surrounded by a liquid nitrogen cooled copper tube[2], Fig. 3e. The gas pressure at the sample can be measured with an ionization gauge, which is not shown. The gas pressure is typically 2×10^{-7} torr.

The stepping motor/encoder, Fig. 3f, h, are coupled to the sample by a Ferrofluidics Corporation ferrofluidic feedthrough, Fig. 3g. The stepping motor/encoder assembly are electrically isolated from the sample by alumina insulators, Fig. 3i. The sample is positively biased with batteries to suppress secondary electrons so true beam currents can be measured during an implant.

An Eastern Air Devices "Incro Step" stepping motor moves the sample between 0° and 90° in 1.8° increments. An encoder verifies the sample's rotation over the same range. The encoder consists of a wheel with slots machined in it every 18°. The angular position sensors, Fig. 3j, consist of light emitting diodes (LED) and light sensitive transistors mounted as a

[2]The cooled copper tube is used in order to minimize the deposition of hydrocarbons on the sample surface during an implantation.

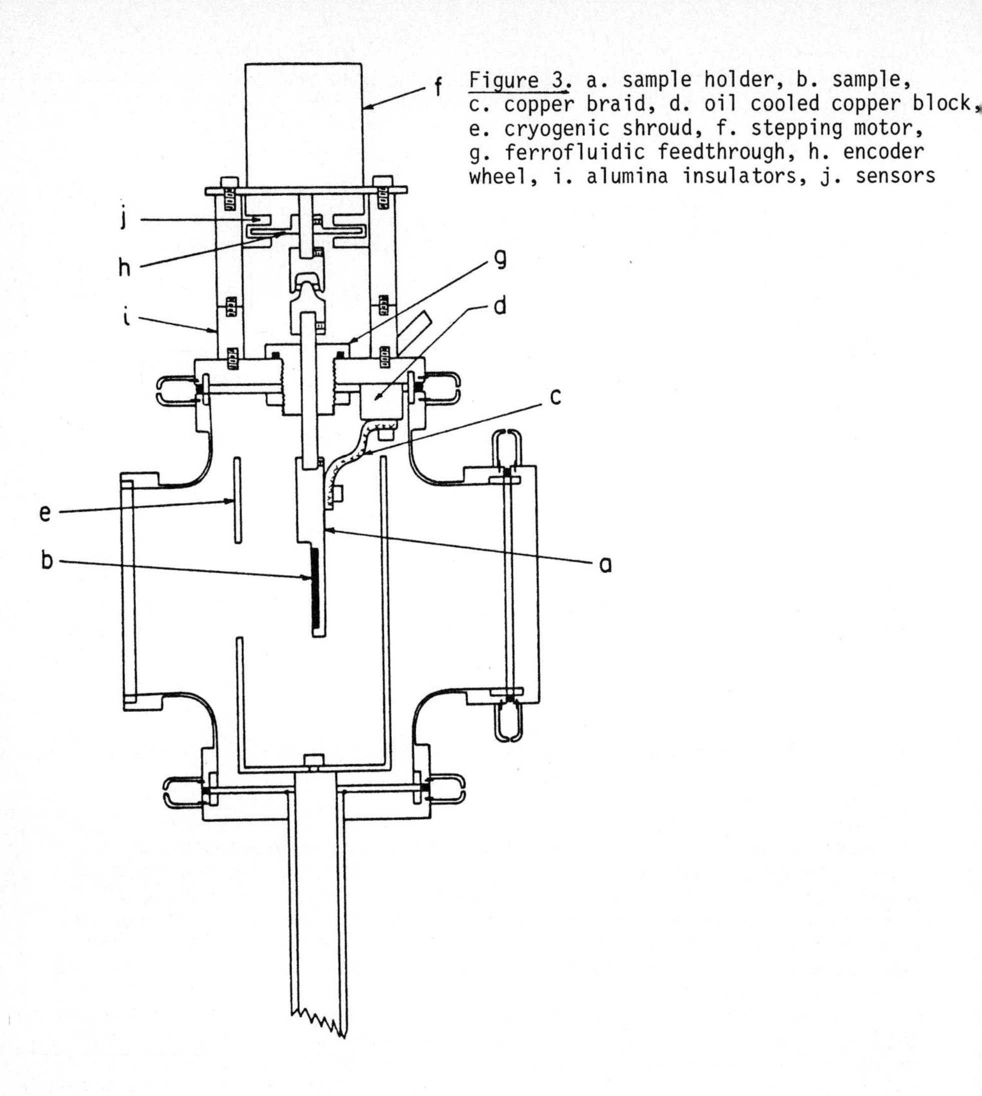

Figure 3. a. sample holder, b. sample, c. copper braid, d. oil cooled copper block, e. cryogenic shroud, f. stepping motor, g. ferrofluidic feedthrough, h. encoder wheel, i. alumina insulators, j. sensors

unit in a "U" shape. As the wheel rotates, periodically a slot in the disk moves in line with the sensor allowing light from the LED to be received by the light sensitive transistor. This sends a pulse to the computer, which is used by the software to check the samples angular position, see Fig. 4 and section 3.2. Two LED/sensor units are mounted, one at 0° and the other at 60°, since these angles are commonly used as the ends of the rocking range.

A DEC DRV11 parallel interface with both input and output capabilities allows communication between the LSI-11/23 microcomputer and the stepping motor/encoder assembly, Fig. 4. One of the outputs of the interface sends pulses to the stepping motor control to rotate the sample in a clockwise direction and another output is used to rotate the sample in a counter-clockwise direction. Two of the inputs to the interface are used to receive pulses from the light sensitive transistors of the encoders.

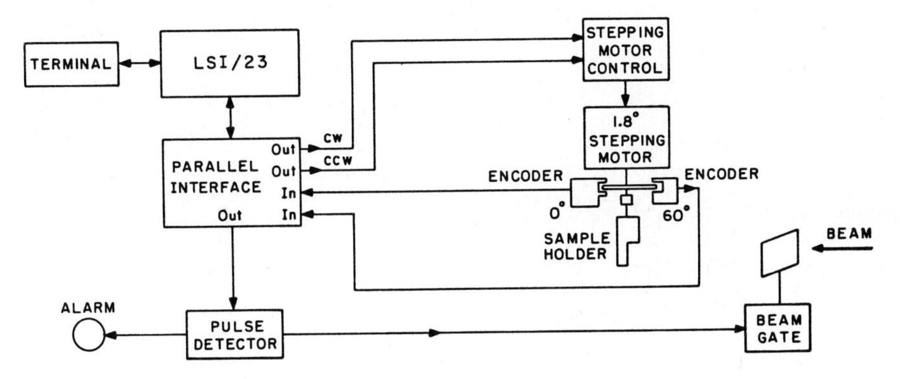

Figure 4. Stepping Motor and Control Electronics

To prevent the actual fluence Ψ from exceeding the desired fluence Ψ_0 in the event of a computer or a mechanical malfunction, an alarm system is incorporated in the design. The computer is programmed to send a pulse, via a third output of the DRV11, to a detector circuit every 0.5 ms. If a pulse is not received from the computer within a fixed time, an alarm sounds and a gate is interposed which prevents the ion beam from impinging on the sample.

3.2 Computer Programs

Two computer programs have been written for the operation of the sample rocker system. Both programs are in standard Fortran.[3]

The first program controls the rotation of the sample during an implant. The dwell times at each angle are controlled either by a software timing loop or by a beam current integrator utilizing a DEC ADV11-A analog to digital converter. If the software timing loop is used, the sample is rocked over the required range of angles many times to smooth out any fluctuations in the ion beam current. The program monitors the encoder system to ensure that the sample is rotating correctly.

A second program calculates the dwell times required to produce the desired dopant depth distribution in a given sample. The program accepts as input the maximum angle to which the sample will be rotated and the range information: R_p, $\Delta R_p^{\parallel}$, $\Delta R_p^{\perp}$; for the required ion energy of the dopant ion into the sample material. The dwell times are calculated using equation (7). The dopant concentration at depth Z' from the surface[4] is obtained by numerically summing the dopant atoms implanted from each Gaussian, whose mean is $R_p \cos\theta$ and standard deviation is ΔR_p (6), into a layer extending from Z' to Z' + ΔZ'. The dopant concentration is calculated for $0 < Z' < 1.25\ R_p$ in steps, $\Delta Z'$, as fine as $5 \times 10^{-4}\ R_p$. For example, a calculation summing 34 Gaussian distributions using steps of $5 \times 10^{-4}\ R_p$ requires approximately 1 hour. This time can be greatly reduced, with no loss of detail, by using coarser steps. The theoretical dopant distribution is plotted on a Houston Instruments DP-10 incremental plotter.

---

[3]Flow charts for the computer programs may be obtained from the authors upon request.

[4]Z' and ΔZ' are similar to Z and ΔZ except that Z' and ΔZ' are not related to an implant angle the way Z and ΔZ (1) are.

4. Discussion

The principle of operation of the rocker can best be elucidated by an example. Suppose a silicon sample is required to have a constant concentration of C_0 nitrogen atoms/cm^3 from a depth of 1.0 μm to 2.0 μm. This can be achieved by using a 1.1 MeV nitrogen beam, $R_p \sim 2.0$ μm,[5] and rocking the sample between the angles of 0° and 60°. In principle, the maximum angle for rocking is 90°, however, owing to the required relationship between ΔR_p and ΔZ explained in section 2, 80° is the practical upper limit. If the desired dopant distribution is wider than that imposed by this limit, namely 0.83 R_p, further implants at different energies will be required. The value of $R_p^{\parallel}$ for 1.1 MeV nitrogen into silicon is 0.18 μm,[5] and while the value for $\Delta R_p^{\perp}$ is not as well known as the value of $\Delta R_p^{\parallel}$, we expect $\Delta R_p^{\perp}$ to be of the same order of magnitude as $\Delta R_p^{\parallel}$. One expects $\Delta R_p^{\perp}$ to be somewhat larger than $\Delta R_p^{\parallel}$ for light implants into a heavy matrix and vice versa [5]. This hypothetical implant is illustrated in Fig. 5a-c where the theoretical dopant distributions are shown assuming $R_p^{\perp} = 2\ R_p^{\parallel}$, $R_p^{\perp} = R_p^{\parallel}$, and $R_p^{\perp} = 1/2\ R_p^{\parallel}$, respectively.

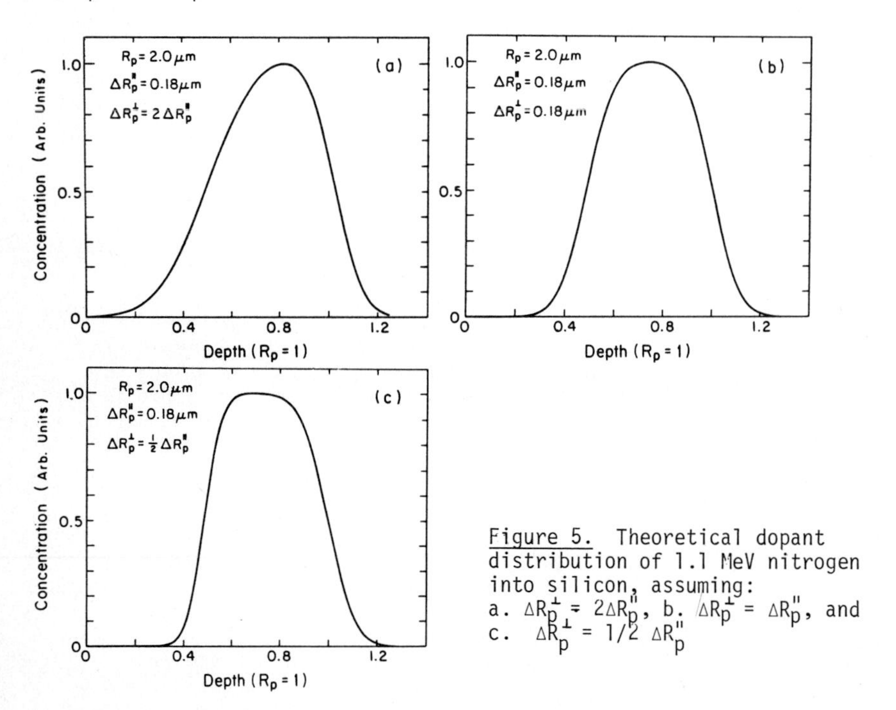

Figure 5. Theoretical dopant distribution of 1.1 MeV nitrogen into silicon, assuming: a. $\Delta R_p^{\perp} = 2\Delta R_p^{\parallel}$, b. $\Delta R_p^{\perp} = \Delta R_p^{\parallel}$, and c. $\Delta R_p^{\perp} = 1/2\ \Delta R_p^{\parallel}$

5. Conclusions/Summary

A technique for implanting a wide range of dopant distributions in solids has been described. The dwell time at each angle has been calculated for a uniform dopant distribution implanted in angular steps of 1.8°. The dwell times for any other desired distribution can be obtained from the uniform

---

[5]From EDEP-1 code of Manning and Mueller[4].

concentration dwell times by multiplying them by the desired ratio of the concentrations at each depth.

The apparatus consists of a sample mount, a stepping motor to rotate the sample, and an encoder to verify the sample rotation. The sample is heat-sinked and is surrounded by a liquid nitrogen cooled shield. Computer programs are written in standard Fortran. They are used to calculate the dwell times and to drive the stepping motor in the required manner during an implant. This rocking technique is useful for producing a wide variety of dopant profiles.

References

1. J.H. Chang, W.J. Choyke, and N.J. Doyle: These Proceedings

2. J.H. Worth: Proc. Uses of Cyclotrons in Chemistry, Metallurgy and Biology (Butterworths, London, 1969) p. 283

3. S. Furukawa and H. Matsumura: Appl. Phys. Lett. 22(1973) No. 2,p. 97

4. I. Manning and G.P. Mueller: Computer Physics Communications 7, (1974) 85

5. S. Furukawa, H. Matsumura, and H. Ishiwara: Jap. J. Appl. Phys. 11 (1972) No. 3, P. 134

Wafer Cooling and Photoresist Masking Problems in Ion Implantation

T.C. Smith

Motorola MOS Group/Advanced Product R&D Labs, Mesa, AZ 85202, USA

Abstract

A review of wafer cooling considerations in ion implantation systems is given, with emphasis on figures of merit for the various schemes. Estimates of maximum wafer temperature are determined for practical cases of interest, where negligible heat transfer, radiation cooling, or conduction cooling takes place. Modeled and measured wafer temperatures are presented for both one wafer at a time X-Y scanning and large batch pre-dep systems. Problems with the use of photoresist masking at high dose levels and high beam powers include degradation of photoresist, outgassing in the implanter, and difficulty in stripping ion implanted photoresist. A simple model for photoresist damage relates some of these effects to the implant parameters (ion, energy and dose) through the width of a carbonized region which is formed as a result of damage to the photoresist.

1. Introduction

In semiconductor device fabrication, one of the unique advantages of ion implantation as a "low temperature" process is the use of photoresist as a masking medium for selective doping. Particularly at high dose levels and high beam powers, wafer temperatures can be encountered which are high enough to cause flow or severe degradation of the photoresist. The basic factors related to heating and cooling of wafers in different types of implantation systems will be reviewed. Consideration of limits and figures of merit is stressed. Practical examples of modeled and measured wafer temperatures will be given in this overview.

The characteristics of photoresist of both positive and negative types are discussed, along with various schemes of pre-treating photoresist coated wafers prior to implantation. The emphasis is on positive photoresists, which are generally less tolerant of high temperatures than negative photoresists. Effects of outgassing in the end station of the ion implanter were investigated for B, P and As ions at energies from 40 to 160 keV in the dose range from 10^{12} to 10^{16} ions per square cm. Results of residual gas analysis of the outgassing products for typical positive and negative resists are summarized. The effect of high beamline pressure upon dose accuracy and uniformity are discussed.

The "difficulty of resist strip" following the implant is related to the implant parameters by means of a simple model proposed for the process of photoresist damage. This same damage model explains the evolution of gas from the photoresist as well as the change in thickness and optical density of the photoresist.

2. Wafer Cooling Considerations

Ion implantation applications in semiconductor processing encompass the range of doses from about 10^{11} to 10^{16} ions per square centimeter and energies from about 10 to 200 kilo-electron-volts. These facts, combined with the wide range of implantation systems employed by different users, mean that their experience can be quite varied. Wafer heating can sometimes lead to serious problems with regard to its effect upon resulting electrical characteristics by self-annealing in the substrate [1]. Localized substrate heating produces enhanced etching of implanted silicon nitride films [2]. High wafer temperatures are a special concern when using photoresist masking to achieve selective doping. Schemes which provide cooling of wafers have been incorporated in the evolution of ion implantation equipment; various approaches will be discussed below. A brief review of the basic power balance is helpful in evaluating the different factors in perspective.

The basic power balance, in terms of power per unit area, is given by Eq. (1) below. The power flux into the wafer equals the rate at which energy is stored per unit area plus the power flux conducted and radiated away from the wafer to its surroundings. The instantaneous power density within the beam spot can be very high — up to 500 W/cm^2 in some implanters. By scanning the beam over large areas, the power density is reduced to manageable levels. The power in the incident beam is the arrival rate of ions times the energy per ion. This is equivalent to beam current times the voltage through which the ions have been accelerated. The effective power density is then the beam power divided by scan area.

$$\left(\frac{P}{A}\right)' = (\rho C th_w)\frac{dT_w}{dt} + \left(\frac{H}{A}\right)(T_w - T_{oc}) + 2\sigma\varepsilon\,(T_w^4 - T_{or}^4) \qquad (1)$$

The first term on the right side of Eq. (1) is the rate at which energy is stored per unit area, ρ is the density of the wafer, C its specific heat, and $(th)_w$ the thickness of the wafer. The last factor is rate of change of wafer temperature. The second term represents the power flux conducted from the wafer to a cooled surface at temperature T_{OC}. The factor (H/A) is a measure of the net thermal conductivity of the materials and interfaces which provide conductive heat flow to a cooled surface. The third term on the right corresponds to the power flux rejected from the wafer by black body radiation. Here, σ is the Stefan-Boltzmann constant, ε is the effective emissivity of the wafer and its surroundings, and the factor of 2 results from the simple assumption that the radiating area is twice the area of the wafer, since both sides radiate.

Detailed solutions of the power balance equation are not always necessary. Much information can be gained by estimating the limiting values of wafer temperature which would be reached in various practical situations. The results of detailed calculations and wafer temperature measurements which verify the validity of this basic treatment have been reported by Bruel et al [3] and Parry [4] for the case of radiative cooling only. King and Rose [5] treated the case of conductive cooling only, using gas behind the wafer as the conductive heat transfer medium. For detailed calculations of non-limiting conditions, it is probably easier, as pointed out by Parry, to use the equation in differential form by iterative calculations of temperature differentials, ΔT, over time increments, Δt, with wafer temperature summed from its initial value to T(t). The analytical solutions to this equation are unwieldy and make it difficult to envision the effect of changing various parameters.

Figure 1 shows the typical characteristics of wafer temperature versus implanting time for several cases of interest. In all instances, the initial rate of rise of wafer

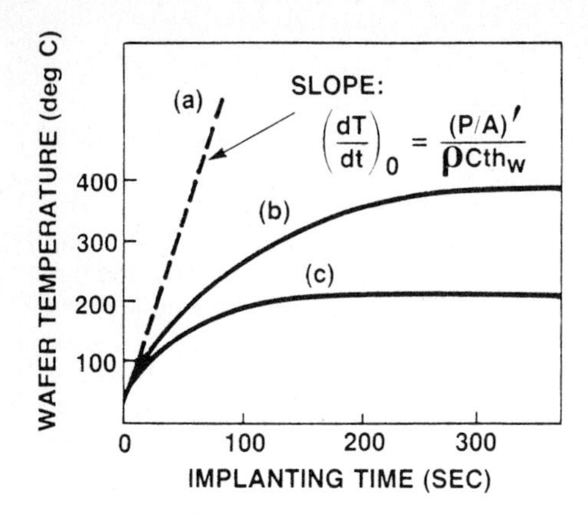

FIGURE 1: TYPICAL CHARACTERISTICS OF WAFER TEMPERATURE versus TIME FOR THREE CASES OF INTEREST.

temperature is the effective power density divided by the heat capacity per unit area. The value of (ρ C th_w) for a 0.5 mm thick silicon wafer is 84 milli-joule per (cm^2, deg). The "time constant", τ, for heating (and cooling) is approximated as the equilibrium temperature difference divided by the initial rate of change of temperature. This time constant is a function of heat capacity and (H/A) for conductive cooling and depends upon (P/A) and ε in the case of radiative cooling.

The limiting values of wafer temperature reached in different situations can be readily estimated if various figures of merit are known or can be reasonably estimated. It is worth noting that the macroscopic wafer temperature is determined by the ion energy, beam current, scan area, dose, etc., but is independent of the ion species being implanted. The resulting maximum wafer temperature can then be compared to the limits imposed by the application being considered and the implanter set up parameters can be readjusted if appropriate. Practical cases of interest are:

(a) No heat transfer (energy stored in wafer)
(b) Radiation only (radiation limited temperature)
(c) Conduction only (conduction limited temperature)

In the latter two cases, the time constant for the applicable heat transfer mechanism should be compared to the actual implanting time, which is determined by the dose and beam current.

Figure 2 shows the calculated temperature rise of a 0.5 mm thick silicon wafer as a function of ion dose and energy when no heat transfer occurs. It can be seen that if photoresist masking were contemplated, doses below 10^{14} ions/cm^2 could probably be tolerated at any energy up to 400 keV. If a certain photoresist had a temperature tolerance of 150°C, a wide range of implant conditions could be specified where this temperature would not be exceeded. Figure 3 shows the theoretical radiation limited temperature as a function of effective power density and effective emissivity. In practical situations, this latter figure of merit may range from 0.20 to 0.35. It can be seen that significant power densities can be rejected only at high temperature levels. Figure 4 shows the computed steady state wafer temperature as a function of effective power density in the conductive cooling case. The inverse of the slope of these lines is (H/A), the most important figure of merit for this instance. High values of (H/A) are obviously desirable when dealing with photoresist masking at high power densities, as when implanting one wafer at a time.

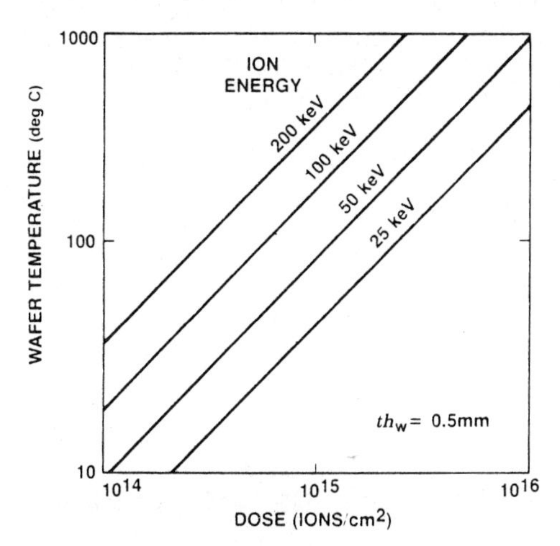

FIGURE 2: WAFER TEMPERATURE RISE versus DOSE AT SEVERAL ENERGIES WITH NO HEAT TRANSFER.

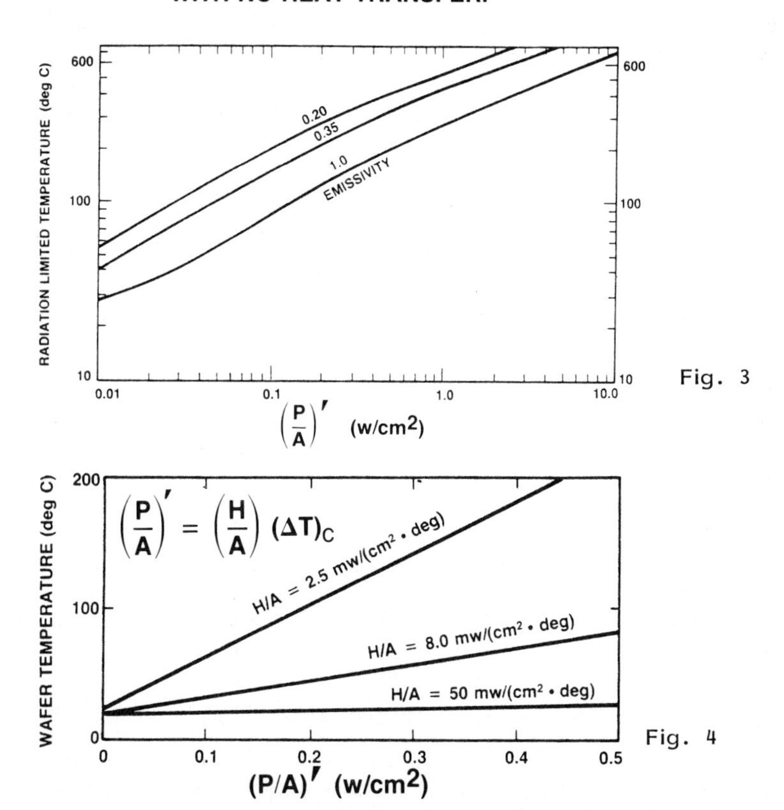

FIGURE 3: RADIATION LIMITED WAFER TEMPERATURE versus EFFECTIVE POWER DENSITY IN RADIATION COOLING CASE

FIGURE 4: STEADY STATE WAFER TEMPERATURE versus EFFECTIVE POWER DENSITY IN CONDUCTION COOLING CASE.

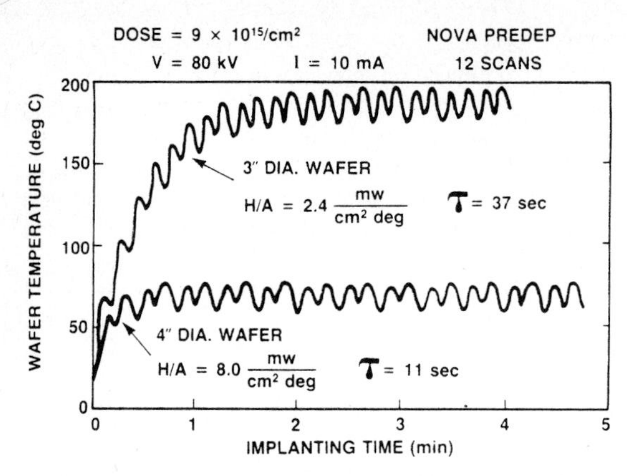

FIGURE 5: MODELED WAFER TEMPERATURE versus IMPLANTING TIME FOR A PRE-DEP IMPLANTER.

The result of a detailed calculation of wafer temperature versus implanting time is shown in Fig. 5 for a pre-dep type implanter. The stated combinations of implanting parameters were employed in actual tests. In the system modeled here, the wafer is clamped onto a disk which spins at high speed and traverses a stationary beam spot. The calculation shows that the wafer temperature would be expected to oscillate about an equilibrium value which is somewhat below the temperature estimated by using the simple limiting form of Eq. (1), with power in equal to power conducted away only. The upper curve shows the effects of higher effective power density, (476 mW/cm^2) and low (H/A), characteristic of a spring loaded clamp with two point wafer hold-down. In the lower curve, the effective power density is lower (407 mW/cm^2), because the scan area is larger, and the value of (H/A) is higher, characteristic of a full-ring circumferential clamp [6].

Wafer temperatures have been measured in situ by various experimenters using attached thermocouples, resistance thermometers, or infrared pyrometers [3, 4, 5]. In this work, adhesive temperature recording labels [7] attached to the backs of the wafers, were the most practical method of measuring the maximum temperature as a function of implanter operating conditions. As shown in Fig. 6a, the temperature tabs turn irreversibly black when the indicated temperature is exceeded. The 1 cm wide by 3 cm long labels fit into the slot for tweezer access under the pedestal on the disk of the pre-dep implanter and did not interfere with the operation of the vacuum locks of the end station of the X-Y scanning implanter.

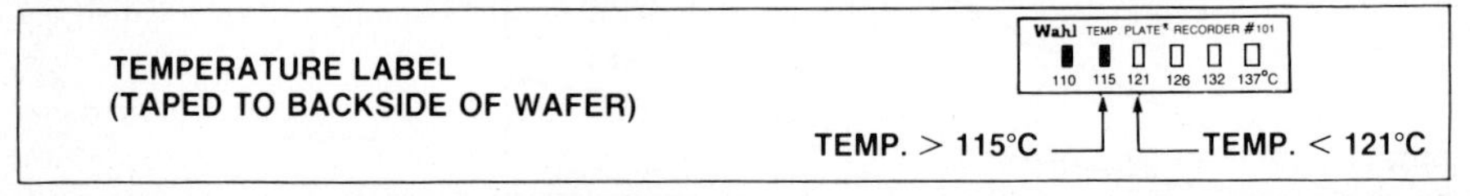

FIGURE 6A: EXAMPLE OF TEMPERATURE RECORDING LABEL

When using these temperature recorders on bare wafers in the X-Y scanning implanter, it was noted that there were pressure bursts which correlated to the point in time at which the indicator tabs turned black. By recording the pressure bursts as indicated by the ionization guage on the end station vacuum system, wafer temperature as a function of time can be inferred. (See Fig. 6b). This fact permits us to plot temperature versus time for several different effective power densities as shown in Fig. 7. In this X-Y scanning system, radiation is the only means of rejecting heat. For the implant conditions given, the expected final wafer temperature, T_f, without heat loss is 203°C and the estimated radiation limited temperature, T_r, for the lowest power density is 121°C. At the two higher power densities, the maximum temperatures reached are less than the radiation limited temperature because the implant is terminated before that limit is reached.

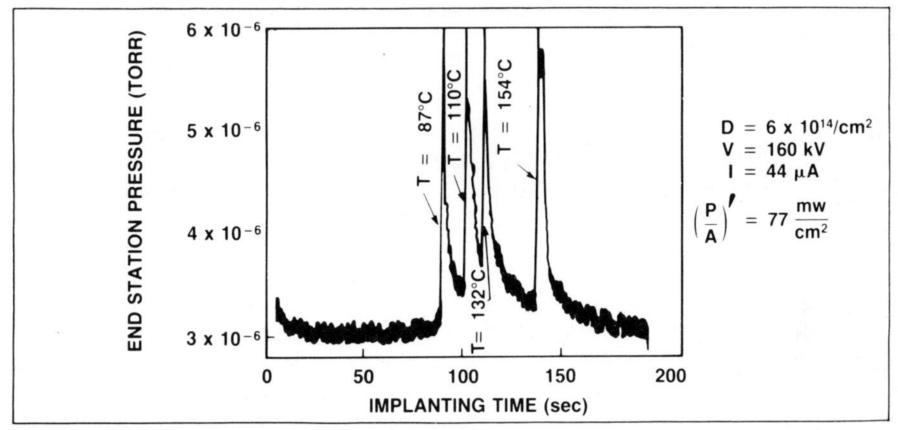

FIGURE 6B: END STATION PRESSURE BURSTS versus IMPLANTING TIME, GIVING T(t).

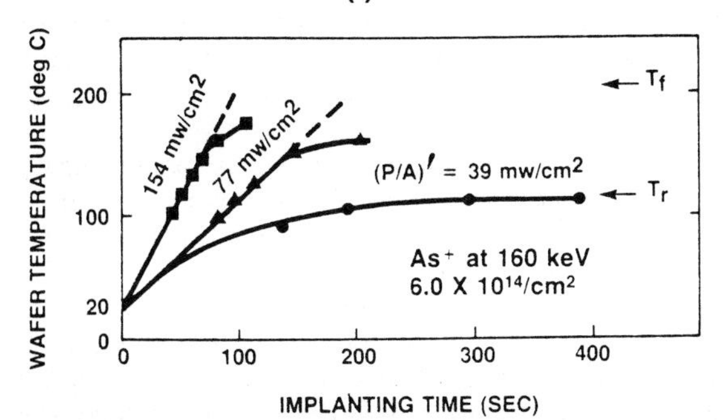

FIGURE 7: MEASURED TEMPERATURE versus IMPLANTING TIME FOR VARIOUS EFFECTIVE POWER DENSITIES.

An example of modeled and measured maximum temperatures for typical parameters in a pre-dep type system is shown in Fig. 8. The solid curves correspond to the calculated maximum temperature for runs of the same dose and beam power made with a different number of scans. Each of the two disks discussed in connection with Fig. 5 were used in these experiments. The dose processor adjusts the speed of traversal of the disk through the beam to be directly proportional to the preset number of scans. The amplitude of the temperature oscillations increases as the number of scans is reduced. The expected increase in maximum recorded wafer temperature is verified by the experimental data. Intuitively, it seems appropriate that lower temper-

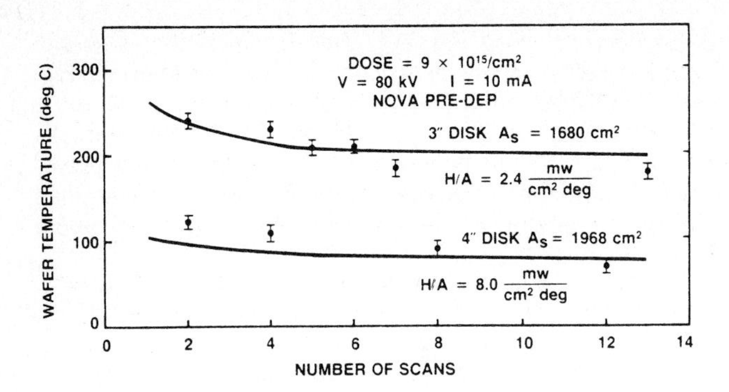

FIGURE 8: MODELED VALUES (SOLID CURVE) AND MEASURED DATA POINTS FOR MAXIMUM WAFER TEMPERATURE versus NUMBER OF SCANS IN PRE-DEP IMPLANTER.

atures are reached when the disk traverses as fast as possible in the radial scanning direction.

The schemes for cooling wafers are as varied as the ion implantation systems which use them, and are covered in more detail elsewhere. Some amount of radiation cooling takes place in all systems, but in practice, temperatures can only be kept low by using large scan areas or limiting the beam power. The interior surfaces adjacent to the wafer may be treated to increase the effective emissivity. In conduction cooling, the wafer is clamped to a cooled plate with heat conducted through a pliable proprietary rubber compound or through gas admitted behind the wafer. Sometimes the incident energy is transferred from the wafer and is stored in a massive heat sink, which in turn is cooled down outside the implanter.

Finally, with regard to wafer cooling capabilities, the interrelationships of various system parameters must be considered. In some large batch systems, where wafers are mounted on a disk or carousel, the fast and slow scanning motions through a stationary beam may be constrained by certain limitations. Not all possible combinations of set-up parameters are allowable.

Ordinarily, the implantation step is simply specified by the ion, energy and dose required for a certain processing application. The incident beam current, involved in the power density, establishes the doping rate, which in turn determines the implanting time. The throughput of the system, (wafers per hour), is determined by implanting time plus the cycle time for venting, unloading, loading, pumping, etc. If beam current must be limited due to thermal considerations, the maximum throughput of the system will not be realized.

3. Photoresist Masking Problems

The use of photoresist (P.R.) to mask implants may lead to some problems, before, during or after the implant step itself. In spite of this, in many cases it is easier to implement P.R. masking than alternative masking methods. The use of thick oxide or nitride layers may require additional deposited films which in turn require P.R. patterning anyway. Anomalous etching characteristics may be encountered after these films are implanted [2]. Problems are sometimes experienced in preserving the P.R. integrity throughout the implant without flowing, blistering, cracking, or other degradation. Outgassing in the end station of the implanter is a concern to be dealt with.

As with other layers, the most difficult implant to mask is boron at high energies. The masking effectiveness of a given P.R. can be estimated if both the projected range, Rp, and straggle, Δ Rp, are known at the energy required for the ion of interest [8]. A conservative "rule of thumb" which requires the thickness of the masking P.R., to be greater than [Rp + 5(Δ Rp)] insures that less than one part per million of the implanted dose will penetrate through the P.R. into the "masked" region. Estimates of Rp and Δ Rp can be made, since Johnson, Gibbons & Mylroie [9] list only AZ111 positive P.R., or suitable tests can be made to insure that the masking is adequate.

The detailed composition of P.R. formulations are regarded as proprietary, but they have certain characteristics in common and are processed in a similar manner [10]. Photoresists consist of a film-forming resin in a solvent system with photosensitizers and additives incorporated for improved performance. In negative-acting P.R., unsaturated polymers are cross-linked by exposure, rendering them insoluble to developer. In positive-acting P.R., the ratio of sensitizer to resin is much higher and react with absorbed radiation to change the solubility of the coating.

As with wafer cooling, the perspectives of those using P.R. masking techniques may vary. In addition to the various schemes for implanting and cooling wafers, different formulations of photoresists exhibit varying degrees of temperature tolerance, resistance to degradation and outgassing characteristics. Special treatments may be used prior to implanting and special techniques may be used to strip implanted P.R. The implant step should be considered as part of a process flow for the P.R., which is very sensitive to thermal effects to begin with [11]. Some trends observed can be generalized however, for certain classes of photoresists or P.R. stripping systems. In the experimental studies discussed below, the independent variables investigated were the implanter parameters, different photoresists, and various pre-treatments.

A simple model for the damage process applicable to P.R. is developed below. The principal factor of interest, the width of the carbonized layer, is determined by the implant parameters of ion, energy, and dose. The following dependent variables are related to the width of the carbonized layer: the total gas evolved, the change in optical density of the damaged P.R., its thickness change, and also the "difficulty of resist strip." In practice, this last item is difficult to quantify.

An experimental study of photoresist coated wafers was made to sort out the various factors and to quantify the P.R. problems as they relate to implanter parameters, particularly wafer temperature effects. The independent variables of the initial experimental matrix are given in Table 1. Arsenic implants with the same energy density were performed in two different systems at a variety of effective power densities, giving five different maximum temperatures. Six photoresist coated wafers were run in each of six implanter set-ups. Positive P.R.s were used because of their lower temperature tolerance. Several resists were given the CF_4 plasma resist image stabilization treatment (PRIST), which is said to improve the temperature tolerance of positive P.R [12]. Additional wafers were implanted later to further investigate various effects.

An overview of the initial results showed that the previous modeling of wafer temperature was verified. In addition, for the six resists used, similar results were obtained with regard to the total gas evolved, the difficulty of resist strip, and the P.R. thickness decrease. The results were the same, within $\pm$10%, and fell into two groups according to the energy and dose of the implant. This was true regardless of the machine type, the effective power density and therefore the maximum wafer temperature reached.

TABLE 1: INITIAL EXPERIMENTAL MATRIX/ION IMPLANTED PHOTORESIST

TWO IMPLANTERS:
1) X–Y SCANNING, EXTRION CF-3000, *w*/RADIATION COOLING
2) PRE-DEP, NOVA NV-10, *w*/CONDUCTION COOLING

SIX As^+ IMPLANTS: (ALL WITH THE SAME ENERGY DENSITY)

ENERGY (keV)	DOSE (IONS/cm^2)	(P/A)′ (mw/cm^2)	Tmax (deg C)	MACHINE TYPE
80	1.2×10^{15}	128	73	PRE-DEP
80	1.2×10^{15}	19	80	X–Y
80	1.2×10^{15}	39	121	X–Y
160	6.0×10^{14}	39	121	X–Y
160	6.0×10^{14}	77	154	X–Y
160	6.0×10^{14}	154	170	X–Y

SIX POSITIVE PHOTORESISTS: (6 WAFERS EACH)

TYPE (I.D.)	THICKNESS (MICRON)	PRE-TREATMENT BEFORE IMPLANT
HUNT HPR 204	1.0	PRIST
HUNT HPR 204	1.0	105°C VAC BAKE
HUNT HPR 206	2.1	PRIST
HUNT HPR 206	2.1	105°C VAC BAKE
KODAK K820	1.9	105°C VAC BAKE
MAC DERMID PR74	1.7	105°C VAC BAKE

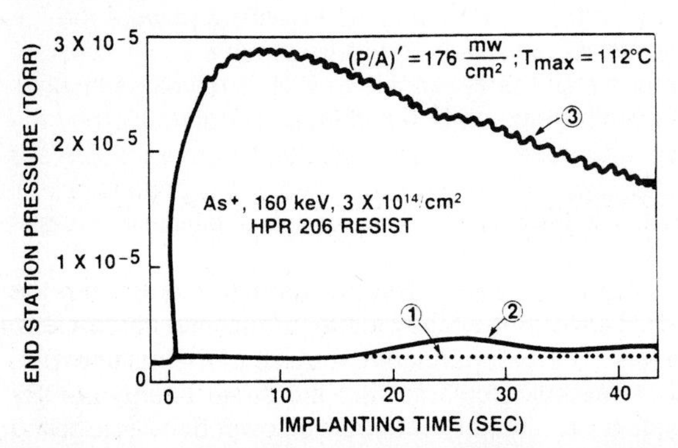

FIGURE 9: P.R. OUTGASSING: END STATION PRESSURE versus IMPLANTING TIME FOR THREE DIFFERENT WAFERS.

Some observations of outgassing are shown in Fig. 9, where end station pressure is plotted against implanting time for three different 100 mm diameter wafers. A bare wafer without P.R. shows a pressure rise which is slightly above base vacuum. For a P.R. coated wafer with the P.R. facing the platen, away from the incident beam, a slight pressure rise is seen at the point where the wafer temperature is about 75°C. When the P.R. coated side faces the beam, a large pressure rise is observed and then the end station pressure begins to decrease. The ripple in the recorded pressure corresponds to the reciprocating motion of the displacers of the cryogenic pump on the end station.

It was noted that if the beam were interrupted, the pressure recovered to base vacuum in a few seconds, and would rise to the same level when the beam was switched back onto the wafer. Since the wafer temperature cannot change this abruptly, this implies that the outgassing is not caused by thermal effects, but is caused by the interaction of the ions with the P.R. Residual gas analysis of the outgassing products showed that the gas evolved from the positive P.R. used here, Hunt HPR 206, is about 90% hydrogen with 5% contributions from nitrogen and water vapor. These facts, in conjunction with some conclusions from the work of Okuyama et al [13], led to the development of a simple model for the P.R. damage which seems to explain these results. They concluded that high energy, high dose implantation changes the P.R. into a disordered carbonized layer, increasing its optical density, but they did not explain the dependence upon the implant parameters.

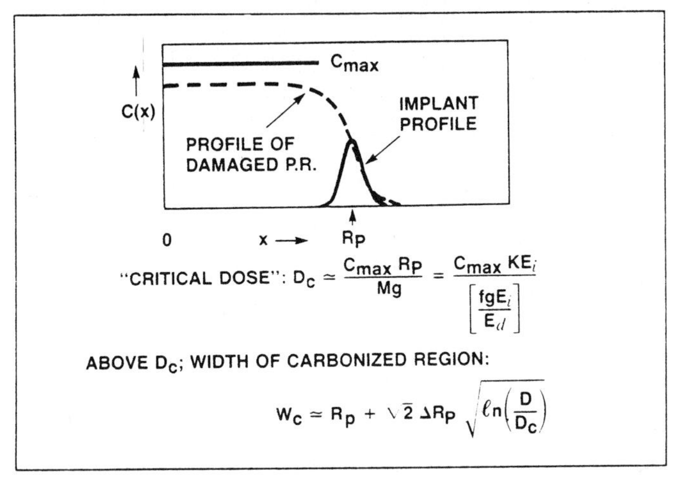

FIGURE 10: SCHEMATIC DIAGRAM OF IMPLANTED ION PROFILE AND DAMAGED P.R. PROFILE. (MODEL FOR D_C AND W_C)

Figure 10 shows a schematic representation of the implant profile of ions stopped in the P.R. along with the damage profile of the P.R. It seems reasonable that if the polymer is "carbonized," hydrogen and other gases evolve from the damaged P.R. One incident ion can cause the release of many gas molecules, so that a "gas multiplier," Mg, is taken to be some fraction, fg, of the incident energy, E_i, divided by an averge displacement energy, E_d, required to liberate gas. As increasingly larger doses are accumulated, the concentration of damaged P.R. increases until the original concentration of hydrogen is depleted and no more gas can be driven from the region from the outer surface to a depth of about Rp. This "critical dose" of the implant, Dc, can be estimated by the approximation given in Fig. 10.

At doses above the critical dose, one could estimate the width of the carbonized region, Wc, as the coordinate of the point at which the implanted ion concentration equals the concentration at the critical dose. Assuming the implant profile to be Gaussian, Wc is related to energy (through Rp and ΔRp) and to dose as stated in Fig. 10. Above Dc, the width of the carbonized layer is slowly varying with dose. Below Dc, fractional carbonization exists to a depth of about Rp. When this model is applied to the results reported by Okuyama et al, which were generally above the critical dose, some interesting results are obtained. The observed trends in optical density as a function of dose at constant energy and as a function of energy at constant dose are predicted by the expression for Wc. Remarkably close agreement is obtained if a few simple assumptions are made about a characteristic attenuation length for the light absorbed in the carbonized layer whose width is calculated using reasonable estimates of Dc, Rp and ΔRp.

The model explains the decrease in pressure as seen in Fig. 11, where pressure calculated from the time derivative of Wc is plotted along with the actual end station pressure. The calculation makes some assumptions about the hydrogen content of the P.R. and the system pumping speed. Assuming a composition similar to AZ111, with a simple formula of $C_8H_{12}O$, the quantity of hydrogen completely released from a one angstrom thickness of P.R. on a 100 mm diameter wafer is 9×10^{-4} Torr liter. For the implant shown, the critical dose was reached when the implant is about one tenth complete.

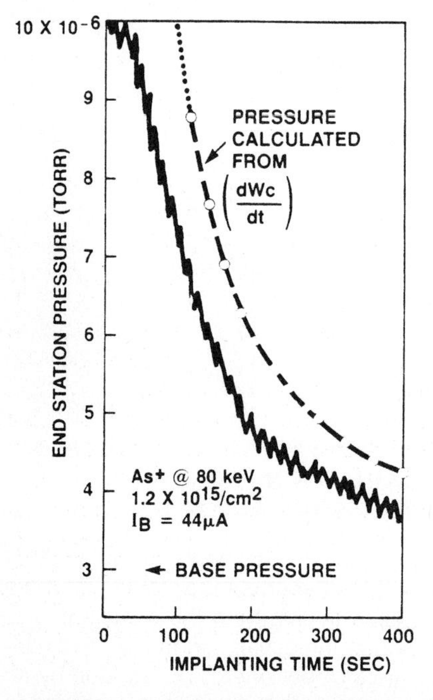

FIGURE 11: P.R. OUTGASSING: ACTUAL AND CALCULATED END STATION PRESSURE versus IMPLANTING TIME.

At low doses, below the critical dose, every incident ion causes the release of gas, so that the rate at which gas evolves depends upon the P.R. used, the fractional coverage of the wafer surface, the doping rate, and the ion energy. So, the pressure in the system is proportional to beam power density, but not because of heating. Figure 12 shows end station pressure versus As^+ ion beam current for several different energies. The values of the gas multiplier are shown on the curves. These steady-state pressures are achieved in about five seconds and will begin to decrease when the critical dose is reached.

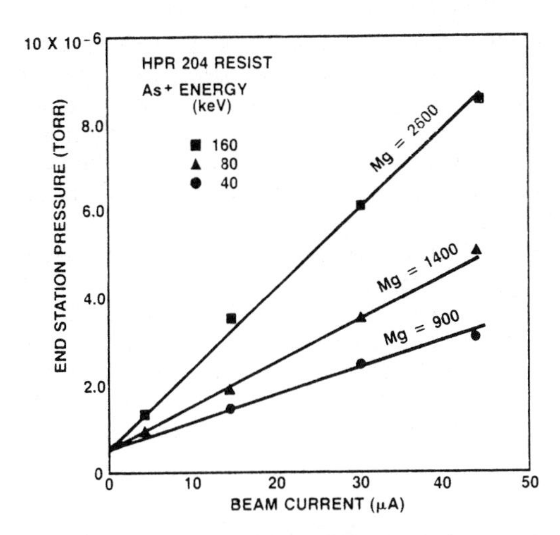

FIGURE 12: P.R. OUTGASSING: END STATION PRESSURE versus BEAM CURRENT FOR SEVERAL ION ENERGIES, AT LOW DOSE.

It was concluded that this model suggests the total quantity of gas evolved from the P.R. for a given implant should be a measure of the fractional carbonization below Dc and the width of carbonized region above Dc. Data on the quantity of gas evolved was obtained by recording end station pressure versus time and integrating the area under the curve. A problem arises with the calculated values, however. As the P.R. approaches a condition of being 100% carbonized to a certain depth, the implant profile is no longer determined by the Rp and ΔRp of virgin (undamaged) P.R. Perhaps the Rp and ΔRp characteristic of amorphous carbon should be used in the Wc calculation. Figure 13 shows the expected characteristic of the time integral of pressure for virgin AZ111 positive P.R. and for amorphous carbon plotted along with actual data for Hunt HPR 206 positive P.R.

With regard to outgassing, another conclusion of the P.R. damage model is that the critical dose for a given ion and P.R. should be relatively independent of energy. The critical dose is the break point between linear behavior and the $\sqrt{\ell n\ (D/Dc)}$ dependence at high doses. Since, to first order, both Rp and Mg can be taken to be proportional to energy, (i.e., Rp $=$ KE_i), the estimated Dc would be independent of energy. This is seen to be the case in Fig. 14 which shows data for the total quantity of gas evolved from HPR 206 for As^+ at various energies.

Similar results on outgassing have been obtained for other ions and other P.R. types. For example, when implanting boron at 160 keV into AZ1350, a critical dose in the low 10^{14} ions/cm^2 dose range is observed, as shown in Fig. 15. The change in optical density for this film is also plotted as a function of dose[1]. A correlation of these two measured parameters is expected above the critical dose since each is an indication of the width of the carbonized region. For doses above the break points, the correlation coefficient for a linear regression fit is 0.995.

[1]Assistance from Physics International Inc., San Leandro, Ca., is acknowledged for optical density data obtained using the IONSCAN system.

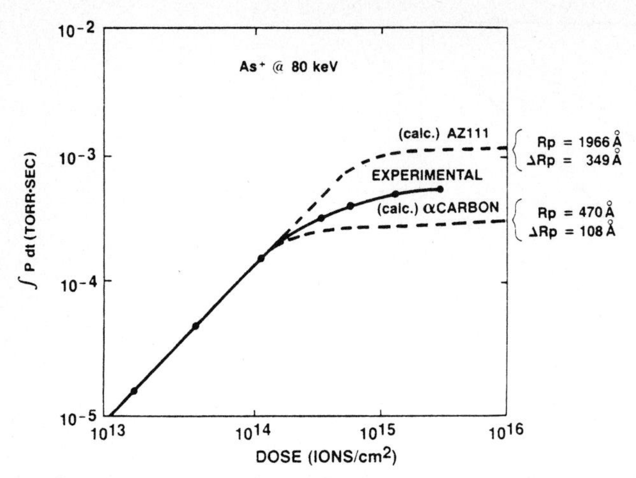

FIGURE 13: TIME INTEGRAL OF PRESSURE versus DOSE, (EXPERIMENTAL AND CALCULATED).

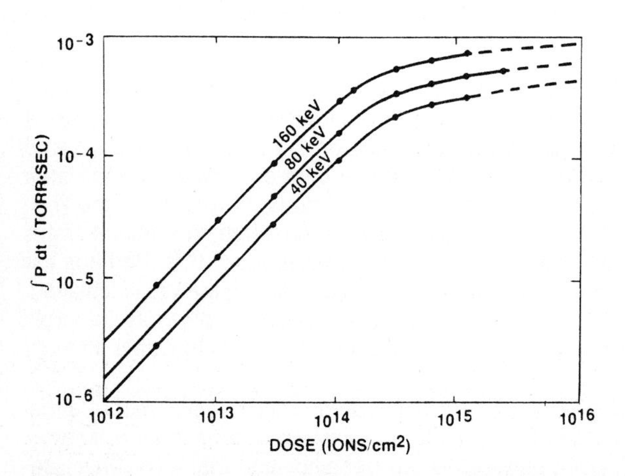

FIGURE 14: TIME INTEGRAL OF PRESSURE versus DOSE FOR ARSENIC AT VARIOUS ENERGIES INTO HPR 206 POSITIVE P.R.

In another series of implants, with doses varied over several orders of magnitude, a correlation was observed between the time integral of pressure and the decrease in P.R. thickness. The density of the damaged region changes from that of the solidified resin to that of amorphous carbon. Here again, the total quantity of gas evolved serves as a "tag" on the width of the damaged P.R. Estimates of the change in P.R. thickness are correct within the limits of our ability to measure it using surface profilometers. (i.e., within $\pm$ 300 angstroms).

Table 2 summarizes the effects of various pre-treatments [14] upon the outgassing for several As implants. The values of the time integral of pressure are normalized to the vacuum bake case as a reference. Other factors to consider are the preservation of the P.R. edge definition [15] and the cross-sectional profile as it is modifed by the pre-treatment in combination with the implant. Elliot [16] has discussed

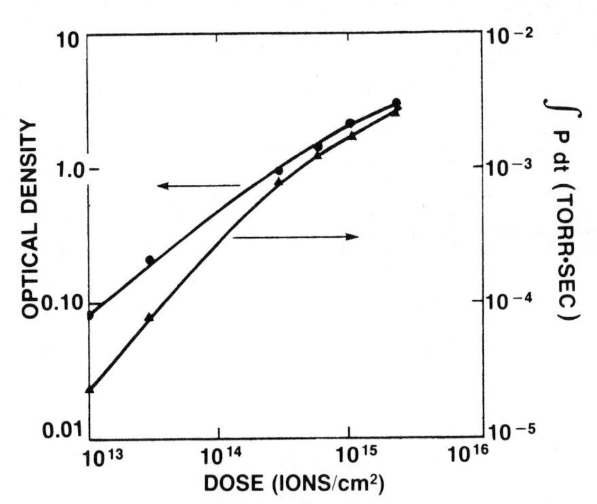

FIGURE 15: TIME INTEGRAL OF PRESSURE AND OPTICAL DENSITY versus DOSE FOR BORON AT 160 keV INTO AZ 1350 POSITIVE P.R.

TABLE 2: EFFECTS OF VARIOUS PRE-TREATMENTS UPON QUANTITY OF GAS EVOLVED

As^+ AT 160 keV INTO HPR 206 POSITIVE P.R.		
PRE-TREATMENT (BEFORE IMPLANT)	RELATIVE OUTGASSING	
	$D = 3 \times 10^{14}/cm^2$	$D = 6 \times 10^{14}/cm^2$
NO BAKE	1.05	1.45
105°C VAC BAKE	1.00 (REF.)	1.29
N_2 PLASMA	0.98	1.38
15 MIN. U.V.	1.10	1.53
30 MIN. U.V.	1.19	1.60

some aspects of this problem. Sometimes the treatment prior to the implant produces the very degradation which one is trying to avoid in the implanter. The time regime for the transient temperature in the implanter is quite different from that encountered in P.R. bake ovens. It is probably safe to say that if the wafer temperature is kept below the maximum temperature recommended by the P.R. supplier, the integrity of the P.R. will be preserved. Because of the wide range of P.R. types and process flows, it is advisable to take scanning electron microscope photos before and after the implant step to check the overall results.

The results of residual gas analysis of the products of outgassing seen in the implanter end station are summarized in Table 3. The two typical P.R.s are Hunt's HPR 206 positive resist and their HNR 120 negative resist. In all cases, the wafers were implanted to a dose of $6 \times 10^{14}/cm^2$ with arsenic at 160 keV. The most prominent peaks were noted from an initial spectrum obtained by repetitive scans. Then, identical wafers were run in sequence with the quadrupole mass analyzer tuned to a different major component each time. The relative percentages of the species listed were inferred from the time integral of the detector currents, corrected for ionization efficiencies. For these two resists, hydrogen is the predominant gas evolving from the damaged P.R. Certain components, such as nitrogen, exhibit a "burst" of about a factor of two in the first few seconds. Otherwise, all species monatonically decrease after rising to their maximum values when the implant is about one tenth complete, for this particular dose.

TABLE 3: SUMMARY OF RESIDUAL GAS ANALYZER RESULTS

ION: As+ ENERGY: 160 keV DOSE: 6 X $10^{14}/cm^2$		BEAM CURRENT: 88 μA MAXIMUM T_w: 170°C IMPLANT TIME: 100 SEC.	
PEAK $\left(\frac{m}{q}\right)$	PROBABLE SPECIE ASSIGNMENT	HPR 206 POSITIVE P.R. % TOTAL $\int I dt$	HNR 120 NEGATIVE P.R. % TOTAL $\int I dt$
1	H	2.7	2.3
2	H_2	87.8	75.6
12	C	0.8	1.1
14	N, CH_2	0.4	1.6
18	H_2O	4.3	1.5
26	CN, C_2H_2	0.4	9.8
28	N_2, CO, C_2H_4	3.6	8.1

The effects of high beamline pressures due to outgassing upon the indicated beam current (and therefore upon the dose accuracy and uniformity) may vary according to the type of implanter and its dose measuring scheme. In the experiments reported here, hydrogen gas was purposely injected into the end station of the X-Y scanning implanter and indicated beam currents decreased when the beam line pressure exceeded 5 x 10^{-6} Torr. The indicated end station pressure is about a factor of two higher. At high pressures, the wafer is being implanted with additional neutralized ions which are not electrically measured in the Faraday cup and instrumental errors can be produced by the motion of ions and electrons in electrostatic fields applied to suppress secondary electrons. Ryding [17] has observed that, with magnetic suppression of secondary electrons in a pre-dep system, the sensitivity of indicated beam current to system pressure is much reduced until 10^{-4} Torr is reached.

In this experiment, the sheet resistance decreases as shown in Fig. 16. The implant was uniform however, since the standard deviation of the measured sheet resistance was less than 0.7% in all cases. These effects should be evaluated since decisions about safe operating conditions depend upon specific applications. For example, in the case of the implant shown in Fig. 9, the pressure in the system is high only in the initial portion of the implant and the actual sheet resistance is at most 2% low, which may be tolerable.

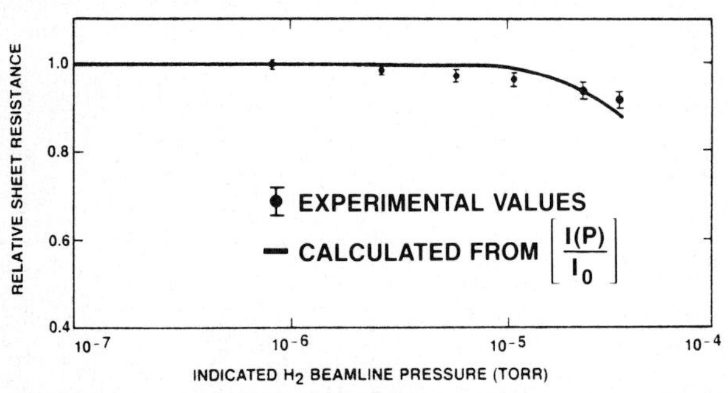

FIGURE 16: P.R. OUTGASSING: EFFECT OF HIGH BEAMLINE PRESSURE UPON SHEET RESISTANCE (THROUGH DOSE ERRORS).

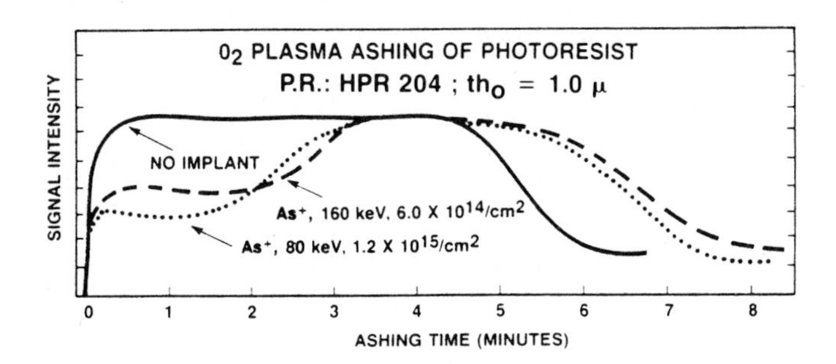

FIGURE 17: P.R. ASHING: INTENSITY OF END POINT DETECTOR SIGNAL versus ASHING TIME FOR NON-IMPLANTED AND IMPLANTED P.R. IN O_2 PLASMA SYSTEM.

Another consideration related to the P.R. damage model is the difficulty of resist strip. In an attempt to quantify this factor, some interesting results were obtained in a Tegal 700 single wafer etcher, running with pure oxygen gas in an ashing mode. Results typical of each group of P.R. used in the initial matrix of Table 1 are shown in Fig. 17. The intensity of the end point detector's signal is shown as a function of time for three types of wafers. In the example shown, the non-implanted P.R. apparently ashes at a constant rate until the end point is approached.

Each of the two different implanted wafers has a repeatable ashing characteristic. As with the total gas evolved, for a given P.R., the ashing characteristics are *identical* for each type of implant. The traces do not vary according to the power density used for the implant and thus are independent of the temperature reached in the implanter. In every instance, for each type of P.R., the wafer with the low dose, higher energy implant takes longer to become cleared of P.R. than the wafer with the high dose, low energy implant. Actually, this is to be expected, since the width of the carbonized layer is greater for 6 x 10^{14}/cm^2 arsenic at 160 keV than for 1.2 x 10^{15}/cm^2 arsenic at 80 keV. This latter fact can be inferred from the curves in Fig. 14. The length of time for the low level signal from the end point detector seems to indicate a narrower carbonized region for the P.R. implanted with low energy arsenic.

It appears reasonable to assume that the P.R. ashing proceeds at a reduced rate through the damaged layer of P.R. on the outside, then recovers to the normal rate later on, when virgin P.R. underneath is encountered. There is no a priori reason to relate the signal intensity to actual ashing rate, but from later work it is known that this is a safe assumption for this ashing system.

In Fig. 18, the calculated values of relative stripping time versus dose are shown for the energies used in the original P.R. matrix of Table 1. The equation given in the figure is a concise way to express the difficulty of resist strip, taking it to be the ratio of the stripping time of carbonized resist to the stripping time of non-implanted resist. The equation involves two figures of merit: Wc/(th)o, the fraction of the original P.R. which is carbonized, and (Ro/Rc), the ratio of the ashing rate of undamaged resist to that of carbonized resist. For this calculation, the ashing rate of the carbonized resist is estimated from Fig. 17 to be 35% of the ashing rate of undamaged resist. Wc was estimated from the data on gas evolved in Fig. 14. Good agreement with these predicted trends, for As to 80 and 160 keV over a wide range of doses, was obtained in this particular ashing system. The same trend is followed for data on P.R. thickness as a function of time in an oxygen gas plasma, reported by Okuyama et al [13]. The char-

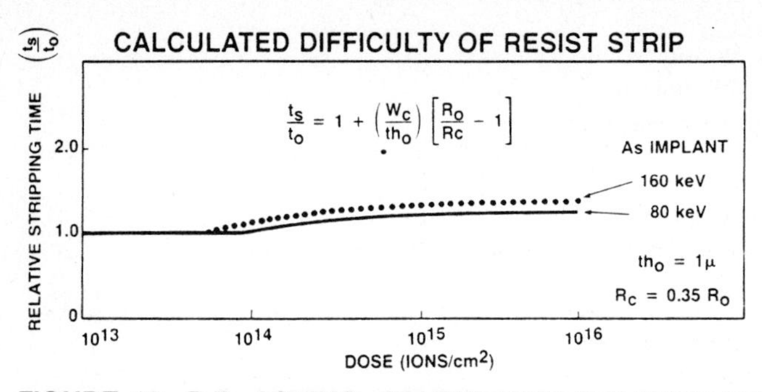

FIGURE 18: P.R. ASHING: CALCULATED RELATIVE STRIPPING TIME versus DOSE FOR ARSENIC IMPLANT AT TWO ENERGIES.

acteristics of stripping ion implanted P.R. can be quantified, and an estimate of the relative difficulty to be expected can be made from a knowledge of Wc.

In general, P.R. removal schemes involve either solvent or oxidizing liquid stripping solutions or dry ashing in an oxygen plasma. The details of these various techniques are reviewed by Elliot [18]. Sometimes, for removal of ion implanted P.R., wet and dry methods are employed sequentially, or in combination with air or oxygen bakes at moderately high temperatures, (400°C). Methods of evaluating the effectivenss of wet strippers, such as "Caro's acid," are discussed by Kaplan and Bergin [19]. Again, the implant should be regarded as a part of the overall process. Results reported for high dose or high energy implants into P.R. are sometimes difficult to analyze, since complete details are not available. In some instances, the wafer temperature may be high enough, for times long enough to modify the P.R. characteristics in subsequent stripping. In the case of the present experiments, the wafer temperature during the implant did not effect the ashing characteristics.

4. Conclusion

A review of wafer cooling considerations for various cases of interest was given. Figures of merit for the estimation of practical limiting values of wafer temperature were discussed and modeling schemes verified. Photoresist problems such as outgassing and "difficulty of resist strip" were analyzed in terms of a model which relates P.R. damage to the implant parameters. The magnitude of these P.R. problems can be estimated from determination of such factors as the gas multiplier, Mg, or critical dose, Dc. Finally, the width of the carbonized region, Wc, is the principal factor with regard to stripping the implanted resist. A correlation between other measured parameters, such as optical density, total quantity of gas evolved, and P.R. thickness change was demonstrated to be related by this P.R. damage model.

Acknowledgements

The author wishes to express thanks to the following individuals for technical help in collection of data and preparation of this paper: J. Alvis, E. Fisk, C. Hart, S. Jenkins, and J. Tsang.

References

1. D. G. Beanland and D. J. Chivers, "Sheet resistance variation on color-banded silicon following high dose implantations at high dose rates," J. Vac. Sci. Technol. *15* (4), pp. 1536–1540 (1978).
2. P. D. Parry, "Localized substrate heating during ion implantation," J. Vac. Sci Technol. *15* (1), pp. 111-115 (1978).
3. M. Bruel, B. Berthet, M. Floccari and J. F. Michaud, "Target heating during ion implantation and related problems," Radiat. Eff. *44*, pp. 173–179 (1979).
4. Peter D. Parry, "Target heating during ion implantation," J. Vac. Sci. Technol. *13* (2), pp. 622-629 (1976).
5. Monty King & Peter H. Rose, "Experiments on gas cooling of wafers," Nucl. Instrum. Methods, *189*, pp. 169–173 (1981).
6. M. Mack, "Wafer cooling in mechanically scanned implantation system," these proceedings.
7. Wahl "Temp-Plate" temperature recorders, Wahl Instruments, Inc., Culver City, CA. 90230.
8. G. Baccarani and K. A. Pickar, "Range and straggle of boron in photoresist," Solid-State Electron., *Vol. 15*, pp. 239–243 (1972).
9. James F. Gibbons, William S. Johnson, & Steven W. Mylroie, *Projected Range Statistics*, 2nd Edition, (Halsted Press 1975).
10. W. S. DeForest, *Photoresist Materials and Processes*, (McGraw-Hill Book Company, 1975).
11. F. H. Dill and J. M. Shaw, "Thermal effects on the photoresist AZ1350J," IBM J. Res. Dev., May, pp. 210–218 (1977).
12. W. H-L. Ma, "Plasma resist image stabilization treatment (PRIST)," Proc. of IEEE Electron Devices Meeting, Dec. 8–10, pp. 574–575 (1980).
13. Y. Okuyama, T. Hashimoto, & T. Koguchi, "High dose ion implanatation into photoresist," J. Electrochem. Soc., *Vol. 125*, No. 8, pp. 1293–1298 (1978).
14. Robert Allen, Marti Foster, and Yung-Tsai Yen, "Deep U. V. hardening of positive photoresist patterns," J. Electrochem. Soc., *Vol. 129*, No. 6, pp. 1379–1381 (1982).
15. H. Hiraoka and J. Pacansky, "High temperature flow resistance of micron sized images in AZ resists," J. Electrochem. Soc., *Vol. 128*, No. 12, pp. 2645–2647 (1981).
16. David J. Elliot, "Positive photoresists as ion implantation masks," SPIE *Vol. 174* Developments in Semiconductor Microlithography IV, pp. 153–172 (1979).
17. G. Ryding, "Dosimetry and beam quality," these proceedings.
18. David J. Elliot, *Integrated Circuit Fabrication Technology*, Chapter 12, "Resist Removal," (McGraw-Hill Book Company, 1982).
19. L. H. Kaplan and B. K. Bergin, "Residues from wet processing of positive resists," J. Electrochem. Soc., *Vol. 127*, No. 2, pp. 386-395 (1980).

Electron-Beam-Induced Recoil Implantation in Semiconductors at 300 K

T. Wada, K. Nakai, and H. Hada
Faculty of Engineering, Mie University, Kamihama, Tsu 514, Japan

Abstract

In the present paper, experimental results for the introduction of In (Sb or Ge, GaSb) impurities into Ge (Si) at 300K,as well as U-shaped diffusion profiles, are reported upon. The technique employs an impurity sheet in contact with a Ge surface which is bombarded with high-energy electrons.

1. Introduction

The technique of recoil implantation is the introduction of impurities into a solid by atomic recoil [1]. 50 and 300 keV krypton ion beams have been used to introduce Sb atoms into silicon from thin evaporated layers deposited on the surface [2]. These experimental results are in good agreement with transmission-sputtering theory [3]. It was originally discoverd by one of the authors, Wada, that the impurities are introduced into Si from the impurity sheet using high-energy electron bombardment [4-6].

The present work describes experimental results for the introduction of In (Sb or Ge, GaSb) impurities into Ge (Si) at 300K, as well as U-shaped diffusion profiles. The technique employs an In (Sb or Ge, GaSb) sheet in contact with the Ge (Si) surface, which is bombarded with high-energy electrons. Whenever a charged particle loses energy in a solid, electron-hole pairs are produced. When such a large number of conduction electrons and / or holes in Ge (Si) recombine at defécts via non-radiative transitions, mobility enhancement of impurity atoms may be caused by the energy released in these processes.

2. Experimental

The samples used in the experiments are summarized in Table 1. t represents thickness of impurity sheets or substrates. The surfaces of the impurity sheets in contact with the Ge (Si) wafer were bombarded with a total dose of about $1 \sim 5\times10^{17}$ electrons/cm^2 at 7 MeV from an electron linear accelerator (Fig.1), with a pulse width of ~ 3.5 μs, a 200 Hz duty cycle and an average electron beam current of 20 μA. The samples were put in a circulating water bath, which was kept at a constant temperature T by using a thermoregulator, as shown in Fig.2. After bombardment, the samples were left at room temperature for a few days to be sure of avoiding the annealing effect. The concentration profiles of impurity atoms in Ge (Si) were measured using Rutherford backscattering spectroscopy (RBS), Auger electron spectroscopy (AES) and secondary ion mass spectroscopy (SIMS).

Table 1. Impurity sheets and substrates used in the experiments

	Material	purity, conduction type, resistivity orientation, thickness
Impurity sheet	Al	99.99 %, t = 0.5 ~ 1.0 mm
	In	99.999 %, t = 0.3 mm
	Sb	99.999 %, t = 0.25, 0.16 mm
	GaP	n type (Te doped), ρ = 0.66 Ω cm t = 0.35 mm
	GaSb	p type (undoped), ρ = 0.0545 Ω cm <100>, t = 0.5 mm
Substrate	Ge	n type (undoped), ρ > 30 Ω cm <111>, t = 0.67 ~ 0.74 mm
		p type (In doped), ρ = 2 ~ 3 Ω cm <111>, t = 0.67 ~ 0.84 mm
	Si	n type (P doped), ρ = 3 ~ 6 Ω cm <100>, t = 0.36 mm
		p type (B doped), ρ = 0.4 ~ 0.6 Ω cm <100>, t = 0.37 mm

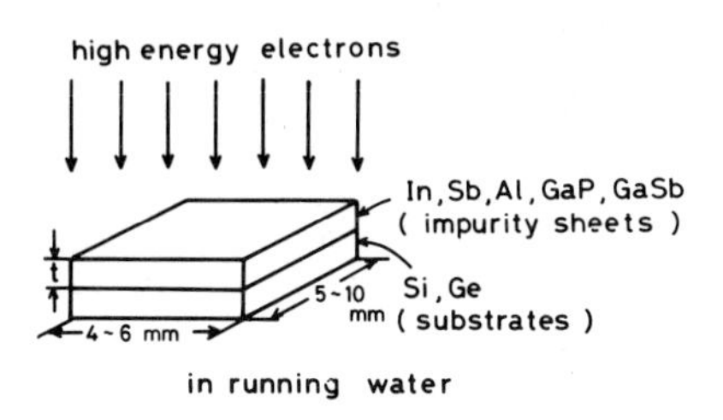

Fig.1. Schematic diagram of electron-beam-induced recoil implantation

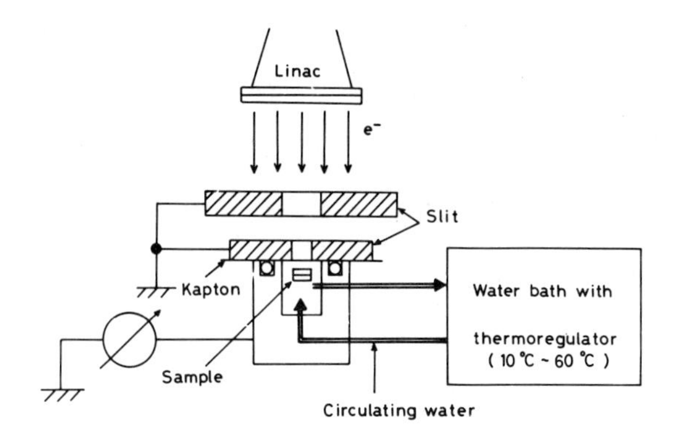

Fig.2. Schematic diagram of electron bombardment

3. Experimental Results

In the cases of In (Sb) overlayers and Ge substrates, the intensity ratios of $^{115}In^+$ ions and $^{121}Sb^+$ ions to $^{74}Ge^+$ ions are shown in Fig.3 for the bombarded specimens as a function of depth measured from the Ge front surface, which is in contact with the overlayer. The SIMS measurements were performed by using the primary ion (O_2^+) beam (diameter 0.5 mmϕ) with an ion energy of 7 keV in a 1.5×10^{-7} Torr vacuum, with an accuracy of within 10%. For Ge wafers bombarded without impurity sheets, the In^+ and Sb^+ peaks disappeared. The concentration profiles of impurity atoms follow two kinds of exponential (-x/L) laws for different impurities. For simplicity, assuming the relationship of $D = L^2/4t$, the diffusivities at

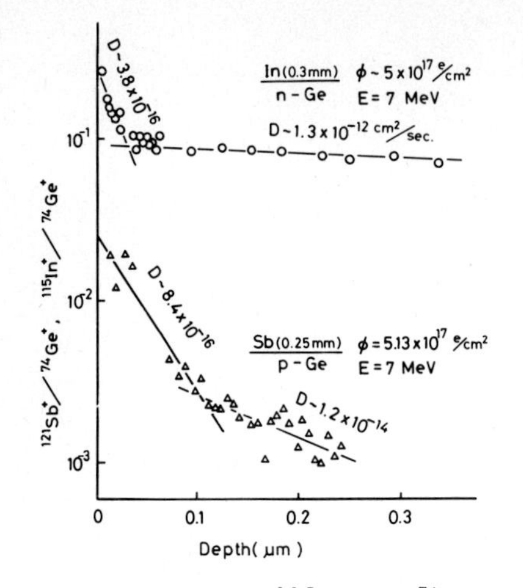

Fig.3. Ratios of $^{115}In^+$ to $^{74}Ge^+$ and $^{121}Sb^+$ to $^{74}Ge^+$ in Ge substrates as a function of depth, from the front surface of Ge

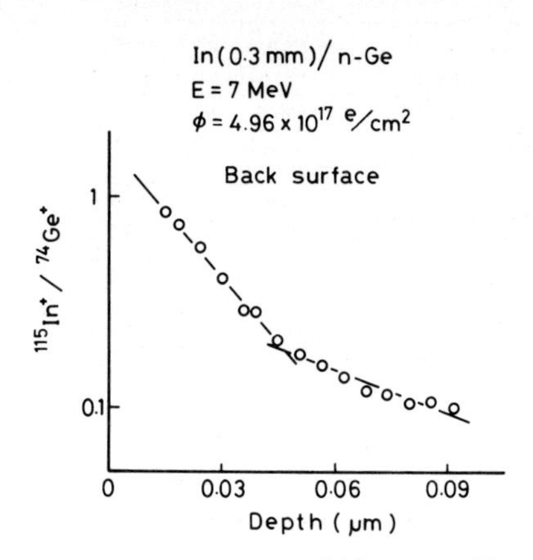

Fig.4. Ratios of $^{115}In^+$ to $^{74}Ge^+$ in Ge substrate as a function of depth, from the back surface of Ge

$x < 0.05$ μm and $x > 0.05$ μm for In are estimated to be about 3.8×10^{-16} cm^2/sec and 1.3×10^{-12} cm^2/sec, respectively. In the similar experiments with In/Ge, the intensity ratios of In^+/Ge^+ are indicated in Fig.4, as a function of depth from the Ge back surface.

The Ga impurity concentration distributions at deeper depths from the Ge front surface in the experiments of GaSb/Ge are shown in Fig.5 as a function of depth. After the bombardment, the Ge surfaces with several different depths from the original surface were fabricated by etching away different small amounts of Ge from the surfaces, which are partially covered with an organic paint so as to protect them from successive etching. Even at the depth of about 8.4 μm, Ga^+ ions are detected.

Auger electron spectroscopy (AES) was combined with ion sputtering to measure the concentration profiles of impurity atoms. Fig.6 shows the observed Auger signal ratio of In (MNN peak-peak) to Ge (LMM peak-peak) for the bombarded sample (overlayer of In) as a function of sputter-etching

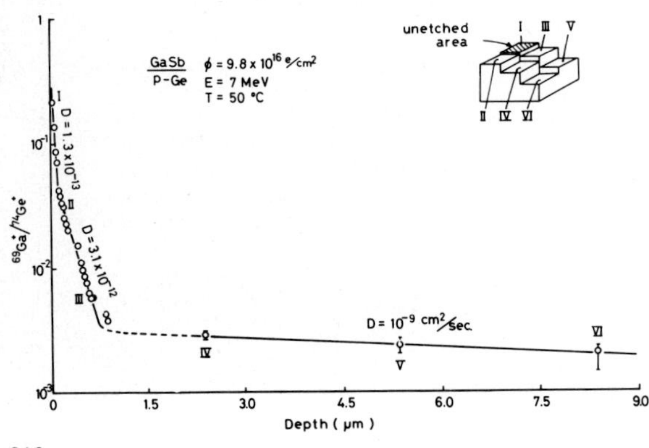

Fig.5. Impurity concentration distributions at deeper depths from the Ge front surface as a function of depth

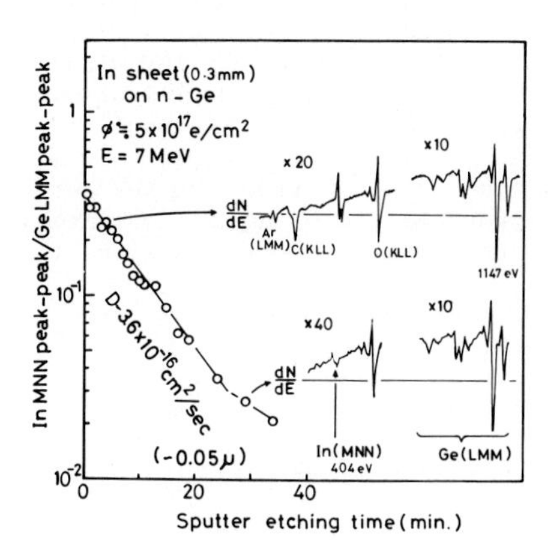

Fig.6. Observed Auger signal ratio of In (MNN peak-peak) to Ge (LMM peak-peak) as a function of sputter-etching time from the Ge surface, together with the Auger electron spectra

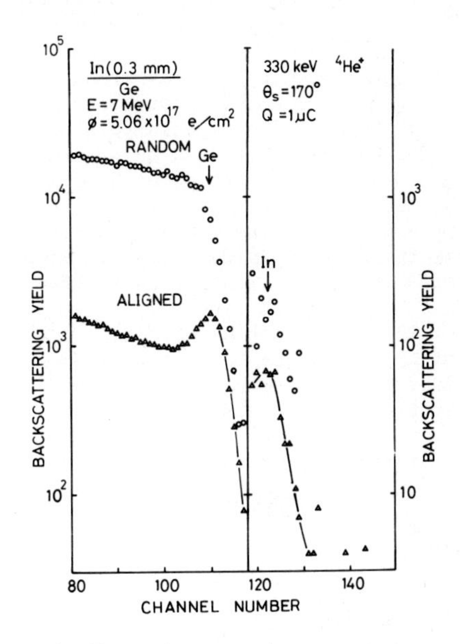

Fig.7. Backscattering spectra for the bombarded Ge (In overlayer) in random and aligned conditions

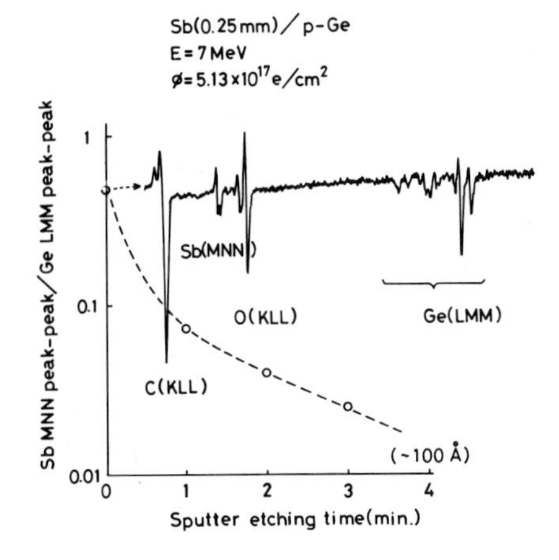

Fig.8. Observed Auger signal ratios of Sb (MNN peak-peak) to Ge (LMM peak-peak) as a function of sputter-etching time from the Ge surface, together with the Auger electron spectrum at the Ge surface

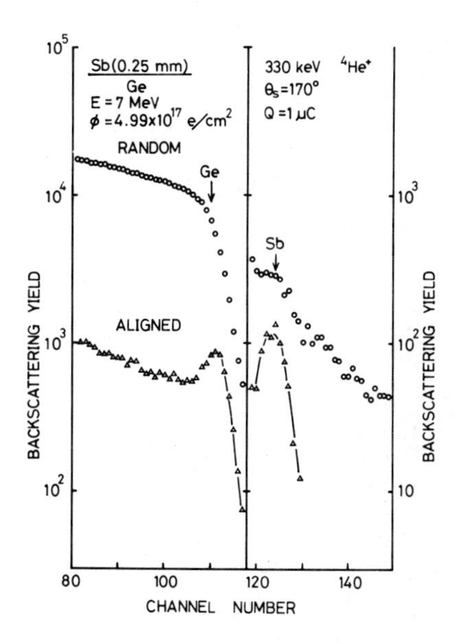

Fig.9. Backscattering spectra for the bombarded Ge (Sb overlayer) in random and aligned conditions

time from the Ge surface, together with the Auger electron spectra. The AES measurements were performed by an incident electron beam (diameter 0.3 mmϕ) at 3 keV energies with a current of ∿10 μA and a pressure of $\sim 1\times10^{-9}$ Torr. The sputter-etching was done by the ion (Ar^+) energy of 2 keV with a current of ∿3 μA and an Ar pressure of $\sim 5\times10^{-5}$ Torr. The distribution profiles also follow an exponential decay curve and D_{In} in Ge is about 3.6×10^{-16} cm^2/sec; it agrees with the results by SIMS. Fig.7 shows backscattering spectra in the random and aligned conditions by 330 keV He^+ in the case of In/Ge. It indicates the introduction of In impurities into Ge. The impurities may be located on both substitutional and interstitial sites in a depth range of $x < 300$ Å.

In the similar experiments with Sb/Ge, the observed Auger signal ratios of Sb (MNN peak-peak) to Ge (LMM peak-peak) are shown in Fig.8 as a function of sputter-etching time and its backscattering spectra are shown in Fig.9. They also indicate the introduction of Sb impurities into Ge.

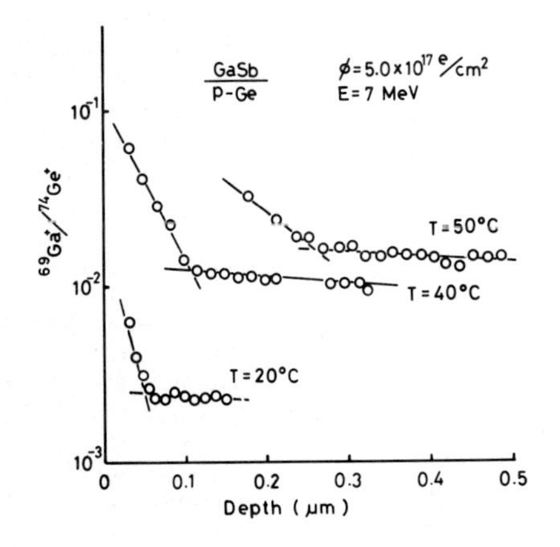

Fig.10. Ratios of $^{69}Ga^+$ to $^{74}Ge^+$ in Ge substrate as a function of depth, from the front surface of Ge, at different bombardment temperatures

Fig.10 shows the intensity ratios of $^{69}Ga^+/^{74}Ge^+$ of the sample in the experiments with GaSb/Ge at different bombardment temperatures. The intensity ratios of Ga^+/Ge^+ increase with increasing bombardment temperature. The results agree well with the temperature dependence of impurity atoms in backscattering spectra for the experiments with Ge/Si [7]. It is suggested from their results that the temperature rises of the sample during bombardment are sufficiently prevented in a circulating water bath.

4. Discussion

The ranges of 7 MeV electrons in Si, Ge and In sheets are about 15, 5.6 and 3.8 mm, respectively [8]. The production rate of defects in Si is about 8 cm^{-1} [9]. The impurity-sheet layer is sufficiently thin here to allow the bombarding electrons to penetrate into the substrate without a significant loss in kinetic energy.

4.1 Recoil Process

Using the theoretical expression for recoil implantation by Mckinley and Feshbach [10], maximum penetration depths for recoil atoms of Al, Ga and In are obtained at about 120 Å,30 Å and 20 Å for 10 MeV electrons, respectively. Mechanisms causing such experimental impurity profiles are not only the recoil process, but also the mobility enhancement of impurity atoms in overlayers and substrates.

4.2 Recombination-Enhanced Diffusion and Recoil

Whenever a charged particle loses energy in a solid, electron-hole pairs (ehp) are produced. For Ge and Si, the energies ε required to produce an ehp were obtained at 2.84 and 3.23 eV/ehp, respectively [11]. The rate of generation G of ehp's by an incident electron beam can be estimated by:

$$G = \frac{1}{\varepsilon} \cdot \frac{dE}{dx} \cdot \frac{d\phi}{dt}$$

where $dE/dx \simeq 1.7$ and 1.6 MeV $cm^2/g \cdot$electron [12] are the energy loss per cm of path by a fast electron in Ge and Si, respectively, and $d\phi/dt$ is the irradiation rate. Irradiation at a rate of $\sim 3.3 \times 10^{11}$ electrons/$cm^2 \cdot$sec (27 mA per 1.77 cm^2, pulse width 3.5 μs) would result in $G \simeq 1.06 \times 10^{18}$ ehp's/$cm^3 \cdot$sec for Ge ($G \simeq 3.8 \times 10^{17}$ ehp's/$cm^3 \cdot$sec for Si) during electron bombardment. When such a number of conduction electrons and/or holes in Ge (Si) recombine at defects via non-radiative transitions, mobility enhancement of impurity atoms may be caused by the energy released in these processes.

4.3 U-Shaped Diffusion Profiles

In these experiments, In (Sb or Ge, GaSb) impurities in Ge diffuse via a substitutional-interstitial (s-i) interchange mechanism. Thermal equilibrium between In_s (A_{tr}) and In_i (A_i) is established via vacancies V according to the Frank-Turnbull mechanism [13]:

$$A_{tr} \underset{k_2}{\overset{k_1}{\rightleftarrows}} A_i + V$$

where k_1 and k_2 are reaction constants. Assuming this mechanism, the calculated profiles agree roughly with experimental **results.**

Acknowledgements

The authors would like to express their thanks to Messrs. M.Takeda, K.Yasuda and H.Masuda, of the Government Industrial Research Institute of Nagoya, for their help in connection with irradiation of the sample, and Dr.O.Ryuzan and Mr.H.Hashimoto, of Fujutsu Laboratory, for their help in RBS measurements.

References

1 R.S.Nelson: Rad. Eff. 2, 47 (1969)
2 A.Grob, J.J.Grob, N.Mesli, and P.Siffert: Proc. 2nd. Int. Conf. on Ion Beam Mod. of Materials (North-Holland Pub. Co, Amsterdam) 1, 85 (1980)
3 P.Sigmund: Phys. Rev. 184, No.2, 383 (1969)
4 T.Wada: Proc. 2nd. Int. Conf. on Ion Beam Mod. of Materials (North-Holland Pub. Co, Amsterdam) 1, 131 (1980)
5 T.Wada: Proc. 3rd. Int. Conf. on Neutron-Transmutation Doped Si (Plenum Press, New York and London), 447 (1980)
6 T.Wada and M,Kaneiwa: Inst. Phys. Conf. Ser. 59, 223 (1981)

7 T.Wada, M.Takeda, K.Yasuda, and H.Masuda: Proc. 6th. Symp. on Ion Sources and Ion-Assisted Technology (Ionics Co, Tokyo), 433 (1982)
8 T.Tabata, R.Ito and S.Okabe: Nucl. Instr. and Meth. 103, 85 (1972)
9 T.Wada, K.Yasuda, S.Ikuta, M.Takeda, and H.Masuda: J. Appl. Phys. 48, 2145 (1977)
10 J.W.Corbett; in: Electron Radiation Damage in Semiconductors and Metals (Academic Press, New York and London, 1966), p.20
11 E.Baldinger, W.Czaja, and A.Z.Farooqi: Helv. Phys. Acta 33, 551 (1960)
12 H.Sugiyama: Research of the Electrotechnical Laboratory, No.724 (Feb. 1972)
13 F.C.Frank and D.Turnbull: Phys. Rev. 104, 617 (1956)

Wafer Cooling in Ion Implantation

M.E. Mack

Eaton Corporation, Ion Implantation Division, 16 Tozer Road,
Beverly, MA 01915, USA

1. Introduction

Recent years have seen a marked increase in the use of ion implantation in semiconductor manufacture. A key element in this rapid growth has been the use of photoresist for masking during implantation. The greatest resolution is achieved with positive photoresists, that is, with resists in which the area exposed in lithography is removed during development. Positive photoresists are generally quite sensitive to temperature. Excessive temperature during implantation can blister resist, alter critical dimensions and render the resist difficult to remove during subsequent processing. Most photoresists are unaffected by temperatures below 100°C. Few positive resists will survive temperatures above 150°C during implantation.

In addition to the requirements imposed by the use of photoresist, the electrical properties of the processed wafer can depend on the temperature of the wafer during implantation. Beanland et al. have reported a variation in sheet resistivity for phosphorus implanted silicon, which depends rather critically on implant temperature [1]. These measurements were performed for channeling implants in <111> silicon. The observed variation of sheet resistivity is the result of the temperature dependence for the formation during implantation of an amorphous surface layer, which progressively diminishes the degree of channeling. In the case of non-channeling implants in <100> silicon the variation of sheet resistivity with implant temperature has proved to be much less significant. Nonetheless, it would seem prudent to minimize temperature excursions and temperature gradients during implantation.

While the need for effective wafer cooling has become more apparent, the requirement for increased throughput has led to the development of implanters with high beam currents and high power loadings. In modern production implanters typical time averaged wafer power loadings range from a few tenths of a watt per square centimeter to several watts per square centimeter. Even at the lowest of these power loadings, wafer temperature will exceed 300°C, if radiative cooling is not enhanced or augmented in some fashion. The implementation of the cooling and the degree of cooling required is very much design dependent. The highest heat loads are developed in the medium current implanters, where only a single wafer is implanted at a given time. The high current implanters typically resort to batch processing. Beam power is spread over a much larger area and a more manageable beam power flux is achieved. However, the implementation of effective cooling is hampered by the mechanical scanning implicit with the batch processing. Even so, by careful design, cooling adequate for implants on photoresist covered wafers at the highest power available today can be provided in either the medium or high current implanters.

A model for the heating and cooling of a wafer during ion implantation is discussed in Section 2. In the case of conduction dominated cooling (Section 2.1.3) the maximum wafer temperature rise is shown to be simply related to the beam power averaged over the total scan area. Conduction cooling by contact to a conductive elastomer is discussed in Section 3. Probably the most effective form of wafer cooling is gas cooling, as is discussed in Section 4. Cooling by elastomeric contact is well suited for the mechanically scanned high current implanters and allows implants at up to 1600W without damage to photoresist. The more complicated but more effective gas cooling is well suited to medium current implanters and likewise allows implants in photoresist at maximum machine currents. Section 5 summarizes the paper.

2. Radiative and Conductive Cooling

2.1. Model for Wafer Heating and Cooling

Figure 1 shows the geometry for ion implantation. For simplicity the beam is assumed to be rectangular with a short dimension a, and a long dimension b. Typically, the beam is substantially smaller in extent than the wafer dimension so that scan in two directions is necessary in order to cover the wafer. In order to minimize doping non-uniformities, a large ratio of scan speeds is required with the slow scan in the long beam direction [2]. Thus, the fast scan speed is V_f and is transverse to a, while the slow scan speed is V_S and is along b. The necessary scanning can be achieved by moving the wafers (mechanical scanning), by moving the beam (electrostatic scanning) or by some combination of the two (hybrid scanning). In any event the heat loading experienced at any point on the wafer will be of the form shown in Fig.2.

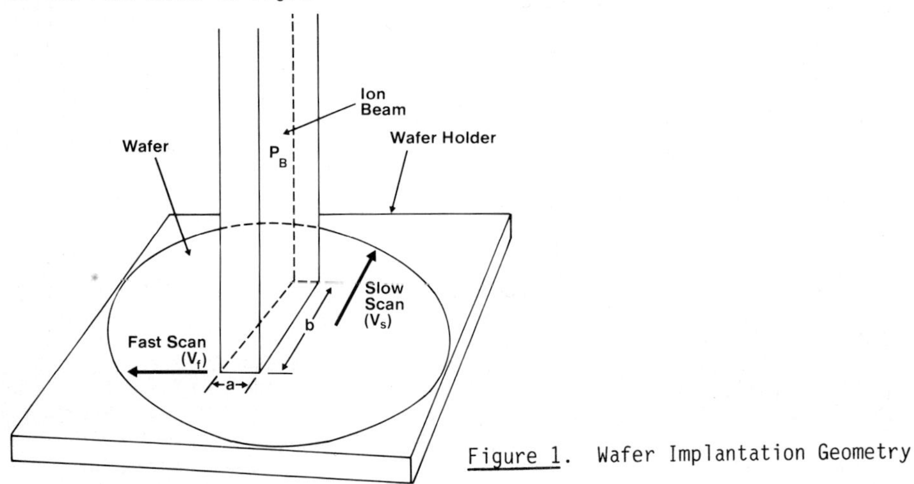

Figure 1. Wafer Implantation Geometry

Each time the beam passes a given point on the wafer the heat flux experienced at that point will be P_B/A_B where P_B is the beam power and A_B=ab is the cross-sectional area of the beam. For the simple rectangular beam of Fig.1, the beam will scan past the given point after a time, $t_1 = a/V_f$. However, the fast scan is assumed to be cyclic as is the case in commercial implanters so that the beam will return to the same point

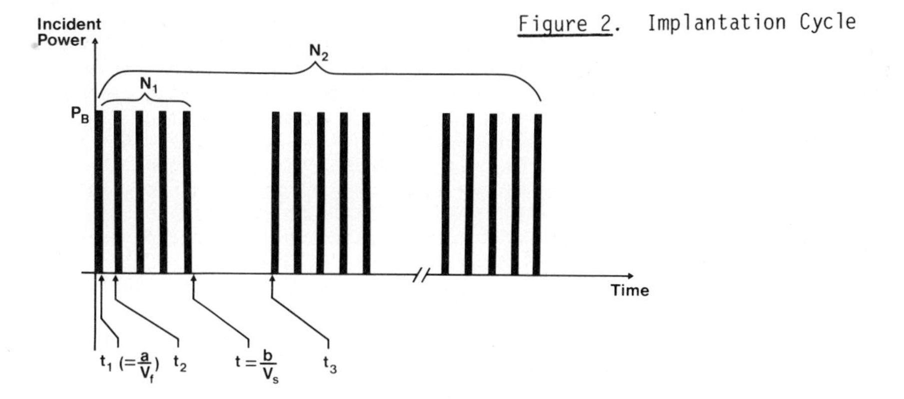

Figure 2. Implantation Cycle

at time t_2. This pattern will repeat until after N_1 cycles at time $t = b/V_s$ the slow scan has moved the beam beyond the point of interest. In general the slow scan will also be cyclical, so that the fast scan cycle will repeat again at time t_3. The slow scan pattern will repeat N_2 times.

When the beam impinges on the wafer, most of the incident ions will be stopped in a fraction of a micron. Since the beam energy is thermalized near the surface, this surface will be hotter than the remainder of the wafer. The greatest temperature gradient will occur when the back side of the wafer is conduction cooled. In this case, the surface temperature $T_s(t)$ will initially increase according to:

$$T_s(t) = \frac{P_B}{k\ A_B} \sqrt{\frac{4kt}{\pi \rho C_P}} , \qquad (1)$$

where k is the thermal conductivity of the wafer, ρ is its density, C_P is its specific heat and t is the time from the onset of the heating [3]. This relationship will hold for times short compared to the thermal diffusion time t_{TD},

$$t_{TD} = \frac{\rho C_P\ L^2}{k} , \qquad (2)$$

where L is the thickness of the wafer. For a 500μm, thick silicon wafer, t_{TD} = 3 msec. For most high current implanters the exposure period t_1 is short compared to the thermal diffusion time and the front to back wafer temperature difference is accurately given by equation (1). The Eaton NV-10 is typical of the mechanical scanning high current implanters. For this machine the nominal beam power is 800 watts, the beam area is approximately 2 cm^2 and the exposure time is $t_1 \leq 0.2$ msec. Thus, the front to back temperature difference is $T_s(t_1) \leq 5^oC$. This temperature difference is small compared to the total wafer temperature rise experienced during the course of a typical implant, and consequently, can be ignored for purposes of analysis. This same conclusion can be reached by direct solution of the heating equations [2,4,5].

Before proceeding it is important to note that there are exceptions where the temperature gradient through the wafer may not be negligible. Wafer surface temperature rise after a single pass of the beam is roughly comparable in the medium current machines to that for the high current machines. However, the retrace time t_2 is much shorter. If this retrace time is also short compared to the thermal diffusion time, the surface temperature rise will accumulate over a number of fast scan cycles and may become significant compared to the average wafer temperature rise. The exact comparison will depend on the details of the scan cycle. A second exception of importance is the case of photoresist. Although the resist is very thin in comparison to the wafer, the thermal conductivity is much less. Data is not available for commercial photoresists but for comparison purposes PMMA, which is used as an ultraviolet region photoresist, has a thermal conductivity of only about 2×10^{-3} W cm^{-1} $^{\circ}C^{-1}$. This is nearly a 1000 times lower than the thermal conductivity of the silicon. The thermal diffusion time for the resist layer will be less than 20 μsec because the layer is so thin (1-1.5μ). Consequently, even in the relatively short beam exposure time t_1, steady state will be reached. In this case, because of the great difference in thermal conductivity between the resist and the silicon, the gradient through the resist is linear and the surface temperature T_S is:

$$T_S = \frac{P_B}{A_B} \frac{l_{PR}}{k_{PR}} , \tag{3}$$

where l_{PR} is the thickness of the photoresist and k_{PR} is the thermal conductivity of the resist. For the example of the NV-10, the surface temperature rise is calculated to be approximately 30°C. Implanters with smaller beam cross sections will suffer proportionately. This temperature rise is not negligible and in instances where maximum surface temperature is of interest, the surface temperature differential must be added to the temperature of the wafer itself.

Neglecting the surface temperature differential, the wafer may be assumed at a constant temperature T_W across its thickness. This case has been analyzed in detail by Parry [4]. The heat flow equation derived by Parry is:

$$\rho A_B L C_p \frac{dT_W}{dt} = P_B(t) - H(T_W - T_{WH}) - \alpha(T_W{}^4 - T_S{}^4) - \beta(T_W{}^4 - T_{WH}{}^4) \tag{4}$$

where $P_B(t)$ is the time-dependent wafer power loading shown in Fig.2, T_{WH} is the wafer holder temperature and T_S is the temperature of the surrounding chamber. The coefficient H represents the conducted heat loss to the wafer holder. The constants α and β determine the radiation loss to the surrounding chamber and the wafer holder respectively. In terms of the wafer emissivity ε_W, the wafer holder emissivity ε_{WH} and the surrounding chamber emissivity ε_S,

$$\alpha = \sigma A_B \frac{\varepsilon_W \varepsilon_S}{\varepsilon_W + \varepsilon_S - \varepsilon_W \varepsilon_S} \tag{5}$$

and $$\beta = \sigma A_B \frac{\varepsilon_W \varepsilon_{WH}}{\varepsilon_W + \varepsilon_{WH} - \varepsilon_W \varepsilon_{WH}} , \tag{6}$$

where σ is the Stefan - Boltzman constant. Equation (4) will give an overestimate of actual wafer temperature, since lateral heat diffusion in the wafer is ignored [4,6].

2.1. Radiation Dominated Cooling

In the case that radiative cooling dominates over conduction, a simple analytical solution of equation (4) is not possible. Instead equation (4) is solved as a difference equation using a computer. The salient features of implanter operation in this regime have been described in the literature [2,4,5]. Figure 3 shows the temperature rise calculated by Glawischnig [5] for a Ferris wheel type implanter at a 300 watt beam power. Wafer temperature increases with each fast scan during the heating cycle and then decays during the remainder of the slow scan cycle. The decay is more rapid at higher temperatures due to the T^4 dependence of the radiative losses. In this instance the maximum wafer temperature is reached after only four slow scan cycles. The relatively low wafer temperature for radiation cooling shown in Fig.3 is the result of the long cooling time, which large batch processing allows.

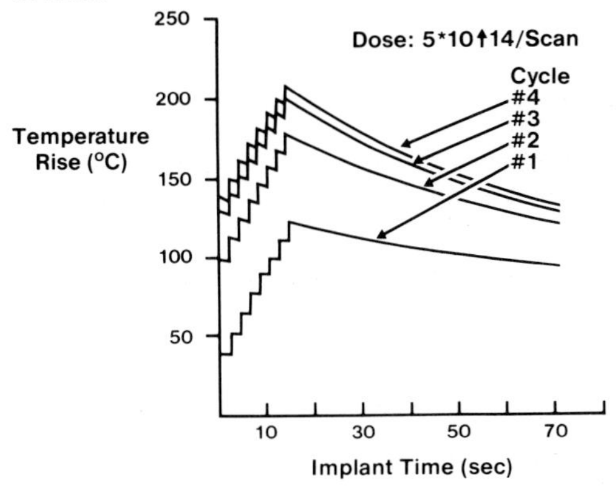

Figure 3. Calculated Temperature in Ferris Wheel Type Implanter (after H. Glawischnig, Low Energy Ion Beams, 1980, Institute for Physics, London (1980)

Parry has performed extensive modeling with varying implant cycles [4]. This modeling highlights the importance of batch processing. Compared to a single wafer implant at a beam power of 50W, the wafer temperature for the case of 20 wafers in a ring on a rotating disk system is reduced nearly 1000°C. If instead of 20 wafers in a single ring, 60 wafers in 3 rings of 20 each are implanted under the same conditions of power and dose, the wafer temperature is reduced another 200°C. Of course, the reason for the dramatic improvement in the cooling is that the heating is periodically interrupted by a cooling cycle of sufficient duration that an appreciable fraction of the absorbed heat can be radiated away.

In addition to enhancing radiational cooling by maximizing batch size and adjusting cycle times, it is also possible to reduce temperature rise by altering the emissivity of the wafer environment. Figure 4 shows radiational cooling in the NV-10 with two different disk arrangements. In the standard configuration the wafer holders, the disk and the chamber walls are all bare aluminum. Under such conditions the emissivity of these surfaces is approximately 0.1, which is rather low. For comparison the nominal emissivity for silicon is of the order of 0.4 [4]. It must be noted that in both configurations of Fig.4, the wafer is held by centrifugal force against the aluminum wafer holder.

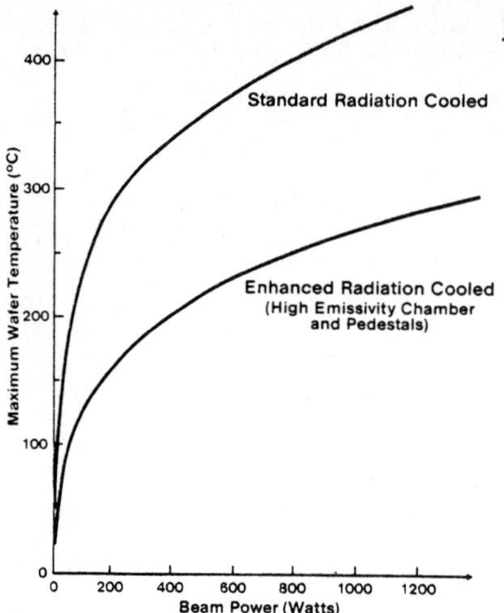

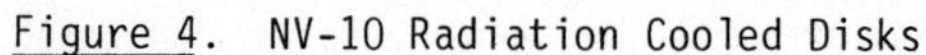

Figure 4. NV-10 Radiation Cooled Disks

However, as discussed in section 2.1.3 conduction cooling is negligible under these circumstances and the primary heat exchange mechanism is radiation. In the enhanced cooling arrangement of Fig.4, the wafer holder is flame sprayed with aluminum oxide and the inside of the chamber is coated with a low vapor pressure black epoxy film. Both coatings have an emissivity in the infrared in excess of 0.7. The increased emissivity results in a decrease in wafer temperature of nearly 200°C.

Thus, the effectiveness of radiational cooling can be enhanced by increasing batch size, by optimizing the implant cycle and by increasing the emissivity of the surfaces surrounding the wafer. However, radiational cooling is most effective for temperatures above 200°C. At lower temperatures the cooling times become inordinately long [4]. In addition at the lower temperatures not all wafers will have a high emissivity. Silicon with a bulk resistivity in excess of 5Ω-cm is generally quite transparent in the 1 to 5μm wavelength region and correspondingly has a low emissivity, 0.1 or less [7]. Consequently, if wafer temperatures of 100°C or less are consistently required, effective conductive cooling is a necessity.

2.1. Conduction Dominated Cooling

If conduction cooling is improved to the point that radiative cooling can be ignored, then the heat flow equation (4) can be solved directly. Setting $\alpha=\beta=0$, inserting the time-dependent wafer power loading of Fig.2 and summing over all of the heating and cooling cycles gives the wafer temperature $T(N_2t_3)$ at the end of the last heating cycle:

$$T(N_2t_3) = \frac{P_B\,\tau\,(1-e^{\frac{-t_1}{\tau}})}{\rho C_p\,A_B\,L} \; \frac{1-e^{\frac{-N_1t_2}{\tau}}}{1-e^{\frac{-t_2}{\tau}}} \; \frac{1-e^{\frac{-N_2t_3}{\tau}}}{1-e^{\frac{-t_3}{\tau}}} \quad . \tag{7}$$

Here the cooling time τ is:

$$\tau = \frac{\rho C_p\,A_B\,L}{H} \quad . \tag{8}$$

Given the conduction coefficient H, and the implant parameters and cycle times, the wafer temperature can be determined directly from (7). The case that the cooling time τ is long compared to t_1, t_2 and t_3 but short compared to N_2t_3 is of interest for rotary scanning high current implanters with a single ring of wafers. In this instance equation (7) can be simplified considerably to give:

$$T(N_2t_3) \cong \frac{P_B}{H} \quad \frac{t_1N_1}{t_3} \quad . \tag{9}$$

In the time N_1t_1 the beam will scan through an area equal to N_1A_B. Similarly, in a time t_3, the beam will scan through an area of N_1A_S*, where A_S* is the total scan area less that portion not scanned with the full redundancy (i.e. less the overscan area). Thus,

$$T(N_2t_3) \cong \frac{P_B/A_S*}{H/A_B} \quad . \tag{10}$$

This is a very intuitive result in that the temperature rise is proportional to the beam flux averaged over the effective scan area and is inversely proportional to the per unit area heat condition out of the wafer, H/A. If the cycle times do not meet the conditions set forth above, the temperature rise will be reduced over that given in (10), so that equation (10) can always be used to give an upper bound on the temperature rise.

For a high current implanter, the beam power flux average over the scan area is of the order of 0.5 Wcm^{-2}. Thus, if the wafer temperature rise is to be kept below 75^oC, giving a final wafer temperature below 100^oC, then H/A must be 7mW cm^{-2} $^oC^{-1}$ or greater. For medium current implanters, the beam power flux is nearly an order of magnitude greater, so H/A must also be proportionally greater. Cooling coefficients of this magnitude can be achieved in practical systems.

3. Conductive Cooling by Elastomeric Contact

It was noted earlier that if a wafer is simply pressed against a cooled aluminum wafer holder, the cooling by the direct conduction to the holder in vacuum is negligible. The reason for this is that the back of the wafer is microscopically rough so that when the wafer is pressed against the aluminum, the contact area is a very small fraction of the total wafer area. This difficulty can be overcome by interposing a thin elastomeric layer between the wafer and the wafer holder. Since the wafer can only be clamped at the edges, the pressure required to drive the wafer protuberances into the elastomer must be developed by forming the wafer over a convex pad as shown in Fig.5. In order to ensure a uniform temperature distribution over the wafer, the contact pressure should be constant across the wafer. In general this requires a slightly aspherical pad surface [8], but for the present application where the radius of curvature is large compared to the wafer diameter, adequate pressure uniformity can be achieved with a spherical pad. The contact pressure to the wafer must be sufficient to achieve adequate thermal contact but must be well below the onset of brittle deformation [9]. This latter limit normally occurs at a stress between 20 to 35% of the normal fracture stress for the wafer. The clamping force at the edge must be adequate to seat the thickest wafer likely to be en-

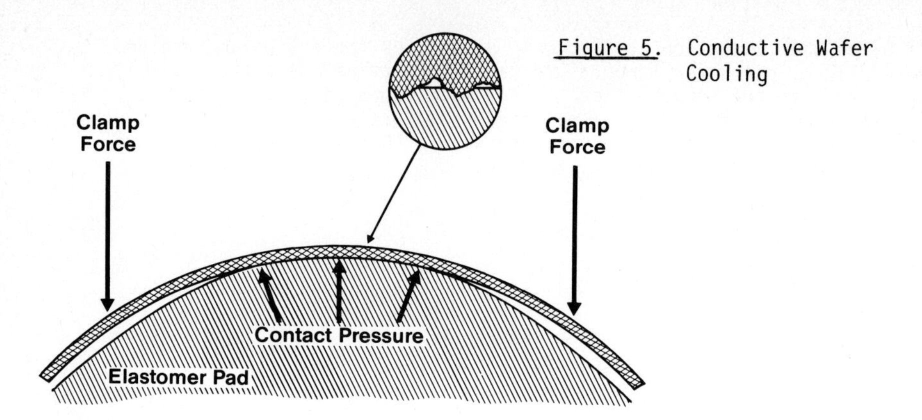

Figure 5. Conductive Wafer Cooling

countered and to develop the full contact pressure across the wafer. In rotary scanning implanters this clamping force is very conveniently developed using centrifugally loaded clamps. This arrangement also minimizes chamber volume and allows the clamps to be opened with very little force when the disk is not spinning.

The thermal conduction through the elastomeric layer is,

$$H/A = \frac{k_E}{l_E} \left(\frac{A^*}{A}\right) \tag{11}$$

where k_E is the thermal conductivity of the elastomer, l_E is its thickness and A^*/A is the effective fractional contact area to the wafer. The elastomers typically used for wafer cooling are RTV formulations. These materials have thermal conductivities of the order of k_E = 10mW cm^{-1} $^oC^{-1}$. With proper pad design $A^*/A \gtrsim 0.05$ can be achieved. Thus, if $l_E \lesssim 0.05$ cm, H/A $\gtrsim$ 10mW $cm^{-2}$$^oC^{-1}$ as required to achieve a final wafer temperature below 100^oC.

Optimization of the cooling pad design is a difficult task. The cooling coefficient depends on the contract pressure, the elastomer conductivity and thickness as well as the Youngs modulus of the elastomer. If the elastomer is made too thin, it will not yield adequately so that the effective contact area will decrease and offset the gain achieved by the shorter conduction path. The thermal conductivity of the elastomer can be increased by a metallic or mineral filling. However, such fillings increase the Youngs modulus and durometer of the elastomer, thus decreasing the contact area. Again a balance must be struck.

Figure 6 shows the performance of an optimized cooling pad design used in the Eaton NV-10. Wafer temperature was measured using backside temperature stickers[1] located in the vacuum chuck notch region of the pad, so as to not reduce contact between the wafer and the pad. These temperatures were also confirmed using an infrared detector similar to an optical pyrometer but more accurate at low temperatures. The data in Fig.6 shows that the heat

---

[1]These stickers are manufactured by several vendors and give an irreversible indication of maximum temperature by changing color. Typically the stickers will have several indicators to cover a range of temperatures. A wider temperature range is achieved with multiple stickers.

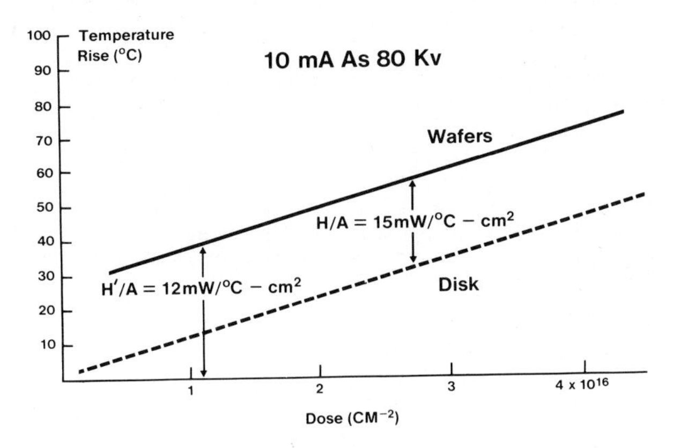

Figure 6. Disk and Wafer Temperature Rise -800 W Input

conductance between the wafer and the pad is H/A = 15 mW cm^{-2} $^{o}C^{-1}$. However, the effective cooling coefficient is reduced because the disk itself heats up during the implant. This heat up is the result of the fact that the disk is cooled only at the center. This latter feature allows simple disk interchange, which makes possible the dedication of a disk to a single implant species to prevent cross contamination. In any event even with the disk heat up, the wafer temperature rise is below 75°C for doses up to 3 x 10^{16} cm^{-2}. Figure 7 shows wafer temperature at fixed dose (1 x 10^{16} cm^{-2}) but varying beam current and, thus, beam power. Since the dose and implant energy are constant, the total energy into the disk is constant. Consequently, the disk temperature rise is fixed. For all beam powers below 1500W (19mA at 80kV) the wafer temperature rise is 75°C or less, giving a final wafer temperature of 100°C or less. This pad design has been used for implanting positive photoresist (KTI III) without damage or excessive distortion at a dose of 1 x 10^{16} cm^{-2} and beam powers of up to 1500W. Both Hunt 204 and Shipley 1470 have been implanted at 800W (80kV and 10mA) and doses up to 2 x 10^{16} cm^{-2} without detriment.

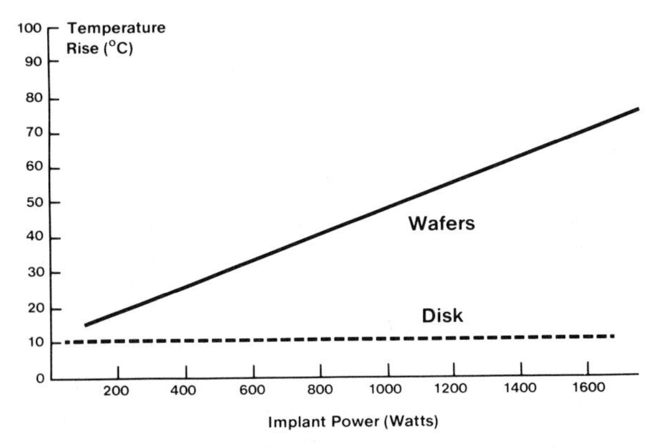

Figure 7. Disk and Wafer Temperature Rise at 1 x 10^{16} cm^{-2} Dose

4. Gas Cooling

Elastomer cooling is adequate for present day high current implanters with batch processing. However, the medium current machines process only a single wafer at a given time and consequently have average beam fluxes an order of magnitude larger than the high current machines. A more effective means of cooling is necessary for these higher beam fluxes. The required cooling can be achieved by using a gas rather than an elastomer as the conductive medium for transporting heat between the wafer and the wafer holder. Conductive cooling by means of a gas has been discussed extensively by King and Rose [10].

In order to use gas cooling for ion implantation, the gas-filled space behind the wafer is sealed with an O-ring at the edge of the wafer. A clamp on the wafer at the edge is necessary to achieve an adequate degree of sealing. To minimize gas leakage into the high vacuum implanter target chamber and to minimize mechanical stress on the wafer [9] a low cooling gas pressure is necessary. Fortunately, thermal conduction in gases, like viscosity, is essentially constant and independent of pressure down to pressures of the order of 5 to 10 Torr. In order to minimize thermal impedance between the wafer and the wafer holder, the gas-filled gap g must be minimized. With a gap in the range of 10 to 30μm and a gas pressure of a few Torr the mean free path λ in the gas will be greater than or comparable to the gap g. Heat condition in this free molecule regime has been analyzed by Knudsen [11].

In the free molecule regime the gas conduction is independent of the gap as long as $g < \lambda$. The heat conduction coefficient is:

$$\frac{H}{A} = \alpha \Lambda_o P \sqrt{\frac{273}{T_{WH}}} , \qquad (12)$$

where P is the pressure in Torr, Λ_o is the free molecule heat conductivity at 0^oC and α is the accomodation coefficient. The accomodation coefficient is a measure of the degree to which molecules striking and reflecting from a wall adjust their kinetic energy to that corresponding to the temperature of the wall. For completely roughened surfaces $\alpha \cong 1$, while for highly polished surfaced $\alpha \ll 1$. For the case of free molecular heat transfer between a silicon wafer and its wafer holder

$$\alpha = \frac{\alpha_W \; \alpha_{WH}}{\alpha_W + \alpha_{WH} - \alpha_W \alpha_{WH}} , \qquad (13)$$

where α_W is the accomodation coefficient for the wafer and α_{WH} is that for the wafer holder. The free molecular heat conductivity can be expressed in terms of more fundamental molecular parameters, that is,

$$\Lambda_o = \frac{1.468}{\sqrt{M}} \left(\frac{\gamma + 1}{\gamma - 1}\right) \quad mW\ cm^{-2}\ {}^oC^{-1}. \qquad (14)$$

Here M is the molecular weight for cooling gas and γ is its specific heat ratio. Table 1 lists mean free path, and molecular heat conductivity for a number of common gases. The high pressure ($g > \lambda$) gas conductivity is also given in Table 1. At higher pressure bowing of the wafer will increase the gap [10]. Curving the cooling platen to prestress the wafer helps to minimize the bowing and gives a more uniform gap when the bowing does occur.

Gas	λ μ-Torr	Λ_o $mWcm^{-2}{}^oC^{-1}Torr^{-1}$	k $mWcm^{-1}{}^oC^{-1}$
H_2	93	60.7	1.62
He	147	29.4	1.35
N_2	46	16.6	0.22
O_2	53	15.6	0.24
H_2O	30	26.5	0.14
A	52	9.3	0.16
CO_2	30	16.7	0.14

Table I

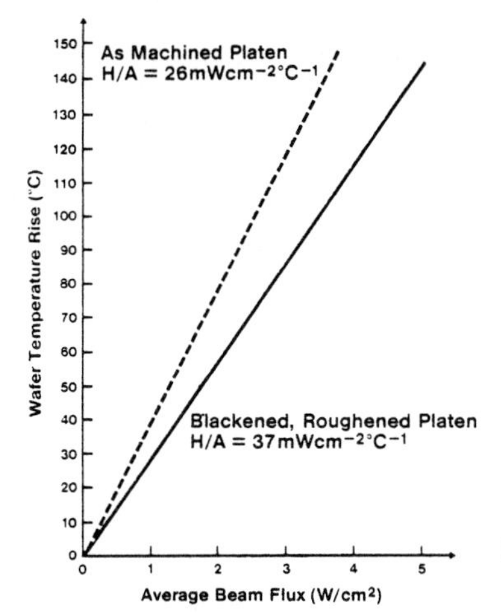

Figure 8.
NV3206 Gas Cooling Performance 5 Torr Hydrogen

From Table 1 it can be seen that hydrogen is significantly more efficient than any other gas for conductive cooling. Figure 8 shows wafer temperature in the Eaton NV3206 implanter using hydrogen gas cooling. The hydrogen gas pressure is 5 Torr and gas consumption is less than 1 scc per hour. The importance of the accomodation coefficient is evident from Fig.8. Because of differing wafer accomodation coefficients a slight variation of cooling dependent on the wafer backside finish is also observed. With H/A = 37mW cm^{-2} $^oC^{-1}$, the cooling is not adequate to hold wafer temperatures below 100°C with a room temperature wafer holder. However, the platen in the NV3206 is freon cooled. By reducing the platen temperature to -20°C, wafer temperature can be held below 100°C at up 4.5W cm^{-2}. In 100mm and 125mm wafers this cooling is adequate to allow implantation of positive photoresist at maximum specified beam currents without damage or distortion to the photoresist.

5. Conclusions

In order to achieve low enough temperatures to successfully implant photoresist masked silicon wafers efficient conductive cooling must be used.

Cooling by contact to a conductive elastomer has proved to be effective in batch processing high current implanters. By such a means positive photoresist can be implanted without damage at beam powers up to 1500 watts. Although beam powers are lower in medium current implanters (since only a single wafer is processed at a time), average beam fluxes are much higher than the high current machines. Consequently, even more effective cooling is required. Gas cooling successfully meets this need.

In terms of future developments, it is likely that the need for still greater throughput will result in high current implanters with significantly higher beam currents than today's machines. Although it may be possible to improve elastomeric contact cooling it is unlikely that the efficiency of cooling will approach that for gas cooling. Consequently, any major increases in high current implanter beam power would probably require a conversion to gas cooling. Such a change does involve engineering complications, but if required, the engineering can be performed [10]. Additional cooling can also be achieved by increasing the batch size.

References

1. D.G. Beanland, W. Temple and D.J. Chivers, Solid State Electronics 21, 357 (1978)

2. R.J. Stocker, Nucl. Inst. Meth. 189, 281 (1981)

3. J.P. Holman, Heat Transfer, Chapter 4.3, McGraw-Hill, New York (1976)

4. P.D. Parry, J. Vac. Sci. Tech. 13, 622 (1975)

5. H. Glawischnig, in Low Energy Ion Beams, 1980, Edited by I.H. Wilson and K.G. Stephens, pg. 60, Institute for Physics, London (1980)

6. P.d. Parry, J. Vac. Sci. Tech. 15, 111 (1978)

7. W.R. Runyan, Silicon Semiconductor Technology, Texas Inst. Electronics Series, Chapter 9, McGraw-Hill, New York (1965)

8. R.J. Roark and W.C. Young, Formulas for Stress and Strain, Chapter 10, McGraw-Hill, New York

9. G.L. Pearson, Acta Metal. 5, 181 (1957)

10. M. King and P.H. Rose, Nucl. Inst. Meth. 189, 169 (1981)

11. S. Dushman, Scientific Foundations of Vacuum Technique, Wiley, New York (1949)

A Rotating Attenuator for Concentration Profiling of Implanted Helium Ions

J.H. Chang[†]

University of Pittsburgh, Pittsburgh, PA 15260, USA

W.J. Choyke

University of Pittsburgh and Westinghouse R&D Center, 1310 Beulah Road, Pittsburgh, PA 15235, USA

N.J. Doyle

Westinghouse R&D Center, 1310 Beulah Road, Pittsburgh, PA 15235, USA

Abstract

An eighteen-sector rotating attenuator which can hold a maximum of thirty-six attenuating foils is described. The foils are of aluminum and are prepared by evaporation onto thin substrates of carbon or salt on glass slides and are subsequently floated free of the slides. Design considerations are presented and a particular He implant designed to match a damage energy profile in 304SS is used as an illustration.

1. Introduction

In charged-particle bombardment experiments aimed at simulating fast-neutron damage in metals and alloys, Helium is implanted in order to simulate the evolution of Helium due to (n, α) reactions. The displacement damage by the fast neutrons can be rapidly simulated by high-energy heavy-ion bombardment. Some years ago we demonstrated [1], [2] that co-implantation of Helium and high-energy heavy ions gives a more realistic simulation of fast-neutron damage than sequential implants. More recently this dual-beam ion implantation technique has been used to study rate and ion beam "History" effects, [3] Helium migration and trapping by extended defects, [4] and critical cavity sizes [5], [6] in stainless steels. In dual-beam experiments of the kind just mentioned it has been found to be very useful to be able to implant the Helium in such a manner as to keep the ratio of Helium dopant to high-energy heavy-ion displacement damage constant over a depth of several μm in the target.

In order to dope a target with He in the manner just described we constructed a rotating attenuator which has now been in constant service for several years. The device consists of a rotating wheel containing aluminum foils of various thicknesses. The foils "chop" a beam of 2 MeV Helium ions so as to vary the energy of the Helium beam in just such a way that the resultant implant gives the desired concentration profile between ∿1 μm and 3.5 μm. Aluminum foils of appropriate thickness are used to obtain a matching of the damage energy deposition profile and the Helium concentration profile over a depth of more than 2 μm. Details of the foil preparation and subsequent calibration will be given in the following sections. Specific examples cited in the text are all based on using

*Work supported in part by NSF grant DMR81-02968

[†]Now at Brooklyn College of CUNY, New York, NY 11210 USA

28 MeV Si^{+6} ions to create the atomic displacement damage in 304SS and simultaneously using He ions for doping the 304SS energies from 0.4 to 2.0 MeV.

2. Description of Foil Wheel

In Fig. 1 we show the foil wheel in its housing and the associated drive mechanism. The housing consists of a large diameter, shallow aluminum dish A, and a stainless steel cap B. Both halves of the housing are made in such a way that they can be readily attached to a 5 cm diameter beam line C. The cap B also has a port which holds a 5 cm diameter pyrex window D. Window D is used to examine the condition and position of the foils mounted on wheel, F. It is possible to replace foils through this port if the housing cannot be disturbed. The foil-wheel shaft is attached to a magnetically coupled rotary feedthrough E, which in turn is used to drive the wheel at 15 RPM. The attenuating aluminum foils H are mounted on frames G with a small amount of vacuum epoxy cement as shown in the inset.

Fig. 2 gives a more detailed picture of the foil-wheel and a particular arrangement of foils to be discussed in some detail. The wheel is composed of two parts; an outer rim A, and an inner disc B. Parts

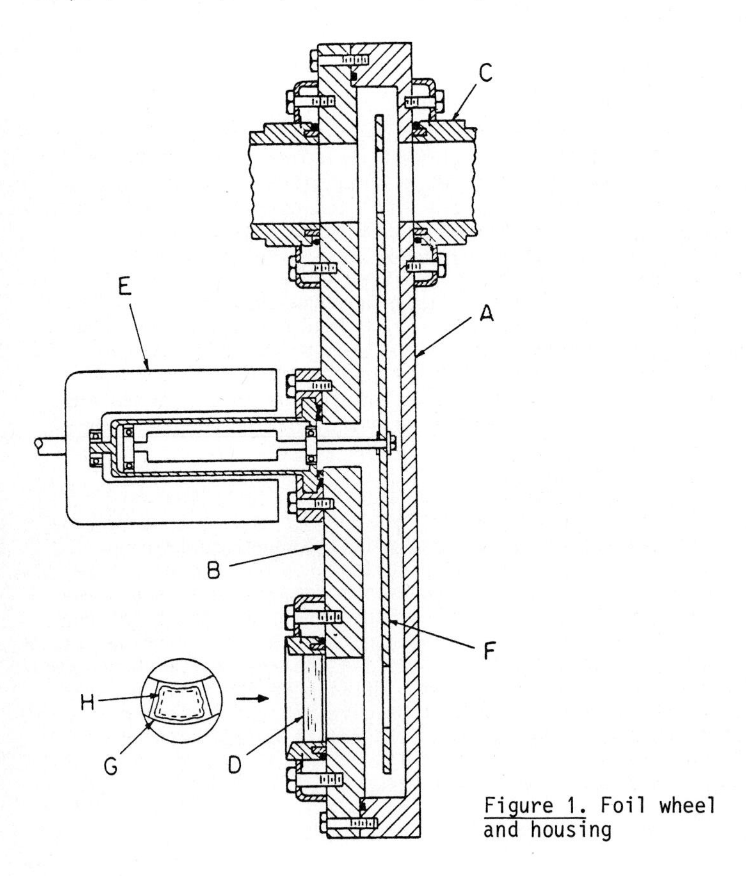

Figure 1. Foil wheel and housing

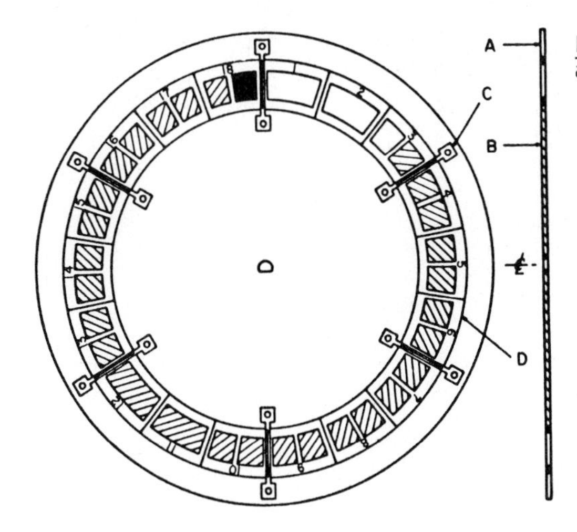

Figure 2. Attenuator wheel and foil arrangement

A and B are held together by six ribs C. Eighteen full-size foil-frames, D, fit on the wheel. In practice these frames may be further divided in order to enable one to mount a larger number of attenuating foils.

By making the aluminum foils of appropriate thicknesses the energy of the transmitted helium beam may be so partitioned as to give a desired spatial implantation profile in a particular sample material. For clarity's sake we shall limit the discussion to a specific set of aluminum foils used for Helium implants into 304SS. The foils are arranged as shown on Fig. 2. Two and a half frames are left open, one half frame is closed, 26 foils cover half frames, and two foils cover full frames. The aluminum foils varied in thickness from 0.75 μm to 5.3 μm. Foils less than 1 μm thick were prepared by evaporating aluminum on to 1000 Å thick carbon layers deposited on specially coated glass slides. The films (aluminum on carbon) were floated off in water. Foils thicker than 1 μm were made using glass slides covered with a 750 Å salt layer and subsequently floated off in water. Combinations of foils are used to obtain some of the thicknesses. Single foils and foil combinations have their thicknesses checked either by means of the energy loss experienced by the transmission of 5.486 MeV alpha particles of Am^{241} or the transmission of the He^+ beam from our 2 MeV Van de Graaff accelerator. Projected-range tables are computed with the stopping powers given by Ziegler [7] and using a modified EDEP-1 code of Manning and Mueller [8]. Since our implantations last for many hours the implants are averaged over thousands of revolutions of the wheel when an angular speed of 15 RPM is used.

3. Design Considerations

In Fig. 3 we plot the calculated damage energy profile for 28 MeV Si^{+6} ions in 304SS. In addition, we plot the schematic concentration profile of the implanted silicon which gives rise to the damage profile and the desired Helium implantation profile. The Helium is produced simultaneously in a separate 2 MeV Van de Graaff accelerator. What considerations are important in choosing the number and thickness of aluminum foils for the attenuator wheel in order to approximate the desired Helium profile shown in Fig. 3?

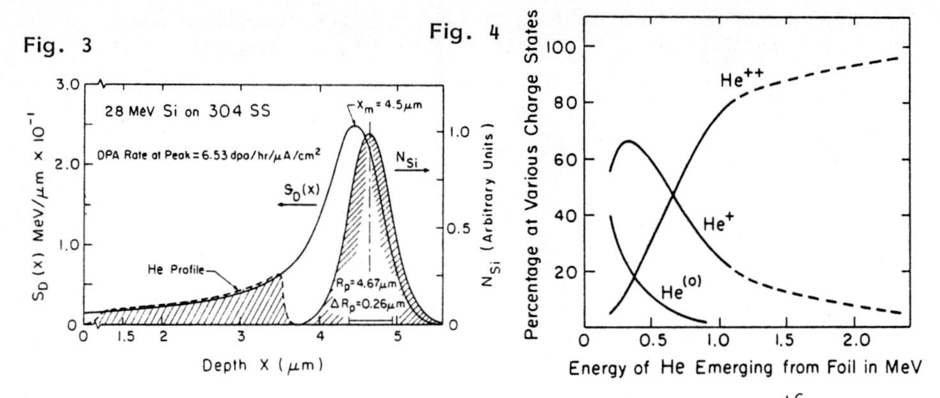

Figure 3. Calculated damage energy profile ($S_D(x)$) for 28 MeV Si^{+6} ions in 304SS and schematic concentration profiles for implanted He and Si

Figure 4. Various charge states of He passing through Al as a function of the energy at which the He is emerging from the foil. (Taken from data by G. A. Dissanaike[11])

The following three factors must be considered in making the choice of the thickness and combination of attenuating foils: (i) the energy straggling of the 2 MeV Helium beam in each foil, (ii) the multiple scattering of the 2 MeV Helium beam in each foil, (iii) the charge exchange of the 2 MeV He^+ ions as they traverse a particular foil thickness. One may obtain an order of magnitude estimate for each of these factors from the literature [9], [10], [11], [12]. We have also used backscattering measurements from thin gold foils to get a measure of the thickness and the energy straggle in our foils. Flux measurements at the actual sample position give a measure of the importance of multiple scattering. To interpret such measurements, however, requires a knowledge of the partitioning of the Helium into He^{++}, He^+, and He° as the particles emerge from a given foil. Fig. 4 gives the percentage of Helium at various charge states as a function of energy of the Helium as it emerges from an aluminum foil. The curves, with some extrapolation, are obtained from the data of G. A. Dissanaike [11].

Let us assume that we have deduced the transmission energy profiles for a large set of aluminum foils using incoming 2 MeV Helium ions. Let us further assume that we have a good measure, or estimate, of the particle flux for each foil at the surface of a 304SS sample. We are now in a position to calculate the Helium implantation profile for a particular choice of foils.

Given a particular choice of foils we first sum the Heilum particle current density transmitted through all the foils for one cycle of the wheel. If the Helium particle current density transmitted through the ith foil is n_i (He/cm^{2}sec), and the total time that the ith foil is exposed to the beam each cycle is τ_i(s), then $n_i \tau_i$ yields the total particle fluence due to the ith foil. The energy distribution of these $n_i\tau_i$ He atoms is reasonably well approximated by a Gaussian distribution centered at $\overline{E}_i$ with a FWHM of ΔE_i. E_i and ΔE_i may be estimated from data in the literature knowing the thickness of the film or may be obtained by means of scattering experiments. τ_i is determined by geometry or by how many frames this particular foil thickness occupies on the attenuator wheel. The energy distribution due to the ith foil may now be expressed as

$$N_i(E) = \frac{n_i \tau_i}{\sigma_{E_i} \sqrt{2\pi}} \exp \left[- \frac{[E - \bar{E}_i]^2}{2\sigma^2_{E_i}} \right] \quad (1)$$

where $\sigma_{E_i} = \frac{\Delta E_i}{2\sqrt{2 \ln 2}}$.

The total energy distribution of the transmitted Helium flux for one cycle of the degrader wheel can be obtained by summing all the individual foil contributions. We obtain

$$N(E) = \sum_i N_i(E) = \sum_i \frac{n_i \tau_i}{\sigma_{E_i} \sqrt{2\pi}} \exp \left[- \frac{[E - \bar{E}_i]^2}{2\sigma^2_{E_i}} \right] \quad . \quad (2)$$

For a particular choice of foils such an energy distribution is illustrated in Fig. 5.

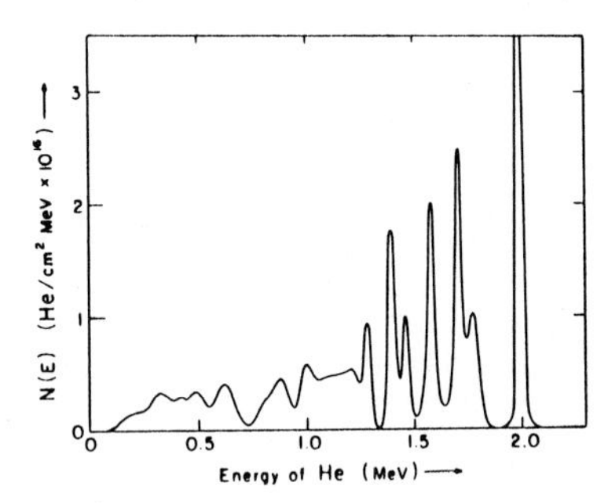

Figure 5. Total energy distribution N(E) of the transmitted He flux, for one cycle of the degrader wheel, using the particular choice of foils shown in Figure 2

We are finally ready to implant our known distribution of Helium atoms in to the 304SS target. Helium atoms with energy E will come to rest in a Gaussian distribution with a projected range $R_p(E)$ and a standard deviation $\Delta R_p(E)$. The depth distribution may be written as

$$f_E(x) = \frac{N(E)}{\sqrt{2\pi}\ \Delta R_p(E)} \exp \left[- \frac{1}{2} \left[\frac{x - R_p(E)}{\Delta R_p(E)} \right]^2 \right] \quad . \quad (3)$$

N(E) may be taken from Figure 5. The overall depth distribution is obtained by summing over all possible energies:

$$f(x) = \sum_E f_E(x) \rightarrow \int_0^\infty f_E(x) dE \quad . \quad (4)$$

This analysis may have to be iterated many times before a set of foils is found which will closely match the desired profile. In our example, the match to the $S_D(x)$ curve for 28 MeV Si in 304SS is shown on Figure 6b. R_p and ΔR_p were obtained using the EDEP-1 code with a fit of the electronic stopping power for aluminum from the data of Northcliffe and Schilling [13]. There is still much uncertainty about the precision to which ΔR_p is known. For that reason we have also calculated the depth distribution for 0.5 ΔR_p and 1.5 ΔR_p (Fig. 6a and 6c) to give the reader a feeling of the role this parameter plays in these fits. It is believed that ΔR_p is normally underestimated in these calculations so that the fit in Fig. 6b is perhaps the best representation of the actual situation.

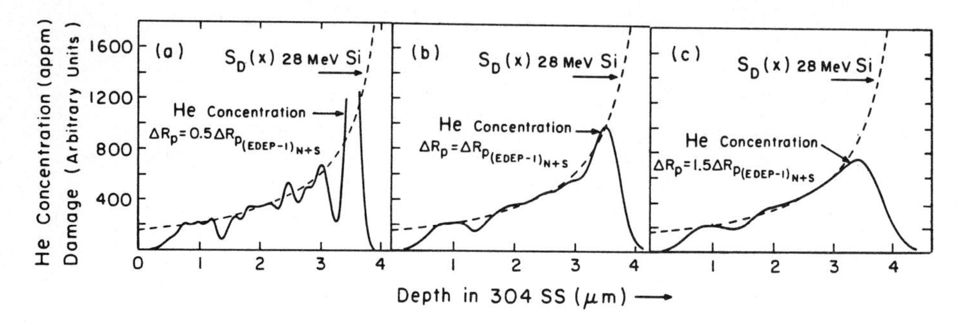

Figure 6. Match of He profile to damage profile $S_D(x)$ produced by 28MeV Si^{+6} ions in 304SS for (a.) $\Delta R_p = 0.5\ \Delta R_p$, (b.) $\Delta R_p = 1.0\ \Delta R_p$ and (c.) $\Delta R_p = 1.5\ \Delta R_p$

4. Summary

An eighteen-sector rotating attenuator which can house a maximum of 36 attenuating foils has been described. The apparatus has been in operation for several years and upon checking individual foils periodically no serious deterioration has been observed. Only one foil has torn in four years of operation. Good vacuum conditions (10^{-7} Torr) are required to keep hydrocarbon deposition to a minimum.

The aluminum foils were prepared by evaporation onto thin substrates of carbon or salt on glass slides and were subsequently floated free of the slides. This yielded far more uniform foils than those commercially available.

Required foil thickness and the relative angular space to be occupied by each thickness of foil may be estimated from published results on energy straggling, multiple scattering, and charge exchange. However, when one deals with thin foils one is never quite certain about foil density, pin-holes, surface texture and purity. These experimental variables may effect the final particle flux at the target in unknown ways. It would therefore be desirable to be able to do very accurate and careful scattering and flux measurements in order to have more confidence in the energy profiles and the effects of multiple scattering. However, this is a very time-consuming process and in the final analysis one still has an uncertainty about the implanted profile due to the uncertainty in ΔR_p. The ideal solution would be to find a way to quickly and accurately profile the implant experimentally.

References

1. J. N. McGruer, W. J. Choyke, J. R. Townsend, J. H. Chang, J. D. Yesso, J. A. Spitznagel, N. J. Doyle and F. J. Venskytis, J. Nucl. Mater. 74, 174 (1978).

2. W. J. Choyke, J. N. McGruer, J. R. Townsend, J. A. Spitznagel, N. J. Doyle and F. J. Venskytis, J. Nucl. Mater. 85 & 86 647 (1979).

3. W. J. Choyke, J. A. Spitznagel, S. Wood, N. J. Doyle, J. N. McGruer, J. R. Townsend, Nucl. Instr. and Methods 182/183 489 (1981).

4. J. A. Spitznagel, S. Wood, N. J. Doyle, W. J. Choyke, J. N. McGruer, J. R. Townsend and R. B. Irwin, J. Nucl. Mater. 103/104, 1463 (1981).

5. J. A. Spitznagel, W. J. Choyke, N. J. Doyle, R. B. Irwin, J. R. Townsend and J. N. McGruer; to be published in Jour. of Nucl. Mater. (1982).

6. J. R. Townsend; to be published in Jour. of Nucl. Mater. (1982).

7. J. F. Ziegler, "Helium Stopping Powers and Ranges in All Elemental Matter" Vol. IV, Pergamon Press, New York (1977).

8. I. Manning and G. P. Mueller, Computer Physics Communications 7, 85 (1974).

9. J. M. Harris and M. A. Nicolet, Phys. Rev. B 11, 1013 (1975).

10. B. L. Cohen, Rev. Sci. Instr. 33, 86 (1962).

11. G. A. Dissanaike, Phil. Mag. Ser 7 44, 1051 (1953).

12. S. K. Allison, Rev. Mod. Phys. 30, 1137 (1958).

13. L. C. Northcliffe and R. F. Schilling, Nuclear Data Tables, A7, 233 (1970).

Part V

Ion Beam Lithography

Ion-Beam Lithography

H. Ryssel and K. Haberger

Fraunhofer-Institut für Festkörpertechnologie, Paul-Gerhardt-Allee 42, D-8000 München 60, Fed. Rep. of Germany

Abstract

Ion-beam lithography is a potential method for producing patterns in photoresist with a higher resolution than that of electron-beam or x-ray lithography. In this paper, the advantages and limitations of ion-beam lithography in respect to resist sensitivity, ranges and lateral speed of ions, as well as resolution, will be discussed.

1. Introduction

Lithography is one of the most important technological steps in semiconductor fabrication. For VLSI circuits, dimensions of 1 to 2 μm are used presently, and the trend is towards still smaller dimensions. Electron-beam writing is used for mask making and also to small extent, for direct resist exposure of the wafer [1-3]. It is limited, by fast backscattered and secondary electrons, to dimensions of about 0.3 μm under practical semiconductor-fabrication conditions. X-ray lithography is a new tool which is being intensely investigated as a future means of mass production for integrated circuits with submicron dimensions; however, it requires a writing system for mask fabrication [4-7].

Ion-beam lithography is a new technique which, although still in an early development stage, already shows great promise for the fabrication of devices with submicron details. The reasons for this are the high resolution possible with ions and the high sensitivity of resists to ions. The sensitivity of resists to ions is higher than to electrons and x rays, because the energy deposition per unit path length is higher for ions. Therefore, a lower exposure dose is required. The reasons for the high resolution are that ions do not suffer from the so-called proximity effect of electrons, which is caused by fast backscattered and secondary electrons, and do not produce photoelectrons as in the case of x rays (200 eV to 2 keV, depending on the wavelength). Ions produce only low-energy secondary electrons (5 eV to 50 eV). Therefore, the structures are defined by the primary ion beam, and are limited only by the straggling of the ions, which is less than the range of the electrons produced by electron beams and x rays.

Ion-beam lithography can be performed in two different ways. By writing with a focused ion beam, mask making or direct writing on the wafer is possible, in competition with electron-beam lithography. This technique has been treated extensively in the most recent paper by Seliger [34]. Masked ion-beam lithography, or ion-beam projection using self-supporting masks [24,31,35], could evolve as a new technique for mass production of VLSI circuits, in competition with x-ray lithography.

2. Resist Sensitivity

Ions deposit their energy in a much smaller volume of the resists than electrons or x rays do. This results in an increased sensitivity, expressed as the number of particles per unit area or charge per unit area needed to expose a certain resist. If no resonance phenomena take place, however, the energy deposition required per unit volume is very similar for all three. Therefore, for ion-beam exposure, all electron-beam and x-ray resists are well suited, with the probable exception of DCOPA, an x-ray resist showing an especially high sensitivity for the palladium L_α (4.37Å) wavelength. Usually, the resists are polymers, and the exposure process results in cross-linking (negative resists), or scission of molecular chains (positive resists). Recently, however, inorganic resists have also been used, mainly GeSe, which work similarly to standard photographic emulsions. Their great disadvantage at present is their low sensitivity.

In Fig.1, typical characteristics are given for hydrogen exposure of different positive resists. The sensitivity lies between 2×10^{11} and $6 \times 10^{12} cm^{-2}$, corresponding to 3.2×10^{-8} and 10^{-6} $Cbcm^{-2}$. All resists show a very high contrast between 3 and 6. Development was performed for 2 min in 1 MIBK:1 IPA [8]. A comparison of exposure characteristics obtained with argon, helium, and electrons is shown in Fig. 2 [9]. It is observed that the sensitivities for helium and argon are about 60 and 120 times higher,

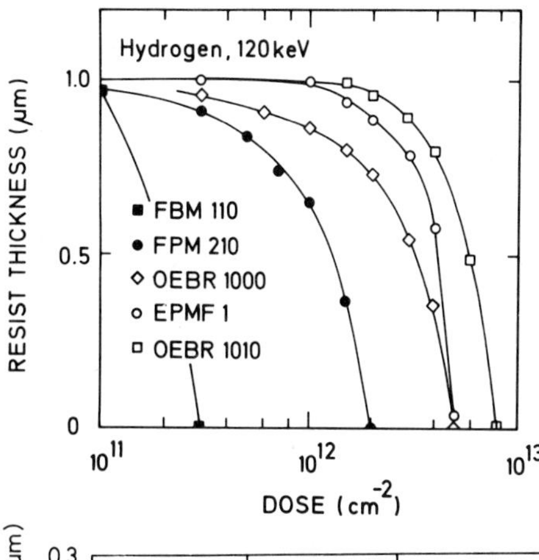

Fig. 1. Exposure of different positive resists with 120 keV hydrogen ions (FBM 110 is a FAMA, FPM 210 is a FAMA, OEBR 1000 a PMMA + ECA, EPMFI a PMMA, and OEBR 1010 a PMIBK + AN resist, respectively)

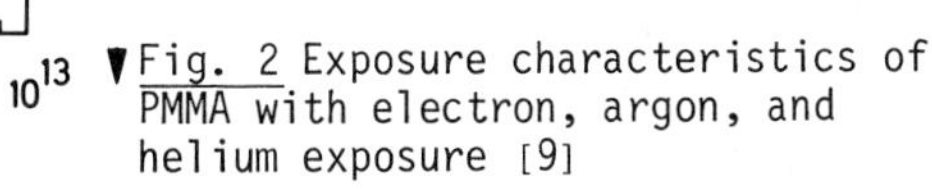

▼Fig. 2 Exposure characteristics of PMMA with electron, argon, and helium exposure [9]

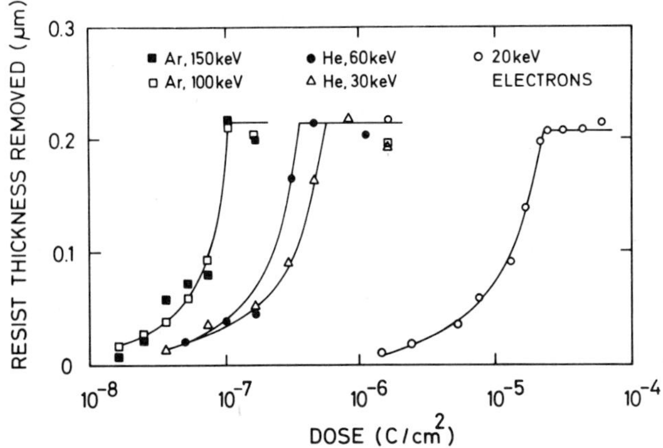

respectively, than for electrons. For other resists, increases in sensitivity up to 100 for hydrogen, 150 for helium, and 300 and 400 for argon and gallium ions, respectively in comparison to exposure by 20 keV electrons, were found [8]. Brault et al. [10] have made a very extensive study of the hydrogen exposure of different resists in comparison to electrons. In Fig. 3, the relationship between proton-beam (100 keV) and electron-beam (20 keV) sensitivity of the investigated resists is shown. They found an enhancement factor between 7.8 and 220. Their data suggest that the increased effectiveness of the proton beam relative to the electron beam is generally greater for resists with low sensitivities than for those with high sensitivities.

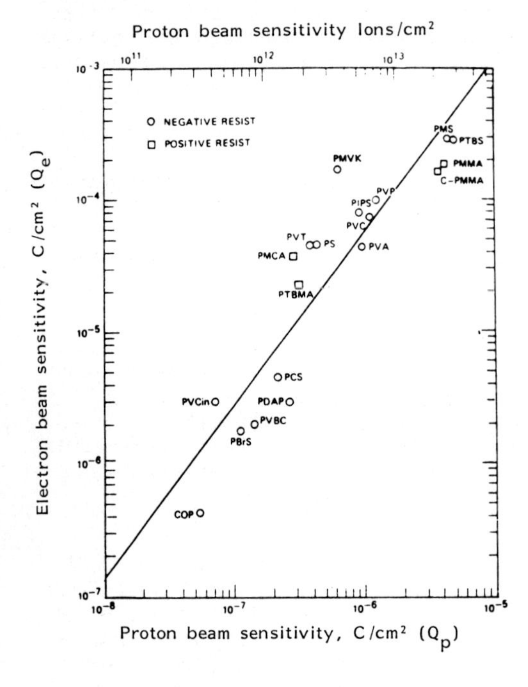

Fig. 3 Relationship between proton-beam (100 keV) and electron-beam (20 keV) sensitivity of photoresists

In general, it is assumed that the increased sensitivity of resists to ions is due to the higher energy deposition per unit volume in comparison to electrons. Hall et al. [17] have found, however, that heavy ions can be more efficient than can be accounted for on the basis of their energy loss. For NOVOLAC, e.g., the required energy deposited for exposure is reduced by 10, whereas for PMMA, it is approximately constant. This effect is so interpreted that for some resists (e.g. NOVOLAC), two sites of adjacent chains have to be activated simultaneously to obtain cross-linking, which is easier with heavy ions than with light ions or electrons; other resists (e.g. PMMA) require only one site to be activated for exposure, and therefore show no energy-dissipation dependence. Hall et al., however, used ion energies in the MeV range, and the relevance of their experiments for practical applications is not clear.

For electron and x-ray exposure, it is assumed that the sensitivity of a resist depends on the molecular weight. This was found to be true for polystyrene resist over more than two orders of magnitude by Brault and

Miller [10]; for the mostly-used positive PMMA resist, however, no clear correlation could be found [8].

Usable in ion-beam lithography are not only polymer resists or inorganic resists such as GeSe which work similarly to silver-based photography films, but virtually any polymer as well; and in addition, many inorganic layers used in semiconductor technology can be used either as a positive or as a negative resist. As positive resists, e.g., SiO_2 and Si_3N_4 can be used [14,15]. Their etch rate is greatly enhanced by ion exposure, due to the breaking of bonds. In contrast to polymer resists, this is caused mainly by nuclear processes; therefore, heavy ions are better suited. The doses required for these resist systems are fairly high, 10^{14} to 10^{16} cm^{-2}, and can only be achieved in a reasonable time using projection systems. Using reactive ion etching, many compounds show the opposite behavior. In a suitable plasma, only the unimplanted areas are etched away, whereas the implanted ions produce non-volatile compounds [16]. However, for these processes too, very high doses between 10^{15} and 10^{16} cm^{-2} are necessary.

In general, various mechanisms are responsible for the ion-beam exposure of different resists. The scission of bonds, by ionization (electronic stopping) or displacement (nuclear stopping), is the main mechanism for polymer resists or inorganic resists such as SiO_2 or Si_3N_4, respectively.

3. Range of Ions

The enhanced sensitivity of resists to ions is caused by the high energy deposition rate. A disadvantage of this is that only a limited resist thickness can be exposed. Depending on the application, resists up to 2 µm thick have to be exposed, unless complicated multilevel resists are used. On silicon wafers, resists of 1 to 2 µm thickness are used, in order to cover the non-planar surface and to provide a mask for etching or implantation; for mask making, thinner resists of several thousand Ångstroms are sufficient.

A comparison between exposable thickness and projected range, for different ions in PMMA, is given as a function of ion energy in Fig. 4. With 200 keV hydrogen ions, resist layers with a thickness of up to 1.5 µm can easily be exposed. Ions with larger masses have a smaller range, and can therefore expose only thinner layers. Therefore, for thick resist layers, hydrogen and helium are best suited. With argon and gallium, resist layers of only up to a few thousand Ångstroms can be exposed. In the case of gallium (for which sources of high brightness exist), resists as thick as in the case of argon can be exposed, although the mass ratio is 1.75. The reason for this is not yet clear. For the other ions, R_p is well suited for a rough estimate of the exposable thickness.

To calculate the exposable thickness more exactly, Monte Carlo calculations of the energy deposition have to be performed and combined with a development model, as will be described in the next section. Such calculations are included in Fig. 4 for comparison, and show a good agreement between experiment and theory, however, again not for gallium.

To circumvent the problem of the low range of heavy ions, inorganic resists can be used, e.g., germanium selenide/silver selenide [10-13]. This resist consists of a thin $GeSe_2$ layer (≈ 2000 Å) covered with a very thin Ag_2Se layer (100 Å). By exposing the resist with ions, silver from the Ag_2Se layer migrates into the underlying $GeSe_2$ film, and makes it insoluble in the developer after stripping the Ag_2Se layer. The advantage of this negative resist is that, in contrast to polymer resists (where the

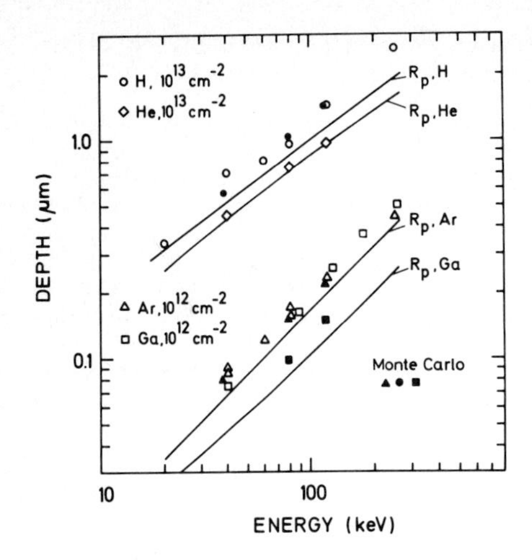

Fig. 4. Removed thickness of Dupont Elvacite 2008 PMMA resist after exposure with 10^{13} cm^{-2} hydrogen and helium, and 10^{12} cm^{-2} argon and gallium, in comparison to projected range data of argon, hydrogen, helium and gallium

ions have to penetrate the entire thickness of the resist), the ions have to penetrate only the thin $AgSe_2$ layer. Additionally, both nuclear and electronic stopping contribute to the exposure process, whereas polymers are mainly exposed by ionization caused by electronic stopping. This is especially important for low-energy heavy ions, which are effectively produced in field ion sources. The sensitivity of this resist is lower than that of polymer resists, and was found to lie between 10^{13} and 10^{15} cm^{-2}. By oblique deposition, it can be enhanced up to a factor of 20 [12].

4. Resolution

Because of the high sensitivity of ion-beam resists, the achievable resolution is limited. This is not caused by secondary phenomena as is the case with electron-beam lithography (fast backscattered and secondary electrons produce a electron cloud around the exposed pixel, causing a widening of the exposure spot and the proximity effect of two pixels exposed close to each other) or x-ray lithography (photoelectrons, however with smaller energies than in electron-beam lithography), but is caused by the high sensitivity itself and by the lateral spread of the exposing ions.

If a resist with a sensitivity S (particles per unit area) is assumed, then the minimum number of particles in a pixel has to be:

$$N_{min} = Sl^2 \quad . \tag{1}$$

The smallest feature size which can be resolved is obtained from Eq. (1) by setting l=1:

$$l_{min} = S^{-1/2} \quad . \tag{2}$$

Equation (2) is plotted in Fig. 5. One can see that, e.g., for a resist with a sensitivity of 10^{10} cm^{-2}, the minimum feature size is 1000 Å; for a resist with a sensitivity of only 10^{13} cm^{-2}, much smaller features of about 30 Å could be resolved.

A restriction upon such high resolution is posed by the lateral spread of the exposing ions. In Fig. 6, results of Monte Carlo calculations for

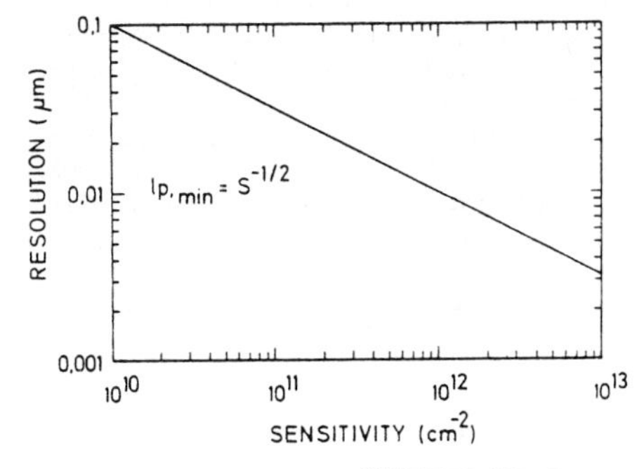

Fig. 5. Resolution vs sensitivity of resists

▼ Fig. 6. Trajectories of 60 keV hydrogen ions passing thru PMMA, PMMA on gold, and PMMA on silicon [20]

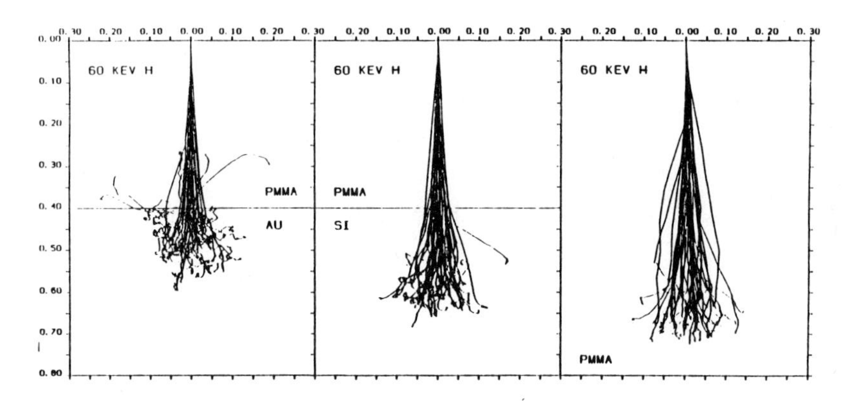

60 keV hydrogen ions in thick PMMA, and in thin PMMA on gold and silicon, are given [20], showing clearly the lateral spread of the ion paths during the slowing-down process. For the exposure, however, not the lateral straggling of the ions themselves, but rather that of the energy deposition into electronic stopping, is relevant. This can be calculated according to the LSS theory [21], as well as by Monte Carlo simulations [20,22]. Together with the known specific energy deposition required for exposure, the resist profile can be calculated; however, only for an infinite development time. For a finite development time, a calculation of

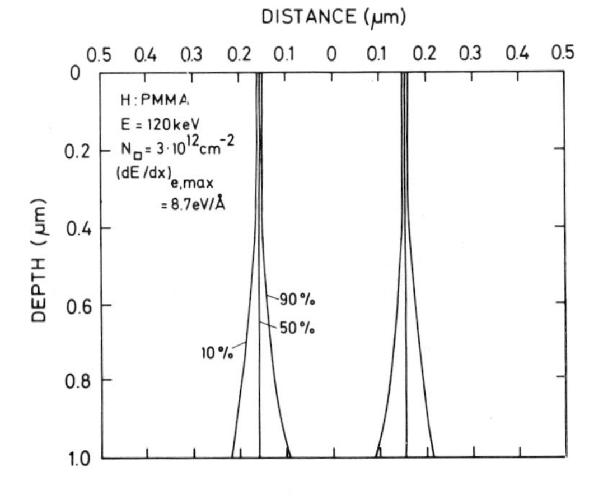

Fig. 7. Energy deposition into electronic processes, for 120 keV hydrogen exposure of a 3000 Å wide line with a dose of $3x10^{12}$ cm^{-2} in PMMA

such profiles is possible, using a suitable development model. Examples for such calculations are given in Figs. 7 and 8, for the energy deposited into electronic processes, as well as the resulting profiles after development for various times [22]. For the simulation, a 3000 Å wide line was assumed. It is clearly seen that the lateral energy deposition and the lateral extent of the developed profiles are smaller than 200 Å, easily allowing the resolution of submicron patterns. More results on Monte Carlo simulations can be found in the papers by Karapiperis et al. [37] and Hoffmann et al. [38].

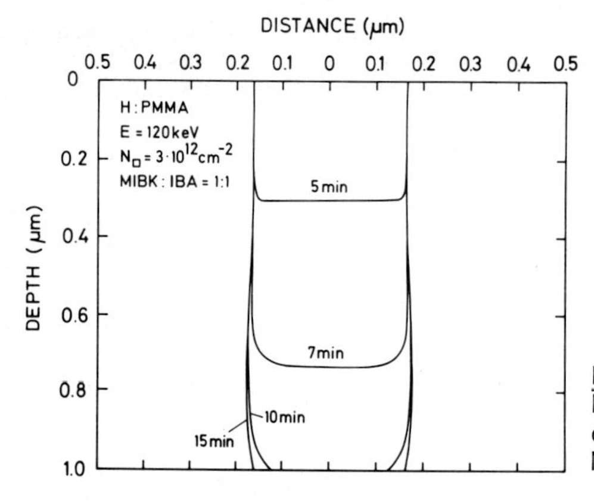

Fig. 8. Developed profiles in PMMA: Exposure with 120 keV hydrogen at a dose of 3×10^{12} cm $^{-2}$, development in MIBK : IPA = 1:1 at 20°C

5. Statistical Limitations

Since the sensitivity of ion-beam resists is high, only a few particles are required for the exposure of a small pixel. Again assuming a resist with a sensitivity of 10^{11} cm^{-2}, only 40 particles are required to expose a 0.2 x 0.2 μm^2 pixel, and only 10 for a 0.1 x 0.1 μm^2 pixel.

The emission of ions from an ion source, however, is a statistical process, i.e., the beam is subjected to shot noise. The mean square deviation of the number of ions is:

$$\sigma = \sqrt{\bar{N}} \qquad (3)$$

where $\bar{N}$ is the average number of particles. The number of particles N arriving in a pixel can be calculated by Poisson statistics to be:

$$p(N,\bar{N}) = \frac{N^{\bar{N}}}{N!} \exp\left[-\bar{N}\right] \qquad (4)$$

The probability of an improper exposure with $N \leq N_{min}$ particles is then given by:

$$P = \sum_{N=0}^{N_{min}-1} p\,(N,\bar{N}) \qquad (5)$$

Numerical calculations of Eq. (5) are given in Fig. 9, yielding the minimum dose required for a proper exposure depending on resist sensitivity and minimum feature size [18]. For calculating the curves, it was assumed that the possibility of a single underexposure is below 1% for an exposed field of 1 cm^2 consisting of 1 cm^2/l^2 pixels. From Fig. 9, it can be seen that the "200 particles per pixel" criterion [19] is much too stringent. The broken line is the limit of the sensitivity for a specific feature size; if lower doses are sufficient for exposure, then the desired feature size cannot be resolved. In contrast to e-beam exposure, an overexposure with ions is easily possible without producing a line broadening caused by the electron cloud.

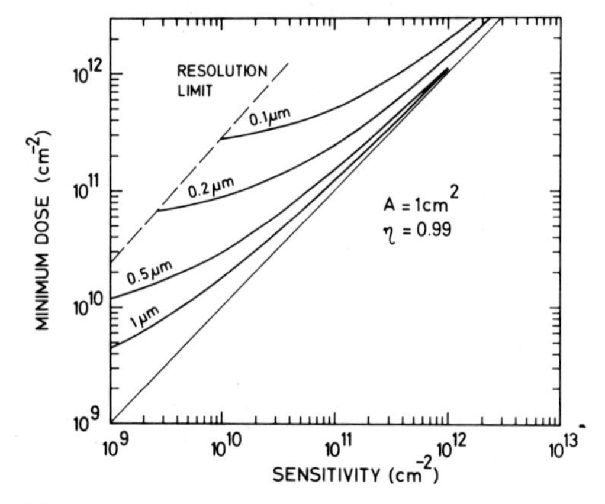

Fig. 9. Minimum exposure dose vs resist sensitivity as a function of minimum line width

6. Radiation Damage

Ions which penetrate the resist deposit their remaining energy in the substrate, and may produce radiation damage. For the exposure of masks, this is of no importance; for semiconductors, and particularly for oxide layers, such damage is serious. The energy of the ions cannot be adjusted in such a way that all energy is deposited into the resist, since due to other technological processes, steps exist in the surface topography of the wafers, and the resist therefore has a varying thickness. For e-beam and x-ray exposure, the formation of fixed charges, surface states, and neutral traps was found in MOS structures [23]. Bartelt et al. [24] have investigated the effect by irradiating MOS devices not covered with resist with hydrogen ions of different energies at doses between 1 and 10 x 10^{13} cm^{-2}. Device parameters were measured prior to irradiation, after irradiation, and after annealing at 450°C. Without annealing, a shift in the threshold voltage and the transconductance was obtained; but after annealing, no observable damage remained.

Similar results obtained with hydrogen and argon exposure of MOS capacitors are shown in Fig. 10, where V_{TP} (the voltage of the turning point of the slope of the capacitance-voltage curve for MOS capacitors) is plotted against exposure dose. This voltage is very sensitive to charged traps near the oxide-silicon interface. All samples, except no. 5, were annealed at 450°C before metallization. As shown in this figure, the capacitance-voltage curve is only affected seriously for argon implanted directly into the thin oxide. Thus, at least for hydrogen irradiation, serious limitations in the use of ion-beam lithography can be excluded.

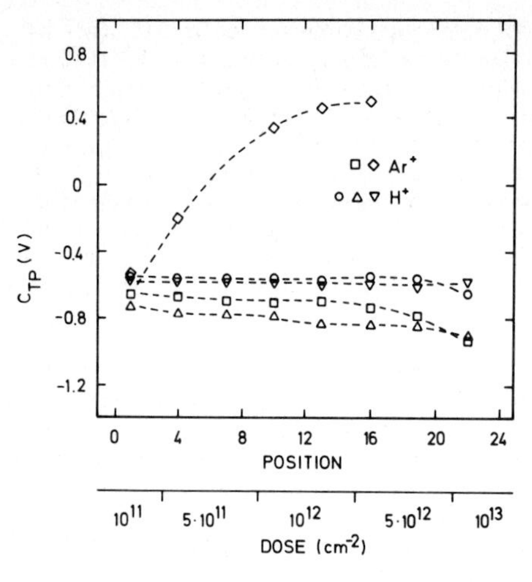

Fig. 10. C-V turning point voltage as a function of exposure dose, measured at 86 kHz

1 ○ H^+ 120 keV through 1 µm PMMA on 70 nm SiO_2
2 ▽ H^+ 120 keV through 70 nm SiO_2
3 △ H^+ 120 keV through 1 µm PMMA on 400 nm Al on 70 nm SiO_2
4 ◇ Ar^+ 120 keV through 70 nm SiO_2
5 □ Ar^+ 120 keV through 400 nm Al on 70 nm SiO_2

7. Ion-Beam Writing and Ion-Beam Projection

The most obvious application of ion-beam lithography is to write with a focused beam. In comparison to electron-beam lithography, this avoids proximity problems, and offers high resolution down to the physical limits of solid-state technology.

With the considerations above regarding ion species and energy, the specifications of a writing system are given if one restricts the design considerations to commonly used organic resists. This means that especially for direct writing on the wafer, hydrogen ions should be used at an energy of 50 to 200 keV, to expose resists thick enough for proper step coverage and low pinhole densities. For the exposure of masks, thinner resists can be used, and heavy ions such as gallium may therefore be applied.

Similarly to e-beam machines, the necessary system consists of an ion source, a beam current regulator, a blanking system, deflectors to guide the writing beam over the wafer, and at least one lens to image the emitter region of the ion source, or the smallest beam-defining aperture, onto the wafer [28,33]. A high brightness of the ion source is very important to obtain a reasonable writing speed. Field ion sources working with hydrogen or gallium have brightnesses up to 10^6 $Acm^{-2}sr^{-1}$ [25 - 28], very close to those of electron sources. However, ion-beam writing is the subject of the preceding paper by Seliger [34], and will therefore not be treated here in detail.

Ion-beam projection is a possible means for mass production of submicron devices by parallel transfer of the mask pattern, as in the case of optical lithography. A parallel transfer of mask patterns is possible by ion-optical imaging and by 1:1 proximity printing. Both methods are very similar to optical exposure.

Two different approaches for the imaging transfer of a mask pattern to a substrate have been studied. Ion optical imaging has been carried out by Bernheim in France [3o]. Here, metal structures, kept at an appropriate electrical potential on an insulating substrate, served as lateral selective mirrors for the ions, and the pattern was demagnified onto a target.

This approach has not been used for lithography purposes. The other method has been developed at Sacher Technik in Vienna [15]. A broad homogeneous ion beam illuminates a mask. The mask consists of a self-supporting metal foil, fabricated by conventional photolithographic techniques. The image of this mask is subsequently demagnified by a factor of 10, and is projected onto the wafer. The ion-beam energy ranges up to 100 keV. With this equipment, a 5x5 cm^2 mask is reduced to an exposure region of 5x5 mm^2. The total calculated aberration of the demagnifying lens system, within the 5x5 mm^2 image area, is in the range of 0.05 µm. However, the fabrication of the transparent mask is difficult, and isolated structures are only possible using two exposure steps.

A more promising approach is to use a transparent channeling mask. This approach is being investigated by Hughes [24,31,35], as well as by our own Institute [32]. Since no self-supporting masks fine enough for submicron fabrication are available, a crystal lattice is used as a support. Based on the silicon-thinning technique, as used for x-ray masks, gold is evaporated and patterned on single-crystal silicon foils. An appropriately-oriented hydrogen beam, at energies up to several 100 keV, is channeled along a crystal axis with a very great reduction in multiple scattering.

A relatively thin metal pattern (Au thickness less than 1000 Å) is sufficient to scatter and dechannel the incident beam [32]. Furthermore, the energy of the incident beam is selected so that the scattered portion of the beam has a very small probability of transmission through the silicon membrane. Another approach uses thick absorbing gold layers [24,38]. Both principles are shown in Fig. 11.

As indicated in the experimental diagram, the channeled particles still have the necessary energy and a small enough angular spread, after traversing the single-crystal silicon foil, to expose the resist layer.

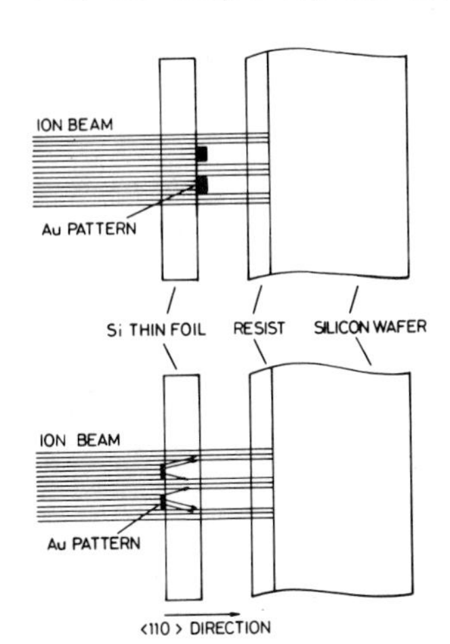

Fig. 11. Comparison of two approaches for channeled-ion-beam lithography. Upper: thick absorbing layer, lower: thin scattering layer

In the case of ion-beam projection lithography (masked ion-beam lithography), the resolution is limited by scattering [35] and diffraction [36]. The ultimate restriction is posed by corpuscular diffraction. The corpuscular wavelength is given by:

$$\lambda = 0.28 / \sqrt{ME} \qquad (6)$$

with M the molecular weight, E the energy in eV, and λ in Å. The diffraction caused by the quantum uncertainty can be estimated to be:

$$d = 1.22\ s\lambda\ /\ r \quad , \tag{7}$$

where r is the effective radius of the channel and s is the proximity distance between wafer and mask. α corresponds to the angle of the particle beam after leaving the channeling mask:

$$\alpha = 1.22\ \lambda\ /\ r \quad . \tag{8}$$

Equation (7) results in an ultimate resolution of about 0.1 µm and a beam divergence of 0.1° for a 100 keV proton beam, assuming a proximity distance of 50 µm and an effective channel radius of 1 Å.

8. Conclusion

The use of ion beams promises many advantages for lithography. Resists are two to three orders of magnitude more sensitive to ions than to electrons, and ions offer very high resolution similar to x-ray lithography. These features can be taken advantage of by proximity printing, as well as by ion-beam writing with a focused beam. Great efforts are being made to develop both approaches. If a need for ultra large-scale integration should arise, ions would be applicable for this purpose too, to the physically feasible limits.

References

1. D.R. Herriott, R.J. Coller, D.S. Alles and J.W. Stafford, IEEE Trans. Electron Devices ED22, 385 (1975)

2. G.L. Varnell, Proc. Kodak Interface '72, 56 (1973)

3. E.V. Weber and H. S. Yourke, Electronics, Nov. 10,96 (1977)

4. D.L. Spears and H.I. Smith, Electronics Lett. 8, 102 (1972)

5. W.D. Buckey and G.P. Hughes, J. Electrochem. Soc. 128, 1106 (1981)

6. A. Heuberger, H. Betz and S. Pongratz in: Advances in Solid State Physics, Vol.XX, p.259, Ed. J. Treusch, Braunschweig (1980)

7. E. Spiller and R. L. Feder in: X-Ray Optics-Applications to Solids, p.35, Ed. H.J. Queisser, Springer, Berlin and New York (1977)

8. H. Ryssel and K. Haberger, J. Vac. Sci. Technol. 19, 1358 (1981)

9. M. Komuro, N. Atoda and H. Kawakatsu, J. Electrochem. Soc. 126, 483 (1979)

10. G.R. Brault and L.J. Miller, Polymer Engineering & Science 20, 1064 (1980)

11. K.L.Tai, W.R. Sinclair, R.G. Vadinsky, J.M. Moran and M.J. Rand, J. Vac. Sci. Technol. 16, 1977 (1979)

12. T. Venkatesan, J. Vac. Sci. Technol. 19, 1368 (1981)

13. K. Balasubramanyam and A.L. Ruoff, J. Vac. Sci. Technol. 19, 1374 (1981)

14. K. Moriwaki, H. Aritome and S. Namba, Microcircuit Engineering 80, Amsterdam (1980)

15. G. Stengel, R. Kaitna, H. Löschner, P. Wolf and R. Sacher, J. Vac. Sci. Technol. 16, 1883 (1979)

16. T. Venkatesan, G.N. Taylor, A. Wagner, B. Wilkens and D. Barr, J. Vac. Sci. Technol. 16, 1379 (1981)

17. T.M. Hall, A. Wagner and L.F. Thompson, J. Vac. Sci. Technol. 16, 1889 (1979)

18. H. Ryssel, G. Prinke, H. Bernt, K. Haberger and K. Hoffmann, Appl. Phys. A 27, 239 (1982)

19. J.S. Greeneich in: Electron Beam Technology in Microelectronic Fabrication, Ed. G.R. Brewer, Acad. Press, New York (1980)

20. K. Karapiperis, L. Adesida, S.A. Lee and E. D. Wolf, J. Vac. Sci. Technol. 19, 1259 (1981)

21. K.B. Winterbon, Ion Implantation Range and Energy Deposition Distributions, Plenum Press, New York (1975)

22. K. Hoffmann, J. Biersack and H. Ryssel, to be published

23. K.F. Galloway et al., J. Electrochem. Soc. 126, 245 (1979)

24. J.L. Bartelt, C.W. Slayman, J. E. Wood, J.Y. Chen, C.M. McKenna, C.P. Minning, J.F. Coakley, R.E. Holman and C.M. Perygo, J. Vac. Sci. Technol. 19, 1166 (1981)

25. R. Clampitt and D.K. Jeffries, Inst. Phys. Conf. Ser. No. 38, p. 12 (1978)

26. J. Orloff and L. W. Swanson, 14th. Symp. on Electron, Ion and Photon Beam Technol., USA, May (1977)

27. G.R. Hanson and B.M. Siegel, Electrochem. Soc. Meeting, St. Louis, (1980)

28. W.L. Brown, T. Venkatesan and A. Wagner, Solid State Technol. 24, 60 (1981)

29. I.L. Berry, J. Vac. Sci. Technol. 19, 1153 (1981)

30. M. Bernheim, Electrochem. Soc. Meeting, Los Angeles (1970)

31. D.B. Rensch, R.L. Seliger, G. Csonsky, R.D. Olney and H.L. Staver, J. Vac. Sci. Technol. 16, 1897 (1979)

32. L. Csepregi, F. Iberl and P. Eichinger, Microcircuit Engineering 80, Amsterdam (1980)

33. R.L. Seliger, J.W. Ward, V. Wang and R.L. Kubena, Appl. Phys. Lett. 34, 310 (1979)

34. R.L. Seliger, C.M. McKenna, and J.W. Ward, these proceedings

35. J. Bartelt, C. McKenna, and C. Slayman, Electrochem. Soc. Spring Meeting, Montreal (1982)

36. H. Ryssel and K. Haberger, Microcircuit Engineering 81, Ed. A. Oosenbrug (1981)

37. L. Karapiperis, I.Adesida, C.D.Lee, and E.D. Wolf, these proceedings

38. K. Hoffmann, K. Haberger, M. Forster, and H. Ryssel, these proceedings

Development Characteristics of Ga^+ Exposed PMMA and Associated Lithographic Resolution Limits

L. Karapiperis*, I. Adesida, C.A. Lee, and E.D. Wolf
National Submicron Facility, Cornell University, Ithaca, NY 14853, USA

With the development of liquid metal sources, Ga has become an important ion species for Ion Beam Lithographic applications. Thin PMMA films are exposed to 250keV Ga^+ ions for a series of doses (0.06×10^{-6} C/cm^2 - 0.14×10^{-6} C/cm^2) and they are subsequently developed in a 1:1 (MIBK:IPA) solution. Development depth versus time curves are determined. A number of conclusions concerning the exposure and development mechanisms are deduced from the particular shape of the above curves. Important differences between heavy and light ions concerning their effectiveness in resist exposure are pointed out. With the help of a Monte Carlo type program, called PIBER , which furnishes three-dimensional energy-loss data for ions traversing amorphous solids, and a specially-developed fitting-scheme, development parameters for Ga^+-irradiated PMMA are derived. Development profiles in PMMA are computer simulated. Lithographic resolution limits due to Ga^+ ion scattering in PMMA are thus established.

1. Introduction

Ion-beam Lithography (IBL) is the latest entry in the already existing variety of lithographic methods. Although still at the development stage, it promises a unique combination of direct writing capability, a resolution superior to that of E-beam lithography and a greater speed.

These properties follow from the simple fact that charged particles (hence deflectable) are employed, whose mass is a few thousand times heavier than that of electrons and whose energy loss per unit length is one to two orders of magnitude higher than that of electrons of comparable energy.

The high resolution capabilities of light ion beams have already been demonstrated experimentally [1, 2, 3, 4] and investigated theoretically in some detail [5]. The problem with light ions is that suitably bright, stable and finely-focused source/column systems are hard to realize, although encouraging progress has been made on the source side [6]. As a consequence, attention has been focused on ion sources of the liquid metal type which, in addition, hold promise for direct implantation [7, 8].

As in the case of E-beam lithography, an important aspect of the IBL development effort is the theoretical simulation of developed profiles in resist. Such a study has already been carried out with H^+ exposure of PMMA [5]. In the present work, the above mentioned study will be extended to a heavy ion, such as Ga^+, whose technological importance derives from the use of liquid gallium emission sources.

As it will be shown later, there exist important differences in the development behaviour of PMMA exposed to light and heavy ions. Lastly, it must be pointed out that the energy loss algorithm employed in the present work does not take into account recoil atoms.

* and Physics Department, Cornell University, Ithaca, NY 14853, USA
Present address:Thomson-CSF,LCR,Domaine de Corbeville,91401 Orsay,France

2. Experimental Results

A standard commercial PMMA powder was used in the course of the experiments. Its nominal molecular weight was given as 950,000. A gel permeatton analysis yielded a weight average molecular weight of 567,248 and a number average molecular weight of 127,663. The 4.4 polydispersity of the sample was judged excessive. For this reason, the PMMA actually used was subjected to "leaching" in a 1:1 (MIBK : IPA)* solution which was kept to be used as developer. Leaching reduced polydispersity to 2.4 and changed the weight average molecular weight to 662,188.

Exposed PMMA films were developed for periods up to 15 min total, in steps varying from 20 sec to 3 min. In order to stop development at each step, samples were quickly removed from the solvent and immediately dipped in IPA for 15 sec, then in distilled water for another 15 sec. Afterwards they were dried in a jet of nitrogen. The step height between exposed and unexposed parts was measured by means of an Alpha step profiler. Unexposed PMMA regions were virtually insoluble in the developer used.

Exposures were done in a standard ion implanter. The incident Ga ion energy was 250keV, and the developed depth vs development time curves for five doses (0.06, 0.08, 0.10, 0.12 and 0.4 x 10^{-6} C/cm ^{2}) are shown in Fig. 1.

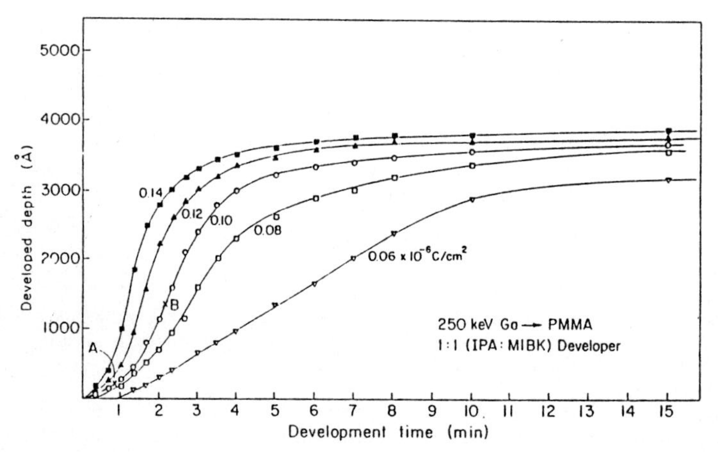

Fig. 1. Development depth vs. development time for five different doses of 250-keV Ga in PMMA

3. Theoretical Energy Loss Density

An indispensable input for the fitting scheme to be described in the next section is the absorbed energy density as a function of resist depth. This input has to be determined theoretically. A Monte-Carlo type computer simulation algorithm called PIBER was used for this purpose. A brief presentation of its features will be given here. For a detailed account, the reader is referred to another publication [9].

PIBER (Program for Ion Beam Exposure of Resists) and hybrids were developed in order to simulate the energy loss and scattering processes that take place during the slowing down of intermediate and low-energy ions in amorphous solids. The program is capable of generating total ranges, projected ranges, straggling, three-dimensional distributions of implanted atoms, energy loss and damage. The physical assumptions on which the Monte Carlo model is based are briefly as follows : (a) separatibility of

* MIBK : Methyl isobutyl ketone,
  IPA : Isopropyl alcohol.

nuclear and electronic stopping according to the Lindhard-Scharff-Schiott (LSS) theory [10]; (b) use of an experimentally fitted nuclear scattering cross section based on the LSS formulation :

$$d\sigma = \frac{\pi a^2 dt}{2t^{3/2}} f(t^{1/2}), \tag{1}$$

$$t^{1/2} = \varepsilon \sin(\theta/2), \quad = \frac{aM_2}{Z_1 Z_2 e^2 (M_1 + M_2)} E, \tag{2}$$

where a is the Thomas-Fermi radius, Z_1 and Z_2 are atomic numbers of projectile and target, respectively, M_1 and M_2 are the mass numbers of projectile and target, respectively, E is the energy of the projectile, and θ is the scattering angle in the center-of-mass frame. $f(t^{1/2})$ is given by the Winterborn formula :

$$f(t^{1/2}) = \lambda t^{1/2 - m} [1 + (2\lambda t^{1-m})^q]^{-1/q}, \tag{3}$$

with $\lambda = 2.54$, m = 0.25, and q = 0.475. (c) Use of the LSS electronic stopping formula. (d) The rigourous validity of the Bragg rule is assumed, whereby each species in a polyatomic target contributes to electronic stopping in proportion to its number density.

Agreement between our theoretical model and experiment, as far as projected ranges and longitudinal straggling are concerned, is quite satisfactory [9].

Figure 2.a shows fifty simulated 250keV Ga^+ trajectories. One should note a number of things : a) The wide spread in path lengths. b) The absence of large angle collisions, and (c) the significant lateral scatter. These features, characteristic of heavy ion implantation in light substrates, are to be contrasted to the behaviour of 60keV H^+ ions implanted in PMMA, Fig. 2.b.

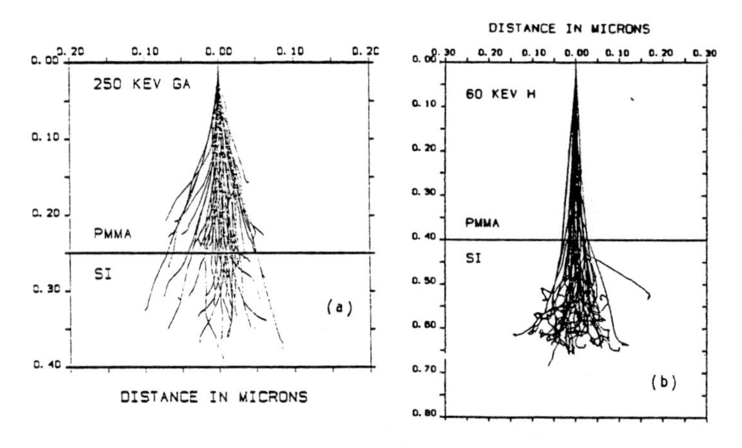

Fig. 2. (a) 250-keV Ga trajectories in PMMA on Si.
(b) 60-keV H trajectories in PMMA on Si.

From the point of view of lithographic resolution, the most important feature is lateral scatter. In order to obtain a quantitative measure of its magnitude for 250keV Ga^+ ions, we plot in Fig. 3 the lateral absorbed energy density at two different depths in PMMA, 1200 and 2800 Å. For comparison, the corresponding energy density distributions are also plotted for 60keV H^+ ions.

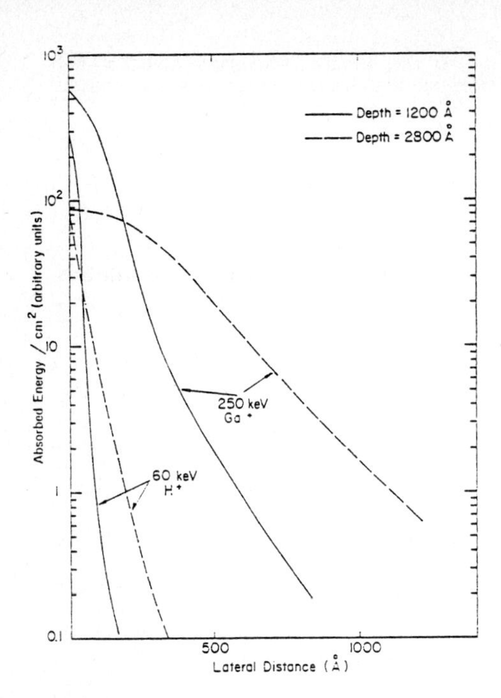

Fig. 3. Absorbed energy vs lateral distance away from "δ-line" exposure at two different depths for 60-keV H-ions and 250-keV Ga-ions

4. Parameter Fitting

A scheme aimed at simulating contours developed in resists after irradiation by various means needs to relate certain physical effects produced by the radiation on the resist with the latter's development behaviour. Perhaps the simplest approach is to postulate the existence of a minimal absorbed energy density beyond which the resist is insoluble by a given developer. This approach has been extensively used in the early stages of electron beam lithography studies. Simulations based on this method suffer from the disadvantage that they cannot deal with the temporal progression of developed profiles.

The time element can be incorporated by using a physical picture of the development process which relates local development rate to locally absorbed energy density. This approach was applied in E-Beam Lithography by Greeneich [11], and others . He related in a simple way molecular weight reduction to absorbed energy density, and speed of development to molecular weight.

For a single type of energy deposition mechanism, Neureuther cast the above model in a particularly convenient form [12],

$$R = R_1 + (C_m + \frac{D}{D_o})^{\alpha} \tag{4}$$

where : R is the local development rate in Å/sec,
R_1 is a constant (Å/sec),
C_m is a constant inversely proportional to molecular weight,
D is the absorbed energy density in J/cm3,
D_o and α are constants.

For high molecular weights C_m is practically zero, and for developers which do not attack unexposed resist R_1 is also zero.

In the LSS formulation of low energy ion stopping, there are two distinct mechanisms of energy loss, electronic and nuclear. In the case of heavy ion irradiation of resists, the nuclear energy loss mechanism dominates. It is natural therefore to envisage a generalization of Eq. (4) in the form,

$$R = R_l + (C_m + \frac{De}{D_{oe}} + \frac{Dn}{D_{on}})^{\alpha} \quad (5)$$

where D_{oe} and D_{on} are constants associated with electronic and nuclear energy loss D_e and D_n, respectively [13].

In a formula of the type Eq. (4) R and R_l can be determined experimentally, D is generated theoretically and parameters D_o and α have to be determined by means of an appropriate fitting scheme.

We developed the following procedure :

(i) The development depth vs. development time data is expressed in analytic form with the use of a variable knot, cubic spline data fitting code named ICSSCU (available as an IMSL routine on the IBM/370 computer by Cornell Computer Services). The analytic approximation comprises a number of spliced sections and has continuous first and second derivatives.

(ii) The above expression is differentiated with respect to time and a rate vs. depth analytic look-up table is obtained.

(iii) The absorbed energy density versus depth data, furnished by PIBER, is analytically fitted as in step (i).

(iv) The rate of development versus absorbed energy density at selected depths is tabulated.

Given the semi-quantitative nature of our investigation, a graphical fitting of log (rate) vs. log (absorbed energy) data will suffice. As it can be seen from Eq. (4).

$$\log (R) = \alpha \log D + \alpha \log D_o \quad (6)$$

Hence, by fitting the above data to a straight line, the slope gives α and the x-intercept gives D_o.

Applied in the case of a light ion like 60keV H^+ ions, where electronic energy loss dominates nuclear energy loss by almost three orders of magnitude, the parameters determined [5] were, not surprisingly, very close to those determined by Neureuther for electrons [12].

Coming now to the case of Ga^+ irradiated PMMA, a number of difficulties is immediately obvious. A glance at Fig. 1 shows a marked dependence of saturation development depth on charge dose. A similar behaviour has been observed with other ions by H. Ryssel et al. [3]. Such a behaviour is not predicted by formulae of the type Eqs. (4), (5). No noticable dose-dependent saturation is observed with H^+ ions and electrons for usual exposure doses.

Secondly, the initial development phase is quite peculiar : according to the theoretical energy loss model, the absorbed energy density at points A (at depth 350 Å) and B (depth 1350 Å - see Fig. 1) is about the same. At A, D_n = 700 J/cm^3, D_e = 160 J/cm^3 and at B, D_n = 800 J/cm^3 and D_e = 100 J/cm^3. The rate of development at point B, however, is about 2.5 times greater than the rate at A.

In an effort to isolate the effect of nuclear stopping and get a rough estimate of its effectiveness, our parameter fitting scheme was applied to data points corresponding to depths greater than 2500 Å where electronic stopping is between 5-10% and, therefore, can be neglected to first order. A formula of the form :

$$R = (D_n/D_{no})^{\alpha_n} \quad (7)$$

with α_n around 1.3, and D_{no} around 75, can represent these points "on the average". This is not very accurate, but adequately indicates that the parameters applicable to electronic stopping cannot be used where nuclear stopping dominates. It is also clear that Eq. (4) cannot reproduce the portions of the curves near the origin where rates are much slower than predicted by the formula.

5. Simulation of Developed Profiles

PIBER outputs represent two-dimensional (x-z plane) energy distribution data for a d-function beam profile. Real-life situations involve beams of finite width whose profile can often be approximated by a Gaussian (focused beams) or a square-wave shape (beams projected through masks). In this paper we will be concerned with square-wave profiles only.

Two-dimensional energy distributions are generated by convoluting the original - function line-exposure with appropriate beam profiles. The convolution scheme was kindly provided by Neureuther and Rosenfield [14].

Having obtained this realistic energy distribution in exposed resist , one can proceed to "develop" the resist. For a time-dependent development simulation, one needs expressions of the type given by Eqs. (4), (5) which relate the rate of development to the locally absorbed energy (the development process is assumed to be isotropic). To the extent that one is performing a computer simulated development, whereby the energy distribution is given on a rectangular x-y grid, a precise algorithm of how to advance the development profile with time is required. A "string-model" algorithm was employed [15].

Before we proceed with the simulation of developed profiles, we should take a look at the significance of the dependence of "saturation" development depth on dose. The simplest explanation is that there exists a critical absorbed energy density below which development is not possible for a given developer. Using the theoretical absorbed energy calculations produced by PIBER, it turns out that an absorbed dose of about 40 J/cm^3 corresponds to all saturation depths shown in Fig. 1. Hence, we postulate a modified rate equation of the form :

$$R = (D/D_o + C)^{\alpha} \tag{8}$$

where D_o = 80 J/cm3, $\alpha = 1.35$ and $C = -40/D_o$ J/sec. When D descends below 40 J/sec, R is assumed to be zero.

In order to obtain a semi-quantitative picture of Ga-exposed resist development, a typical dose, 0.1×10^{-6} C/cm^2, was chosen. The development depth vs time curve was approximated by a zero rate initial portion from 0-80 sec, which was followed by a curve depicting development according to Eq.(8) . As it is shown in Fig. 4 , the resultant curve is a reasonable approximation to the actual one and reminiscent of the curves obtained with low electron or H^+ doses.

One possible explanation for the initial slow "incubation" period in development, is the low density of incident ions. A dose of 0.1×10^{-6} C/cm^2 corresponds to 0.5 incident ions in a square measuring 100 Å a side.

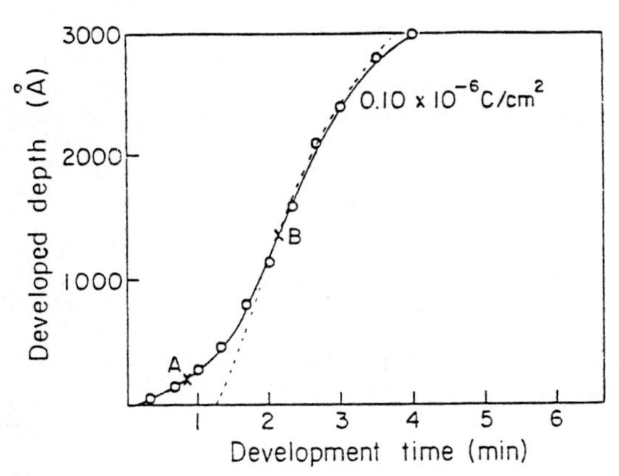

Fig. 4. Developed depth vs. development time curve (solid line) and approximation for 0.10×10^{-6} C/cm^2 of 250-keV Ga ions (dotted line)

Using the above equation, development profiles after exposure with a rectangular profile 1000-Å-wide line of charge were simulated at 3.33 - 9.33 min (in steps of one min) of development time, Fig. 5.a. Given the symmetry of the situation, only the right hand sides of the profiles are shown .

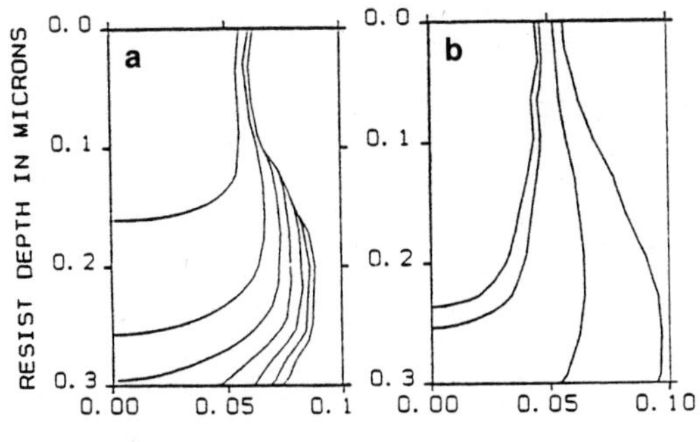

Fig. 5. Developed contours in PMMA exposed by a 1000 Å-wide line of 250-keV Ga ions. Dose-0.10×10^{-6} C/cm^2, t=m + 2.33 min, m=1,2,...,7. (b) Equi-energy contours at 800, 600, 200 and 40 J/cm^3

Saturated developed profiles can also be generated by plotting the appropriate two-dimensional equi-energy contours. Fig. 5.b shows a number of such curves. The outer curve represents the saturated profile.

6. Conclusion

The developed profile simulations presented in the previous section indicate that heavy ion IBL may produce line broadening exceeding 500 Å per side and noticeable undercutting. In fact, theoretical profiles will be broader than those shown here when recoil atoms are taken into account. Therefore, proximity effects may become important at line-widths and line-spacings of 1000-1500A in resist layers a few thousand angstroms thick, especially when high ion-doses and strong developers are used.

By contrast, experimental and theorical studies on 40-60keV H^+ IBL indicate a line broadening of the order of 200 Å or less [5, 16].

In our simulations, we have used a rather high-energy Ga^+ beam. If lower energy liquid metal columns are used, thinner resist films will have to be used. This fact, together with undesirable Ga implantation in the substrate, will probably restrict the lithographic use of liquid metal sources to multi-layer processes, whereby ions will expose a top thin layer to define a mask for dry etching of underlying buffer layers.

Ultimately, liquid metal sources may prove most useful for direct implantation purposes.

Acknowledgement

This work was supported by the National Science Foundation under Grant N° 77-09688.

References

1. R.L. Seliger, R.L. Kubena, R.D. Olney, J.W. Ward and V. Wang : J. Vac. Sci. Technol. 16, 1610 (1979)
2. L. Karapiperis and C.A. Lee : Appl. Phys. Lett. 35, 395 (1979)
3. H. Ryssel, K. Haberger and H. Kranz : J. Vac. Sci. Technol. 19, 1358 (1981)
4. K. Moriwaki, H. Aritome, S. Namba and L. Karapiperis : Jap. J. Appl. Phys. 20, L881 (1981)

5. L. Karapiperis, I. Adesida, C.A. Lee and E.D. Wolf : J. Vac. Sci. Technol. 19, 1263 (1981)
6. G.R. Hanson and B.M. Siegel : J. Vac. Sci. Technol. 19, 1176 (1981)
7. V. Wang and R.L. Seliger : J. Vac. Sci. Technol. 19, 1158 (1981)
8. K. Gamo : J. Vac. Sci. Technol. 19, 1182 (1981)
9. I. Adesida and L. Karapiperis : Radiat. Eff. 61, 223 (1982)
10. J. Lindhard, M. Scharff and H.E. Schiøtt : Mat-Fys. Medd. Dan. Vidensk. Selsk. 33, 1 (1963)
11. J.S. Greeneich : J. Electrochem. Soc. 122, 970 (1975)
12. A.N. Neureuther, D.F. Kyser and C.H. Ting : IEEE Trans. Electron Devices ED-26, 686 (1979)
13. M. Komuro, N. Atoda and H. Kawakatsu : J. Electrochem. Soc. 126, 483 (1979)
14. M. Rosenfield, Master's Thesis, Univ. of Calif. Berkeley (1981)
15. R. Jewett, Memorandum No. UCB/ERL M79/68, Univ. of Calif. Berkeley
16. N.P. Economou, D.C. Flanders and J.P. Donnelly : J. Vac. Sci. Technol. 19, 1172 (1981)

Simulation of the Lithographic Properties of Ion-Beam Resists

K. Haberger, K. Hoffmann, M. Forster, and H. Ryssel

Fraunhofer-Institut für Festkörpertechnologie, Paul-Gerhardt-Allee 42, D-8000 München 60, Fed. Rep. of Germany

Abstract

Monte Carlo simulations of ion scattering are used, together with a model for energy loss along the ion path, to calculate the spatial energy deposition caused by the ion beam in the resist. To simulate the time evolution of the exposed profile during development, the energy-deposition profile is converted into a resist-solubility rate for different ions. In addition, the predicted sensitivity and lateral resolution are investigated and compared with experimental results obtained with hydrogen, helium, argon, and gallium ions in several PMMA resists.

1. Introduction

Since high-brightness field-emission ion sources are available, ion-beam lithography could become a serious alternative to electron-beam lithography. Ion-beam lithography offers two main principal features which make its use worth serious consideration: high resist sensitivity and superior pattern resolution. These two advantages result from the low penetration range of ions in resists. Incident ions deposit their energy into a more restricted volume region than is the case for electrons at proper energies. Thus, the energy absorbed in a given volume element is much higher, which results in sensitivities two to three orders of magnitude higher than with electrons. This high sensitivity can be attained by focused ion-beam writing [1,2], as well as by masked ion-beam proximity printing using crystal channeling masks [3,4]. If a future need for ultra-fine pattern fabrication should arise, ions could be used for lithography down to the physically feasible limits.

We have obtained a set of experimental results on the exposure of different resists by various ions. For a better understanding of the related possibilities, we tried to simulate these results. To simulate the lithographic properties of a resist, the first step is to calculate the actual energy deposited in the volume element of the resist, and the second step is to find an equation to convert this energy deposition into a local dissolution rate.

The lithographic process is a combination of exposure and developer treatment. Positive organic resists such as PMMA are formed by long chains of polymer molecules having an average molecular weight of several thousands to a million. The chain bonds are covalent, with a binding energy of approx. 3.7 eV. These chains are mutually linked by non-covalent bonds, such as dipole forces and H-H bridges, with binding energies up to several tenths of an eV. Through exposure, the molecular chains are broken, which results in a decrease of the molecular weight of the polymer. Development is accomplished using an organic solvent, which removes molecular fractions depending on their individual molecular weight.

2. Energy Deposition

When a positive resist is exposed to an ion beam, random scission occurs, producing a decrease in the average molecular weight. Ions penetrating the resist lose energy through nuclear scattering as well as a "viscous" electron scattering. The cross sections of both processes depend on the resist density, the atomic composition, and the actual velocity of the ion which is being slowed down. The energy dissipated in a small resist volume causes chain scission via secondary electrons and direct energy transfer to atoms of the molecular chains.

The simplest way to calculate the energy deposition is to use Monte Carlo simulation. To reduce the computation time, a sophisticated program called TRIM (Transport of Ions in Matter), developed by Biersack and Haggmark [5], has been used. With this program, the target is considered to be amorphous with randomly distributed atoms, having the stoichiometric ratio of 5:8:2 for carbon, hydrogen, and oxygen, respectively, in the case of PMMA.

The nuclear scattering, which determines the spatial distribution of the particle trajectories, is calculated by a time-saving semianalytical approximation. For nuclear scattering, the Molière approximation to the Thomas-Fermi potential is used. The electronic energy loss is related to the distance travelled between nuclear collisions. The calculation is stopped when the energy drops below 5 eV.

A typical result of these Monte Carlo simulations is shown in Fig. 1, where the simulated particle distribution for hydrogen at 120 keV is given for 1000 particles. In this figure the final positions of the particles

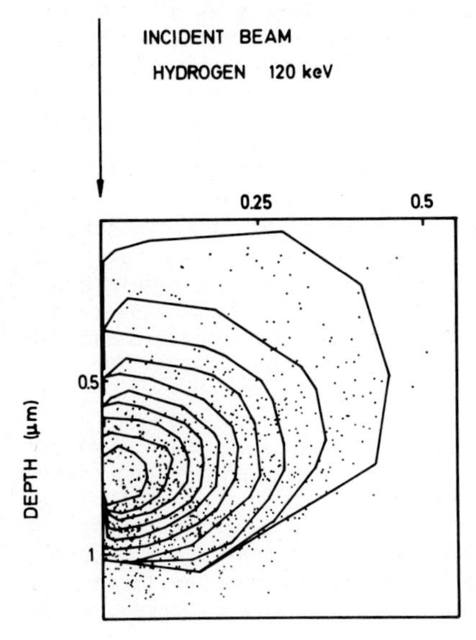

Fig. 1. Simulated particle distribution for hydrogen at 120 keV in PMMA. The solid lines represent isoconcentration lines

after their slowing down are plotted, and not the trajectories usually shown. Because of the symmetry of the problem, only the positive x axis is drawn.

3. Developer Process

If simultaneous crosslinking does not occur, the number of molecules increases by one per main-chain scission. Since one gram of polymer contains N_A/M_Q molecules after exposure with a local energy of Q (in eV per gram), and contains N_A/M_0 molecules at the beginning, one obtains:

$$\frac{1}{M_Q} = \frac{1}{M_0} + \frac{G(s) \cdot Q}{100\ N_A} \qquad (1)$$

where M_0 and M_Q are the average molecular weights before and after irradiation with dose Q, respectively, and N_A is the Avogadro number. G(s) is the number of main-chain bonds broken per 100 eV of absorbed energy (approx. 2 $(eV)^{-1}$ for PMMA). After exposure, an average molecular weight of:

$$M_Q = \frac{M_0}{1 + G(s) \cdot Q \cdot M_0/N_A} \qquad (2)$$

results, where Q is the locally absorbed energy.

As the developer, an organic solvent is used to dissolve the polymer, depending on the latter's molecular weight. It has been proposed [6] that over a wide range of molecular weights, the dissolution speed $\dot{s}$ of a polymer is related to M by:

$$\dot{s} = kM^{-\alpha} \quad . \qquad (3)$$

In Eq. (3), k is a temperature-dependent parameter which is mainly determined by the polymer-solvent combination and M is the molecular weight; the exponent α is between approx. 0.5 and 2, and does not depend on the temperature over a wide temperature range. The underlying idea of Eq. (3) is that the solvent penetrates the polymer and forms an adhesive swollen layer of polymer in front of the polymer-solvent interface from which the molecular coils are removed into the solvent. The rate-limiting factor is the transport of the separated molecules from the dissolution front; therefore, α should be related to the viscosity of the polymer-solvent system, and thus, also related to the length and entanglement of the molecular chains [7].

Combining Eqs. (2) and (3), the local development rate $\dot{s}$ is related to the locally absorbed energy as follows:

$$\dot{s} = \frac{k}{M_0} \left(1 + \frac{G(s) \cdot M_0}{100\ N_A} Q\right)^{\alpha} \quad . \qquad (4)$$

According to this formula, $\dot{s} \sim Q^{\alpha}$ and therefore, $s \sim N_{\square}{}^{\alpha}$, where $N_{\square}$ is the exposure dose. Moreover, for a fixed developer composition and developer temperature, the dark rate should be reciprocal to M_0.

4. Experimental Results

To investigate the validity of this developer model, ions of different mass were implanted with different doses into several PMMA resists. The total resist thickness on the spin-coated wafers was approx. one micron. For each ion species, the different doses were all implanted on the same wafer, which was moved step by step to obtain the desired doses. All of these experiments were made using a standard implanter. A small mesh in front of the wafer was imaged as a shadow pattern of exposed and unexposed areas, in order to measure the removed resist thickness by the mechanical Talystep technique.

In order to simulate the development behavior of the resists, the locally absorbed energy density was incorporated into a simple development model according to Eq. (4):

$$\dot{s} = s_0(1 + s_1 Q)^{\alpha} \quad . \tag{5}$$

In this model, s_0 (nm/sec), s_1, and α are regarded as fitting parameters, whereas Q, the total amount of energy absorbed by nuclear as well as electronic stopping, was taken from Monte Carlo simulation.

In Fig. 2, a result is shown for 120 keV hydrogen in Esschemical PMMA, which has an average molecular weight of 678,000. In this figure, the removed resist thickness is indicated vs development time, and is compared with the drawn lines from the simulation.

Another example, for hydrogen at 120 keV in Elvacite 2041 PMMA having an average molecular weight of 350,000, is shown in Fig. 3. Similar curves

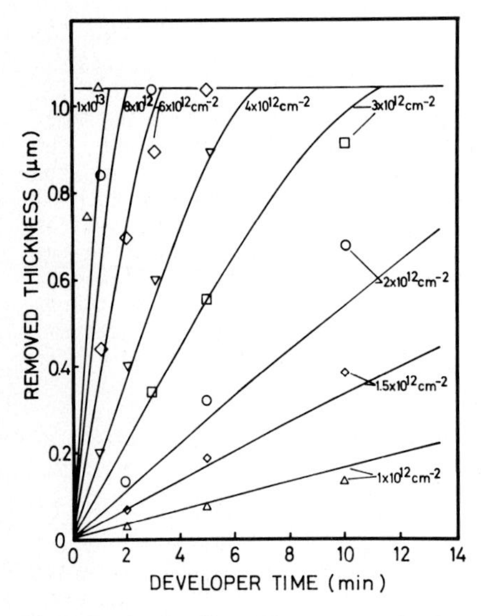

Fig. 2. Comparison between calculated and measured development curves, for hydrogen at 120 keV in Esschemical PMMA

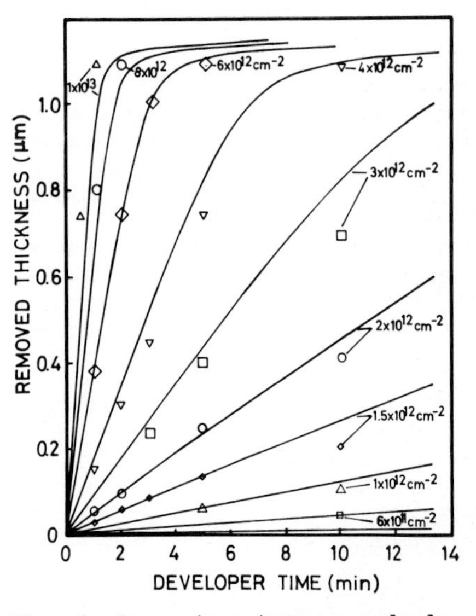

Fig. 3. Comparison between calculated and measured development curves, for hydrogen at 120 keV in Elvacite 2041 PMMA

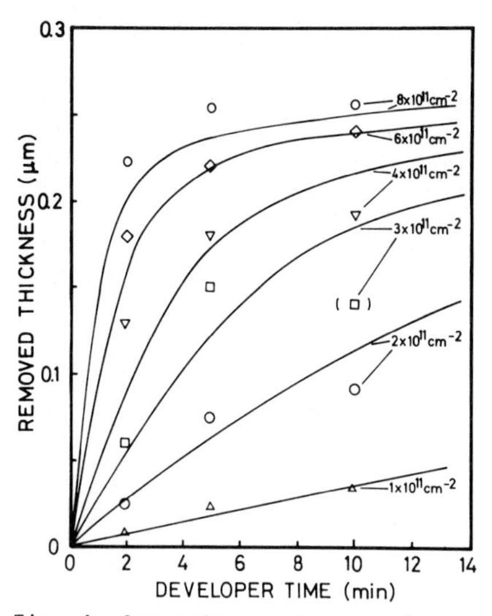

Fig. 4. Comparison between calculated and measured development curves, for argon at 120 keV in Esschemical PMMA

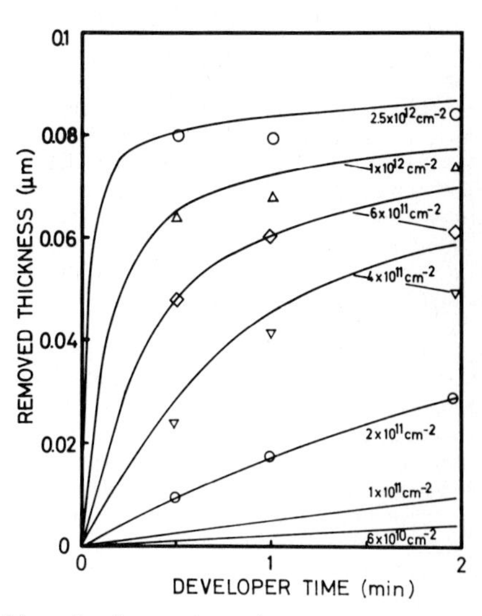

Fig. 5. Comparison between calculated and measured development curves, for gallium at 40 keV in Elvacite 2008

were obtained with argon in Esschemical PMMA. An example for argon exposure is shown in Fig. 4. In these three cases, development was done in 1:1 MIBK:IPA at 20°C. After different periods, the samples were removed from the developer bath, rinsed, dried, and measured.

The example shown in Fig. 5 is a result for gallium in Elvacite 2008 PMMA, having an average molecular weight of 250,000. Development was performed in 1:1 MIPK:IPA at 17°C. The low exposure energy of 40 keV was chosen to investigate resist sensitivity and removable thickness in connection with low-energy gallium field-emission ion columns.

Important for practical applications of ion-beam lithography is the resist-layer thickness exposable by different ion species and energies. In Fig. 6, the removed thickness after exposure with hydrogen, helium, argon,

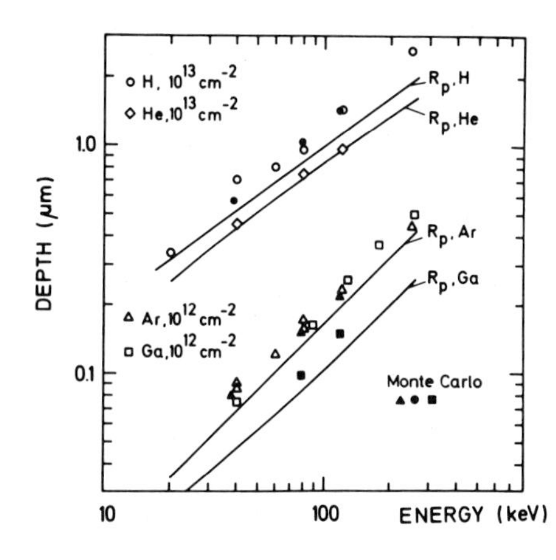

Fig. 6. Removed thickness of PMMA resist (Dupont Elvacite 2008) after exposure with $10^{13} cm^{-2}$ hydrogen and helium, and $10^{12} cm^{-2}$ argon and gallium, in comparison to projected range data (drawn lines) and Monte Carlo simulation (filled symbols)

and gallium ions as a function of the energy is shown for a developing time of 2 min in 1 MIBK: 1 IPA. The exposure doses used were 10^{13} cm^{-2} for hydrogen and helium, and $10^{12} cm^{-2}$ for argon and gallium. For comparison, the LSS ranges of these ions are also given. One can see that as a first approximation of the exposable depth, the LSS range can be used. A better agreement is found between the experimental data and Monte Carlo calculations together with the development simulation results.

5. Conclusions

We obtained reasonable agreement between the the results of our calculations and the experimental data, with the crude developer model which was used. In all cases, including gallium, the results could be fitted with an exponent of α = 1.93. The constant s_o was fitted within a range of 30% for three resists which were investigated and evaluated. This difference seems to be due to the molecular-weight distribution, or to different prebakes. In accordance with Eq. (4), in the case of gallium (where a relatively low-molecular-weight PMMA was used), a dark removal rate was measured. However, despite this reasonable fitting of the exposure and development processes, much additional work has to be done to evolve the physical background, which is oversimplified in the present crude developer model.

References

1. G.R. Hanson and B.M. Siegel, Electrochem. Soc. Meeting, St. Louis (1980)
2. M. Komuro, Thin Solid Films 92, 155 (1982)
3. D.B. Rensch, R.L. Seliger, G. Csonky, R.D. Oleny, and H.L. Staver, J. Vac. Sci. Technol. 16, 1897 (1979)
4. L. Csepregi, F. Iberl, and P. Eichinger, Microcircuit Engineering 80, Amsterdam (1980)
5. J.P. Biersack and L.G. Haggmark, Nucl. Instr. and Meth. 174, 257 (1980)
6. K. Überreiter and F. Asmussen, J. Polymer Sci. 23, 75 (1957)
7. J. Schurz, Hochpolymere, Springer, Berlin (1974)

Deposition of Masking Films by Ion-Beam Induced Polymerization

C.R. Fritzsche and K.M. Eisele

Fraunhofer-Institut für Angewandte Festkörperphysik, Eckerstraße 4,
D-7800 Freiburg, Fed. Rep. of Germany

1. Introduction

It is known, both from electron microscopy and from ion implantation, that through the action of a particle beam a contamination layer can be deposited from the residual gas onto the sample. These layers are confined to the area exposed to the beam, and can withstand very strong etch processes. They could therefore be used as masks in microlithography, provided a process with sufficiently high growth rates of the masking film could be found.

This paper reports on layer deposition from well-defined gases. The factors influencing the growth rate are discussed, and the problems of developing an economical dry-masking technique are sketched.

2. Experimental Technique

Vapor from liquid divinyl benzene (DVB) or methyl siloxane[1] was fed through a needle valve into a "gradient tube" within the target chamber of a normal ion implanter. The "gradient tube" is closed by the target holder on the side where the gas enters. It narrows at the beam entrance, thus providing a pressure gradient. The ion current could be measured in front of the gradient tube, as well as in front of the target inside the tube. A diminished current density at the target would indicate the loss of charge or particles within the gas. This however, was not observed below 1×10^{-3} mbar for 55 keV Ne ions. The target was cooled to 0°C. Silicon was used as the target material.

3. Results

The ratio of the growth rate R of the film to the current density j may be described as efficiency η. Qualitatively, R and η were found to depend upon current density and gas pressure, as already known from electron-beam induced deposition [1, 2]. With increasing current density, the growth rate increases while the efficiency decreases. Figure 1 shows this for DVB and 55 keV Ne ions at a pressure of 7×10^{-4} mbar. For comparison, data for 0.51 keV electrons [3] are included in the figure. The solid lines were calculated from

$R = R_0/(1 + \alpha/j)$, the constants R_0 and α being fitted to the experimental data.

[1]The material used in our experiments is commercially available under the name "silicone oil type 3".

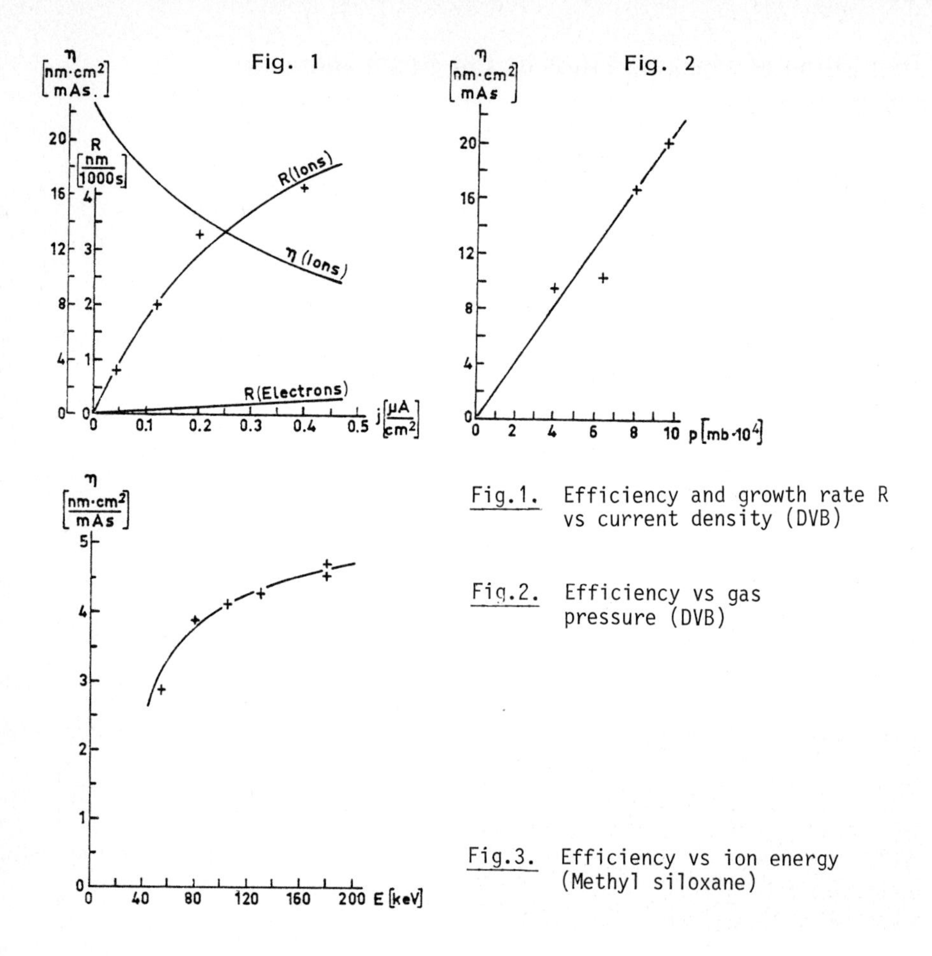

Fig.1. Efficiency and growth rate R vs current density (DVB)

Fig.2. Efficiency vs gas pressure (DVB)

Fig.3. Efficiency vs ion energy (Methyl siloxane)

The efficiency is proportional to the pressure of the monomer gas, as shown in Fig. 2.

The influence of ion energy on the efficiency of film deposition was studied using methyl siloxane as the monomer. Figure 3 shows that a pronounced increase in efficiency with increasing energy can be observed between 55 and 105 keV. The influence of current density and vapor pressure is qualitatively the same as for DVB.

Films deposited from DVB withstand plasma etching in SF_6 and CHF_3. A precise determination of the very low etch rate was not possible, since no reference material sufficiently resistant to act as a reference plane was provided in our experiments and ellipsometric measurements are influenced by the radiation damage in the substrate. The visible interference color was changed only slightly after etching. Films from methyl siloxane are less resistant and the etch rate could be estimated from the time necessary to remove the entire film. Both types of films can be removed in an Ar-O_2 plasma. A gas-flow-rate ratio of 1 : 1 was chosen, and the uncovered parts of the substrate were used as a reference plane. Some data on etch resistance are presented in Table 1.

Table 1. Plasma etch rates of polymer films (nm/min)

	divinyl benzene	methyl siloxane	silicon	SiO_2
SF_6 [4]	very low	72	700	20
CHF_3	very low	< 1.7	6.5	80
$Ar + O_2$ (1:1)	3	0.3	0	0

To demonstrate that ion beams produce localized film deposition, a grid was mounted in front of the target at a distance of about 70 μm so that the gas flow itself could not cause an image of the grid. The deposited polymer pattern was copied onto the silicon substrate by plasma etching in SF_6. An example is shown in Fig.4. A poly-DVB layer of 31 nm thickness was used in this experiment, and the silicon was etched to a depth of 200 nm. The edge length of the holes in the grid is 6 μm.

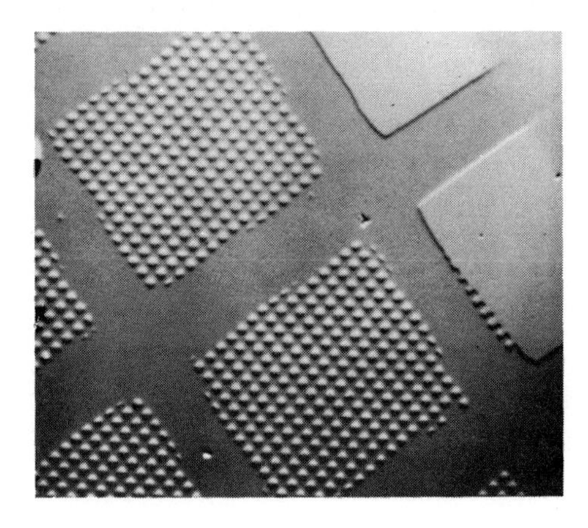

Fig.4. Pattern copied from a poly-DVB mask onto silicon

4. Discussion

A sensitivity equivalent for the masking process can be deduced by dividing the minimum thickness necessary for masking by the efficiency of layer deposition. Combination of the highest efficiency obtained up to now (35.3 nm · cm/mAs) with the film thickness used for the structure shown in Fig.4 results in a sensitivity equivalent of 880 $\mu C/cm^2$. This value needs to be improved substantially if the technique of structured deposition is to be useable in VLSI technology. However, in comparing this sensitivity equivalent with the sensitivity of electron resists, one must take into account that the proposed technique replaces the three conventional processes of deposition, irradiation, and development by one single and completely dry process.

The efficiency could possibly be improved by optimizing the deposition parameters. Furthermore, the choice of DVB and siloxane in the experiments described here was only a first attempt. We supposed that the presence of groups such as the vinyl group in DVB could provide a contribution of normal polymerization to the deposition process, while for the siloxanes, the process might consist mainly in crosslinking of single molecules. It has already been shown [3] that, for both processes, the dependence upon current density follows the same law, and pulsed deposition is necessary to investigate the contribution of normal polymerization. It has also been shown [3] that under pulsed electron irradiation, the film deposition from DVB continues during the pauses, according to the lifetime of the active species (free radicals or ions). Clearly, a high efficiency will be obtained if the lifetime can be made long. Also, from the theoretical work on electron-beam induced polymerization [1,2], the relations between vapor pressure of the monomer, operating pressure, and target temperature can be understood. They may serve as a guideline for the choice of the monomer. For ion irradiation, the mechanism may be similar. Additionally, nuclear interactions have to be taken into account in this case. They may contribute to the formation of volatile fragments of the polymer, and the observed increase in efficiency with increasing energy can be explained by the corresponding decrease in the nuclear stopping power.

In summary, we can state that etch-resistant masks can be deposited by ion-beam induced polymerization, but the speed is still too low for practical application. Future development should concentrate on long lifetimes of the active species, reduced production of volatile fragments, and optimal matching of the process parameters to the properties of the monomer.

Acknowledgements

This work was supported by the Ministry of Research and Technology of the Federal Republic of Germany. The authors are indebted to J. Schaub and E. Olander for their assistance in the experimental work.

References

1 R.W. Christy: J. Appl. Phys. 31, 1680 (1960)

2 J. Haller, P. White: J. Phys. Chem. 67, 1784 (1963)

3 C.R. Fritzsche: J. Appl. Phys., to be published

4 K.M. Eisele: J. Electrochem. Soc. 128, 123 (1981)

Part VI

Measuring Techniques

Dosimetry and Beam Quality

G. Ryding

Eaton Corporation, Ion Implantation Division, 16 Tozer Road,
Beverly, MA 01915, USA

Abstract

The ability to control dose in terms of absolute value, repeatability from wafer to wafer, and uniformity across a wafer is the most important characteristic of any implanter.

During implantation wafers can also be exposed to particles originating from the residual gases and the interior surfaces of the vacuum system in addition to the particles generated in the ion source itself. Furthermore the measurement accuracy of the primary ion beam can be complicated by beam interaction with the residual gases and secondary particle effects at the target surface.

The magnitude of these effects will be reviewed and different methods of beam measurement will be discussed.

1. Introduction

In all commercial implanters the ion dose is controlled by measurement of the electrical current associated with the ion beam. In recent years there has been some excellent reviews on the subject of beam detection and dose control [1-7]. In the following sections some of the complications of dose control in a high current implanter will be discussed. First the various Faraday suppression techniques will be briefly reviewed. Then, after discussing the vacuum environment, the performance of several Faraday designs will be summarized giving particular attention to the influence of residual gases along the beamline. Dose control results determined by four point probe sheet resistance measurements will then be presented. Finally design techniques to enhance beam quality and reduce neutral beam and sputter effects will be discussed.

2. Faraday Designs

A selection of Faraday designs which have been developed for ion implantation is shown in Fig.1. In all cases the beam enters through a defining aperture at ground potential and proceeds to the target where the net current flow I is measured. Unfortunately this measurement is complicated by a variety of secondary and tertiary effects, the most significant of which are listed as follows:

a. Secondary electrons ejected from the target.

b. Secondary negative and positive ions ejected from the target.

c. Secondary electrons generated at the beam defining aperture.

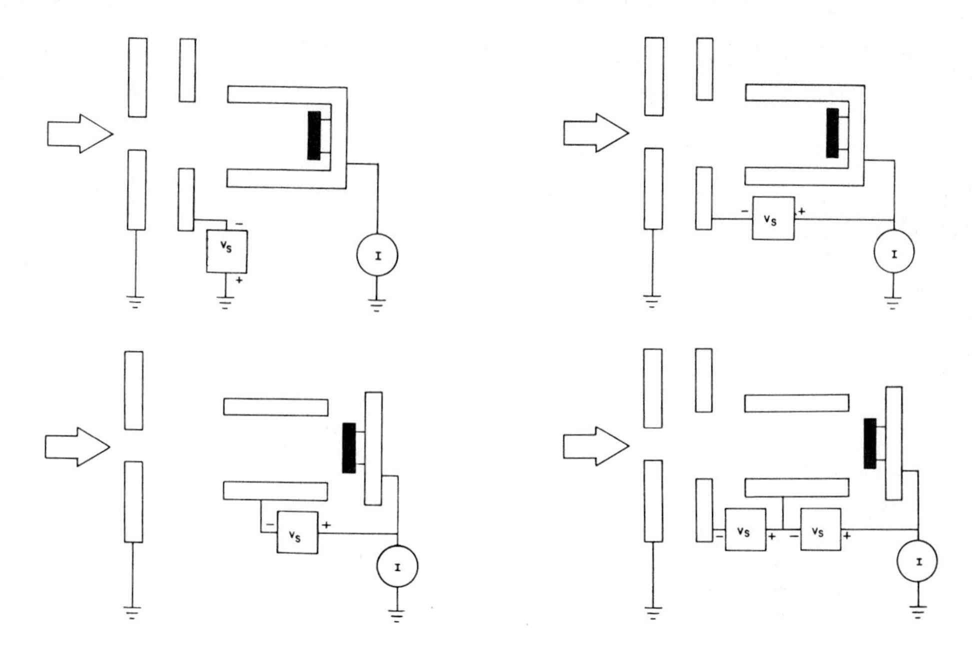

Figure 1. Examples of Faraday Cup Designs Incorporating Electrostatic Suppression of Secondary Particles

d. Leakage currents.

e. Slow electrons and ions resulting from collisions between the incident ions and background gases along the beamline.

In order to minimize these effects the basic Faraday cup containment technique has been augmented by a variety of bias electrode configurations as shown in Fig.1. In general these electrodes are arranged with the primary objective of minimizing the effects of secondary electrons and ions emanating from the target and secondary electrons emanating from the beam defining aperture. In the more sophisticated designs [3] full consideration is given to the interaction of fields from the beam space charge with fields from the suppression electrodes.

Regrettably the measurement of intense beams ($\geq$1mA) is further complicated by the following interrelated problems.

a. The suppression fields can interfere with the low-energy electrons which are trapped within the beam and which neutralize the space charge of the beam ions. When this delicate space charge balance is disturbed, beam blow-up is inevitable [7].

b. Axial suppression fields are intended to inhibit the flow of low-energy electrons along the beamline and may therefore enhance surface charging on insulated regions of "device" wafers [3].

c. Good vacuum is generally more difficult to preserve in industrial high throughput, high current implanters. A significant number of ions and electrons are generated along the beamline and can influence the primary beam measurement in the Faraday.

In order to solve these problems, magnetic field suppression is sometimes used as an alternative to electrostatic suppression for high beam currents [3,7,8,9]. As an example, the arrangement used on the Applied Implant Technology machines [10] is shown schematically in Fig.2. In this case a low-energy electron gun has been added inside the Faraday to prevent surface charging of the wafers. The magnetic field lines are arranged so as to prevent slow secondary particles from entering or leaving the Faraday entrance but they do not inhibit the flow of electrons between the gun and the wafers.

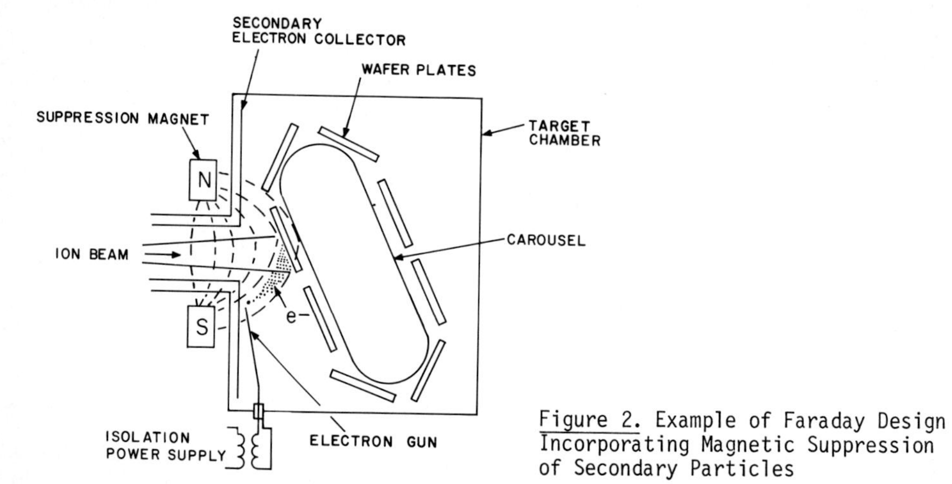

Figure 2. Example of Faraday Design Incorporating Magnetic Suppression of Secondary Particles

3. The Vacuum Environment

In order to discuss the influence of collisions between the beam and residual gases, it is useful first to examine the vacuum environment of an implanter.

All high current systems use the concept of batch processing whereby a large number of wafers are scanned through the ion beam. Even static outgassing of clean wafer batches presents a significant gas load on the pumping system ($\sim 10^{-2}$ Torr l/sec) and conflicts with high throughput requirements. Furthermore there has been an increasing interest in the use of photoresist masking for high dose process steps such as M.O.S. source and drain, polysilicon conductors, bipolar transistor emitters and buried layers. Positive photoresist in particular is increasingly used by V.L.S.I. process engineers for high resolution pattern definition. Now the use of photoresist masking in conjunction with high dose applications presents the implanter designer with a formidable challenge. First of all mask integrity must be maintained under high beam power exposure. Then, in addition to this thermal problem, there is the complication of measuring beam accurately at high pressures. The static outgassing rates for photoresist are significantly higher than for bare silicon or silicon dioxide and, what is more important, when photoresist is bombarded with a high power beam, outgassing rates increase by orders of magnitude.

In the case of positive photoresist the masking pattern which remains on the wafer has not been exposed during lithography and unpolymerized molecules, sensitizers and solvents are present. In the case of negative resist the masking area has been exposed to ultra violet light leaving polymerized molecules and less volatile constituents which generally result in slightly less outgassing under ion beam impact than positive type. Monitoring of the outgassing products has been performed using a Bayard-Alpert ionization gauge and a quadrupole residual gas analyzer [11]. A typical pressure plot is shown in Fig.3 which displays pressure above the end station pump during an implant when an 800 watt beam strikes a full disk of positive photoresist covered wafers. For comparison a similar plot using blank silicon wafers is shown in Fig.4. The undulations correspond to radial scans of the spinning disk and analysis of the outgassing products indicates that nitrogen is the dominant component. Assuming a nominal pumping speed of 10^3 l/sec it can be seen that the outgassing rate for photoresist exceeds 10^{-1} Torr l/sec^{-1} in the first scan. It should be noted that in many implanter designs, a Faraday cup surrounds the point of impact where the ion beam strikes the wafer, restricting pumping and producing even higher pressures within the Faraday region.

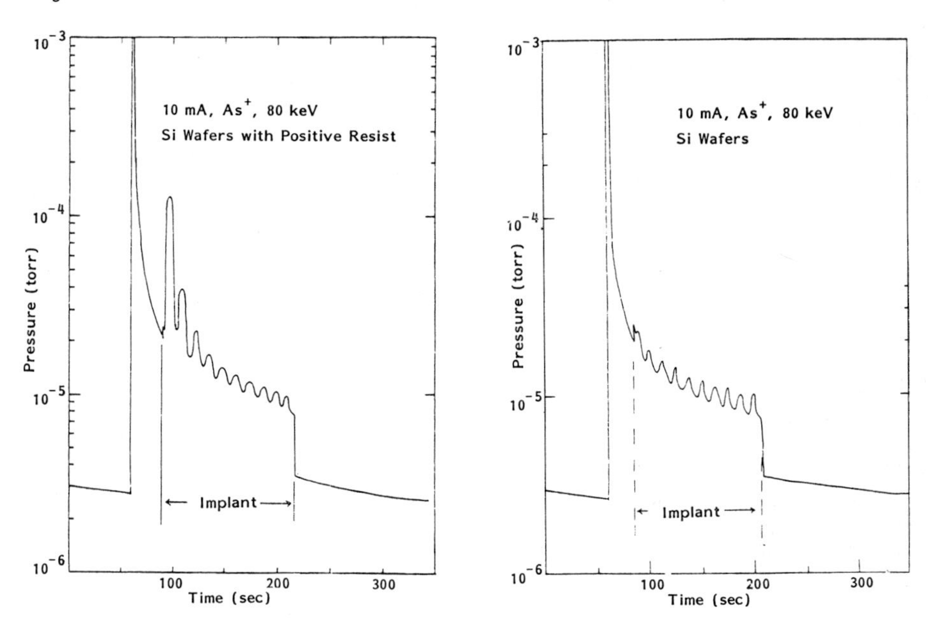

Figure 3. End Station Pressure As a Function of Time During Pump-Down and Implantation of a Batch of Positive Photoresist Covered Wafers

Figure 4. End Station Pressure As a Function of Time During Pump-Down and Implantation of a Batch of Clean Silicon Wafers

4. Faraday Performance Results

Collisions between incident ions (A) and residual gases (B) result in a variety of reactions including the following:

$A^+ + B \rightarrow A^+ + B^+ + e$ (ionization) --(1)

$A^+ + B \rightarrow A + B^+$ (electron capture, charge exchange) --(2)

$A^+ + B \rightarrow A^{++} + B + e$ (electron loss, stripping) --(3)

In order to study the influence of these collisions on dose control, a commercial implanter [12] was used to evaluate different Faraday designs using beams of boron, phosphorus and arsenic with intensities between 0.1 and 20mA and energies between 40 and 80 KeV. Major elements of the system are shown schematically in Fig.5. It contains two Faradays, F_1 and F_2 for dose control [13]. This convenient feature was exploited to compare different secondary suppression schemes as the pressure in the target region was varied by admitting air through a fine control leak valve. The beam resolving aperture, which has a conductance of ~10 l/sec, is the only vacuum connection between the independently pumped beam line region P_2, and the target region P_3. Consequently, the resulting pressure rise in the beam line is two orders of magnitude less than the pressure rise in the end station. During the measurements a calorimeter detector, which gave a beam signal response independent of the charge of the incident particles, could be inserted into the beam to ensure that the total incident flux had not changed.

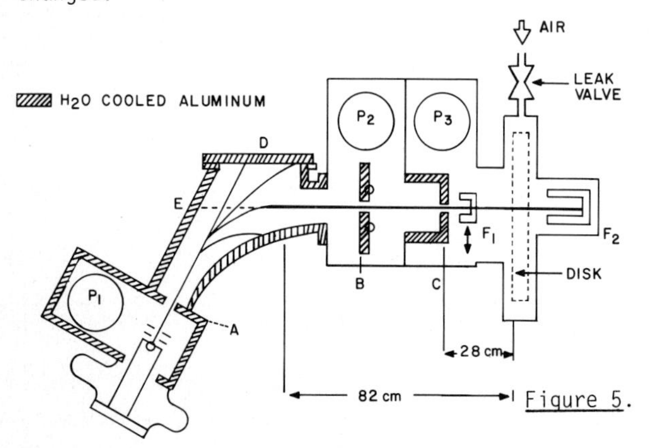

Figure 5. Beamline Schematic of the Implanter

A typical result is shown in Fig.6 which displays the relative beam intensity measured in F_2 as a function of target pressure when the conventional suppression scheme of Fig.1a is used with a 10mA beam of 80KeV As^+ ions.

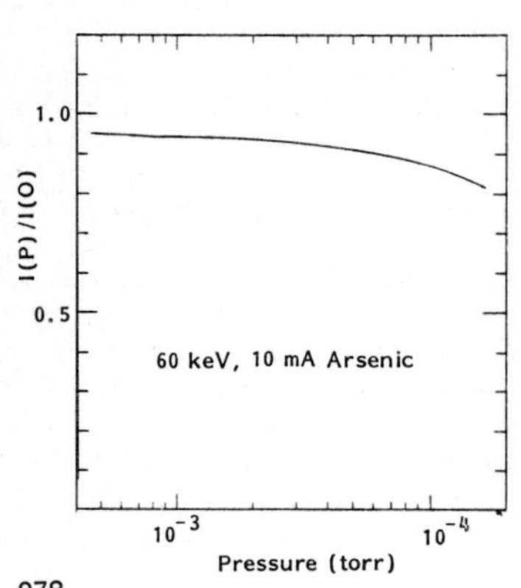

Figure 6. Relative Beam Intensity vs. End Station Pressure for the Faraday Cup Design of Fig.1a

It can be seen that the signal from F_2 is attenuated by approximately 13% at a pressure of $\sim 10^{-4}$ Torr. Now the neutral fraction F_0 generated along a section of beam path is given by:

$$F_0 = 3.3\ 10^{16}\ P\ L\ \sigma \qquad \text{--(4)}$$

where P = Pressure (Torr)
L = Path Length (cm)
and σ = the collision cross section (cm^2).

Assuming a typical [6] electron capture cross section of $\sim 2 \times 10^{-16}$ cm^2, the neutral component at F_2 is expected to be less than $\sim 2\%$. Clearly, the observed signal attenuation is not the result of beam neutralization. Instead it is postulated that the attenuation is the result of residual gas ionization (equation 1) in the entrance region of the Faradays. This phenomenon is illustrated in Fig.7 which shows that slow ions generated in collisions with the residual beamline gases are drawn out of the Faraday by the negative suppression electrode whereas slow electrons generated in the same collisions are pushed into the Faraday. Both effects result in a reduction of the measured current I.

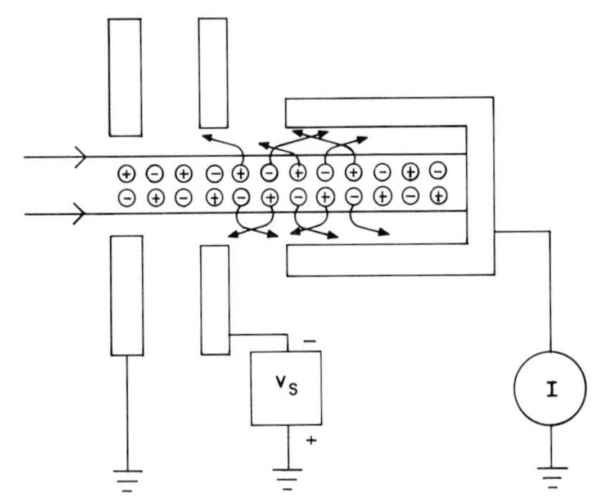

Figure 7. Schematic Showing the Separation of Secondary Charged Particles Produced in Residual Gas - Ion Beam Collisions

In order to estimate the magnitude of this effect the region of field penetration between the bias electrode and the Faraday F_2 was estimated to be 15cm. Assuming a total ionization cross section [14] of $\sim 2 \times 10^{-15}$ cm^2, the expected signal reduction at 10^{-4} Torr is $\sim 10\%$ which is reasonably consistent with the observations.

The suppression scheme of Fig.1b in which the bias supply current is returned to the Faraday was then investigated and typical results are shown in Fig.8. The measured current increases as the pressure increases and in this case it is explained by residual gas ionization in the region between the ground-defining aperture and the suppression electrode as shown in Fig.9. Charge particle flow in this region results in a net increase in the measured current I, whereas particle flow in the region between the bias electrode and the Faraday leads to circulating currents which do not influence the measured current I.

In order to test this model the double electrode suppression scheme illustrated in Fig.10 was evaluated. As shown the flow of slow charge

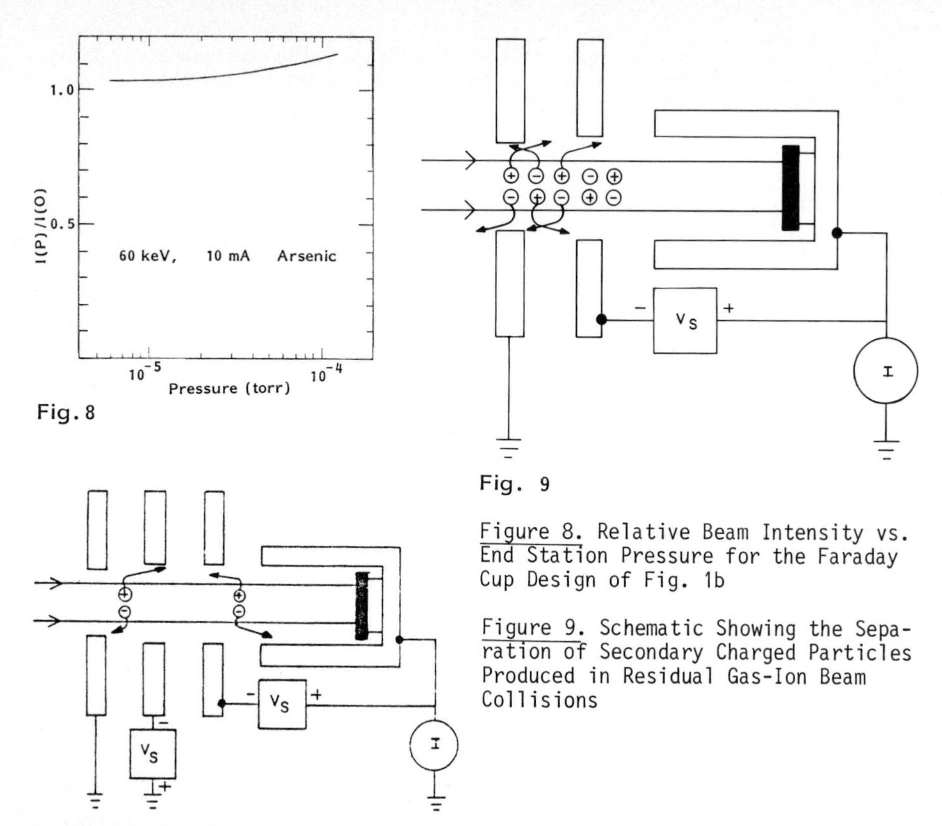

Figure 8. Relative Beam Intensity vs. End Station Pressure for the Faraday Cup Design of Fig. 1b

Figure 9. Schematic Showing the Separation of Secondary Charged Particles Produced in Residual Gas-Ion Beam Collisions

Figure 10. Schematic of Faraday with Double Electrode Suppression Scheme Showing that the Separation of Secondary Charged Particles has Minimum Influence on the Measured Current I

particles no longer influences the measured current I and the results of Fig.11 confirm that the sensitivity to pressure variations is greatly reduced. In this case the slight attenuation of beam signal is entirely consistent with beam neutralization (equation 2) as previously discussed.

Finally the electrostatic suppression designs were replaced by the magnetic design shown schematically in Fig.12. The permanent magnet arrangement produced transverse fields of 400G along the length of the Faraday cup and excellent flat response characteristics were observed as shown in Fig.13. Since the measured beam intensity is independent of pressure over such a broad range, a significant advantage is achieved with this design in that implantation can be initiated earlier in the pump down cycle and system throughput can be increased. The effects of outgassing are also minimal over rather broad limits when photoresist masked wafers are implanted. A further advantage of magnetic suppression is that the dangerous suppression voltages and breakdown complications of conventional electrostatic designs are avoided. Furthermore the magnetic field in the region of the wafers can be minimized if magnetic suppression is used in conjunction with the sampling slot technique [13]. In this way auxiliary electrons can be readily supplied from an electron gun in order to prevent surface charging of the wafers.

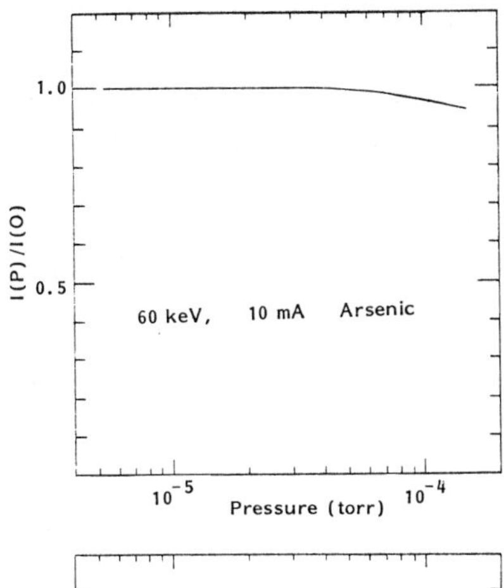

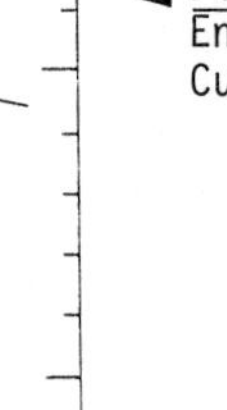

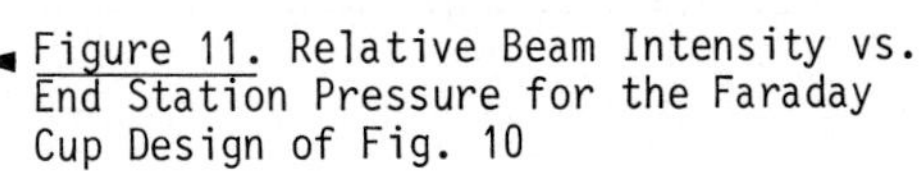

Figure 11. Relative Beam Intensity vs. End Station Pressure for the Faraday Cup Design of Fig. 10

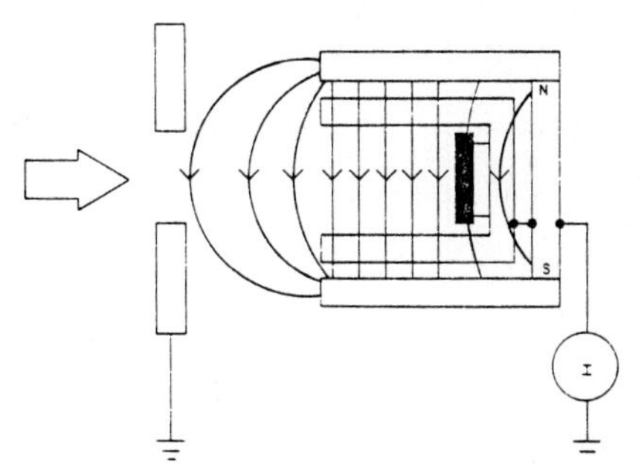

Figure 12. Faraday Cup Design Using Magnetic Suppression

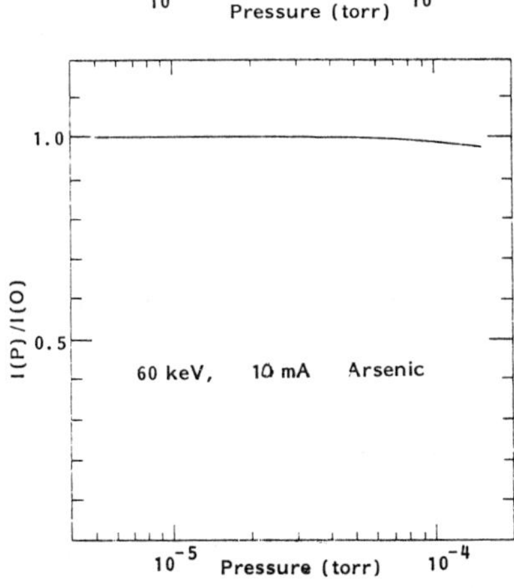

Figure 13. Relative Beam Intensity vs. End Station Pressure for the Faraday Cup Design of Fig. 12

5. Dose Control Results

The ultimate measure of success for any Faraday design is the accuracy and repeatability with which dopant atoms are implanted into the wafer surface under typical production conditions. This is complicated by reflection of incident ions or subsequent sputtering of implanted ions but these effects are generally small and repeatable for a given application.

Absolute measurement of retained dose can be attempted using the following techniques:

a. SIMS. Secondary ion mass spectrometry

b. NAA. Nuclear activation analysis

c. PIXE. Proton-induced X-ray emission

d. RBS. Rutherford backscattering .

A typical implant profile obtained by SIMS analysis is shown in Fig.14 (provided by courtesy of G. Jung and R. H. Kastl of I.B.M. East Fishkill). Unfortunately attempts at absolute measurement are often limited in accuracy, expensive, and in the case of NAA, very time consuming.

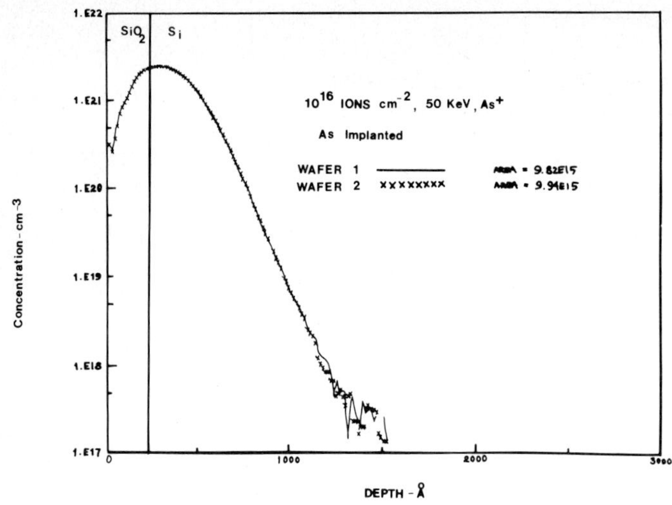

Figure 14. SIMS Profile for 50 KeV, 10^{16} ions cm^{-2}, As^+ Implant

Consequently it has been more common to study the electrical characteristics [15] of the implanted layer with a variety of techniques including the following:

a. Sheet resistance

b. Spreading resistance

c. C-V Profiling

d. Hall measurements

e. Device measurements (MOS threshold, etc.) .

Of these sheet resistance has been most commonly used to evaluate implanter performance [16,17]. However, as with other electrical techniques, only relative data is provided since the final dopant profile depends on annealing conditions and there is no complete theoretical description of carrier mobility in the concentration range in question. Despite this, sheet resistance measurements are a powerful aid in studying implant uniformity and repeatability. Furthermore, if a set of process parameters and measurement standards could be established, then the performance of different implanters could be readily compared. Many individual implanter users have established such standards but to date only one has been published for 150 KeV boron at a doping level of 5 x 10^{14} ions cm^{-2} [15].

The Faraday designs discussed in section 2 have been evaluated using sheet resistance measurements for the test conditions listed in Table 1. These sheet resistance results will now be discussed in terms of dose variation, pressure effects, beam current and temperature effects, process effects, and energy effects.

Table 1

Test Conditions for Sheet Resistance Measurements

Ion Species	B, P, and As
Dose Range	10^{12} - 10^{16} ions cm^{-2}
Energy Range	20 - 80 KeV
End Station Pressures	10^{-6} - 10^{-4} Torr
Wafer Size	100mm
Wafer Type	Czochralski <100> ,p and n-type
Background Resistivity	1-60 ohm cm
SiO_2 Thickness	B^+ implants : 1200Å P^+, As^+ implants: native
Tilt Angle	0 - 7°
Implant Temperature	20 - 400°C
Anneal Temperature	950 - 1050°C
Anneal Duration	30 mins. (10 min - 180 min)
Furnace Gas Flow	B^+ implants : 1 sl/min N_2 P^+, As implants : 1 sl/min N_2 0.1 sl/min O_2
Test Vehicle	4 Point Probe
Test Sites Per Wafer	81 to 161

5.1 The Dependence on Dose

The primary objective was to investigate the influence of doping level on sheet resistance. Typical results using magnetic suppression for 50 KeV boron, 80 KeV phosphorus and 80 KeV arsenic are shown in Figs.15, 16 and 17 respectively. Since there is little published data

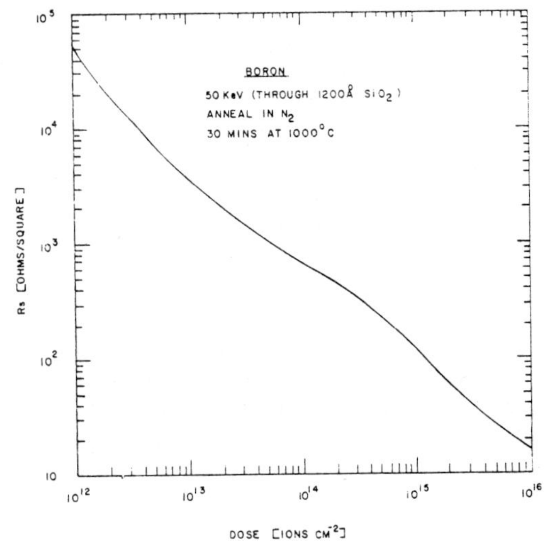

Figure 15. Sheet Resistance vs. Dose for 50 KeV B^+

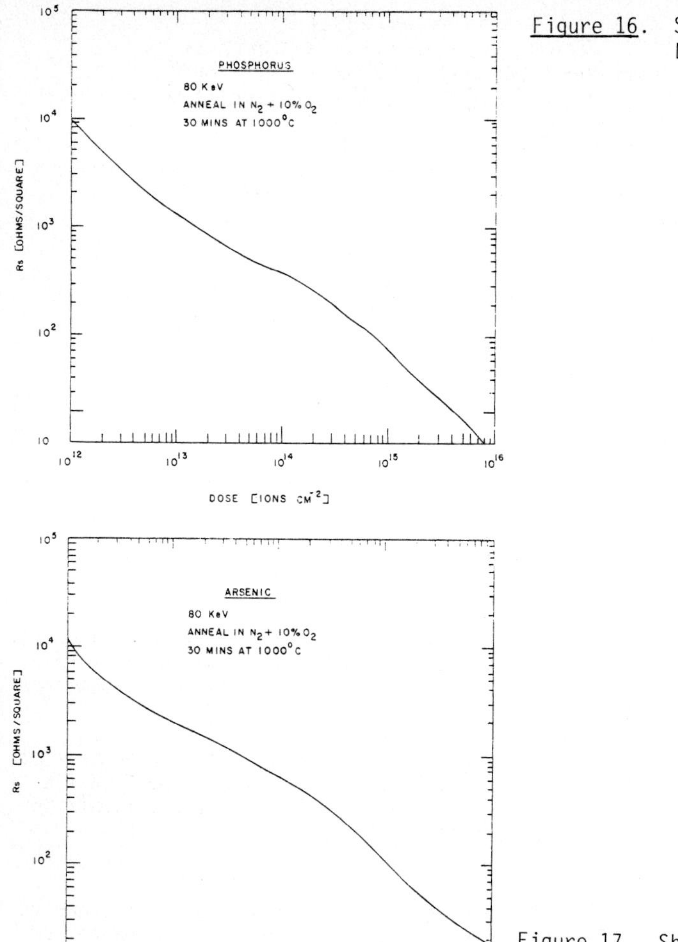

Figure 16. Sheet Resistance vs. Dose for 80 KeV P^+

Figure 17. Sheet Resistance vs. Dose for 80 KeV As^+

for comparison, sheet resistance values were converted to bulk resistivity values using a depth concentration profile obtained by anodic oxidation and chemical stripping. Excellent agreement with the published bulk resistivity data has been obtained particularly in regard to the slope and shape of the curves [18].

5.2 Pressure Effects

The Faraday designs were also investigated under different end station pressure conditions by admitting air through a leak valve. Typical results are displayed in Figs.18, 19 and 20 in which performance of a conventional electrostatic suppression design (Fig.1a) is compared with the magnetic design (Fig.12). As expected the magnetic design is significantly less sensitive to end station pressure. In the case of phosphorus and arsenic, errors are less than 1% even under worst-case conditions when positive photoresist is used and the average pressure during a short implant may be as high as 3 x 10^{-5} Torr (see Fig.3). In the case of boron the pressure dependence is more pronounced but outgassing is less on account of the lower beam power and dose errors should not exceed ~5% for similar worst-case conditions.

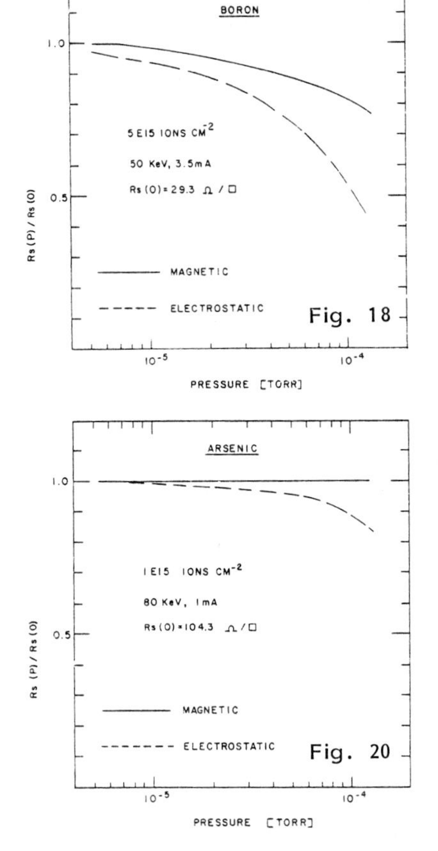

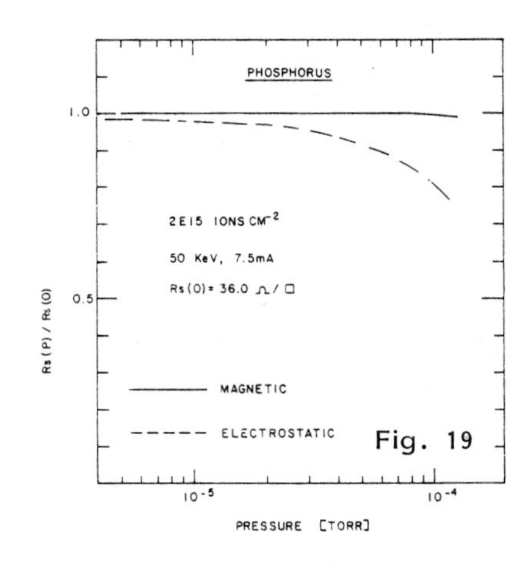

Figure 18. Relative Sheet Resistance vs. End Station Pressure for the Magnetic Faraday (Fig.12) and the Electrostatic Faraday (Fig. 1a)

Figure 19. Relative Sheet Resistance vs. End Station Pressure for the Magnetic Faraday (Fig.12) and the Electrostatic Faraday (Fig.1a)

Figure 20. Relative Sheet Resistance vs. End Station Pressure for the Magnetic Faraday (Fig.12) and the Electrostatic Faraday (Fig.1a)

In order to investigate further pressure effects, test wafers were implanted with 80 keV As^+ ions using a 10mA beam under widely different vacuum conditions as follows. First a control wafer was implanted on a disk loaded with clean bare silicon wafers. The average pressure during the implant was 8 x 10^{-6} Torr. Then a second wafer was implanted under similar conditions but this time air was leaked into the end station so that the average pressure was 4 x 10^{-5} Torr. Finally a third wafer was implanted on a disk surrounded by wafers coated to a thickness of 1.1 microns with Shipley AZ1470J positive photoresist.

The average pressure under these conditions was 3 x 10^{-5} Torr. The sheet resistance results are presented in Table 2 and once again it can be seen that performance of the magnetic Faraday is essentially immune to pressure effects.

Table 2. Sheet Resistance Under Different Vacuum Conditions for 80 keV As^+ Implants

IMPLANT PRESSURE CONDITIONS		R_S (OHMS/SQUARE)
Clean Wafers	8×10^{-6} Torr	39.3
Air Leak	4×10^{-5} Torr	40.3
Photoresist Wafers	3×10^{-5} Torr	38.8

5.3 Beam Current and Temperature Effects

The variations in sheet resistivity with incident beam current and wafer temperature has also been examined. Wafer temperature effects were investigated qualitalively by comparing the results of uncooled wafers and those of cooled wafers. In the case of uncooled wafers the temperature ranges from 20°C to 400°C depending on beam power whereas with cooled wafers the temperature ranges from 20°C to 100°C [19]. The results are summarized in Table 3.

It can be seen that there is no systematic variation in sheet resistance. Typically all values lie within $\pm 3\%$ (including measurement errors) even though the beam current and wafer temperature each vary over approximately one order of magnitude. In similar investigations with phosphorus implants, Beanland et al. [20] observed a substantial variation of the sheet resistance as a function of the wafer temperature during implant. This phenomenon was not observed in the present experiments.

Table 3. Sheet Resistance Values at Different Beam Currents and Wafer Temperatures

ION	ENERGY (KeV)	BEAM CURRENT (mA)	R_S (UNCOOLED) (ohms/square)	R_S (COOLED) (ohms/square)
B	50	0.64	53.8	52.6
	(1200 A SiO_2)	1.61	51.8	51.9
		4.00	52.1	51.3
P	80	1.6	27.5	27.5
		4.0	27.2	27.2
		10.0	25.8	25.7
As	80	1.6	46.3	45.6
		4.0	46.9	47.1
		10.0	44.2	45.2

5.4 Process Effects

Apart from implantation effects, the final sheet resistance depends on several process variables including the initial substrate concentrations, oxide thickness, anneal temperature, anneal duration and ambient gas. The sensitivity to anneal temperature was measured for 80 KeV, 1E16 ions cm^{-2} implants into p-type silicon (1-10 ohm cm). For thermal deviations in the range 950 to 1050°C a gradient of 0.14 ohms/square/°C was measured. It has also been shown that thermal gradients in a furnace resulting from inadequate insulation, end effects, or the influence of the wafers on the temperature profiles can produce systematic variations of approximately 1 ohm/square across a wafer.

In recent years there has been a growing interest in alternate methods of repairing the crystal damage and producing the required electrical activity of the dopant atoms after implantation. Pulsed and CW laser and electron beams have been investigated and more recently the use of incoherent light sources has been evaluated. It is interesting to note that recent results of wafers annealed with a directed incoherent light source have shown that rapid, uniform heating of the wafer from the face can result in superior uniformity as compared to conventional furnace annealing [21].

5.5 The Dependence on Energy

The variation of sheet resistance with incident ion energy and oxide thickness has also been briefly investigated. Preliminary results are displayed in Table 4.

Table 4. Sheet Resistance Values for Different Implant Energies and Oxide Thicknesses

ION	DOSE (ions cm^{-2})	OXIDE THICKNESS (A)	ENERGY (KeV)	R_s (ohms/square)
B	2E15	1200	20	99.5
			30	83
			40	77
			50	67
			60	61
			70	57
			80	55
	4E14	1200	50	231
		200	30	276
			50	233
			80	201
		native	50	232
As	6E15	native	20	26.7
			30	26.0
			40	25.8
			50	25.8
			60	26.3
			70	26.7
			80	27.2
	1E16	225	80	20.5
			50	15.1
P	5E14	native	80	136.5
			50	138.2
		200	80	139.2

6. Contamination and Memory Effects

During implantation a wafer is exposed to a variety of particles including of course the primary ion beam. Atoms or molecules which reach the silicon surface are conveniently grouped into three categories illustrated schematically in Fig.21 and described as follows:

a. Particles originating from the ion source.

b. Particles originating from the residual gases of the vacuum system.

c. Particles originating from the internal surfaces of the vacuum system, including the surface of the wafer itself.

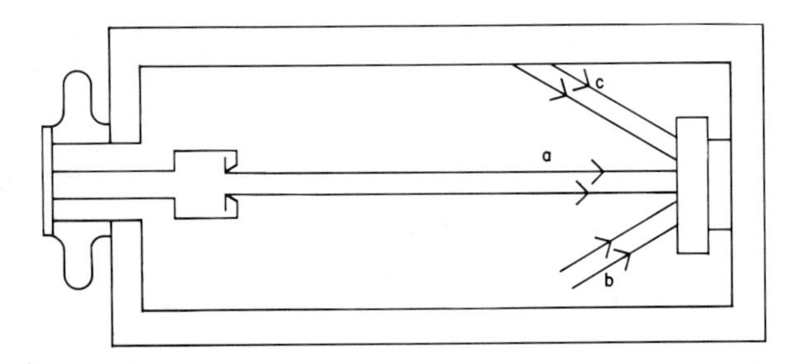

Figure 21. Schematic Illustrating the Sources of Particles Which Reach the Silicon Surface

The general subject of beam quality and the various circumstances under which unexpected ions are transported from the ion source to the wafer has been reviewed in detail by Freeman [6]. Some of the precautions which can be taken to minimize these effects are illustrated schematically in Fig.5. In this system the entire beamline and wafer fixturing is constructed of aluminum or graphite, which are relatively benign materials, and the use of heavy metals has been avoided. Whenever possible the regions of beam impact are water cooled so that local heating and re-evaporation of previously deposited materials is minimized.

Contamination by sputtering is not so easy to control and occurs to some extent in all implanters [22, 23]. As expected the amount of material transferred to the wafer from a surface exposed to the beam is a strong function of its distance from the wafer. Consequently beam defining apertures or masks are generally placed at the maximum convenient distance in front of the wafer.

A more difficult situation is encountered with wafer fixturing when a support clip or cooling clamp is required in close proximity to the wafer. In this case it is again advisable to use benign materials and add a protection lip so that the portion of the clamp or clip in contact with the wafer is shadowed from the beam [19].

In addition, the solid angle from which secondary sputtered or evaporated particles can directly reach the wafer can be reduced by adding water-cooled baffles such as the one shown at B (Fig.5). With such an arrangement the direct line of sight access to the wafer is possible only from the resolving aperture at C and the distant region E which is never subjected to beam bombardment.

Secondary particles are a particular problem when the beam sputters dopant materials which were implanted in the surfaces during previous use of the machine. This phenomenon is often referred to as the "memory effect". In regard to this effect the automatic disk interchange scheme used on the Nova NV-10-80 offers a particularly attractive feature [24]. The double disk arrangement enables disks to be easily changed without reducing throughput since one disk is being loaded while the second disk is being implanted. Consequently the memory effect can be minimized by the use of "dedicated" disks for each dopant ion type. R.B.S. analysis techniques have been used to study the "memory" characteristic of this system [25]. In the first test the system was operated with arsenic for several hours under typical production conditions. The ion beam was then changed to argon and test wafers were implanted. Under these conditions the initial surface concentration of arsenic ions was found to be ~1% of the argon ion dose. In the second test the procedure was repeated. However when the ion beam was changed from arsenic to argon the disks were also replaced by clean disks which had previously been operated with argon. In this case the initial concentration of Arsenic was 0.2% of the argon dose, a value comparable to the detection limit of the R.B.S. instrument.

7. Conclusions

The final electrical characteristics produced by ion implantation in silicon are a complex function of implant parameters, implant variables and process parameters. The more important of these are summarized in Table 5.

Table 5. Parameters and Variables Influencing R_S

Implant Parameters	Ion Species Ion Energies Doping Level Implant Angle
Implanter Variables	Beam Current System Pressure System Memory (Contamination)
Process Parameters	Wafer Type Oxide Thickness Anneal Temperature Anneal Duration Anneal Atmosphere

In this paper, the influence of these parameters and variables has been reviewed. In particular, the common methods of beam detection have been investigated and some recent attempts to eliminate the influence of implanter variables during high current implantation have been described.

8. Acknowledgements

This paper includes contributions from many scientists and engineers. Although unable to acknowledge all individually, the author would like to express appreciation for the machine development provided by Marvin Farley and the wafer evaluation provided by Ken Steeples.

1. P.L.F. Hemment, Radiation Effects 44, 31 (1979).

2. P.L.F. Hemment, Inst. Phys. Conf. Ser. 54 77 (1980).

3. C.M. McKenna, Radiation Effects 44 93 (1979).

4. D.M. Jamba, Nucl. Instr. and Meth. 189 253 (1981).

5. S. Matteson and M.A. Nicolet, Nucl. Inst. and Meth. 160 301 (1979).

6. J.H. Freeman, Inst. Phys. Conf. Ser 28 340 (1976).

7. W.C. Ko and E. Sawatzky, 7th International Conference on Electron and Ion Beam Science and Technology. Electrochem. Soc. Washington(1976).

8. G. Dearnaley, J.H. Freeman, R.S. Nelson and J. Stephen. Ion Implantation. Amersterdam: North Holland, 416-421 (1973).

9. Applied Implant Technology. Series III Implanters.

10. D. Aitken, Private communication.

11. K. Steeples and G. Ryding, To be published.

12. Eaton Corporation. Nova Implanter Model NV-10-80.

13. G. Ryding and M. Farley, Nucl. Instr. and Meth. 189 319 (1981).

14. H.S.W. Massey and H.B. Gilbody, Electronic and Ionic Phenomena, Vol. IV, University Press, Oxford (1974).

15. J.N. Gan and D.S. Perloff, Nucl. Instr. and Meth. 189 265 (1981).

16. B.J. Smith, J. Stephen, and G.W. Hinder, Harwell AERE Report 7085 (1974).

17. D.S. Perloff, F.E. Wahl and J.T. Kerr, 7th International Conference on Electron and Ion Beam Science and Technology. Electrochem. Soc. Washington (1976).

18. K. Steeples and G. Ryding, To be published.

19. M. Mack. This conference.

20. D.G. Beanland, W. Temple and D.J. Chivers, Solid State Electronics 21 357 (1978).

21. J.C. Gelpey, P.O. Stump, D.M. Camm, S.L.F. Richards, G.G. Albach and N.P. Halpin. First Canadian Semiconductor Technology Conference, Ottawa (1982).

22. P.L.F. Hemment. Vacuum 29 439 (1979).

23. E.W. Haas, H. Glawischnig, G. Lichti and A. Bleier, J. Electronic Mater 7 525 (1978).

24. G. Ryding and A. Armstrong. Nucl. Instr. and Meth. 189 319 (1981).

25. M. Current, Private Communication.

A New Facility for Ion Beam Surface Analysis

P.L.F. Hemment, J.E. Mynard, E.A. Maydell-Ondrusz*, and K.G. Stephens

Department of Electronic and Electrical Engineering, University of Surrey, Guildford, Surrey, England

Abstract: The surface analysis facility on the 2 MeV Van de Graaff accelerator at the University of Surrey is described. Two beam lines, including a microbeam capability, are dedicated to this application and the target chambers house 2- and 3-axis goniometers and linear drives for rapid sample changing. Rutherford backscattering and PIXE techniques may be combined with ion channelling for the analysis of semiconductor, metal, insulator and biological samples. Data is processed and stored on a DEC LSI 11-03 computer, which is linked to main frame computers with software for data interpretation.

1. Introduction

The University of Surrey has possessed a Rutherford backscatter facility since 1970(1), and during this period semiconductor, metal, insulator and biological samples have been analysed. Ion beam techniques(2) combined with ion channelling in single crystal samples, provide a quick and non-destructive method of surface analysis. In particular Rutherford backscattering(3) enables concentration profiles of heavy impurities, damage profiles and the atomic site location of impurities in single crystals to be determined to a depth of about 0.5 μm, with a depth resolution of about 300Å. This depth resolution may be improved by an order of magnitude when working at a glancing angle of incidence or when a magnetic spectrometer is used to analyse the backscattered ions. These features make backscattering an attractive technique for studies of diffusion and crystal regrowth in semiconductors and thin film systems.

In order to extend the scope of the facility at Surrey the equipment has been upgraded and now includes analysis by proton induced X-ray emission(3) (PIXE) and a microbeam capability, using a magnetic quadrupole lens. The addition of an interactive data handling system and a new specimen manipulator enables samples to be rapidly analysed.

2. Description of the Facility

2.1 Design Features

The following decisions were taken before commencing the upgrading of the surface analysis facility:

1. Two beam lines (target chambers) to be available with minimal delays to be incurred when switching between these lines.

---

*Institute of Nuclear Physics, Krakow, Poland

2. Rapid sample changing with fast data collection and storage to be provided.

3. Interchangeable goniometer and linear drives to be available.

4. Rutherford backscatter and PIXE techniques both to be available in one target chamber.

5. The beam to be focussed to give a lateral resolution of order 10μm.

6. Direct viewing of samples to be available using an optical microscope or TV system.

7. Standard formats to be used for storage, plotting and listing of experimental data.

2.2 Description

Figure 1 is a schematic diagram of the surface analysis facility, showing the major components. The ion beam, which may be H^+, He^+ or O^+ is extracted from an r.f. source in the top terminal of a 2 MeV High Voltage Engineering Corporation, Van de Graaff, which is 25 years old. The vacuum system on this machine has been modified and now includes an Edwards Diffstak(4) oil diffusion pump, with a liquid nitrogen trap, plus additional pumps along the beam lines to give a base pressure of better than 5×10^{-7} torr. The analysing magnet serves as a beam switch to deflect the ions into one of four lines. Two of these beam lines are used for high energy light ion irradiations and complement the facilities available on the other (low energy) accelerators within the laboratory. Lines 3 and 4 are used for surface analysis and are now described in detail.

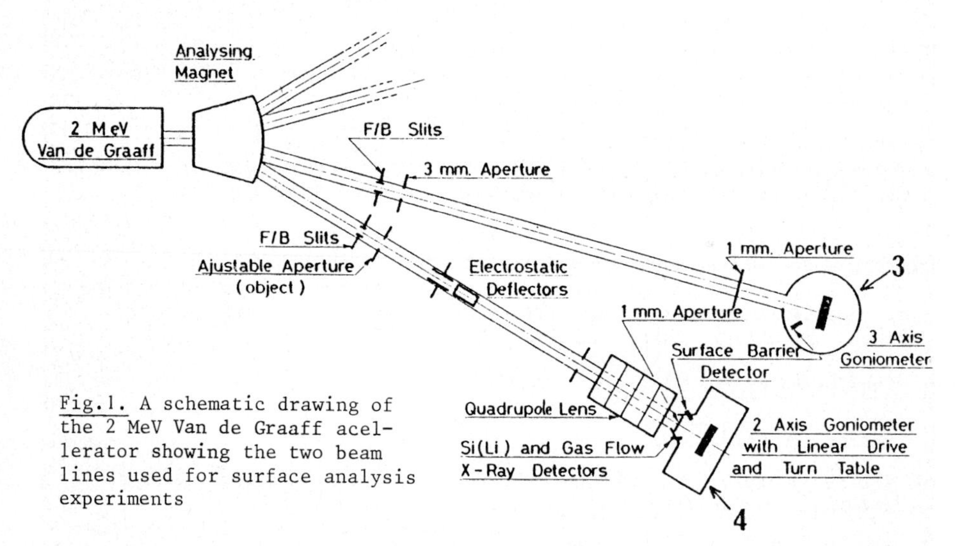

Fig.1. A schematic drawing of the 2 MeV Van de Graaff acelerator showing the two beam lines used for surface analysis experiments

Line 3

This line includes two fixed apertures which collimate the beam, to a half angle of 0.025°, and define a beam diameter of 1mm in the plane of the sample. The target chamber contains a three-axis goniometer(5) for sample alignment in a channelling direction or to incline samples at a glancing angle of incidence, to improve the depth resolution. A silicon surface barrier detector is used for backscatter measurements. This target chamber is to be modified soon and no further mention will be made in this paper.

Line 4

Included in this line is a magnetic quadrupole lens of a design developed by Cookson(6) at AERE, Harwell. When the lens is arranged as a "Russian Quadruplet" it gives a demagnified image (x5.6) of an object aperture which is mounted just behind the feedback slits. The image is focussed at a distance of 210mm beyond the lens and this fixed dimension has called for a target chamber of a compact design. In an alternative configuration (triplet) the lens gives a larger and asymmetric demagnification of × 18 and x8 in two orthogonal planes. Beam spot sizes of 15 to 20 μm are produced using an electron microscope aperture as the object. When this high lateral resolution is not required, two apertures which are 3.9 metres apart are used to collimate the beam to a similar divergence and spot size as on line 3.

Two pairs of electrodes are mounted in the beam line, between the object aperture and the quadrupole lens. These plates provide electrostatic analysis, to remove high velocity ions with the same mv/q value(7) and also enable the beam to be raster scanned, for imaging purposes.

Fig. 2. The line 4 target chamber with the back plate removed and the 2-axis goniometer pivoted through 90° to show the good accessibility to components within the chamber

Figure 2 is a photograph of the rectangular target chamber on line 4 and shows the 2-axis goniometer, radiation detectors and the optical microscope used to view the samples. The circular frames on the far side of the chamber are the outer yokes of the quadrupole lens. The target chamber, with internal dimensions of 33cm x 24cm x 17 cm, was machined from a single ingot of dural and no vacuum problems have been encountered, either due to the choice of material or to the use of O-ring seals. The front plate is also dural and has a conical section with six extrance ports, arranged symmetrically around the beam axis, which accept the radiation detectors and the window for the optical microscope. The chamber accepts various designs of sample manipulator which are located by pivots,on a rectangular frame. This frame has 5cm of travel along the beam axis which enables samples to be moved into the focal plane of the quadrupole lens. When the back plate is removed, as shown in the photograph, the manipulator may be pivoted through 90° to facilitate sample loading.

Figure 3 is a schematic drawing of the two-axis goniometer which provides $\pm 15^{\circ}$ of rotation about 2 axes (θ and ϕ), linear travel over 90mm plus a turntable for continuous rotation of the sample during analysis. This latter feature is of value when reproducible backscatter spectra, typical of amorphous material, are required from crystalline targets(8).

The translational and rotational movements on the goniometer are actuated by two stepper motors(9) and two dc motors(10) situated inside the vacuum chamber. No serious surface contamination has been observed and a base pressure of $2x10^{-6}$ torr routinely is achieved. Irregular shaped samples can be accommodated but it is usual to work with 5mm x 5mm squares when up to 14 samples may be mounted on the interchangeable sample plates. Upon loading a new batch of samples, a pump down time of 15 minutes is required to achieve a working pressure of $4x10^{-5}$ torr.

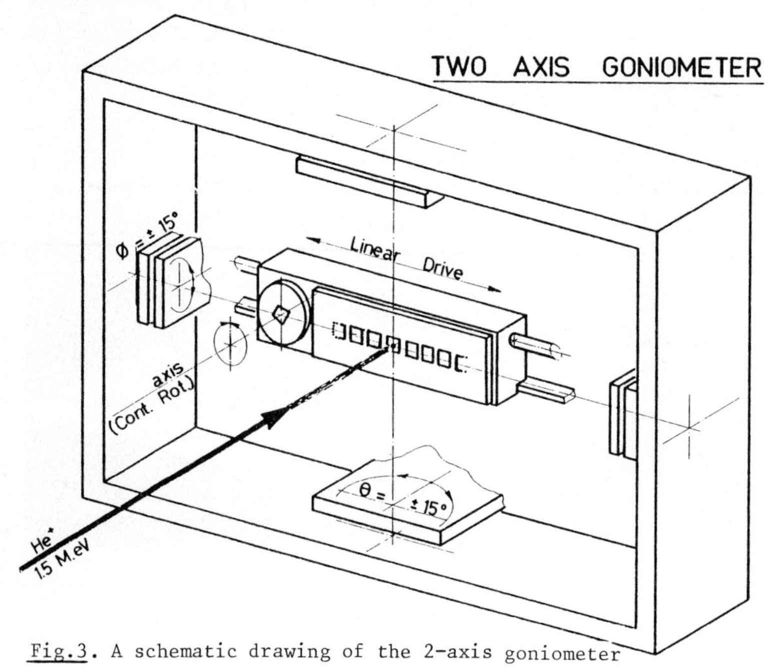

Fig.3. A schematic drawing of the 2-axis goniometer

Three radiation detectors are available, these being a silicon surface barrier detector for Rutherford backscattering and a Si(Li) detector plus a gas flow proportional detector(11) for X-ray analysis. Characteristic X-rays may be detected over the photon energy range 100 eV to 50 keV, effectively covering all elements heavier than boron. Both X-ray detectors have variable geometry with the gas flow detector having an end window configuration which permits the sensitivity to be optimised to detect photons of a particular energy in a selective manner.

Data collection and processing is under the control of software(12) run on a dedicated DEC LSI 11-03 computer, which is interfaced to the University network of five PRIME computers (Fig.4). The interactive software runs in the foreground/background mode with Terminal 1 having priority for collection and storage of data on floppy disks. A second user may access the computer from Terminal 2 and with the use of a few simple commands, stored data may be manipulated and plotted. In the case of Rutherford backscattering, mass identification and depth scales may be added to the energy spectrum.

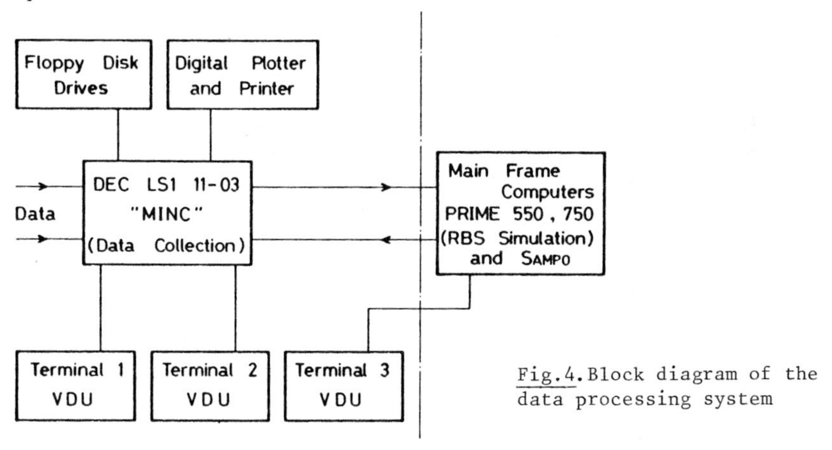

Fig.4. Block diagram of the data processing system

Software is available to simulate Rutherford backscattering by generating (theoretical) energy spectra for test structures, which may consist of up to 5 elements in 99 discrete layers(13). Additional software has been implemented on the PRIME computers to interpret the X-ray spectra.

3. Applications

The facility is used by physicists and engineers from within the University and by collaborators from Industry and other University laboratories. In addition the department provides a service for staff working on projects funded by the U.K. Science and Engineering Research Council. Thus many different types of sample are presented for analysis and it is the availability of two beam lines/target chambers and the use of a dedicated computer that gives us the flexibility to maintain a specialist service and also an ability to carry out routine analysis of large batches of samples.

Examples of the use made of the facility are now described.

3.1 Synthesis of SiO_2

There is considerable interest in the formation of Silicon on Insulator (SOI) structures by the synthesis of a buried SiO_2 layer using ion implantation(14). When assessing these structures it is desirable to know the depth profile of the implanted oxygen and the conditions under which reordering of the implantation damage takes place.

Figure 5 shows the random and channelling energy spectra of 1.5 MeV He^+ ions backscattered from a sample implanted at 500°C with a dose of 1.8 x 10^{18} O^+ cm^{-2} at 200 keV. The oxygen signal is evident between channels 70 and 130, but is poorly defined as it is superimposed upon the signal from the silicon substrate. The dip between channels 160 and 240 is due to the lower atomic density of silicon in the implanted layer and the oxygen distribution also may be inferred from the shape of this part of the spectrum. Computer simulations show that the gradient of the oxygen concentration at the interface is a decade in 1700Å. A detailed examination of the channelled spectra between channels 230 and 280 confirms that after implantation the top layer is a highly defective single crystal, but after a prolonged high temperature anneal recovery of the implantation damage occurs.

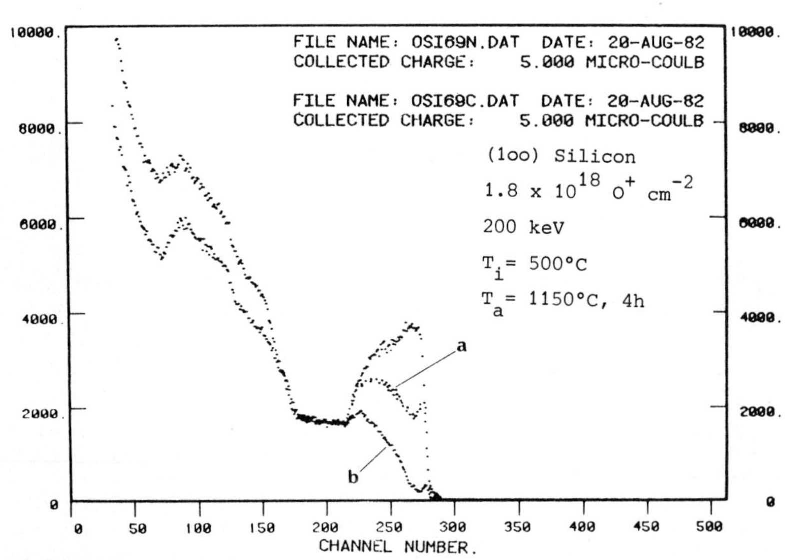

Fig.5. Random and channelled backscatter spectra of silicon samples implanted at 500°C with 1.8x10^{18} O^+ cm^{-2} at 200 keV. The channelled spectra were recorded (a) before and (b) after annealing at 1150°C for 4 hours, using a SiO_2 cap

3.2 Thin Films

In many areas of semiconductor device technology it is necessary to study the reaction of thin films deposited on silicon. An example is the formation of metal silicides for contacts and interconnects and Fig.6 shows Rutherford backscatter spectra of a thin film of titanium deposited on silicon and subsequently processed to form $TiSi_2$, by irradiation with a

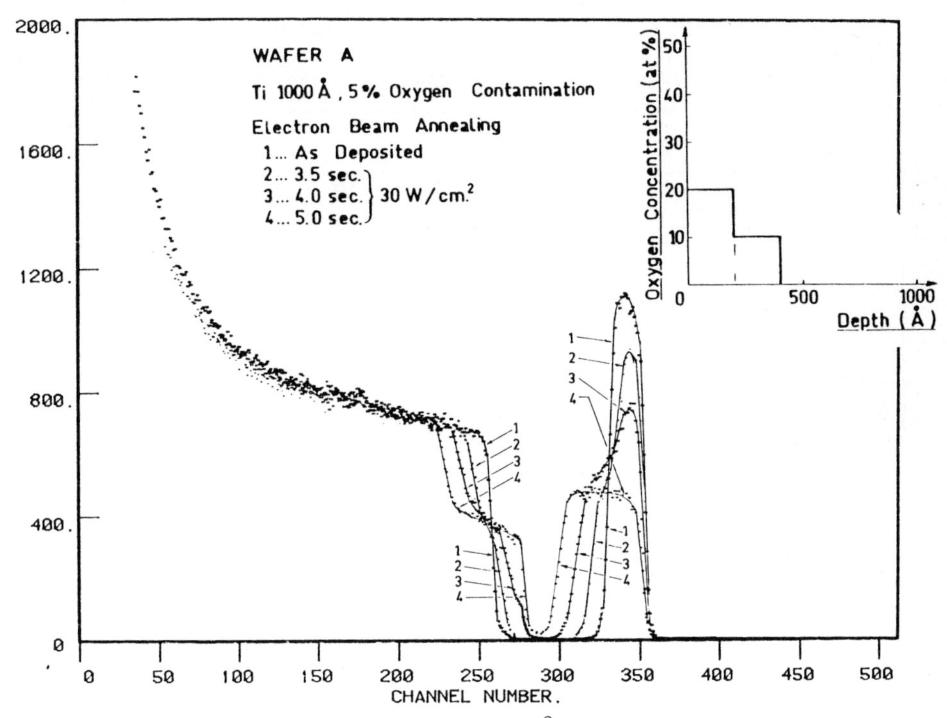

Fig.6. Random backscatter spectra from a 1000Å Ti layer on silicon after processing with a multi-scanned electron beam

multiscanned electron beam. The interdiffusion may be modelled by following the evolution of spectrum 1 (Ti on Si) through to spectrum 4 ($TiSi_2$). In this example the changes in the depth distributions of the reacting species have been followed by fitting computer generated spectra, shown as solid lines, to the experimental data.

The oxygen concentration within the films may be deduced from the area under the small peak centred on channel 180 and also from the shape of the titanium signal. It is found that this contaminant is driven out of the system during the rapid heating achieved with the electron beam to leave a stoichiometric film of $TiSi_2$, which is 2400Å thick and contains oxygen below the detection limit of about 5% atomic.

3.3 Ion Implantation Dosimetry

A particular strength of Rutherford backscatter analysis is that impurity concentrations may be determined directly from known values of the scattering cross-section and measured values of the experimental parameters. Therefore the technique offers a direct method of determining the absolute areal density of implanted impurities and may be used to determine the accuracy of the ion beam dosimetry on ion implantation equipment. A problem frequently encountered in the analysis of single crystal targets is that channelling can give an erroneous backscatter yield. Blood et al.(8) have demonstrated that continuous rotation of the

Table 1 . Variation in the areal density of As^+ implanted into silicon to a nominal dose of 5.0×10^{15} As^+ cm^2 at 150 keV. The data was recorded for samples implanted under different experimental conditions

	SUPPRESSION SUPPLY			
	CONFIGURATION (A)		CONFIGURATION (B)	CONFIGURATION (C)
SAMPLE HOLDER 1	5.22×10^{15} (+ 4.4%)		4.38×10^{15} (-12.4%)	4.18×10^{15} (-16.4%)
SAMPLE HOLDER 2	5.45×10^{15} (+ 9%)		4.93×10^{15} (- 1.4%)	4.73×10^{15} (- 5.4%)
SAMPLE HOLDER 3	AMP. SATURATED 5.41×10^{15} (+ 8.2%)	IN RANGE 5.74×10^{15} (+ 14.8%)	$4.62 \pm 0.03 \times 10^{15}$ (- 7.6%)	(ESTIMATE) 4.42×10^{15} (-11.6%)

THE SPREAD ON REPEATED MEASUREMENTS IS $\pm 0.07 \times 10^{15}$ As^+/cm^2 (± 1.5%), EXCEPT WHERE SHOWN.

sample during data collection gives reproducible random spectra, which show an energy dependence typical of an amorphous target. The turntable incorporated in the 2-axis goniometer (Fig.3) provides the facility and data has been collected from samples inclined at angles of $\theta = -3^o$ and $\phi = +7^o$ to the beam axis and with a rotational period of 90 seconds.

The results of analysis of (100) silicon wafers implanted with a nominal dose of 5×10^{15} As^+ cm^{-2} at 150 keV are listed in Table 1. Measurements of the retained dose show a short term repeatability of better than ± 0.40% and have an overall spread of less than ± 1.5%, which is due primarily to the statistical spread in the individual measurements. This good reproducibility has enabled variations in the retained dose, due to different geometric configurations within the target chamber of an implanter, to be measured. Direct comparison of samples implanted in different machines is also possible.

4. Summary

A surface analysis facility at the University of Surrey has been described. Two target chambers are available and these house 2- and 3-axis goniometers, which incorporate linear drives for rapid sample changing. Surface analysis is by Rutherford backscattering and Proton Induced X-ray Emission (PIXE) with data collection and plotting being under software control, which is run on a DEC LSI 11-03. Various applications have been described which illustrate the scope of the facility and show the value of computer simulations when interpreting Rutherford backscatter spectra.

Acknowledgements

The authors are pleased to acknowledge the technical assistance given by the staff of the D.R. Chick Laboratory, University of Surrey and thank D.W. Wellby and J. Morris for writing many of the computer programmes. Part of this work is funded by the U.K. Science and Engineering Council.

References

1. P.J. Cracknell, M. Gettings and K.G. Stephens: Nucl. Instr. Meths. *92*, 465, 1971.

2. J.F. Ziegler: *New Uses of Ion Accelerators*, Plenum Press, New York, 1975.

3. J.W. Mayer, E. Rimini: *Ion Beam Handbook for Material Analysis*, Acad. Press, London, 1977.

4. Edwards High Vacuum, Manor Royal, Crawley, Sussex, England.

5. Panmure Instruments Ltd., Bone Lane Industrial Estate, Newbury, Berks, England.

6. J.A. Cookson, A.T.G. Ferguson and F.D. Pilling: J. Radioanal. Chem. *12*, 39, 1972.

7. P.L.F. Hemment, J.F. Singleton and K.G. Stephens: Thin Solid Films, 1975.

8. P. Blood, L.C. Feldman, G.L. Miller, J.P. Remeika: Nucl. Inst. Meths. *149*, 225, 1978.

9. M. Calderon Ltd., Sebastian House, Sebastian Street, London EC1V OHN.

10. Portescap (UK) Ltd., 204 Elgar Road, Reading, Berks, England.

11. J.A. Cairns, C.L. Desborough, D.F. Holloway, Nucl. Inst. Meths. *88*, 239, 1970.

12. D.W. Wellby, Internal Report, University of Surrey, 1981.

13. J. Morris, to be published.

14. P.L.F. Hemment, E.A. Maydell-Ondrusz, K.G. Stephens, J. Ioannou, J. Butcher, J. Alderman, IBMM 82, Grenoble 1982.

15. E.A. Maydell-Ondrusz, P.L.F. Hemment, K.G. Stephens, S. Moffatt: Electronics Lett. *18*, 17, 752, 1982.

16. M. Tolson, private communication.

Non-Destructive Techniques for Measuring the Parameters of Low-Energy Continuous Ion Beams

W.J. Szajnowski

Institute of Telecommunications, Technical University of Warsaw, Nowowiejska 15/19, 00-665 Warsaw, Poland

1. Introduction

The commercial significance of ion implantation as a production tool has caused an increasing interest in fully automated systems. The design of such systems requires that special attention be given to methods ensuring the reproducibility of ion-beam parameters. In order to measure the beam parameters in real time during implantation, special devices have been developed. The information about the beam parameters is extracted from the electromagnetic field associated with the moving charged particles. Another source of information is visible light emitted following collisions of the beam particles with the residual gas molecules.

The non-destructive devices can be classified into several groups on the basis of the type of beam-device interaction:

- electrostatic induction electrodes [1] - [11], [20]
- magnetic sensors [12], [20]
- wall-current monitors [13] - [15], [20]
- Hall-effect devices [16], [20]
- resonant cavity monitors [17], [18], [20]
- beam-induced light processors [19].

These devices are capable of measuring or at least monitoring such beam parameters as current, transverse coordinates of center of charge, ion velocity, and beam profile.

In developing optimum techniques for processing the observable signals provided by non-destructive devices, account must be taken of the statistical nature of continuous ion beams. Consequently, the signal processors proposed should implement algorithms based on statistical-inference theory.

This paper describes some new non-destructive techniques to estimate the transverse coordinates of center of charge of continuous ion beams. The information is extracted from noise-like signals induced on specially shaped electrostatic induction electrodes positioned around the beam. The techniques proposed offer a new approach to signal processing without some of the complications associated with conventional methods. Experiments performed with the use of the prototype processors evolved from considerations outlined in the paper have provided ample proof of the soundness of the concepts presented.

2. Information Provided by Electrostatic Induction Electrodes

Consider a grounded conducting pipe of a circular cross-section in which a line charge is parallel to the pipe axis. An equivalent two-dimensional system consists of a point charge located inside a circle of unit radius - Fig.1. The point charge exerts a field of force derived from a logarithmic potential. On the circumference of the circle, a countercharge is induced, and the potential of the total field thus created is equal to the Green's function of the circle [22].

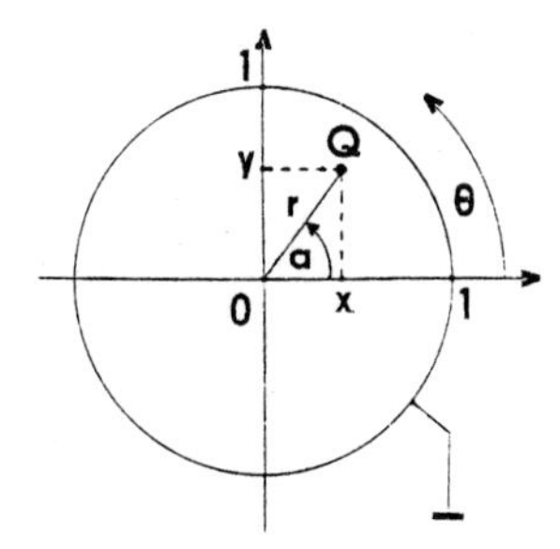

Fig.1 Two-dimensional electrostatic model for a beam inside a pipe

It can be shown that the density of the charge induced on the circumference of the circle is of the form

$$g(\theta;r,a) = -\frac{Q}{2\pi}\,\frac{1-r^2}{1-2r\cos(\theta-a)+r^2} \tag{1}$$

where (r,a) are the polar coordinates of the line charge and Q is the charge density (per unit length in the z direction). Assume that the density $g(\theta;r,a)$ can be processed by an electrode system performing the following operation

$$u(r,a) = \int_0^{2\pi} g(\theta;r,a)w(\theta)\,d\theta \tag{2}$$

where $w(\theta)$ is the weighting function of the system. Substituting (1) into (2) yields the Poisson integral which is the solution to the boundary value problem of the first kind [23]. The function $u(r,a)$, which can be regarded as the response of an electrode system characterised by the weighting function $w(\theta)$, satisfies the Laplace equation and the boundary condition

$$\nabla^2 u(r,a) = 0; \quad u(1,a) = w(a) \quad . \tag{3}$$

From the above discussion it follows that irrespective of the weighting function, the response $u(r,a)$ is a harmonic function; any search for an electrode system with a response which is not harmonic will, therefore, be fruitless. This is a general result, since all bounded domains of interest can be mapped onto a circle by means of a conformal mapping.

If a line charge is replaced by a charge with density $q(x,y)$, then the superposition considerations show that the electrode response U_q can be evaluated from

$$U_q = \int\int q(x,y)u(x,y)dx\,dy \quad . \tag{4}$$

Some useful information about the beam parameters can be inferred from charge induced on electrodes, implementing the following weighting functions

$w(\theta)$	$u(x,y)$	U_q
1	Q	total charge
$Q^{-1}\cos\theta$	x	x coordinate of center of charge
$Q^{-1}\sin\theta$	y	y coordinate of center of charge
$Q^{-1}\cos 2\theta$	x^2-y^2	coefficient of "ellipticity"
$Q^{-1}\sin 2\theta$	2xy	tilt of the elliptical cross-section of a beam.

In the above electrostatic model for an ion beam the time variations have been neglected. Each ion passing close to an electrode makes an incremental contribution to a noise-like signal $s(t)$ observed at the output of a sensing amplifier driven by the electrode. The form of impulse response $h_o(t)$ is a function of the electrode geometry, transfer function of the amplifier and ion velocity. The signal $s(t)$ can be regarded as a filtered Poisson process defined by

$$s(t) = \sum_i h_o(t-t_i) \tag{5}$$

where t_i are random times of a Poisson process with average rate I. According to Campbell's theorem, the mean value and variance of $s(t)$ are given by [21]

$$E(s) = I\int_0^\infty h_o(t)dt \tag{6}$$

$$\mathrm{var}(s) \triangleq \sigma_s^2 = I\int_0^\infty h_o^2(t)dt \tag{7}$$

where E is the statistical expectation operator. A filtered Poisson process as a superposition of independent components can tend to a Gaussian process under relatively weak conditions. For example, it is known that as I increases, or the bandwidth of the system decreases, $s(t)$ tends to a Gaussian process. It should be pointed out that a signal $s(t)$ formed by linear filtering contains the same information about the beam parameters as charges induced on electrodes. Furthermore, some other parameters, e.g. ion velocity or velocity spread, can be estimated from the power spectrum of the signal $s(t)$. To obtain reliable estimates of such parameters, a spatial filtering concept should be used.

In the following section, an estimation of the transverse beam position will be discussed as an example of various nondestructive techniques to measure ion-beam parameters.

3. Transverse Beam Position Estimation

The response u(x,y) of a single electrode with the weighting function cos θ is proportional both to the x coordinate and the beam intensity. In order to eliminate the dependence on the beam intensity, one may use two electrodes with weighting functions of the form

$$w_1(\theta) = 1 + \cos\theta \tag{8}$$

$$w_2(\theta) = 1 - \cos\theta \ . \tag{9}$$

The above weighting functions are non-negative, and the corresponding electrodes can easily be implemented [1].

The observable signals at the outputs of two identical sensing amplifiers driven by the electrodes can be expressed as

$$v_1(t) = (1+x)s(t) + n_1(t) \tag{10}$$

$$v_2(t) = (1-x)s(t) + n_2(t) \tag{11}$$

where $n_k(t)$; k=1,2; are the amplifier noises and s(t) is the signal observed when the beam is at central position (x=0). Signals s(t) and $n_k(t)$ are realisations of zero-mean mutually independent stochastic processes. The noise processes are Gaussian, and it is assumed that their variances are equal to σ_n^2. The problem is how best to process the observable signals $v_1(t)$ and $v_2(t)$ to obtain an estimate $\hat{x}$ of a beam transverse coordinate x.

One standard solution to the problem is to base an estimate $\hat{x}$ on estimates of the following second-order statistical moments of the random variables v_1 and v_2

$$E(v_1^2) = (1+x)^2\sigma_s^2 + \sigma_n^2 \tag{12}$$

$$E(v_2^2) = (1-x)^2\sigma_s^2 + \sigma_n^2 \tag{13}$$

$$E(v_1 v_2) = (1-x^2)\sigma_s^2 \ . \tag{14}$$

Modifications of such a method have been proposed in [9].

When two orthogonal coordinates are to be estimated, a two-dimensional electrode system can be built as shown in Fig.2. The four electrodes are identical, and the system is invariant with respect to rotation of $\pi/2$. The symmetry in the z direction of beam transport reduces any problems due to difference between the impulse responses of the electrodes.

In the following, two different approaches to the problem of signal processing to estimate the beam position will be presented briefly. Discussion will be confined to one dimension.

3.1. Scatter Diagram Method

The numerical estimate of the beam coordinate x can be determined by an inspection of a bright pattern (so-called scatter diagram) observed on an oscilloscope, whose deflecting plates are driven directly by signals $v_1(t)$ and $v_2(t)$ [10]. The time average of the luminosity at any point on the oscilloscope de-

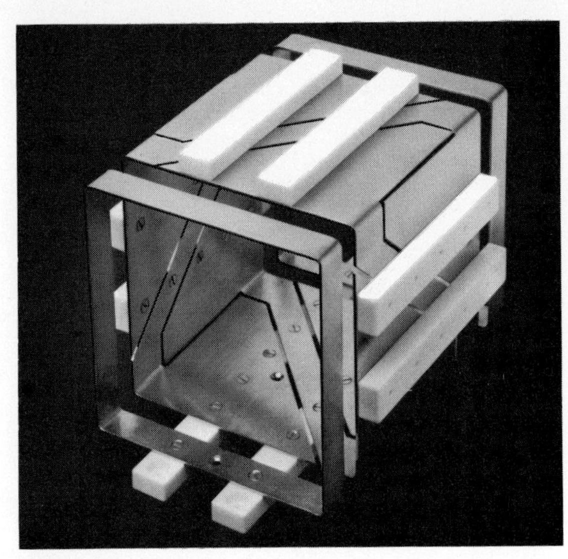

Fig.2 Two-dimensional, orthogonal electrode system. Shown are two auxiliary electrodes on both sides of the main structure

pends on the two-dimensional probability density function of the signals $v_1(t)$ and $v_2(t)$. It can be shown that irrespective of the statistical characteristics of a process s(t), the angle of inclination of the scatter diagram is a function of the beam coordinate. Furthermore, the scatter diagram is symmetric with respect to the line of maximum probability (luminosity).

In the case of electrodes implementing the weighting functions (8) and (9), the angle ϕ of inclination - Fig.3 - is

$$\phi = -x - \sum_{i=1}^{\infty} (-1)^i (2i+1)^{-1} x^{2i+1} \quad . \tag{15}$$

This function can be well approximated by a linear function, and as an estimate of a coordinate x one may use an estimate of an angle ϕ. For example, for $|x| < 0.3$, the error of this approximation is less than 3%.

The accuracy of estimating a beam coordinate from a scatter diagram depends generally on the two factors:

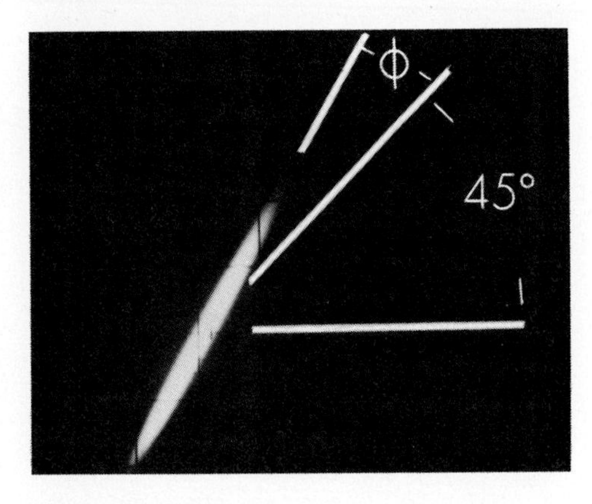

Fig.3 Scatter diagram for a 2 µA beam of 200 keV argon ions

- the shape of the scatter diagram, which is narrower for high signal-to-noise ratios;
- the definition of the scatter diagram, which is better if the product of the sensing-amplifier bandwidth and the averaging time of the phosphor of the CRT is large.

In the special case when the process s(t) can be modelled as a Gaussian process, the scatter diagram is an ellipse. The ratio R of the major to minor semiaxes is given by

$$R = \left[2d(1+x^2) + 1\right]^{1/2} \tag{16}$$

where d is the signal-to-noise ratio defined by

$$d \triangleq \sigma_s^2 \sigma_n^{-2} . \tag{17}$$

This quantity can be regarded as a measure of the "narrowness" of the elliptical pattern. A different measure, based on the angular spread of the pattern, is proposed in [10].

3.2. Estimation of Time-Varying Beam Coordinates [11]

The method of scatter diagrams cannot be easily implemented for a two-dimensional case. Moreover, the information provided by an inclination angle is not suitable for transmission and processing, especially in the case of time-varying coordinates.

Let us assume that the time-varying coordinate x(t) can be modelled by a lowpass process, with the power spectrum confined within a B_x bandwidth. The estimate $\hat{x}(t)$ can be computed as follows. First, the variances of $v_k(t)$ are estimated as

$$z_k(t) = v_k^2(t) * h_T(t), \quad k=1,2 \tag{18}$$

where * is the convolution operator and $h_T(t)$ is the impulse response of an averaging filter with the equivalent integration time T. Next, the estimate $\hat{x}(t)$ is evaluated as

$$\hat{x}(t) = \frac{1}{4} \left[\ln z_1(t) - \ln z_2(t)\right] . \tag{19}$$

It should be pointed out that the estimate thus made is independent of the beam intensity. To obtain a satisfactory performance of the algorithm, the integration time T should be chosen as

$$B_s^{-1} < T < B_x^{-1} \tag{20}$$

where B_s is the cutoff frequency of the sensing amplifiers.

For large processing gains B_sT and high signal-to-noise ratios d, the bias b of the estimator $\hat{x}$ can be expressed as

$$b = -xd^{-1}(1-x^2)^{-2} + \sum_{i=1}^{\infty} (2i+1)^{-1} x^{2i+1} . \tag{21}$$

In the case when the process s(t) is Gaussian, the variance of the estimator $\hat{x}$ can be bounded as

$$\mathrm{var}(\hat{x}) < (4B_sTd)^{-1}(1+x^2)(1-x^2)^{-2} . \tag{22}$$

The algorithm presented has been implemented with the use of commercially available IC rms-to-dc converters with logarithmic outputs. Experiments have shown that the technique discussed makes it possible to observe the time fluctuations in beam coordinates - Fig.4 - or to display the beam scan pattern - Fig.5.

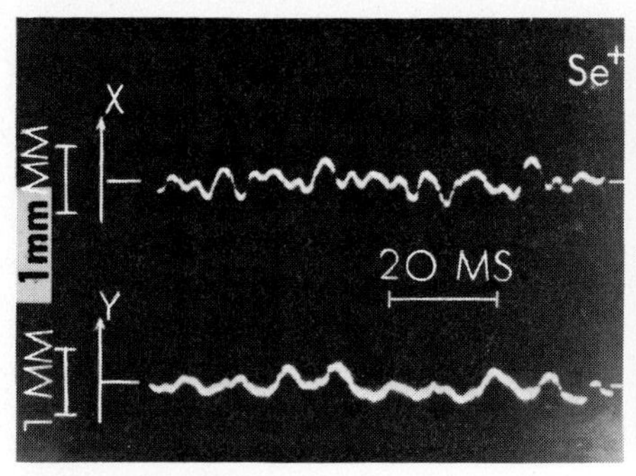

Fig.4 Short-term fluctuations of beam coordinates

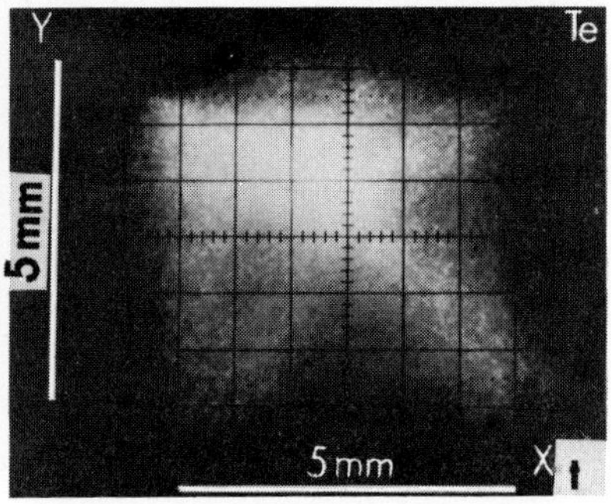

Fig.5 Scan pattern as a result of deliberate scanning and coordinate instabilities

The information about beam coordinates can be used as well in an active closed-loop system to stabilise the beam position, or to obtain an optimum scan pattern.

Acknowledgements

The author would like to acknowledge the support of the UK SERC, and helpful discussions with M.S. Hodgart, P.L.F. Hemment and K.G. Stephens from the University of Surrey.

References

1 A.J. Sherwood: IEEE Trans. NS-12, 925 (1965)
2 R.E. Shafer, R.C. Webber, T.H. Nicol: IEEE Trans. NS-28, 2290 (1981)
3 E.F. Higgins, T.H. Nicol; IEEE Trans. NS-26, 3426 (1979)
4 A.V. Rauchas, F.R. Brumwell, Y. Cho, W.S. Czyz: IEEE Trans. NS-28, 2338 (1981)
5 F.R. Brumwell, R.M. Kliss, D.R. Schmitt: IEEE Trans. NS-24, 1739 (1977)
6 C. Carter, C. Christiansen, J. Donnat et al.: IEEE Trans. NS-28, 2270 (1981)
7 T. Katsura, H. Nakagawa, S. Shibata: IEEE Trans. NS-28, 2353 (1981)
8 J.H. Cuperus: Rev. Sci. Instrum. 44, 626 (1973)
9 M.S. Hodgart, A. Andrews, R.W. Haining: Inst. Phys. Conf. Ser. 38, 125 (1978)
10 W.J. Szajnowski, M.S. Hodgart, K.G. Stephens: Electron. Lett. 16, 674 (1980)
11 W.J. Szajnowski: Electron. Lett. 17, 489 (1981)
12 W. Radloff: IEEE Trans. NS-28, 2287 (1981)
13 T.J. Fessenden, B.W. Stallard, G.G. Berg: Rev. Sci. Instrum. 43, 1789 (1972)

14 K. Satoh: Rev. Sci. Instrum. 50, 450 (1979)
15 K. Satoh: IEEE Trans. NS-26, 3364 (1979)
16 W.S. Whitlock, C. Hilsum: Nature 185, 302 (1960)
17 K.C.D. Chan, R.T.F. Bird, M.F. Coulas et al.: IEEE Trans. NS-28, 2328 (1981)
18 F.B. Kroes, A. Maaskant, T. Sluyk, J.B. Spelt: IEEE Trans. NS-28, 2362 (1981)
19 J.S. Fraser: IEEE Trans. NS-28, 2137 (1981)
20 W.A. Moskalev, G.I. Sergeev, W.G. Shestakov: Measurements of Parameters of Charged Particle Beams (Atomizdat, Moscow 1980) - in Russian
21 D.L. Snyder: Random Point Processes (J. Wiley, New York 1975) p. 171
22 R. Courant: Dirichlet's Principle, Conformal Mapping, and Minimal Surfaces (Interscience, New York, 1950), p. 250
23 R. Courant: ibid. p. 9

Investigation of the Lifetime of Photocurrent Carriers in Si During Ion Implantation

T. Giedrys, V. Grivickas, L. Pranevicius, and J. Vaitkus
Polytechnic Institute of Kaunas, Lithuania, USSR

This paper describes a method for lifetime measurement of photocurrent carriers in semiconductors during implantation (in situ). With this method, the kinetics of recombination-level formation in the surface layer of a semiconductor can be investigated with relatively high time resolution, depending on ion-beam parameters and sample temperature. In the case of silicon, it is shown that during Ar+ ion implantation at an energy of 50 keV, the efficiency of recombination-level formation in doped p-Si (ρ = 10 Ω cm) is considerably higher than in undoped n-Si (ρ = 220 Ω cm).

The proposed method can be used to control accumulation kinetics of recombination levels in the semiconductor surface layer during implantation. It makes possible, by means of ion implantation, the fabrication of surface layers with a controllable carrier lifetime.

1. Introduction

One of the most important parameters of semiconducting materials which determine the characteristics of the finished device is the charge-carrier lifetime. It is known [1] that this parameter, especially for the surface layer of the semiconductor, depends considerably on many difficult-to-determine parameters which characterize the surface. In this connection, from the practical point of view, it is very desirable to obtain surface layers with the charge-carrier lifetime known and determined beforehand. Ion implantation is widely applied for this purpose. However, since the accumulation kinetics of radiation defects during the implantation process considerably depend on the initial sample parameters, it is often difficult to estimate the values of the ion implantation (total dose, ion species, energy) needed to obtain a given carrier lifetime in the implanted layer. Thus, the development of nondestructive surface-layer diagnostic methods for semiconductors, making it possible to record changes in charge-carrier lifetime during ion implantation (in situ), is very desirable. Development of such a method can make new data available regarding the kinetics of radiation-defect accumulation during the ion implantation process which have an influence upon the charge-carrier lifetime.

The experimental technique, as well as some results on charge-carrier lifetime changes in Si during Ar+ ion implantation at an energy of 50 keV, are described in this paper.

2. Experimental Technique

Measurements were carried out using the experimental arrangement diagrammed in Fig. 1. The investigated sample (1) is placed inside the vacuum chamber of an ion accelerator at a residual gas pressure of 10^{-3} Pa.

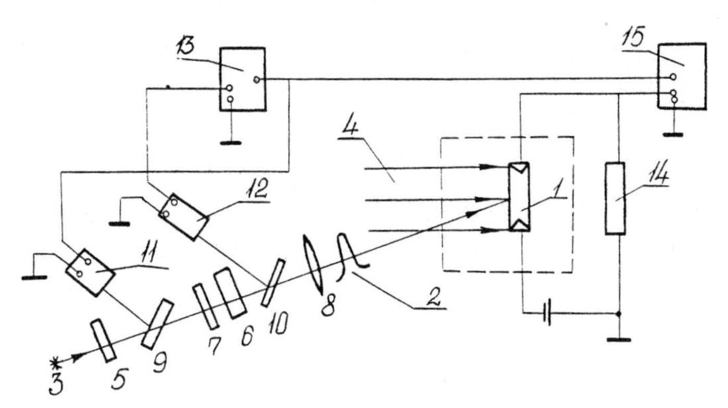

Fig. 1. Experimental arrangement for carrier-lifetime measurement (see text for item explanation)

It is stimulated by light pulses (2) of a second-harmonic YAG laser (3) ($h\nu$ = 2.33 eV), with a pulse duration of τ_L = 10-15 ns on a 0.5 level. The light-pulse frequency is 12.5 Hz. The wavelength is determined by a cutoff filter (5). At the same time, the sample is irradiated by the ion beam (4). The intensity of the light pulses is changed by use of filters (6). A phase screen (7) and a focusing lens (8) allow an even illumination of the investigated sample. A portion of the light pulse is directed by plates (9 and 10) to coaxial photocells (11 and 12), for recording of intensity and sychronization through oscilloscopes (13 and 15). Photoconductivity signals from a resistor (14) are transmitted to a velocity oscilloscope (15).

The energy of the Ar+ ions employed was 50 keV, implanted doses varied from $5x10^{10}$ to $1x10^{16}cm^{-2}$. The ion-current density in the beam was between 0.01 and 0.5 μA cm-2, depending on the value of the dose. The sample temperature during implantation was 295 K. Single crystals of p-Si (ρ = 100 Ωcm), n-Si (ρ = 250 Ωcm) grown by the Czochralski method, and n-Si (ρ = 220 Ωcm) grown by the floate zone method, were investigated. The latter single crystals were simply neutron-doped and then annealed. After annealing, the phosphorus concentration was $4x10^{13}cm^{-3}$ the compensation degree was Nd/Na ≈ 65%. The surfaces of all samples were mechanically-chemically cleaned and polished. The samples were shaped into parallelepipeds measuring $12x4x0.3mm^3$ or $8x2x1mm^3$. Ion irradiation was carried out approximately perpendicularly to the large surface, coinciding with the <111> direction for p-Si and the <110> direction for n-Si. The contacts were fabricated by depositing narrow strips of aluminum on the surface of p-Si, and by alloying gold eutectics on the surface of n-Si. Resistivity of the contacts was preserved at the employed stimulation levels, at values of 15 V or more. Photoconductivity kinetics were directly measured during ion implantation.

Figure 2 shows typical characteristics of the following signals: the first curve indicates the light pulse emanating from the laser, with duration τ_L = 10-15 ns.

The second characteristic indicates the relaxation curve for a unirradiated sample; the third is the relaxation curve showing photoconductivity in silicon implanted with Ar+ ions at a dose of $5x10^{14}cm^{-2}$. The amplitude decrease, as well as changes in the relaxation-time constant, are observed during the ion-implantation process. The photoconductivity relaxation curves were obtained with a constant number of quanta in the laser pulse at $10^{14}cm^{-2}$. It is

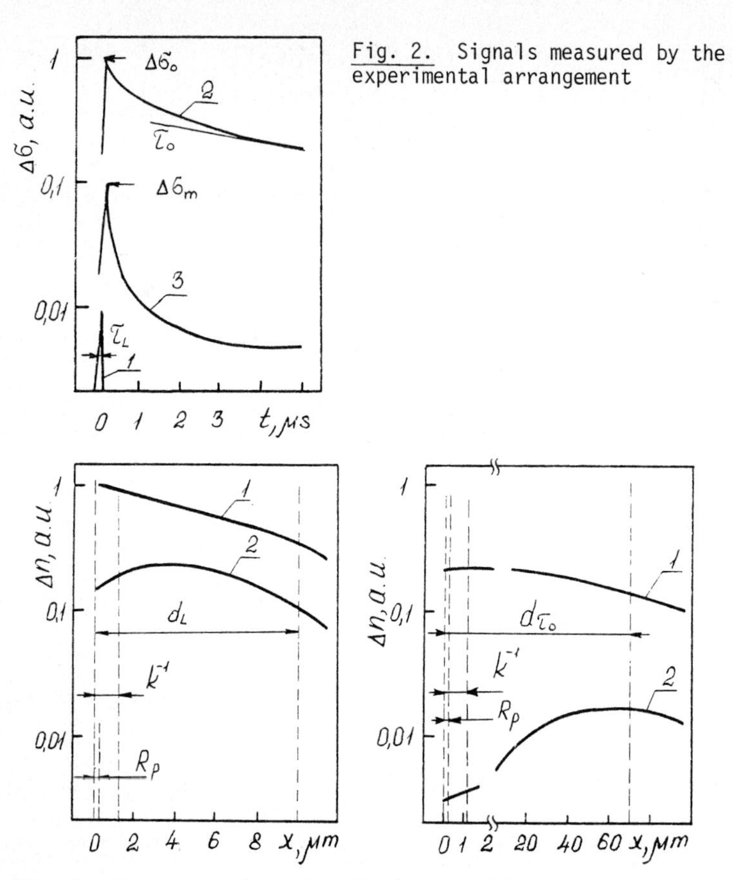

Fig. 2. Signals measured by the experimental arrangement

Fig. 3. Charge-carrier distribution at different sample depths or different time invervals: a) 30 ns, b) 1 μs

worth mentioning that the depth of light quantum absorption, k^{-1} = 1-1.2 μm, i.e., it is nearly twenty times higher than the projected ion range, Rp = 0.05 μm. During the generation time $2\tau_L \simeq$ 30 ns, the stimulated carriers diffuse to the depth $d_L \simeq$ 10 μm, Fig. 3. Under the given conditions, maximum concentration of nonequilibrium carriers was $\Delta n_o = \Delta p_o \simeq 10^{17} cm^{-3}$ up to the beginning of implantation. Maximum photoconductivity, at the end of the light pulse, was calculated from the equation $\Delta\sigma = e\Delta n_0(\mu_e + \mu_h)$ where μ_e and μ_h are the mobilities of electrons and holes, respectively. Assuming that at a given injection level the zones are linearized, it is possible to evaluate the rate of surface recombination (s_0) by means of the linear equation of diffusion, recombination, and volume lifetime τ_0 /2-4/. This model, to some approximation, can be applied to the implanted samples, taking the inequality into account $R_p \ll k^{-1} \ll d_L$.

Figure 3 shows the charge-carrier distribution at different depths in the sample as a function of time, plotted from the beginning of the light pulse.

We assume that changes in charge-scattering mechanisms within the implanted layer do not significantly influence the charge-carrier concentration distributic and $\Delta\delta_m$. Referring to the relaxation curves for undoped silicon, we obtain:

p-Si (ρ = 100 Ωcm): $s_o=(3.5\pm1).10^3 cm.s^{-1}$, τ_o = (4.5$\pm$0.5) s;

n-Si (ρ = 220 Ωcm): $s_o=(2\pm0.5).10^4 cm.s^{-1}$, τ_o = (34$\pm$4) s.

These values represent typical silicon parameters for the given fabrication technology and surface-processing method.

3. Results

Figure 4 shows photoconductivity as a function of dose, measured during implantation with 50 keV in p-type silicon (curve 1) and n-type silicon (curve 2).

Figure 5 indicates experimental and theoretical time-dependence curves for photoconductivity in silicon implanted with various doses. The calculated surface-recombination velocities are 10^2cm/s for curve 1, 10^3cm/s for curve 2, and 10^4cm/s for curve 3.

It can be seen from Fig. 4 that photoconductivity amplitude changes, depending on the implanted ion dose, are more pronounced in p-type silicon than in n-type silicon. The observed photoconductivity amplitude variations in the dose ranges of 10^{14} - 10^{15}cm^{-2} and 10^{15} - 10^{16}cm^{-2} are explainable by the fact that the photoconductivity amplitude during implantation depends not only on the implanted ion dose, but also on the intensity of the ion irradiation. For a dose up to 10^{13}cm^{-2} , the ion-current density in the beam was 0.01 μA/cm^2; in the dose interval 10^{14}-10^{15}cm^{-2} , the value was 0.05 μA/cm^2; and in the dose interval 10^{15} - 10^{16}cm^{-2} it was 0.5 μA/cm^2.

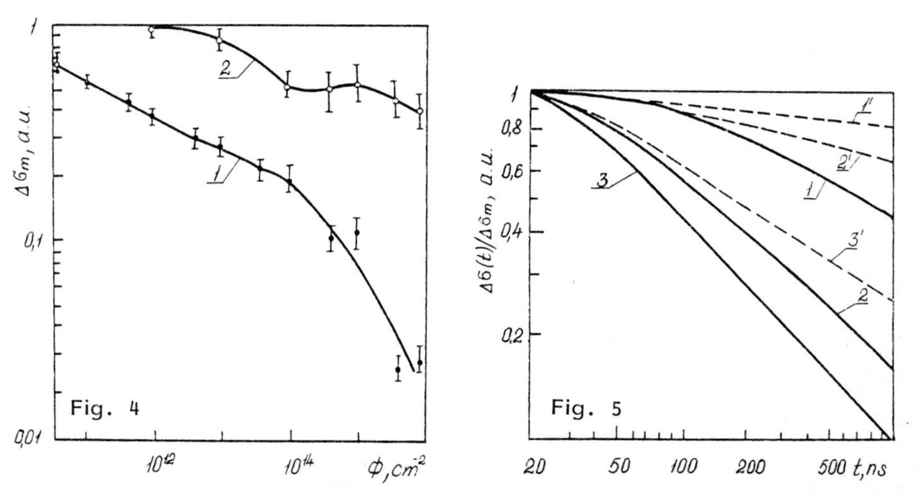

Fig. 4. Amplitude dependence of photoconductivity on implanted ion dose: curve 1 = p-Si (ρ = 10 Ωcm), curve 2 = n-Si (ρ = 200 Ωcm)

Fig. 5. Theoretical (solid line) and experimental (dotted line) dependences of photoconductivity on time in silicon: curves 1 = without implantation; curves 2 = implantation dose: 10^{11}cm^{-2} ; curves 3 = implantation dose: 10^{14}cm^{-2}

4. Discussion

Since the values of ion penetration depth, generation depth, and nonequilibrium charge carrier diffusion during the time period of a laser pulse satisfy the condition $R_p \ll k^{-1} \ll d_L$, the experimental results for the implanted samples can be interpreted assuming that the kinetic photoconductivity variations are only influenced by recombination processes in the implanted layer. We consider that average charge mobility and bipolar diffusion coefficient do not depend on the coordinate. Nonequilibrium carriers diffuse from the bulk to the implanted layer, and recombine in the latter with a certain effective lifetime τ. Since $d_L/R_p \geq 10^2$, it is possible to determine the applicable effective surface-recombination velocity (Fig. 5). The decrease of τ in the implanted layer is determined by the formation efficiency of the recombination centers. The role of the recombination centers is probably represented by radiation defects of various kinds, or their complexes, having concentrations much higher than those of the implanted ions.

When $\tau \leq \tau_L$, the charge-carrier distribution profile changes greatly. The nonequilibrium carrier concentration in the implanted layer may be several times less than the average concentration at the diffusion depth. If we assume the recombination-level concentration N_I to be one percent of all Frenkel-type radiation defects, then the calculation indicates that inequality $N_I \gg \Delta n$ is fulfilled when $\phi \geq 10^{12}cm^{-2}$, i.e., throughout the whole range of the doses used. Thus, the effective lifetime at higher doses coincides with the lifetime of faster trapping carriers. Approximate calculations show that in our samples at $\phi = 10^{14}cm^{-2}$, $\tau = 10^{-8}s$ in n-Si samples, and $10^{-9}s$ in p-Si samples. In regard to $\Delta\sigma(t)$ kinetics (Fig. 5), at $t > 20$ ns, inequality $N_I \gg \Delta n$ increases, so that the recombination carrier flow determines the exponential tail of the recombination centers. This explaines the observed weaker correlation between $\Delta\sigma(t)$ kinetics and lifetime, in comparison with amplitude dependence.

If the above observations are correct, then we can draw the conclusion that recombination-level formation effectiveness in the investigated p-Si crystals is much higher than formation effectiveness in undoped n-Si crystals. We believe that the observed difference can be explained by two factors. Apparently, complex radiation-defect influences or conductivity-type conversion in an implanted layer is the first factor. The conductivity conversion may only take place in pure crystals [5]. Thus, the barrier appearing at $N_I \gg \Delta n$ will divide electrons and holes and increase τ. The second factor is the increase in radiation-level recombination activity during complex formation with doped impurities or unfixed initial deep impurities. Such effects have been observed in previous research [6]. A more detailed investigation of τ for various types of samples and doping levels would be desirable to obtain further information on this topic.

References

1. L.S.Smirnov: Problems of Semiconductor Radiation Technology (in Russian), "Nauka", Novosibirsk (1980)
2. J.Vaitkus, V. Grivickas: Sov.Phys.Collect. (Litov.Fiz.Sb.) 17, 613 (1977)
3. J.Vaitkus, V. Grivickas et al: Sov.Phys.Collect. (Litov.Fiz.Sb), to be published in 1982
4. J.Vaitkus: Phys.Stat.Sol. (a) 34, 769 (1976)
5. V.L.Vinecki, A.S. Smirnov: Fiz.Tech.Poluprov. 5, 176 (1971)
6. V.V.Bolotov et al: Fiz.Tech.Poluprov. 14, 2257 (1980)

A Mössbauer Spectrometer for in situ Low Temperature Studies of Ion-Bombarded Metals

G.K. Wolf, F. Schreyer, and G. Frech

Institut für Physikalische Chemie, Universität Heidelberg,
Im Neuenheimer Feld 500, D-6900 Heidelberg, Fed. Rep. of Germany

F. Wagner

Physik Department der TU München, D-8000 München, Fed. Rep. of Germany

1. Introduction

Mössbauer spectroscopy has been used in a number of cases for studying ion-implanted metals [1-3]. It is possible by this technique to obtain information on the lattice position of implanted elements, as well as on the defect structure of the target metal. Such information can also come from Rutherford backscattering and channeling experiments. In addition, Mössbauer spectroscopy has the unique feature to yield results on the state of binding of implanted atoms and the chemistry of the systems under study.

Nearly all investigations, up to now, have been performed at or above room temperature (RT). But often the situation at much lower temperature is specially interesting because

- the annealing of the majority of point defects originating from the implantation takes place in most metals below RT;
- metastable alloys and compounds may be formed during implantation but survive only at low temperature. Under certain conditions, one can expect a special low-temperature chemistry or physics to exist. This fact is quite well known from conductivity or superconductivity studies [4]. knowledge of the state of binding, however, is very scarce.

We decided, therefore, to construct a Mössbauer spectrometer to be coupled directly to an ion-implantation machine, in order to measure Mössbauer absorption spectra at low temperature directly after the end of the implantation into cooled targets. A comparable instrument has been used earlier by Gütlich et al. [3] for the recording of emission spectra of implanted radioactive elements. Van Rossum et al. [5] used a similar technique for low-temperature implantation of ^{57}Fe into frozen gases.

2. Equipment and Experimental Technique

2.1 The Mössbauer Spectrometer on Line with an Ion Implanter

A commercially available low-temperature Mössbauer cryostat (Leybold) was attached to a vacuum chamber, which was connected to the target chamber of a 60keV ion implanter (Danfysik). A plate valve enabled one to shut off the Mössbauer chamber and remove it without warming or breaking the vacuum. The tempera-

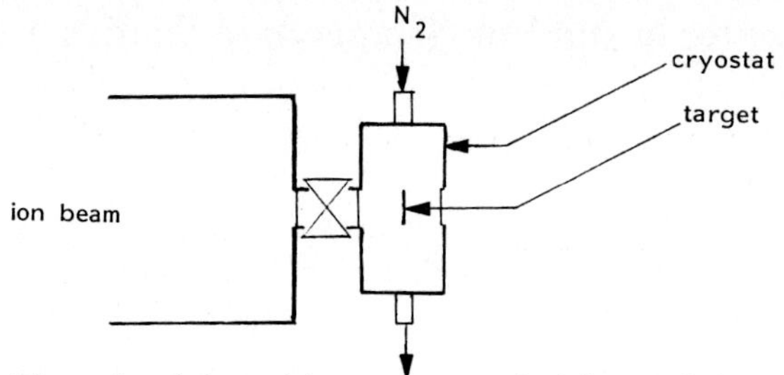

Fig. 1. Schematic representation of the Mössbauer spectrometer in bombardment position

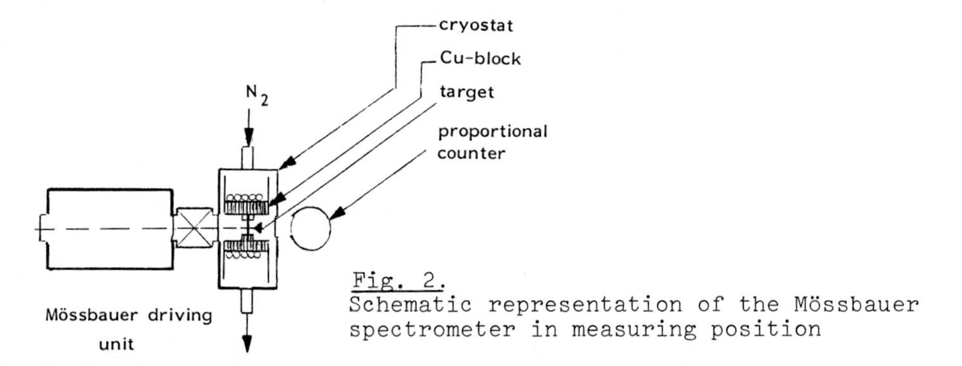

Fig. 2. Schematic representation of the Mössbauer spectrometer in measuring position

ture was adjusted by means of a liquid-nitrogen flow, regulated with an electrically controlled automatic valve.

The construction and the experimental arrangement are shown in figures 1 and 2. The temperature during implantation can be measured with a thermocouple attached to the target holder, the implantation dose recorded by the current measured at the target. Secondary electrons were suppressed by a negatively charged screen.

The Mössbauer velocity drive carried a 20mCi ^{57}Co Rh source, and the γ rays from the source were measured with a rare-gas proportional counter.

2.2 The Experimental Procedure

As targets, thin films of a metal were used, attached to a backing of aluminium or beryllium in order not to disturb the passage of the γ rays. We used iron foils of $\cong$ 1mg/cm^2 as well as iron evaporated on a thin layer of copper. In some cases, another copper layer was evaporated on top of the target to avoid oxidation. A typical sandwich consists of a beryllium backing and 30nm Cu/90nm Fe/30nm Cu.

The targets were mounted to the cryostat and the chamber attached to the ion accelerator and evacuated. Later on, the irradiation temperature was adjusted to the wanted value. This was done very carefully under good vacuum conditions because every condensing layer on top of the targets makes a controlled implantation impossible. The lowest temperature to be reached with liquid N_2 is 73K. In principle, liquid He can be used too, but an additional cooling shield has to be installed to avoid condensation of gases.

The bombarding particles hit the target exactly under the same geometrical arrangement which is used afterwards during the measurement. After the implantation, the gate valve was closed and the chamber removed under vacuum from the accelerator without changing the temperature. The chamber was attached to the Mössbauer velocity drive with the γ-ray source. Thus, the passage of the γ rays was exactly the same as before the one of the ions. All Mössbauer spectra were recorded with the source at room temperature and the target (absorber) at 77K. The sample temperature could be raised in between two measurements up to 320K for in situ annealing.

3. Selected Examples of Applications

3.1 The Implantation Synthesis of "Iron-hydride"

Iron is one of the few metals which are not able to form hydrides under normal conditions. In addition, the solubility of hydrogen in iron at RT and standard pressure is extremely small, far below 1 atom ppm. The only possibility to study the iron/hydrogen system in more detail is the production of extremely supersaturated mixtures. One possibility to do this is hydrogen implantation.

We prepared therefore thin iron films, as described in section 2, and implanted at 73-77K 4.5×10^{17} H_2^+ with an energy of 18-25keV. The ranges of these ions are chosen to permit a homogeneous filling of the 90 nm thick target with hydrogen. The estimated resulting H/Fe ratio was roughly 0.6.

The spectra measured from this sample are displayed in fig. 3. Comparing the unimplanted sample with the hydrogen-bombarded one (77K) one realizes immediately in the latter case the development of a superimposed spectrum consisting of an iron-like species and a species with a smaller hyperfine field, and an isomer shift indicating a decrease of the electron density at the iron site. We attribute the first spectrum to "normal" iron, modified by irradiation effects and the second one to a new compound, FeH_x.

A He implantation, shown for comparison in fig. 3, does not lead to this compound, but has many similarities with the "normal" but slightly modified iron spectrum.

Annealing of the hydrogen bombarded target causes the FeH_x spectrum to disappear already above 100K, while the irradiation effects, as in the He-implanted sample, disappear completely only above 200K.

During the course of our experiments, the work of Antonov et al. [6,7] was published on iron hydride prepared by high pressure synthesis at 35kbar and only stable at low temperature. From the detailed analysis of our measurements, which will be published elsewhere [8], we conclude to have formed, by low-

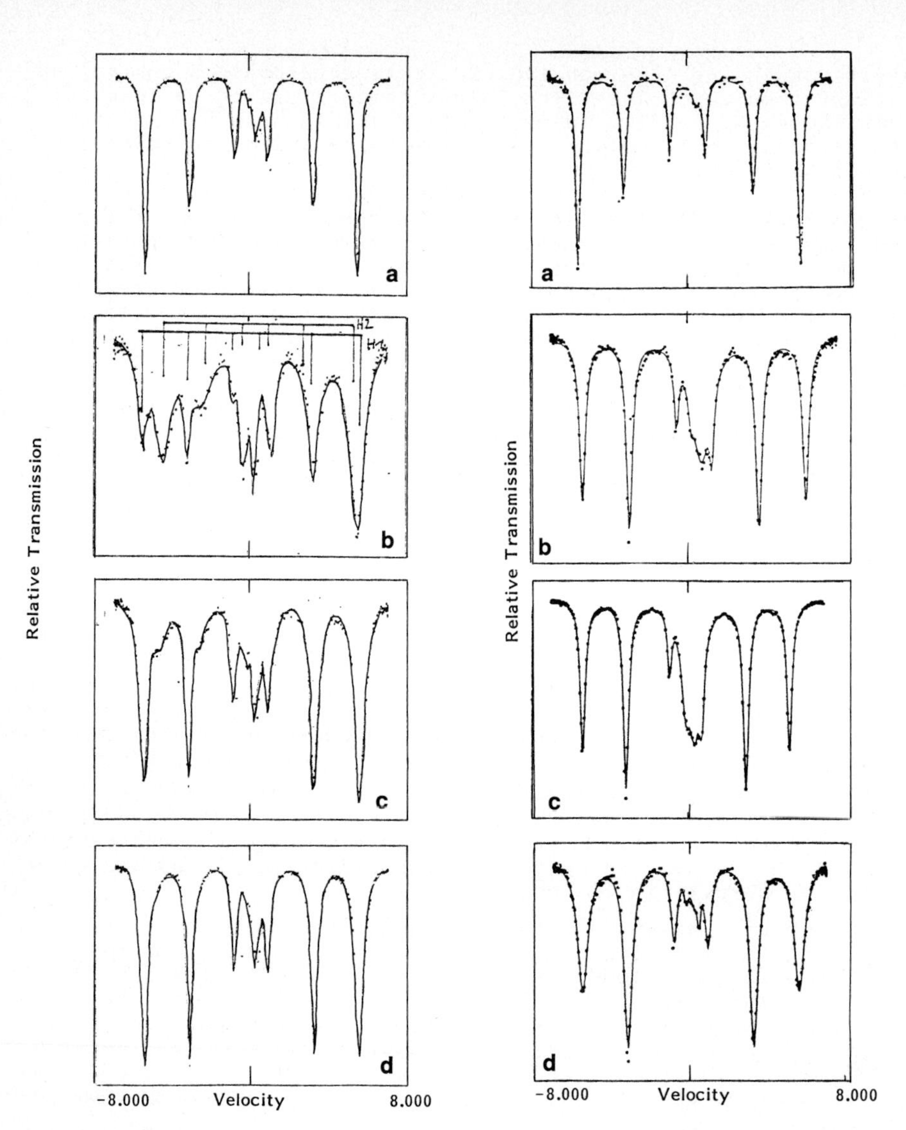

Fig. 3. Mössbauer spectra of unimplanted iron (a), iron implanted with $4.5x10^{17}$ H_2^+at 77 K (b), annealed 3H at 132 K (c), and 300 K (d), He^+ implantation see Fig. 4

Fig. 4. Mössbauer spectra of unimplanted iron (a), iron bombarded with $4x10^{17}$ N_2^+ ions at 77 K (b), annealed at 233 K (c), and bombarded with $8x10^{17}$ He^+ ions (d)

temperature implantation of hydrogen in iron, the same species FeH_{07}, which was so far only accessible by applying extremely high pressures.

3.2 The Implantation Synthesis of "Iron-nitride"

Recently we were interested in the question whether a nitride of iron would by formed during low-temperature bombardment of thin iron films. Using the same technique as mentioned above, a thin iron film (in this case without Cu overlayer) was bombarded with ≅ 3×10^{17} N_2^+ ions/cm^2 at 73-77K. Again, the Mössbauer spectra of the resulting species were recorded.

Fig. 4 shows the spectra as implanted and annealed to RT, in comparison with the unimplanted sample and a He-implanted sample, already presented in Fig. 3.

Similar to the Fe/H case, the spectrum consists of a superposition of a "normal" iron spectrum, slightly modified by irradiation effects, and a new set of middle lines which we attribute to FeN_x. The evaluation of these spectra is not completed by now; therefore a detailed analysis and comparison with the literature on Mössbauer spectra of "iron nitride" will be presented in a future publication.

References:

1 H. de Waard, L.C. Feldman: In Application of Ion Beams to Metals, p. 317, Plenum Press, New York (1974)

2 B.D. Sawicka: Nucl. Instr. Meth. 182/183, 1039 (1981)

3 P. Gütlich, R. Link, T. Fritsch, G.K. Wolf: Nucl. Instr. Meth. 148, 573 (1978)

4 H. Bernas, P. Nedellec: Nucl. Instr. Meth. 182/183, 845 (1981)

5 M. Van Rossum, E. Verbiest, H. Pattyn, H. Coussement, S. Bukshpan: To be published in Rad. Effects (1982)

6 V.E. Antonov, I.T. Belash, E.G. Ponyatovskii, V.G. Thiessen, V.I. Shiryaev: Phys. Stat. Sol. (a) 65, K43 (1981)

7 V.E. Antonov, I.T. Belash, E.G. Ponyatovskii: Scripta Met. 16, 203 (1982)

8 F. Schreyer, G. Frech, G.K. Wolf, T.E. Wagner: To be published (1982)

Background in (*n,p*) and (*n,α*) Spectrometry

D. Fink and J.P. Biersack

Hahn-Meitner-Institut für Kernforschung Berlin GmbH, Glienicker Straße 100, D-1000 Berlin 39, Fed. Rep. of Germany

H. Liebl

Max-Planck-Institut für Plasmaphysik, D-8046 Garching, Fed. Rep. of Germany

1. Introduction

In exoenergetic (n,p) and (n,α) reactions, such as ^{3}He(n,p)t, ^{6}Li(n,α)t and ^{10}B(n,αγ)^{7}Li, a thermal neutron is captured by the target nucleus with a high cross section. The created compound nuclei then decay by emission of monoenergetic α particles (or protons) and recoil nuclei with a Q value of typically 1...5 MeV. As the momentum transfer from the thermal neutrons to the compound nucleus is negligible, the reaction products are emitted isotropically from the site of the non-displaced compound nucleus. These are optimal conditions for the examination of depth distributions and lattice positions of the above-mentioned light nuclei [1]. This technique has been described already in previous publications [2] - [10].

2. Experimental Arrangement

2.1 Neutron Sources

In simple cases, when distributions of impurities at very high concentrations (more than 10%) are examined, a paraffin-clad radium/beryllium neutron source is sufficient [11]. For more sophisticated applications, however, it is preferable to use a nuclear research reactor as a neutron source. In this case,samples can be placed either into the interior of the reactor or outside of the reactor into an extracted neutron beam. Both methods have been applied. The advantage of irradiating samples inside the reactor is the high neutron flux leading to reasonably short measuring times,which is essential for channeling/blocking experiments. On the other hand, however, the experimental equipment is subjected to a high background of fast neutrons and gammas,which induces radiation damage and limits the detection sensitivity considerably. Also,components have to be miniaturized [12] due to the limited space and the high activation, and the materials have to be selected carefully.

Performing experiments outside the reactor has the disadvantage of lower neutron flux and, hence, longer measuring times, but there is little limitation in size for the equipment which is scarcely activated, and the neutron flux can be purified from background radiation by filter crystals or neutron guides so that the detection sensitivity is greatly improved.

2.1.1 Irradiation inside a Reactor

The fraction of fast neutrons which creates an unwanted background due to nuclear reactions and due to emission of knock-on particles from sample, instrument and detector can be reduced by a suitable geometrical arrangement inside the reactor. The assembly should be placed inside or near the thermal column to enhance the thermal neutron flux, and the direct irradiation of the detector with the fast neutrons is prevented by inserting the equipment into a tangential instead of a radial beam tube. In Table I,the neutron and γ fluxes for experimental sites inside reactors are compared to other experimental positions outside reactors. Due to low activation, Al-99 is a commonly-used reactor material. Because of the background of protons and α particles (from (n,p) and (n,α) reactions with fast neutrons), free Al surfaces facing the detectors have to be avoided or covered with lacquer.

Table 1: Neutron and gamma fluxes at the sites of our (n,p) and (n,α) experiments (given for full reactor power)

Type and year of experiment	Reactor	Position	Thermal neutrons [neutr./cm^{2}s]	Fast neutr. [neutr./cm^{2}s]	γ-flux [r/h]
channel./block. 1969/70	BER I (Berlin)	SNO (thermal column) (in-pile experiment)	$3\cdot10^{11}$	$6\cdot10^{9}$	$3\cdot10^{5}$
channel./block. 1971/74	FMRB (Braunschweig)	S11 (thermal column) (in-pile experiment)	$1.3\cdot10^{11}$	$2\cdot10^{7}$	?
depth profiling 1974/75	FMRB (Braunschweig)	S7 (neutron guide)	$3\cdot10^{4}$	-	-
depth profiling 1975/81	BER II (Berlin)	T3 (tangential tube)	$3\cdot10^{7}$	$< 10^{3}$	3
depth profiling since 1976[1)]	ILL (Grenoble)	S30 (thermal neutron guide tube)	$8\cdot10^{8}$	-	0.03-0.05
channel./block. since 1978[1)]	ILL (Grenoble)	S44 (cold neutron guide tube)	$1\cdot10^{10}$	-	0.5-1

[1)] in cooperation with R. Henkelmann, K. Müller and F. Jahnel, Institut für Radiochemie, TU München

2.1.2 Irradiation Outside a Reactor in a Neutron Beam

Again, the fraction of unwanted fast neutron and γ radiation in the neutron beam has to be reduced as far as possible. This can be done either by inserting a Bi single-crystalline filter into the beam,which absorbs gammas and deflects fast neutrons to a high percentage, or by construction of a neutron-guide tube which deflects only the thermal neutrons slightly,so that fast neutrons and gammas from the reactor can be extinguished perfectly. There is no doubt that a neutron guide is preferable to a Bi filter, but the neutron guide is more space consuming and more expensive. We tried both, depending on the available facilities of the reactor stations (Bi filter in the installation at the reactor BER II, HMI Berlin,and neutron-guide tubes at the FMRB, PTB Braunschweig, and at the high-flux reactor of the ILL Grenoble). Besides purification, the neutron beam has to be sufficiently collimated to avoid nuclear reactions of scattered neutrons with the walls of the experimental chamber which would create an additional background. It was found that the neutron beam could be transmitted through 20...100 cm air before entering the experimental chamber without affecting the measuring accuracy.

2.1.3 Beam Collimators, Filters and Neutron-Guide Tubes

For the first experiments at the Berlin reactor BER I and the Braunschweig reactor FMRB, only collimators were inserted into the irradiation beam tubes. They consisted of a one-meter long sequence of different absorbing layers: Pb-Cd - ($CaSO_4$ + H_2O + H_3BO_3) - Pb-Cd - ($CaSO_4$ + H_2O + H_3BO_4) - Pb-Cd, clad by Al, with an aperture of 3.1 cm diameter. For the new Berlin reactor BER II a collimator was combined with a filter. In this case, the tangential beam tube T3 is facing a scattering body of graphite beside the core. The neutron collimator consists of boron-enriched wooden discs, their inner diameters converging from 15...2 cm diameter. Before the collimator discs, a single-crystalline Bi filter was inserted. The thickness of the Bi layer was optimized until the ratio of thermal neutron flux to γ flux became a maximum, see Fig. 1. The neutron beam has a divergence of about $\pm$ 1.5°. By its construction, the collimator acts like a pinhole camera, depicting the source neutron-flux distribution at the emitting surface (graphite scattering body). Therefore, the emitted neutron beam is slightly inhomogeneous, see Fig. 2,

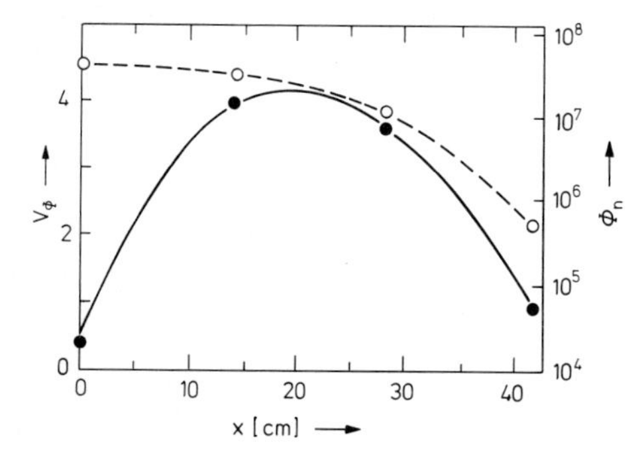

Fig. 1. Thermal neutron flux ϕ_n (dashed line) in [neutrons/cm^2s] and ratio of neutron flux to gamma flux V_ϕ (solid line) in [(10^6 neutrons/cm^2s)/(R/h)] as a function of Bi filter thickness x (BER II, 5 MWatt)

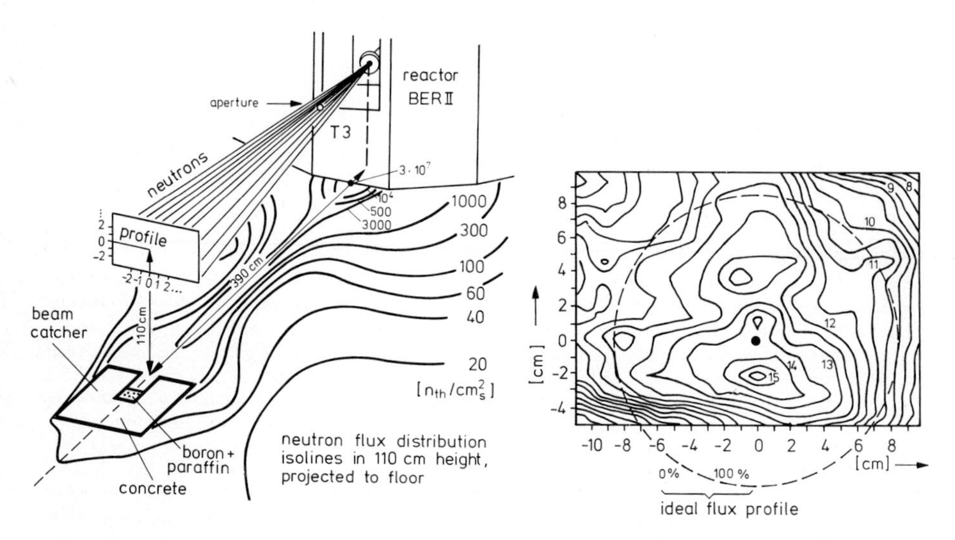

Fig. 2. Flux distribution of thermal neutrons emitted from beam tube T3 of the Berlin reactor BER II (a,b) and the geometry of measurement (a). Due to the construction of the collimator, the measured flux distribution is an image of the distribution of the neutron flux emerging from the graphite scattering body inside the reactor (no Bi filter inserted into beam tube T3). The numbers are intensities in arbitrary units

if no Bi filter is inserted. With the Bi filter, however, the inhomogeneities are smoothed out. Figure 3, finally, shows how the different collimator and filter compositions affect the measured energy spectra. By additional shielding of the detector (distance to the neutron beam: 5...10 cm) with boric acid in paraffin against scattered neutrons, the background is reduced by 10...20% for energies below 1 MeV.

At the high-flux reactor of the Institute Laue-Langevin in Grenoble, eight evacuated neutron-guide tubes are installed. They are described elsewhere [9]. Our neutron-guide tubes are enclosed completely with bricks of concrete and lead. The background radiation of the neutron-guide tubes is mainly due to

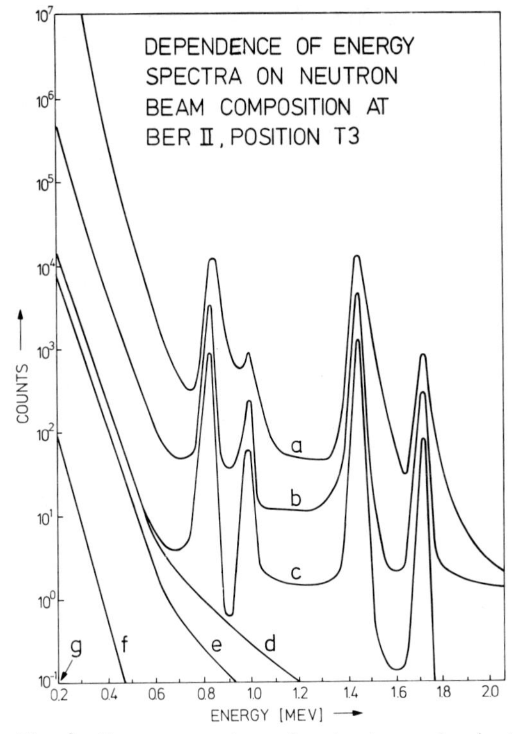

Fig.3. Energy spectra of a test sample (natural boron, thickness about 300 Å, on a quartz disc) under various conditions at beam tube T3 of the Berlin reactor BER II. The measurement is performed with an ORTEC surface barrier detector with 100 µm depletion depth for 4 min at 5 MWatt, in all cases.

a) spectrum without collimation and filter
b) spectrum without collimation, with filter
c) spectrum with collimation and filter
d) additional: 2 mm Cd sheet in neutron beam for extinguishing thermal neutrons
e) additional: 10 cm boron-enriched paraffin for extinguishing fast neutrons
f) background of activated material (sample, sample holder and walls of experimental chamber) by the direct beam and scattered neutrons after reactor shut off, slowly decreasing with time
g) the thermal noise of the electronics, measured with an unactivated vessel and without sample, is just beyond the picture's frame. As the background of the measurement is affected by other factors much stronger than the thermal noise, detector and preamplifier were not cooled

neutron activation of the environment (see Table 1), ranging from 30 mrad to 1 rad. This is crucial for the accessibility of the experiments during reactor operation.

2.2 Instruments for Depth Profile Measurements

2.2.1 Instruments

The schematic set-up for depth profile measurements is this: The sample is placed in a vessel flooded by the thermal neutron beam. A detector in the vicinity collects the emitted particles; the electronic signals are processed in a multichannel analyzer. The vessel has to be evacuated to at least a few torr to prevent straggling and energy loss of particles during their flight to the detector. The vacuum should be oil-free to prevent contamination of the detectors and samples. To reduce scattering of the neutron beam, it has to be properly collimated. Entrance and exit windows of the vessel are made of thin (0.2 mm) Kapton and Al foils, and the sample holder is made of thin Al or lucite parts.

At the Berlin facility, the apparatus is constructed completely of standard vacuum parts. Here, we assembled several irradiation vessels, one behind the other, to measure several samples simultaneously. As the neutron-beam intensity decreases after passing a sample with its holder, the samples at successive vessels have to be displaced for some millimeters from the preceding positions.

The maximum area of the samples to be measured is about 40 x 40 mm^2, both at the Grenoble and the Berlin facilities. The maximum thickness of the samples can range up to 20 mm. To reduce background by nuclear reactions from neutrons at the sample, the sample should not be thicker than necessary. The emitting sample surface should, however, be as large as possible.

At the ILL Grenoble, the need for measuring several samples simultaneously is not so urgent, due to the higher neutron flux. Here, an automatic sample changer was constructed to use the instrument more efficiently and to avoid unnecessary radiation exposure of the experimenters [9]. For monitoring the neutron flux, another detector was added in the vessel which faces a well-calibrated sample.

2.2.2 Detectors

The proper choice of the detector is of great importance for the measurements. Figure 4 shows energy spectra of a 10 Å thick B layer on SiO_2, measured at the FMRB (PTB), BER II (HMI), and the high-flux reactor (ILL) under the same conditions, but with different detectors. The intense background of the spectra measured by partially-depleted detectors with 100 µm depletion depth is probably due to the accumulation of a high concentration of electron-hole pairs, produced by the incident high-energetic ions, which cannot be swept away from the sensitive detector zone fast enough. For the same reason, the background is higher for detectors with larger surface area. Additionally, the detectors are constantly bombarded by a high flux of energetic photons and electrons, resulting mainly from activation of sample and vessel materials by the neutrons.

Due to the lower depletion depth and hence the higher capacity of the totally depleted detectors, their energy resolution is slightly worse than that of the partially depleted ones (21 keV compared to 15 keV). As a resumé, we may say that small totally depleted detectors with 20...50 µm depletion depth are best suited for application in (n,p) and (n,α) spectrometry. A sensitivity down to about 1 ppm and a depth resolution of about 100 Å are obtained in optimal cases. For Li and B, the replacement of natural impurities by the enriched isotopes (6-Li and 10-B) frequently makes measurements possible for which otherwise the detection sensitivity would already be too low.

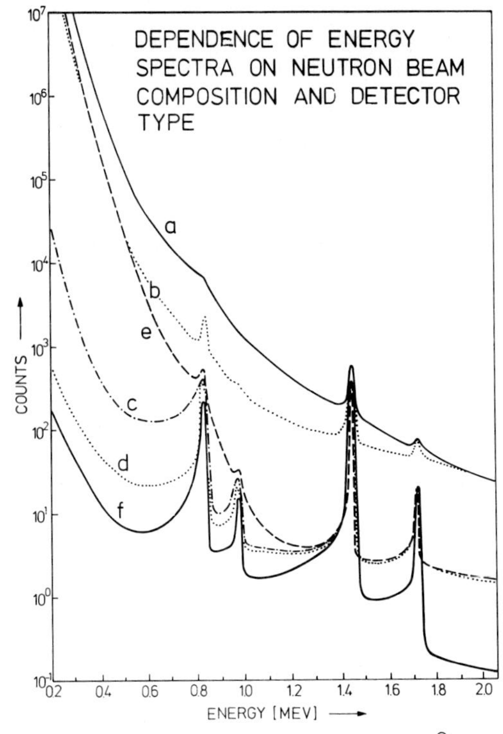

Fig.4. Energy spectra of a thin (10 Å thick) boron layer, evaporated onto a quartz disc, measured under various conditions:

a) partially depleted detector, 100 μm depletion depth, 50 mm^2 active area (detector A), BER II, T3, without collimation and filter;
b) totally depleted detector, 50 μm depletion depth, 50 mm^2 active area (det. B), BER II, T3, without collimation and filter;
c) partially depleted detector, 100 μm depletion depth, 300 mm^2 active area, FMRB, S7 (neutron guide tube);
d) det. A, FMRB, S7
e) det. A, ILL, S30 (neutron guide tube)
f) det. B, ILL, S30

The comparison of spectra 4e) and f) illustrates the influence of the detector type (partially or totally depleted), the comparison of 4c) and d) demonstrates the influence of the detector size (and hence capacity), Figs. 4a) and b), compared to the others, show the advantage of using neutron-guide tubes, and a comparison of Figs. 4d) to e) shows that the background apparently depends even on the type of neutron guide used. Figs. 4a) and b) show that the proper choice of the detector alone yields only minor improvements, if the thermal neutron-beam quality is not sufficient. The spectrum 4f) has about the same signal/noise ratio as the one found by Ziegler et al. in their work [2], and gives an example for the best results obtainable with this simple experimental arrangement.

2.3 Improvements by Ion Optical Devices

As we discussed above, the background in (n,p) and (n,α) spectrometry is essentially due to capture of unwanted particles such as scattered thermal and fast neutrons as well as secondary electrons, and due to β and γ radiation in the detector. By separating this from the nuclear-reaction products to be measured (MeV-p, α, and recoil nuclei), the instrumental sensitivity is greatly enhanced. A simple construction to realize this separation is shown in Fig. 5. The (n,p) and (n,α) reaction products emerging from the irradiated sample penetrate into a coaxial cylindrical condenser through longitudinal slots in the inner electrode. A voltage of about 10...20 keV applied to the outer electrode deflects the transmitted ions by a few degrees along a path length of 10...40 cm. The ions leave the condenser through other slots in the inner electrode, and are registered in a subsequent solid-state surface-barrier detector. The direct path from the sample to the detector along the axis of the coaxial condenser is blocked by inserted polyethylene, ^{6}Li metal and lead, thus preventing direct irradiation of the detector by unwanted fast and thermal neutrons and γ radiation. Because of their negative charge, electrons hit the outer electrode and cannot reach the detector. The outer electrode is completely shielded from the surroundings by enclosure within the inner electrode and the vacuum vessel, which are both grounded. Thus, stray fields outside the ion-transmission tube are prevented, and maximum safety for handling is obtained. Additionally, the detector is shielded by lead and boron carbide to reduce isotropic background radiation from diffusely scattered particles in its vicinity.

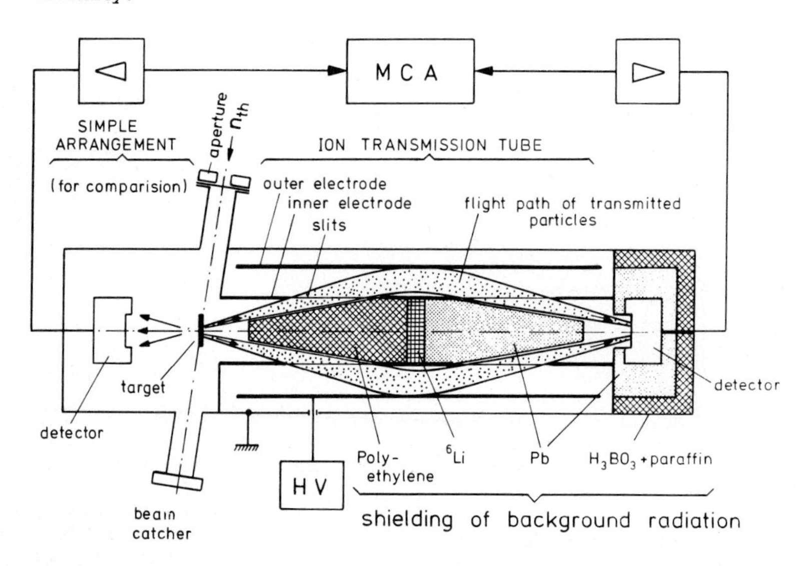

Fig.5. Principle diagram of the ion transmission tube and the paths of the transmitted ions

This device is designed for optimum transparency for fast light ions, but has nearly no spectroscopic properties. Hence, ions in a broad energy interval are transmitted simultaneously. After reduction of the radiation background by this arrangement, the electronic noise is now one of the limiting factors for the instrumental sensitivity. Hence, cooling of the detection system may further improve the signal/noise ratio. If, additionally, good

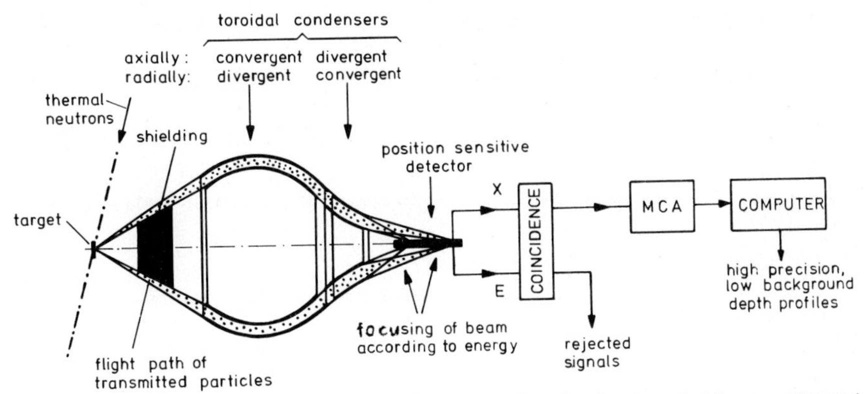

Fig.6. Principle diagram of the (n,p) and (n,α) electrostatic spectrometer now under construction

energy resolution is required, the ion optics have to be more sophisticated. An initial sketch of this (n,p) and (n,α) spectrometer now under construction is given in Fig. 6. The principle is the same as above. However, the cylindrical condenser is replaced by two toroidal condensers, by which all particles emerging from the sample within a certain solid angle range with the same energy are focused at the same distance. Thus, position-sensitive detectors can be applied for high-precision spectroscopy. Due to the rotational symmetry of the instrument, several detectors can operate parallel to each other, each facing a certain segment. Each position of the detectors corresponding to a certain energy, the background can in this case be further reduced by a coincidence circuit, comparing the position and the energy signals. With this spectrometer, depth resolutions of less than 50 Å and a sensitivity in the lower ppb region should be obtainable.

3. Conclusions

1. (n,p) and (n,α) spectrometric measurements can be performed both at irradiation positions inside and outside reactors. In general, however, positions outside reactors will be preferable.
2. A high-purity thermal neutron beam and a small totally depleted detector with a small depletion depth are essential for high quality measurements.
3. By applying even a simple ion optical device, the background of the measurements may be considerably decreased.

Acknowledgements

We acknowledge the kind support of the reactor divisions at the Institute Laue-Langevin, Grenoble, Physikalisch-Technische Bundesanstalt, Braunschweig, and Hahn-Meitner-Institut, Berlin, enabling us to perform the tests reported here.

References

[1] J.P. Biersack, D. Fink, R. Henkelmann, K. Müller: J. Nucl. Instr. Meth. 149, 93 (1978)

[2] J.F. Ziegler, G.W. Cole, J.E.E. Baglin: J. Appl. Phys. 43,9, 3809 (1972)

[3] J.P. Biersack, D. Fink: J. Nucl. Instr. Meth. 108, 397 (1973)

[4] D. Fink, Thesis, Free University Berlin (1974)

[5] J.P. Biersack, D. Fink in: Applications of Ion Beams to Metals, ed. by S.T. Picraux, E.P. Eer Nisse, F.L. Vook (1974), p. 307

[6] J.P. Biersack, D. Fink in: Atomic Collisions in Solids, Vol. 2, ed. by S. Datz, B.R. Appleton, C.D. Moak (1974), p. 737

[7] J. Bogancs et al., Reprint P14-8295, Joint Inst. f. Nucl. Res., Dubna (1974)

[8] J. Kvitek, V. Hnatowicz, P. Kotas, Radiochem. Radioanalyt. Lett. 24,3, 205 (1974)

[9] K. Müller, Thesis, Technical University Munich (1979)

[10] J.P. Biersack, D. Fink, J. Lauch, R. Henkelmann, K. Müller: J. Nucl. Instr. Meth. 188, 411 (1981)

[11] H. Grawe (HMI Berlin), personal communication (1978)

[12] D. Fink, U. Fischmann: J. Nucl. Instr. Meth. 100, 549 (1972)

Monitoring of X-Y-Scan Quality by Amorphization Contrast on Silicon Wafers

J.D. Hoepfner

Siemens AG, Otto-Hahn-Ring 6, D-8000 München 83, Fed. Rep. of Germany

Introduction

The exact control of the scanned ion beam on the wafer is an important factor influencing the dose accuracy across the wafer, and must be checked carefully. In order to achieve uniformity of dopant concentration, the ratio of the scan line distance to the beam spot diameter for a Gaussian beam must be optimized.

Faraday cups used for beam monitoring have limited spatial resolution. The oscilloscope displays an indirect image of the real scan pattern and its variation across the wafer. But one needs a fast and simple ion-beam diagnostic technique [1].

Single-crystal silicon covered with a thin SiO_2-layer visualizes the scanned ion beam, with very high lateral resolution, because the ion-implantation process changes the refractive index of the silicon substrate. Possible methods of inspection of damaged silicon or SiO_2 surfaces are visual inspection, ellipsometry or reflectrometry. In this paper,ellipsometry was used to investigate the crystal damage resulting from ion implantation in silicon.

The conventional method of using wafers with van der Pauw structures gives information of high accuracy, but involves an extended masking and preparation procedure.

In contrast, the method presented here gives first information immediately after implantation, and hence may serve as a very convenient, fast and economical in-line process evaluation.

Experimental Procedure

Arsenic implantation was performed at a 7° tilting angle with a standard medium-current implanter. Good results are obtained with arsenic at doses from 5×10^{13}-5×10^{15} ions cm^{-2} and energies fixed at 100 keV. The substrate was maintained at room temperature. The substrate material used is p type <100>, 20 Ωcm. The 3-inch diameter wafers were cleaned chemically and oxidized up to 80 nm in thickness. Ellipsometry is a sensitive, rapid and non-destructive method to measure the relative change in the refractive index and thickness of a SiO_2 layer on a damaged substrate. This method was used to quantitatively investigate the colouration in SiO_2 resulting from radiation damage in silicon. Fig.1 shows the multilayer structure consisting of the bulk silicon, the damaged Si layer and the transparent SiO_2 film.

Ellipsometric measurements were made using a Rudolph Research Auto EL III ellipsometer; the angle of incidence was $\phi_0 = 70^{\circ}$. The light source was a He-Ne laser; the wavelength, $\lambda = 632.8$ nm.

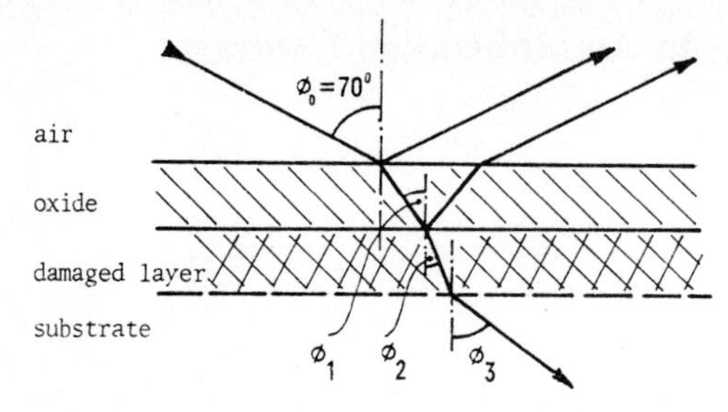

Fig. 1. Reflection and transmission of a wave by a transparent film. $\phi_0 - \phi_3$ are the angles of refraction in the parallel plane oxide and damaged layer films

Results and Discussion

The projected range R_p of arsenic implanted through SiO_2 at normal incidence is 58 nm at 100 keV effective energy [2]. The relative change of refractive index versus ion dose is shown in Fig. 2. The corresponding value of unimplanted SiO_2 is given for comparison.

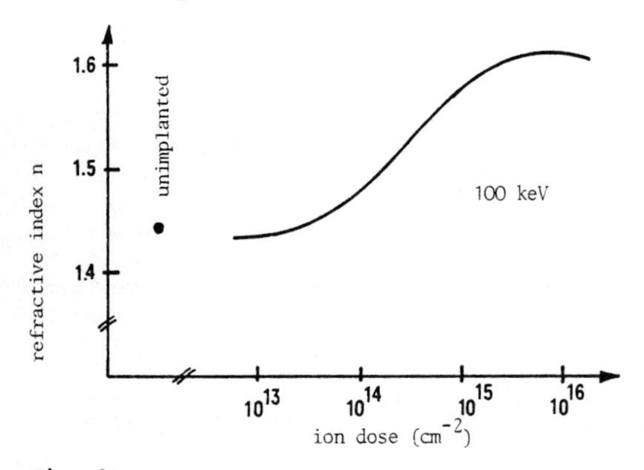

Fig. 2.
Dependence of the refractive index n upon the arsenic ion dose for a fixed energy at 100 keV

The increase of the refractive index at $1x10^{14}$ ions cm^{-2} suggests the onset of a quasi-amorphous state in the silicon. For ion doses above 10^{15} ions cm^{-2}, the refractive index begins to saturate. From this it may be concluded that the high-dose implants heat the wafer so much that some annealing of the defects occurs, if the wafer is not cooled properly.

It should be mentioned here that these ellipsometric measurements do not yield true changes in the refractive index and the thickness of SiO_2 when the material below that film, i.e. silicon, changes its properties too. Therefore we attribute "pseudo" to the values of refractive index and thickness. Indeed, by assuming for the implanted silicon the refractive index of poly Si and the penetration depth of arsenic in Si for thickness, one obtains for the thickness of the SiO_2 about the same value as was measured before implan-

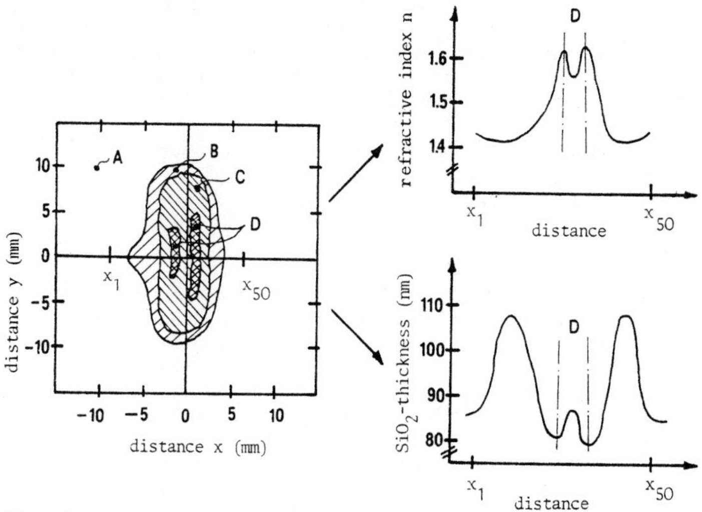

Fig. 3. Unscanned beam shape image with hot spots caused by a defocused ion beam

tation, while the increase in the refractive index of SiO_2 is reduced by about 50%.

The correlation between the increase of the pseudo refractive index and the decrease of the pseudo SiO_2 thickness is shown in Fig.3 for an unscanned beam spot with two hot spots caused by a defocused ion beam.

The colouration of the beam spot corresponds to the local flux density of the ion beam caused by radiation damage in the silicon layer. The colouration of the unimplanted oxide was violet (point A), the edge of the beam shape was metallic (point B), the beam spot center metallic blue (point C), with two "hot spots" which are ion-beam annealed with brownish color (point D).

The same measurements were made using a scanned beam with scan frequencies in the X direction of about 100 Hz and in the Y direction fixed at

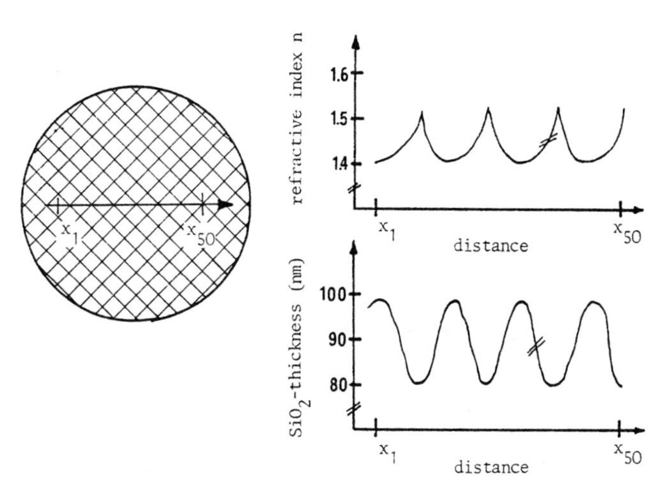

Fig.4. Topography of the optical constants of the damaged silicon wafer

1086 Hz (Fig.4). The beam shape corresponds to that shown in Fig.3. It is shown that the beam profile influences the dose homogeneity across the wafer. The remarkable non- uniformities of the electrostatic X-Y-deflection systems are caused by the random frequency scanners.

This method may be applied to the construction of contour maps across the wafer.

Summary and Conclusions

For implantations, e.g. 10^{14} ions cm^{-2} of As, changes in the optical behavior of silicon wafers covered with a thin layer of SiO_2 can be used to readily detect inhomogeneities in the implantation dose across the wafer. Ellipsometric measurements reveal an increase in the refractive index and a decrease in the effective thickness of the SiO_2, which correspond to these local dose variations. The modifications of the optical behavior are attributed to implantation damage and ion-beam annealing as well. Beam annealing compensates the effect of implantation damage in part. They can therefore be used for a quick characterization of an implanter with respect to scanning technique and beam homogeneity.

References

1 R. Badalec, H. Runge, J. Phys. E 12, 1146-7 (1979)

2 J.F. Gibbons, W.S. Johnson, S.W. Mylroie, Projected Range Statistics: Semiconductors and Related Materials, 2nd Edition, Halsted Press Stroudsbury, PA, USA (1975)

Part VII

Implantation into Metals

Techniques and Equipment for Implantation into Metals

G. Dearnaley
Harwell Laboratory, Didcot, OX11 0RA, England

1. Introduction

Since the last conference in the present series was held, in 1980, there has been considerable progress in the field of ion implantation of metals for industrial applications. Aspects that will be included in this review comprise continuing ion source development, the advent of the first commercial machines for ion implantation now installed for industrial use, and the relatively novel concept of ion beam mixing which extends greatly the versatility of the implantation process and the equipment developed.

There has, at the same time, been a growth in understanding of how ion implantation brings about a hardening of metals. It is now established that two species, one substitutional and one interstitial, can reinforce each other in providing resistance to wear, and sometimes also to oxidation. This has stimulated experiments aimed at finding the most appropriate combinations of ion species for such dual implantations, and the development of ion sources suitable for delivering these particles simultaneously.

The most widespread industrial application for ion implantation into metals and composites such as cemented tungsten carbide is for improving the wear resistance of many kinds of relatively expensive tools, and a more limited number of metallic components. Although ion implantation of suitably chosen species can have a strong and often surprisingly long-lasting effect on corrosion behaviour, the number of practical applications in this field is much more limited and specialized so far. It has been limited to critical parts of costly systems, such as bearings and turbine blades for military equipment since in the case of mass produced items the areas to be treated would be very large. Each corrosion problem requires extensive testing, preferably under realistic conditions, and simply produced gaseous ions are rarely effective. A requirement has therefore arisen for versatile equipment that can be used in development work on the implantation of any ion species into metallic components for the necessary tests. Dedicated equipment for carrying out the treatment may then be required at a subsequent stage.

2. The Hardening of Metals

Improvement in the wear resistance of metals and alloys is achieved by techniques which effectively harden them and hinder the fatigue-like processes involved during the creation of particles of debris. To achieve this, it is necessary to pin dislocations and to influence the mechanism of work hardening which takes place as a result of plastic deformation of load-bearing asperities.

The first successful implantation treatments [1] involved the injection of interstitial species such as nitrogen, carbon, or boron into steels.

Such atoms segregate to dislocations which may either pre-exist in the metal or may be formed during wear. The effective implanted doses ($\sim 10^{17}$ ions/cm^2 implanted to a depth of ~ 2000 Å) are sufficient to decorate every available atomic site along all the dislocations even at the maximum sustainable densities of about 10^{12} line cm/cm^3. This has a strong damping effect on dislocation movement, and because the implanted atoms are very finely dispersed and easily dissolve to form an interstitial solid solution (as segregation proceeds) the interaction between dislocations and impurity atoms is partially inelastic. This beneficially dissipates mechanical energy in the form of heat. For this reason we can understand how the ion implantation of nitrogen can reinforce conventional nitriding of steel, because in the latter case relatively macroscopic nitride precipitates are produced, which can interact mainly elastically with dislocations.

Another consequence of the mobility of implanted interstitials, particularly along dislocations ('pipe diffusion'), is that the effectiveness of the treatment often persists well beyond the shallow implanted depth. The forward migration of impurities is driven by the very strong concentration gradient that exists, and the availability of vacant lattice sites along forest dislocations being created continuously at progressively greater depths as wear goes on. Migration is assisted by the local temperature rise, which may easily reach 500°C, due to the dissipation of frictional energy at the very points, or asperities, at which plastic deformation and dislocation propagation are taking place [2].

Under atmospheric conditions, there will furthermore be at least some oxidative wear due to the high local temperatures combined with pressure and the production of defective, non-protective oxide. In the case of steel, such oxides are a useful barrier to prevent the loss of mobile nitrogen. In alloy steels, containing chromium, the growth of spinels or Cr_2O_3 at the surface provides an even better diffusion barrier to retain nitrogen.

Experiments on the migration of implanted nitrogen during wear suggest that frictional heating is necessary, and very mild abrasive wear such as occurs during vibratory polishing is not sufficient to stimulate diffusion [3]. Even during dry adhesive wear tests [4] only about 10-15 per cent of the implanted atoms seem able to move forward, but this fraction appears to remain constant throughout the course of the experiment. This observation suggests that it is necessary for the implanted nitrogen to be in a particular type of site, possibly associated with a bombardment-induced defect, in order to possess the required mobility or freedom to segregate.

A growing number of experiments has shown that a considerable improvement in wear resistance can be achieved if certain metallic atoms are implanted in addition to the interstitial (nitrogen). Wale-Evans investigated rare earths in iron and steel [5], Watkins and Dearnaley found that tin and nitrogen are very effective in titanium [6] and Baumvol [7] has shown that the same combination of atoms improves the wear of iron. More recently Peacock [8] has been able to show that implanted tin alone gives no improvement in the wear resistance of titanium alloy, and so it must be the combination of the two that is effective. It is not the damage, due to implantation with heavy tin atoms, that accounts for the difference, because the same result is obtained by ion-beam mixing a tin coating on iron (or titanium) by bombardment with nitrogen ions, usually at elevated temperatures.

This led Dearnaley [9] to suggest that oversized impurities such as tin or rare earths may create favourable sites in their neighbourhood for interstitial nitrogen. Such substitutional-interstitial (S-i) pairing is well established in zirconium containing tin and nitrogen [10]. Such an atomic pair can then undergo an inelastic reorientation under an applied mechanical stress, and so relieve local cyclically applied stresses which occur during wear. The same conclusion was arrived at independently by Dastur and Leslie [11] in an explanation of the unusual work-hardening properties of manganese-carbon steel (Hadfield alloy). They argued that the reorientation of Mn-C pairs in the strain field of a nearby dislocation can be an important mechanism in work-hardening, and one that imparts excellent wear resistance.

Impurities can therefore influence strongly the work-hardening behaviour of steels, and the argument can be taken further and generalised somewhat. In order to pin dislocations successfully it is necessary to have an impurity that will segregate to and be trapped by the dislocation in such a way that subsequent unpinning is difficult. An inelastic behaviour under applied mechanical stresses is also desirable, as we have seen. The least mobile (or sessile) points of a dislocation network are certain intersections, known as Lomer-Cottrell locks (and other related structures). If such points can be decorated by suitably-chosen oversized impurities, their stability may be improved. The objective would then be to achieve the maximum density of pinned Lomer-Cottrells during work-hardening under chosen thermal conditions, which may for instance allow diffusion along dislocations but trapping at the locking point. The work-hardening behaviour of metals depends also on their structure, and the larger number of slip systems available in fcc or hcp lattices (compared with bcc structures) favours the production of three-dimensional dislocation locks. Conditions for favourable implantation therefore include:

(i) oversized impurities that will segregate at appropriate temperatures to dislocations;

(ii) a local fcc or hcp structure that can work harden effectively;

(iii) plastic deformation at a suitable temperature to create as many pinning points as possible;

(iv) interstitial impurities (e.g. N or C) to form S-i pairs which can reorient by the Snoek relaxation under stress and convert mechanical energy inelastically into heat;

(v) the possibility of pipe diffusion from the reservoir of implanted material in order to decorate dislocations at greater depths during wear.

On this basis of mechanisms and criteria we can understand better how tin and nitrogen have been effective in hcp titanium, why ε carbonitride is a favourable structure in implanted steels [12], why yttrium and nitrogen are highly beneficial in fcc austenitic stainless steel, and why γ-phase fcc Hadfield steel shows such good work-hardening behaviour. On the basis of these arguments it should be possible to devise treatments for many different alloys, not only in steel, but also aluminium, copper, nickel, etc. Experiments are now in progress along these lines, and the results are beginning to dictate requirements for ion sources and implantation equipment, as will be discussed below.

3. Corrosion of Metals

There are two principal regimes of corrosion in which protection of metallic components is required: these are high-temperature oxidation (e.g. turbine blades) and aqueous corrosion (e.g. marine applications). Of these two, the first is probably the simpler because thermal energy is available for the redistribution of implanted material during oxidation, to maintain the protection, and there is no lateral transport such as can occur during galvanic action through the medium of an electrolyte or aqueous solution. Under aqueous attack, there is the fear that abrasion of shallow ion-implanted layers can lead to a rapid attack due to differences in surface composition and corrosion potential. Intermediate between the two are corrosion problems that arise during atmospheric exposure, or localized pitting due to chloride contamination of lubricants in bearings, etc.

Many experiments over the past ten years have demonstrated that substantial improvements in corrosion resistance can be achieved by means of ion implantation [13, 14]. The mechanisms by which these effects are obtained are broadly understood, and in several cases the work has provided better understanding of the corrosion behaviour. In the case of aqueous attack, the guiding principle is to alter the rates of either the anodic or cathodic reactions at the surface and thus the ion implantation of species such as chromium into iron, or insoluble tantalum into iron has been successful [15]. Localized, or pitting corrosion by chloride ions has been overcome by the implantation of high concentrations of Cr, or of Mo into steels and aluminium. Mo^+ implantation also reduces pitting corrosion in magnesium [16]. During thermal oxidation, the most useful guiding principle is to provide a barrier layer that hinders atomic transport of the appropriate atomic species. This may be done locally, if this transport occurs along dislocations or grain boundaries, or more homogeneously if the diffusion is a bulk phenomenon. Coherent diffusion barriers of SiO_2, Al_2O_3 or Cr_2O_3 are commonly involved, and in each case substantial amounts ($> 10^{17}$ atoms/cm^2) of Si, Al or Cr are required in order to establish an efficient barrier. When the oxidation takes place by short-circuit diffusion, particularly along linear defects such as dislocations (as in the case of titanium) then oversized impurities (barium, rare earths) can be implanted so that they will segregate to and block these dislocation paths by the formation of impermeable precipitates of binary oxide (such as $BaTiO_3$). The doses required are then substantially lower, around 10^{16} ions/cm^2, because this is quite sufficient to decorate the atomic sites involved.

The outcome of these experiments is to show that a relatively small number of ion species (e.g. Cr, Al, Si, Ba, rare earths, Ta, Mo, Y) will be likely to provide corrosion resistance under a variety of conditions. However, these are not particularly easy ion species to produce as an ion beam of high intensity, and under industrial conditions. For this reason, there is now a growing interest in the use of ion beam mixing as an alternative method of introducing chosen species into the surface layers of a material.

4. Ion Beam Mixing and Bombardment-diffused Coatings

The purpose of this approach [17] is to introduce a selected additive into a given material by the ion bombardment of a deposited coating. Because it is a non-equilibrium process in which many point defects are created, the final result is generally very similar to that achievable by direct implantation. However, atoms of the ion beam (usually gaseous) and of the coating are present together, and insofar as they lie at similar depths there may be physico-chemical interactions between them. Such interaction may, as we have seen above, lead to beneficial pairing associations.

The process of ion beam mixing is somewhat akin to ion plating, but there are some important distinctions: (i) the process is carried out with much more energetic ions in a relatively hard vacuum, and (ii) the purpose is usually (though not necessarily) to achieve complete intermixing of the coating and substrate, rather than to produce a coating layer of a distinct composition. Just as in ion plating, however, it is possible to envisage the coating atoms being deposited (by evaporation or sputtering) throughout the ion bombardment.

There are three basic mechanisms of ion beam mixing: (i) recoil implantation or 'primary recoil mixing' [18] in which atoms are transported by a direct collision between the projectile ion and an atom of the coating, (ii) cascade mixing, which occurs within the collision cascade of energetic heavy ions due to the random-walk consequences of collisional atomic displacements [18, 19], and (iii) radiation-enhanced diffusion, taking place by various thermally assisted mechanisms of transport involving the point defect fluxes created by bombardment.

These effects were all exploited initially for the ion beam mixing of metallic coatings on silicon, for the purpose of producing conductive metal silicides for contacts and interconnections [20]. It is possible to envisage a more widespread use for the techniques in the treatment of metals.

Sometimes a relatively shallow layer may be sufficient to provide protection, for example during mild aqueous corrosion conditions. Then the small amount of interpenetration produced by collisional cascade mixing may be adequate. It is advantageous in this case to use relatively energetic heavy ions, such as xenon, which will induce a massive amount of atomic displacements along the ion trajectory. Mazzoldi et al. [21] have recently reported a significant amount of mixing of coatings of Pb deposited on aluminium by such an irradiation, using a dose of only 10^{15} Xe^+ ions/cm^2.

This example shows how the non-equilibrium nature of the process overrides normal considerations of solubility and alloy formation, since lead has a very small solubility indeed in aluminium. The same has been reported for the enhanced diffusion of mutually insoluble iridium and gold, by Dearnaley [17] under argon ion bombardment.

Much greater thicknesses of coating can be mixed by using enhanced diffusion at temperatures at which point defects, such as vacancies, become mobile. Complexes formed by the binding of an impurity to a vacancy may be relatively mobile, and can transport material even beyond the range over which bombardment-induced defects are produced. The diffusion length is dependent upon the density of sinks at which the defects can become annihilated.

Another mechanism of transport is by the inverse Kirkendall effect [22, 23], in which impurity atoms that jump frequently into a neighbouring vacancy site can be redistributed towards the peak of the vacancy concentration profile. A buried peak can be produced in this way, as has been observed with cobalt in gold [17].

Since in these experiments each bombarding ion produces many defects and displacements, it is possible to achieve a 'transport ratio', which is the number of coating atoms significantly relocated for each incident ion, that can be appreciably greater than unity. Galerie and Dearnaley [24] obtained a transport ratio of 3 for silicon introduced to a mean depth of nearly 2000 Å under argon bombardment, and even larger ratios are possible during cascade mixing to smaller depths (up to about 300 Å). The advantages of ion beam mixing are therefore that it may be much more efficient than direct implantation, and the gaseous ion beams required (usually argon, xenon or nitrogen) are readily generated with long-life ion sources. The process adds little in the way of complexity to an industrial implantation facility. Perhaps the least simple requirement is that for heating the workpiece in order to induce enhanced diffusion. In steels, vacancy migration and enhanced diffusion commence above 200-250°C, but in titanium alloys a temperature of 450°C is required. Aluminium vacancies are mobile at room temperature, however, and so no auxiliary heating is necessary in this material.

Some concern was felt initially that the almost inevitable presence of oxide films between the coating and substrate would impede interdiffusion: this is certainly the case in purely thermal intermixing. However, the cascade mixing of the oxide barrier and perhaps defect-assisted transport across the film have been found to overcome this problem and, in fact, ion bombardment is a good means of ensuring a uniform and predictable degree of thermal diffusion across the interfacial barrier [25].

Several successful applications of ion beam mixing of coatings into metals have now been reported, and others are under investigation. Thus Watkins and Dearnaley [in ref. 17] have achieved major improvements in the adhesive wear of titanium alloy by enhanced diffusion of tin by nitrogen bombardment at 450°C. Approximately 4.10^{17} atoms/cm^2 of both tin and nitrogen were introduced to a depth of several thousand Ångstroms. Baumvol [26] found that tin and nitrogen have beneficial effects on wear in iron, and that the oxidation resistance at 500°C is much improved. In this case the ion bombardment was carried out at only 200°C. A recent industrial test of a component of stainless steel treated in this manner gave a figure for the reduction in wear rate of 320 times. Galerie and Dearnaley [24] mixed silicon into iron to achieve a reduction in thermal oxidation at 600°C of 45 times, and this work is now being extended to titanium (for possible application to compressor blades).

Another application of ion beam mixing is to create a graded composition in which the surface concentration of additive is high (almost 100 per cent). This would be the case at the final stage of intermixing, and it can be considered as a useful method of improving adhesion of a subsequently-deposited coating. By this means, ion beam mixing can be combined with electrodeposition or ion plating in order to overcome problems which sometimes arise in the achievement of a satisfactory bond.

Li et al. [27] have successfully mixed Ti into iron in order to improve the aqueous corrosion resistance of the surface. This gave a strong effect, and there is good reason to believe that the titanium, by interaction with carbon in a steel, would at the same time improve the abrasion resistance of the metal [28]. The retention of the treated surface during practical use would thereby be increased.

5. Industrial Application of Ion Implantation

The past few years of activity have further consolidated the usefulness of ion implantation particularly for improving the wear resistance of tools. On the basis of production tests, and a careful consideration of the economics of the process, several new commercial enterprises have been initiated. A few examples can be presented here to illustrate the savings which can result from the use of ion implantation. Industrial interest now provides, at least in the UK, and to a growing degree in the USA, the driving force for continued development of equipment and techniques.

One of the most uniformly successful areas of application has been to steel tools used in the injection moulding and extrusion of plastics. Mineral fillers and glass fibre lead to remarkably rapid wear of hardened steel tools, many of which are now highly expensive. Filled plastics are being used to a greater extent in automobiles and elsewhere for lightness and to eliminate costly machining. The universal tool used in this work is the screw which forces plastics material into a mould or through a die Fig.1.

Fig. 1. A steel screw of the type widely used for the injection moulding of plastics. Such tools have lasted 12 times longer than normal after implantation

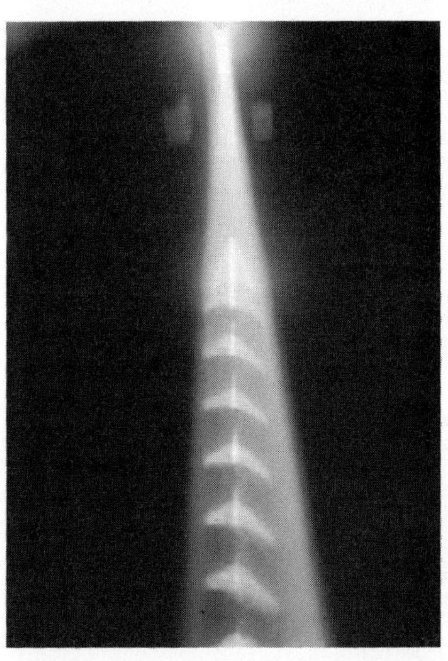

Fig. 2. An injection moulding screw undergoing nitrogen implantation, by rotation in the ion beam, inclined at an angle to the axis of the screw

About 20,000 of these are estimated to be in use in the UK alone, mostly imported and costing about $5000 each. Treatment by rotation in a nitrogen ion beam Fig.2 costs about $1000 with present-day small scale equipment, and increases the life by a factor of 10 or more. One company in Britain has implanted screws in use after two years whereas the normal life is two months. Nozzles through which the plastics flows have similarly been improved, despite the fact that the tolerated wear can be up to 1 mm: for reasons which are probably not yet understood, the implantation process continues to provide wear resistance over remarkable depths, perhaps by initiating a novel wear regime during the early stages. Moulds used for plastics manufacture may cost $100,000 and here the cost of nitrogen ion implantation is usually less than 10 per cent of the mould cost, and has increased life in numerous cases by a factor of ten. Extrusion dies, Fig.3, are also expensive components, and their wear results in a departure from

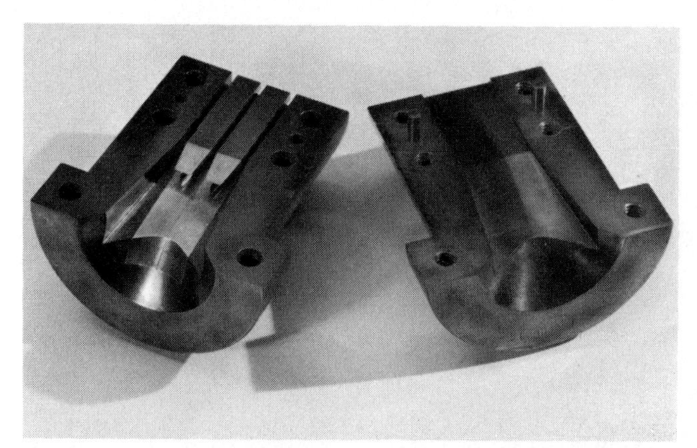

Fig. 3. A die used for the extrusion of plastics. This tool has since successfully processed 144 tons of material (800 km of product) without measurable wear, following nitrogen ion implantation

accepted tolerances and a waste of plastics. The disc illustrated has performed extremely well in terms of the dimensional stability of extruded sections.

Punches and dies are used in considerable numbers, and are subject to adhesive wear. Nitrogen ion implantation has increased the output of dies used for stamping electric motor laminations by a factor of six [29] and the treatment of the flank of the punch has enabled it to be reground (on the face) several times without loss of effectiveness [30].

Press tools sometimes give rise to problems which are associated with the flow of metal across the surface of the tool. Reduced pickup and better flow is frequently reported after nitrogen ion implantation, and thus better results are achieved. Figure 4 shows a large press tool which has been implanted recently at Harwell for this purpose. Not only are tool costs high, but the product quality is a major criterion of success.

Tungsten carbide tools are also costly, and ion implantation of back extrusion punches has been highly successful in production tests. Here again pickup is noticeably lessened and the tool life is extended by factors up to three.

Extension of the process to low-cost tools, such as wire dies, and to mass-produced components will be dependent upon the development of dedicated machines rather than the general-purpose facilities illustrated in Fig.4. Operating costs of $100 to $200 per hour for the larger, specialized equipment are acceptable only if the machines are loaded for most of the time. The integration of ion implantation into industrial metal finishing is therefore an essential factor in its adoption. Jobbing centres, strategically located in industrial countries, will be important in gaining acceptance and in treating work for customers who could never justify a machine of their own. Appropriate scientific back-up for these centres will be required if they are to be in a position to apply the more sophisticated ion beam treatments such as ion beam mixing. This is because the number of possible additives then becomes very high. It is important, therefore, that the straightforward process of nitrogen ion implantation is so effective in

Fig. 4. A high-chromium steel press tool, 1200 mm by 600 mm, after ion implantation with nitrogen in the large 2.5 m facility at Harwell

steels and tungsten carbide in order to provide a base for industrial experience. On this base the extending versatility of the process can be built as experience grows.

Problems sometimes arise in the preparation of tools for ion implantation, particularly if they are as large as the one shown in Fig.4. Complex tools may be made up of many component parts fitted together and it is not always practicable to disassemble them. Lubricant may seep or evaporate from the interstices and result in a cracked hydrocarbon film on the bombarded surface. Normally, in a well-designed implantation chamber there is no visible film of carbon on ion implanted steel components. Contaminant films up to about 500 Å in thickness are not, in practice, deleterious and they can even provide a temporary protection from wear, adhesion or corrosion. Films greater than this will, however, impede the penetration of nitrogen into the metal, and they should be avoided. The best procedure is to clean the item as thoroughly as possible in an organic solvent, and to pump for at least 23 hours in vacuum, preferably with moderate heating to about 150°C, before implantation. An auxiliary chamber is justifiable if this problem is often encountered. The requirements in regard to preparation for ion implantation are, however, much less stringent than those for plating or coating processes.

It is our experience that a commercial service in ion implantation into metals needs initially a well-planned advertising procedure, but that after a sufficient number of successful trials have been carried out news about the process spreads spontaneously and customers return with larger batches of work. As the next stage, it is possible to envisage a network of centres equipped to carry out the process and cooperating with each other to extend the market, while sharing the work on a geographical basis. Communication with industrial customers is an essential part of this development, since the market is far more diversified and more conservative than the semi-conductor device market for implantation.

Demand for the ion implantation of metallic components for protection against wear is steadily growing in countries such as the UK, USA and W.Germany. The increased utilisation of the process depends upon the availability of appropriate equipment, and the prospect that the technique will become more economical with further developments in ion sources and work handling facilities. These aspects are considered next.

6. Ion Source Developments

Ion sources for gaseous ions, such as nitrogen, present few difficulties. A simple discharge source, comprising a DC potential sufficient to ionize the gas at a suitable pressure, is capable of delivering useful currents of nitrogen ions. Somewhat more elaborate versions incorporate magnetic fields to confine the plasma and so reduce recombination at the walls. Duoplasmatron sources for gaseous ions have long been in existence and can supply multi-milliampère currents.

The situation is less well developed in regard to metallic ions, particularly when a reasonable ion source life ($\sim$ 1000 hours) is required. In a mass-analysed system, such as is nowadays conventional for the ion implantation of semiconductors, the Freeman source offers the possibility of achieving milliampere currents of many elements from appropriate volatile compounds, such as metal chlorides. As the temperature range of Freeman sources increases [31], so the prospect for the more difficult metal ions improves.

The alternative is to generate ions by sputtering of the metal, to release what are mainly neutral atoms into a discharge of rare gas ions (e.g. argon) in which, by electron collision or charge exchange with argon ions, the required metal ions are generated. One very promising source design is based upon early work by Bernas [32], and is shown in Fig.5. Electrons from a filament, external to the source, ionize argon gas from which ions are drawn to a cylindrical sputtering electrode of the appropriate metal. Atoms, mainly neutral, released by this intense sputtering, can become ionized in the argon discharge and then extracted through the aperture by an applied external field.

For the dual implantation of metallic ions and interstitial nitrogen, as discussed above, the sputtering source can be operated with nitrogen gas, though the sputtering efficiency is thereby reduced. This has been the principle of a development by Goode and Ledbury [33], which is to be tested shortly.

The extraction of metallic ions by field emission from molten metals has so far failed to live up to expectations. Apart from the easily fusible metals, such as gallium, caesium, etc. it has not proved feasible to extract large (i.e. multi-milliampère) currents of metallic ions from such sources.

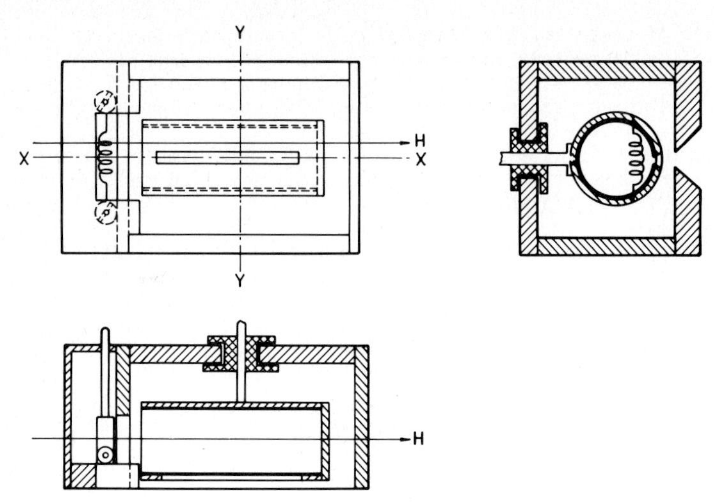

Fig. 5. A diagram of the cylindrical sputtering source, designed by Druaux and Bernas [32] which has formed the basis for recent ion source developments at Harwell

Further ion source developments, for the non-gaseous species, seem sure to be stimulated by the requirements of ion implantation. Some, which it would be premature to describe, are under way, and the objectives are to achieve about 30 mA of various non-gaseous ion species during the next year or two. This current intensity would improve dramatically the economics of ion implantation for such applications as corrosion resistance or high temperature wear resistance.

7. Ion Implantation Facilities

In this final section we consider the development of complete systems for industrial ion implantation (in the non-semiconductor area). It will be apparent from the consideration of the sizes and complex shapes of workpieces that are often to be treated that work handling equipment is a most important feature of an industrial facility. There are two situations: (i) a general purpose machine that is versatile enough to treat many kinds of component, and (ii) a dedicated machine in which the emphasis is upon one particular category of workpiece. Versatility is achievable by the use of several basic types of manipulator such as an X-Y table, a rotatable wheel or face-plate, and a rotatable drum. These require to be speedily interchangeable, and perhaps operated from a standardized drive controller. Lubrication of the moving parts is not easy in vacuum and it is necessary to design a system which will operate reliably without sticking.

Ion sources for gaseous species such as nitrogen can be of the simple discharge variety, and it is advantageous if they can be compact enough to be able to arrange two or more of them to provide beams that impinge at controllable angles to the workpiece surface. In this way, for instance, both faces of a cutting wheel or saw can be implanted simultaneously, rather than in two sequential operations.

Heating of components during ion implantation presents some problems since it is generally desirable to keep the surface below 200°C in order to prevent thermal diffusion of nitrogen. Exceptions to this are stainless steel, which can safely be implanted at up to 500°C, or cemented tungsten carbide, which will withstand at least this temperature. We have demonstrated that nitrogen remains immobile in tungsten carbide even at 1000°C.

With a beam current density of 20 μA per cm^2 and an ion energy of 100 keV, the resulting power dissipation of 2 W per cm^2 is sufficient to raise the temperature of small components to well over 300°C. The solution is to mount as many of these small items as possible in the workchamber, on a suitably designed manipulator so that each spends only a small fraction of the time within the ion beam.

Safety aspects of equipment which may often need to be used by relatively unskilled personnel also require careful attention. Shielding and full electrical interlocks are essential, together with a straightforward means of gaining access for maintenance.

These, and many of the features discussed above, are incorporated into the commercially available design of implanter shown in Fig.6. This 100 keV machine has a workchamber 60 cm cube, and particularly simple controls. It is intended as a small, general-purpose machine for light duty jobbing work or developmental use. Modules such as the ion gun, high voltage supply and controllers can readily be assembled into a more dedicated machine, designed around the particular work-handling required, e.g. for the treatment of wire dies. The commercial possibilities have been reviewed by Charter, Thompson and Dearnaley [34] who estimate the costs and benefits of the ion implantation process for a number of typical examples.

In the ion beam mixing of coatings it is important to avoid too much contamination at the coating-substrate interface, due either to oxidation

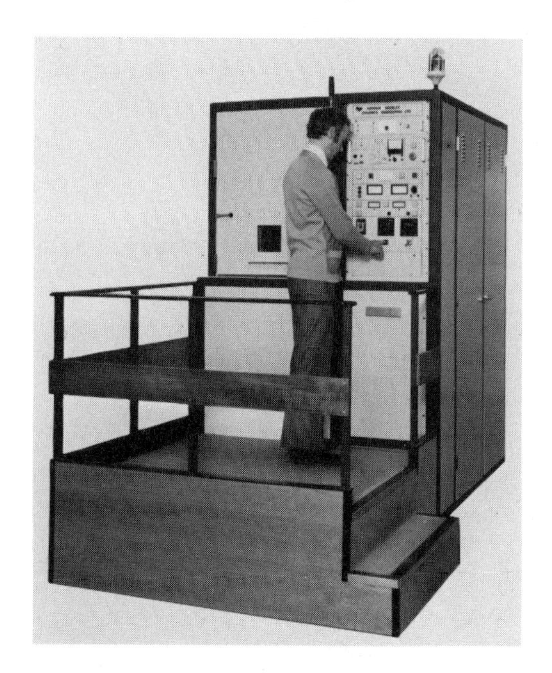

Fig.6. A 100 kV implantation machine for industrial use, and designed primarily for the implantation of nitrogen into steels and carbides. The work-chamber size is 600 mm cube. (Photography by courtesy of Hawker Siddeley Dynamics Engineering Ltd. Welwyn, UK)

Fig.7. A large implantation facility at Harwell with a work-chamber diameter of 2.5 metres. The beam area is approximately 1000 cm^2. A rotary table for manipulation of items up to 1500 kg in weight can be seen on the right

or hydrocarbon deposition. It is also necessary in the case of rather reactive coatings (such as titanium) to prevent significant oxidation. For this reason, a facility which is to be used for ion beam mixing should have a superior pumping system, such as a large cryo-pump. This offers the other advantage that the pump-down time for conventional implantation work can be speeded up. A monitor system for control of the deposition rate is another requirement.

A calibration procedure is advisable for any implantation machine, whether of the mass-analyzed design or not. Non-analyzed systems can generate a variety of beams, molecular or neutral, and a measurement of the ion current alone is then not enough. An analysis, by nuclear reaction techniques or

XPS, of the total quantity of implanted atoms is a useful technique which allows the true particle flux to be determined as a function of workchamber pressure. Other simple calibration procedures have been developed on the basis of the secondary electron emission from bombarded surfaces, or the method of calorimetry in which the heating effect of the beam is measured.

The emphasis in this review has been upon the design and use of non-analyzed implantation systems, because at the present time these offer the most economic means of treating metals and carbides and they have therefore been developed for the industrial market. Ion beam mixing techniques, or ion sources capable of delivering more than one species simultaneously, increase the versatility of the process to a point which is still far from being well explored. At this final stage, however, it is useful to discuss the role of mass-analyzed equipment for the implantation of non-semiconductor materials.

Mass-analyzed machines offer greater versatility because, with ion sources of the Freeman type milliampere currents of most elements can be generated from appropriate volatile compounds (such as chlorides). In the latest designs [35] good progress has been made in reducing the cost and in providing workchamber facilities to suit customer requirements: hitherto the emphasis lay so much upon the semiconductor device market that it was difficult to obtain equipment for other purposes. This type of equipment will undoubtedly be very useful for research and development. The only reason why it may not be favoured for industrial applications is that it may be more economic to use ion beam mixing of coatings under bombardment with gaseous ion beams generated from long-life ion sources. The transport ratios that have been achieved, well in excess of unity and sometimes as great as 100 coating atoms per ion, make it less attractive to treat surfaces by direct ion implantation. However, the enhanced diffusion process involves elevated temperatures and demands relatively high diffusivities that cannot always be realized, and there may also be difficulties with the more reactive coatings (as discussed above). In these cases, the direct implantation of ions may prove to be the best solution.

In conclusion, it can be said that progress in the field of ion implantation into metals and carbide composites has been very rapid. It is increasingly coupled to the market for improved material performance. New techniques, such as ion beam mixing, appear to offer great promise, and the degree to which success is achieved with gaseous ion bombardment will determine the relative importance of analyzed and non-analyzed implantation systems. During the developmental stage there is certainly scope for both.

Acknowledgements

Support by the Materials and Chemicals Requirements Board of the UK Department of Industry is acknowledged.

References

1 G.Dearnaley, N.E.W.Hartley, Proc. 4th Conf. on Sci. & Indust. Applns. of Small Accelerators, Denton, 1976 (IEEE, New York) p.20.
2 D.M.Rowson, T.F.J.Quinn, J. Phys. D. *13*, 209 (1980).
3 R.N.Bolster, I.L.Singer, Appl. Phys. Lett. *36*, 208 (1980).
4 S.Lo Russo, P.Mazzoldi, I.Scotoni, C.Tosello, S.Tosto, Appl. Phys. Lett. *34*, 629 (1979).
5 G.Wale-Evans, M.Sc. Thesis, Brighton Poly. (1979).
6 R.E.J.Watkins, G.Dearnaley, unpublished work summarised in Nucl.Instr. & Meth.

7 I.J.R.Baumvol, Phys. Stat. Sol. (a) *67*, 287 (1981).
8 A.T.Peacock, AERE priv. comm. (1982).
9 G.Dearnaley, Rad. Effects, (to be published).
10 S.Mishra, M.K.Asundi, Can. Met. Quarterly *11*, 69 (1972).
11 Y.N.Dastur, W.C.Leslie, Met. Trans. *12A*, 749 (1981).
12 C.A.dos Santos, B.A.S.de Barros, J.P.de Souza, I.J.R.Baumvol. Appl. Phys. Lett. *41*, 237 (1982).
13 V.Ashworth in *Treatise on Materials Science & Technology*, Vol. 18, ed. J.K.Hirvonen (Academic Press, New York, 1980) p.215.
14 G.Dearnaley, Nucl. Instr. & Meth. *182/183*, 899 (1981).
15 V.Ashworth, D.Baxter, W.A.Grant, R.P.M.Procter, Corros. Sci. *17*, 947 (1977).
16 H.Ferber, priv. comm. (1982).
17 G.Dearnaley, Rad. Effects, to be published (1982).
18 P.K.Haff, Z.E.Switkowski, J. Appl. Phys. *48*, 3383 (1977).
19 P.Sigmund, A.Gras-Marti, Nucl. Instr. & Meth. *182/183*, 25 (1981).
20 J.W.Mayer, Nucl. Instr. & Meth. *182/183*, 1 (1981).
21 P.Mazzoldi, priv. comm. (1982), to be published in proc. IBMM Conference, Grenoble (1982).
22 G.Dearnaley, Appl. Phys. Lett. *28*, 244 (1976).
23 A.D.Marwick, J. Phys. F. *8*, 1849 (1978).
24 A.Galerie, G.Dearnaley, Proc. Conf. on Ion Beam Modification of Materials, Grenoble (1982), to be published.
25 L.S.Wielunski, C-D. Lien, B-X.Liu, M.A.Nicolet, Proc. Symposium Mater. Res. Soc. Boston, Vol. 7 (North-Holland, Amsterdam, 1982) p.139.
26 I.J.R.Baumvol, R.E.J.Watkins, G.Longworth, G.Dearnaley, Inst. of Physics (London) Conference Series *54*, 201 (1980).
27 J-Y. Feng, H-D. Li, H-H.Wang, H-M.Chen, Qinghua University Beijing, priv. comm.(1982).
28 J.K.Hirvonen, C.A.Carosella, R.A.Kant, I.Singer, R.Vardiman, B.B.Rath, Thin Solid Films *63*, 5 (1979).
29 R.E.Fromson, R.Kossowsky, Proc. 9th North American, Manufacturing Research Conf., Pennsylvania State University (1981).
30 R.E.Fromson, priv. comm. (1981).
31 P.Byers, Whickham Engineering Ltd. Newcastle-upon-Tyne, priv. comm. (1982).
32 J.Druaux, R.H.Bernas, in *Electromagnetically Enriched Isotopes*, ed. by M.L.Smith (Butterworth, London, 1956).
33 P.D.Goode, A.Ledbury, AERE Harwell (unpublished work).
34 S.Charter, L.R.Thompson, G.Dearnaley, Thin Solid Films *84*, 355 (1981).
35 Whickham Engineering Ltd., Newcastle-upon-Tyne NE16 6EA.

Nitriding of Steels: Conventional Processes and Ion Implantation

C.A. dos Santos and I.J.R. Baumvol
Instituto de Fisica-UFRGS, Av. Luiz Englert S/N, 90000 Porto Alegre, Brasil

1. Introduction

There is at present an increasing interest in ion implantation treatments of the surface of steels. Many laboratories and industries are reporting results on the production of very hard and wear-resistant engineering components using ion implantation as a hard finishing coating.

Between the different atomic species that bring about beneficial effects when implanted into steels, nitrogen is of particular practical interest. Besides all the common advantages of ion implantation (the process is carried out at low temperatures and so there is no distortion, the surface polish and dimensions are unaffected, the treatment is made in high vacuum assuring cleanness), nitrogen presents the additional advantage of being effective in a wide range of materials, and there are also designs of gas ion sources which can be readily adapted to produce the large current-large area beams required for most of the industrial applications [1].

The wear and fatigue performances of nitrogen implanted steels resemble those obtained by gas and salt bath nitriding, the normal heat treatment processes used to harden steels. However, nitriding of steels by means of ion implantation is very distinctive as compared to all other conventional nitriding methods. Moreover, it has been recently reported that synergistic effects exist when nitrogen is implanted into the surface of steels which have been previously nitrided by conventional processes. In order to place adequately the ion implantation technique in the wide field of metal surface coatings, we first review briefly the basic facts about heat treatment nitriding and nitrocarburising of steels; next we discuss the characteristics of nitrogen ion implantation into the surface layers of steels, and finally we compare the two processes.

2. Ferritic Nitriding and Nitrocarburizing

Nitriding of steels has been for a long time a well known and successful practice in metallurgy. The diffusional addition of nitrogen to the surface of ferrous materials, performed at temperatures characteristic of the ferrite phase (500-550 ^{o}C), causes hardening to depths up to 1 mm and confers both wear and fatigue resistance on engineering components. The basic mechanism is that at nitriding temperatures, ammonia (NH_3) is metastable and decomposes in contact with iron, producing molecular hydrogen plus either molecular nitrogen or nitrogen dissolved interstitially in iron [2].

The advantage of nitriding over other surface hardening methods is the reduced risk of distortion and the elimination of quenching. The disadvantages are long process times (typically 24-72 h), the need to use special steels containing chromium and/or aluminium, and the formation of the so-called "white layer". This is an outer compound layer with thickness up to 100 μ consisting of ε-$Fe_{2+x}N$ ($0 < x < 1.2$) and γ'-Fe_4N iron nitrides which form on the surface in grains whose size ranges from 10 to 100 μ. The white layer is soft and brittle and must be removed because it spalls easily in service leading to accelerated wear and seizure. The cost of removing the white layer has been estimated to be comparable to the cost of the nitriding treatment itself.

It is possible to limit and even to avoid the formation of ε - and γ'-iron nitrides by controlling the nitrogen potential of the nitriding atmosphere. This is accomplished by diluting the ammonia with hydrogen gas. Unfortunately, full hardening of the surface layers (resulting from a fine dispersion of chromium and/or aluminium nitrides) can only be achieved at nitrogen potentials where the constituents of the white layer are stable as it is illustrated in Fig. 1 [3], [4].

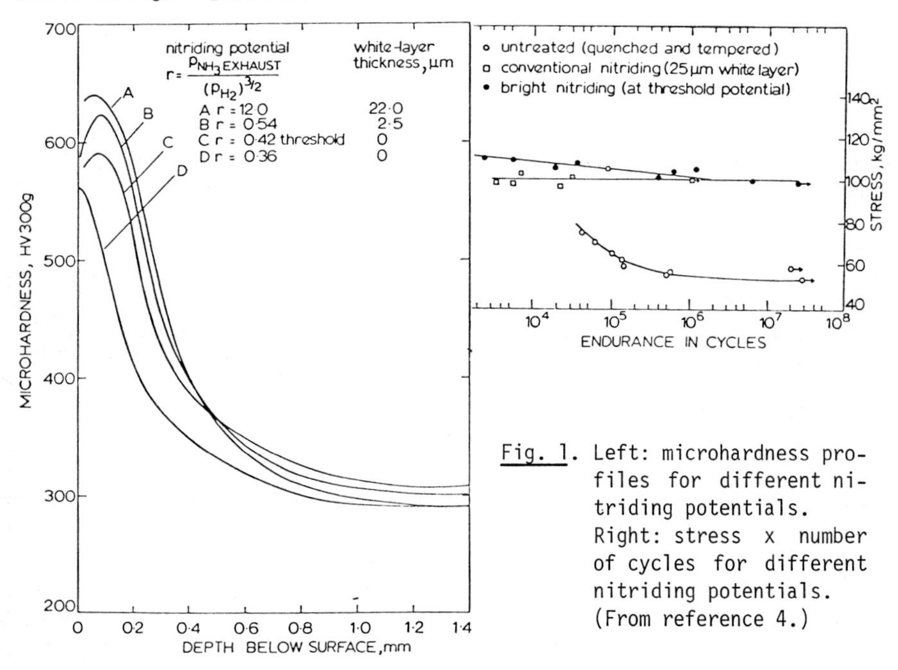

Fig. 1. Left: microhardness profiles for different nitriding potentials. Right: stress x number of cycles for different nitriding potentials. (From reference 4.)

The rate of nitriding of the steel depends on the concentration of the alloying elements (chromium, aluminium...) the ease with which precipitates can nucleate and grow, the nitriding potential of the gas and the temperature at which nitriding is carried out.

In order to overcome the long treatment time inconvenience, short cycle nitriding processes were developed, reducing the treatment times to 4 h in some cases. Short cycle nitriding produces a nitrided case consisting of two regions. The outer ("compound") layer consists primarily of an ε-iron nitride, ε-Fe_3N (thickness around 10 μ) which is hard and wear resistant, and is stable between 6-10% N. As the N content is increased above this range ε-Fe_2N starts to be formed and there is more of a tendency for spalling of the surface layer. That is the reason why compound layer compositions of entirely ε-Fe_3N are generally the aim in short cycle nitriding. The inner ("diffusion") zone consists of nitrogen in solid solution with the matrix and it is responsible for the fatigue crack propagation resistance. The depth of the diffusion zone ranges from 0.2 to 1.0 mm depending upon time, temperature and base material [5].

Ion nitriding is another process developed as an alternative nitriding method, capable of producing a hard nitrided case in a reduced period of time. The basic principle is as follows: if two electrodes of differing potential are placed in a gas at reduced pressure (0.1 to 10 Torr) and an increasing voltage is applied, at a certain minimum voltage (typically 1000 V) a glow is set up around the electrode of lower potential. Ion nitriding is then carried out in the region of abnormal glow discharge where the workpiece to be ion-nitrided is completely covered with glow, and voltage and current increase simultaneously. The temperatures employed are in the same range (500--550 °C) as in ammonia nitriding but the time is considerably reduced. Usually a soft white layer is produced that must also be removed [6],[7].

Finally, in recent years there has been much activity in developing nitrocarburizing processes which set out to produce a compound layer which is not brittle and possesses good wear properties. Nitrocarburizing treatments are not designed specifically for nitriding steel. Indeed their main attraction is that they can be applied to plain carbon and even to mild steels. The fatigue characteristics of the material are also considerably improved, particularly when nitrogen is retained in the "diffusion" zone beneath the compound layer [8].

The result of these nitrocarburizing treatments is the formation of a nitrogen and carbon rich compound layer on the surface of the components. The

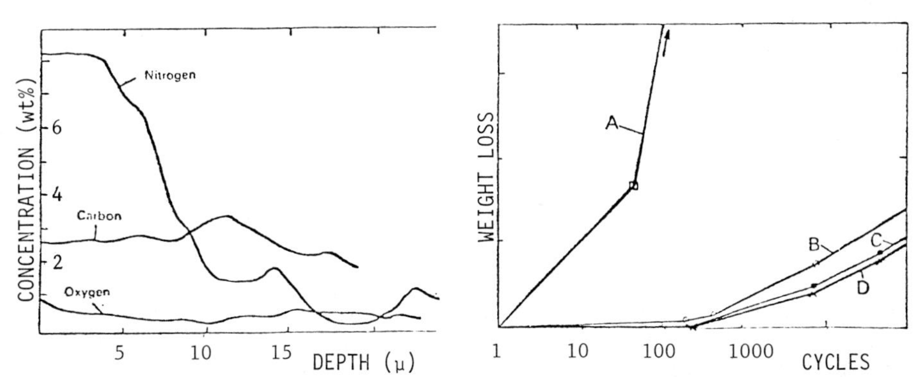

Fig. 2. Left: nitrogen, carbon and oxygen concentrations in the compound layer formed by a three-hour gaseous nitrocarburizing treatment in an ammonia/endothermic gas mixture. Right: modified four ball wear tests on En32 steel. A-untreated, B and C-gaseous nitrocarburizing for three hours atmosphere and oil quenched respectively, D-idem, 8 hours. (From reference 8)

thickness of the layer (typically in the range 8 to 20 μ) depends on the material being treated and on the process time, which is usually less than three hours. Grain sizes range between 3 and 20 μ. The composition of the compound layer can be seen in Fig. 2 below, for a cyanide-bath nitrocarburizing treatment (Tufftride) together with the wear behaviour of untreated and treated steel surfaces.

A systematic study of cyanide nitrocarburizing treatments indicated that the best anti-scuffing properties were obtained when the compound layer consisted mainly of a close-packed hexagonal phase of variable carbon and nitrogen concentration. Examination of the appropriate isothermal section of the Fe-C-N ternary phase diagram indicates that the phase in question is the epsilon carbonitride phase [9]. Provided this epsilon phase is predominant within the compound layer, the presence of small amounts of other phases, particularly Fe_4N and Fe_3C, have no serious adverse effects on the anti--scuffing behaviour [10].

3. Ion Implantation Nitriding

3.1 Surface Characteristics of Steels Implanted with Nitrogen

The beneficial influence of nitrogen ion implantation on several mechanical characteristics of steels has been recognized by the Harwell group in the middle 1970's [11],[12]. These characteristics include stress fatigue life, friction, adhesive, erosive and abrasive wear and other. Laboratory and industry tests have been performed on steels implanted at rather different conditions. Not only the implantation dose and beam energy have been varied (10^{16} to 10^{18} $N^+.cm^{-2}$ and 40 to 400 keV, respectively) but also other parameters like beam current density (2-200 $\mu A.cm^2$), sample temperature (20-500 ^oC) and base pressure at the implantation chamber ($1x10^{-7}$ to $3x10^{-6}$ Torr). All these parameters and the different combinations of them have shown to be determinant on the mechanical performance of the steel surface [13].

Measurements of the concentration (retained dose) as a function of fluence (implanted dose) in low-carbon, tool (medium-carbon) and stainless steels showed that the average concentration of N increases linearly with the fluence up to around $4x10^{17}$ cm^{-2} and then it saturates. The magnitude of the saturation average concentration depends on the alloy composition and it is 40% for implantation into a low-carbon steel at low current density (<10 $\mu A.cm^{-2}$) and low substrate temperature (<100 ^oC) [14],[15].

Depth profiles of the concentration can be significantly different depending on the composition of the steel and on the implantation parameters. The profiles usually peak deeper than the LSS range calculation R_p, being from 1.5 to 5 times this value. In Fig. 3 we give an idea on how the depth profiles depend on the implantation parameters. More complete data can be obtained in Refs. [13] and [14].

In stainless steel most of the implanted nitrogen is found occupying octahedral interstitial sites. The nitrogen atoms are bonded in the nitrided state at all doses between 10^{16} and 10^{18} cm^{-2}. Precipitation has been found to be limited to the region near the peak nitrogen concentration, the pre-

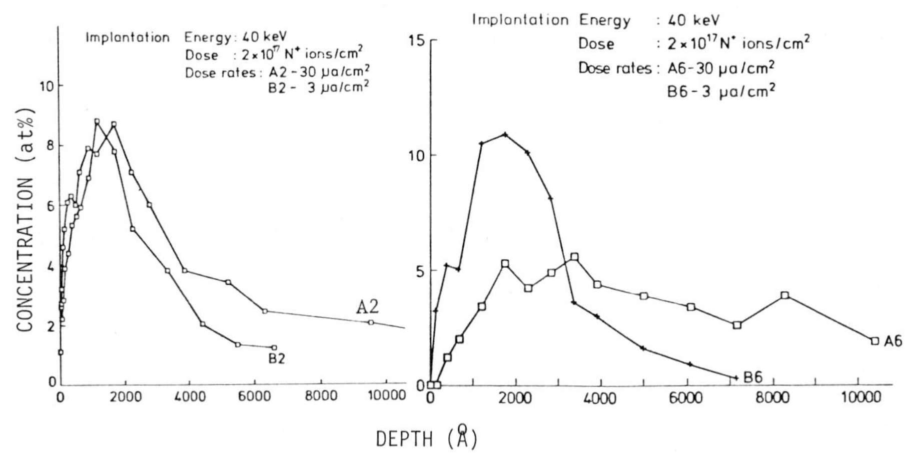

Fig. 3. Profiles of nitrogen implanted into mild steel (left) and stainless steel (right) at different current densities. (From reference 14)

cipitates appearing to be isomorphic to CrN and distributed incoherently with particle sizes between 10-100 Å [16].

Nitrogen implantation into carbon steels was also studied by several authors. Its understanding must take into account the most complex metallurgical situation of these steels. Cementite (Fe_3C) grains existent in the steel previous to ion implantation will be largely dissolved by the N^+ ions bombardment and in some manner reprecipitated. Evidence from transmission electron microscopy support the existence of iron nitride precipitates of particle sizes between 20 and 100 Å as well as nitrogen martensite [17].

Mössbauer spectroscopy studies of nitrogen implanted carbon steels observed not only iron nitrides as Fe_2N, Fe_3N and Fe_4N, but also carbonitride precipitates of various particle sizes. Some general trends are already apparent from these observations: i) nitrogen and carbon-nitrogen martensites are formed in all cases; ii) above a certain implanted dose ($\sim 4\times10^{17}$ cm^{-2}) most of the nitrogen is seen in the ε-Fe_2N phase; iii) the ε-Fe_2N phase formed during implantation is decomposed at rather low temperatures (<200 °C) and the nitrogen can be seen in the ε-$Fe_3(C,N)$ and γ'-Fe_4N phases as well as in solid solution; iv) in pure iron large amounts γ'-Fe_4N are formed during ion implantation, whereas very little is observed in carbon steels and no Fe_4N is seen in high (>10%) chromium steels [18].

3.2 Hardness, Fatigue and Wear Measurements of Nitrogen Implanted Steels

There are very few microhardness measurements on nitrogen implanted steels due to technical difficulties in assessing the hardness of the very shallow implanted layer. Recently some experimental results have been reported. Pethica [19] shows that for stainless steels with a variety of chromium contents, N^+ implantation (4×10^{17} cm^{-2}, 90 keV) produces little or no change on the hardness of mechanically polished surfaces. Newey et al. [20] have measured the microhardness of lapped and electropolished iron specimens implanted with 300 keV N_2^+ molecular ions. There was a large increase in hardness at an implanted dose of 10^{17} cm^{-2}, but at higher doses the effect was considerably reduced.

Fatigue experiments are also not very numerous in N^+ implanted steels. Here, however, the existent results lead to a very elucidative picture in the case of carbon steels. Using a rotating-bend machine Hu et al. [21] measured the fatigue life for samples implanted with $2x10^{17}$ $N^+.cm^{-2}$ and artificially aged at 100 ^0C for 6 h, having observed a large modification on the stress-number of cycles curve, as it is shown in Fig. 4(a). Lo Russo et al. [22] obtained similar results and, in addition, showed that the dose dependence of the fatigue life is as shown in Fig. 4(b), being the maximum number of cycles reached for a dose around 1 to $2x10^{17}$ cm^{-2}.

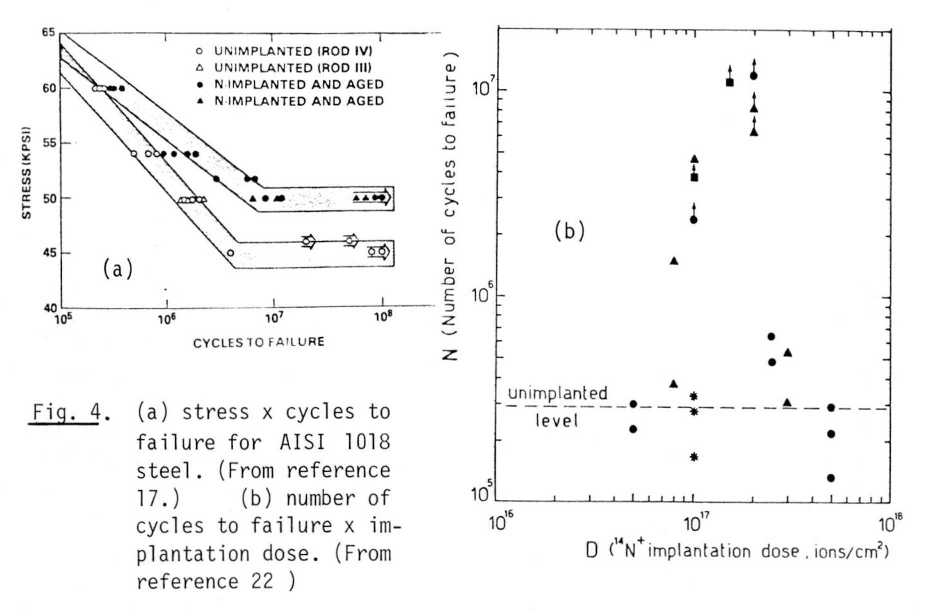

Fig. 4. (a) stress x cycles to failure for AISI 1018 steel. (From reference 17.) (b) number of cycles to failure x implantation dose. (From reference 22)

The wear behaviour has been investigated for many different kinds of steels, implanted in different conditions and also submitted to various tribologic situations. We give here some elucidative examples. Hirvonen [23] reported crossed cylinders wear tests, lubricated, for 416 stainless steel rubbing against 304 stainless steel. The results are summarized in Fig. 5(a). In this case the large reduction in the wear rate is not believed to be merely the result of a nitriding of the alloy skin since the amount of material removed from the rotating member of the tribologic couple is much greater than the penetration depth of the implanted nitrogen ions. The reduction has been atrributed to the mobile-interstitial-implanted nitrogen decorating dislocations produced during the wear, impeding their motion, and producing a hard skin. The persistence of the effect is attributed to the inward migration of the implanted (interstitial) nitrogen atoms under the high pressures and stresses produced during the wear process.

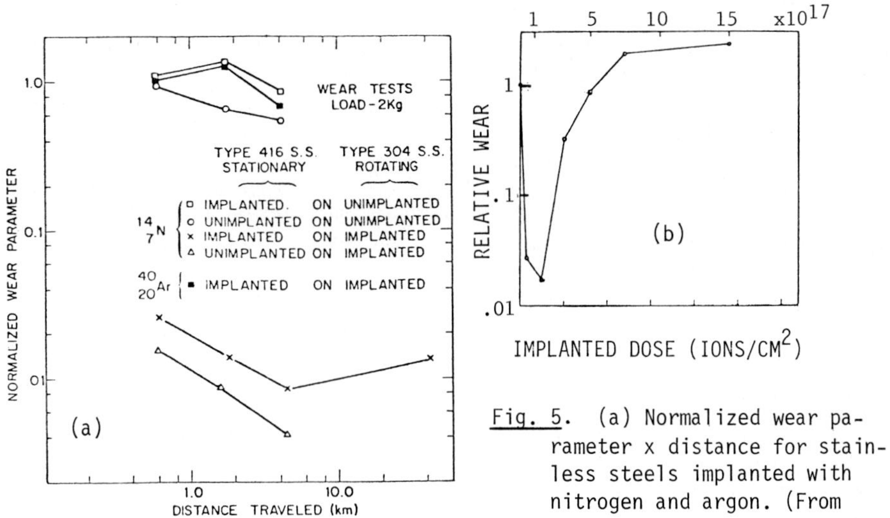

Fig. 5. (a) Normalized wear parameter x distance for stainless steels implanted with nitrogen and argon. (From reference 23.) (b) Relative wear x implanted dose for a 1015-steel implanted with nitrogen. (From reference 15)

Hartley has measured the wear of nitriding steel discs rubbing against stainless steel pins. The discs were implanted with 2.7×10^{17} $N^+.cm^{-2}$ and also with 2×10^{17} $C^+.cm^{-2}$. The results for lubricated tests show a reduction up to a factor of 100 in wear rate [12].

Lo Russo et al. [24] performed dry wear measurements of a carbon steel (Italian standard 38NCD4) like-on-like tests. The wear reduction persisted after removal of some microns of material. This thickness is orders of magnitudes higher than the implanted nitrogen range. To check the nitrogen migration the author used nuclear reactions and observed the presence of 20% of the implanted nitrogen after removing some 5 μ from the worn surface. Lo Russo et al. also showed that the wear reduction has a maximum for doses around 2×10^{17} $N^+.cm^{-2}$. Far below or above this dose the wear rate is the same as in the unimplanted case. Exactly the same implanted-dose dependence was observed by Varjoranta et al. [15] for a low-carbon (1015) steel, as showed in Fig. 5(b) above.

Goode and Baumvol [13] have performed pin-on-disc, like-on-like wear tests on stainless and tool steels implanted with 4×10^{17} $N.cm^{-2}$ having varied the current density and sample temperature. The results show that the wear rate is reduced by a factor of more than 10. In addition it seems to be more advantageous to implant stainless steel at high temperature (300 ^{o}C) in order to obtain long lasting reduction in wear rate which correlates with broad nitrogen distributions. In tool steel, however, the implantation temperature should not exceed 200 ^{o}C in order to prevent excessive out-diffusion of nitrogen from the worn surface region.

Finally we mention the synergistic effect of implanting N^+ into thermally nitrided stainless steel. In this case the wear rate is much lower than for the same steel thermally nitrided only or ion implanted only. It is now also in practical use, with excellent results, to implant nitrogen into certain moulds that have been previously treated by a carbonitriding ("Tufftriding") process [25].

4. Comparison and Conclusions

The above described studies of the mechanical characteristics of steels nitrided by heat treatment and ion implantation methods show that the practical results are, in many aspects, comparable. This is the case, for instance, for the stress fatigue and for the lubricated and dry wear of many different kinds of steels. If we consider that ion implantation confers these properties by treating the steel component in very clean conditions (high vacuum), without any risk of distortion (the treatment is performed at room temperature) and also without altering the dimensions and the surface polishing, we can certainly foresee a place for ion implantation as a method of treating the surface of steels.

Although the economical aspects are beyond the scope of the present work, it is worth remarking that in many cases a high ion current density is acceptable and even desirable (e.g. stainless steel). So, with the development of large current - large area nitrogen implanters, we can bring the treatment time necessary to implant an optimum dose of 1 to 2×10^{17} $N^{+}.cm^{-2}$ down to a few minutes, a fact of major economical importance.

This optimum dose is implanted to a maximum depth of about 1000 Å as compared to nitrided cases of several hundreds of microns formed in conventional nitriding. In surface layers nitrided by ion implantation the matrix structure coexists with nitride (or carbonitride) precipitates and supersaturated solid solution of interstitial nitrogen formed during implantation. There is not a well-defined interface. Essentially the same kind of nitrides are observed, but the plain compound layers with large grains formed in the outer surface by heat treatment methods give place to a very fine dispersion of nitride precipitates in the case of ion implantation. Typical grain sizes are 10-100 Å in ion implantation and 1-100 μ in conventional nitriding. As the hardening, the wear and the fatigue resistance obtained in conventional nitriding are many times attributed to finely dispersed nitrides in the diffusion zone beneath the compound layer, it seems that the ability to form very small precipitates dispersed in the matrix is another important advantage of ion implantation. These small precipitates can be more effective in pinning the dislocations by interacting elastically with them [25].

This is apparently the physical mechanism that underlies the already mentioned synergistic effect of implanting nitrogen into the surface layers of steels that were previously nitrided by conventional methods. Nitrogen ion bombardment leads to the formation of dispersed nitrides, at the same time as it transforms the large grains of nitrides of the compound layer formed by conventional methods in finely dispersed precipitates. So, in practical terms, nitrogen implantation is rendering the compound ("white") layer hard and wear resistant. Undoubtedly this is a most desirable and economically convenient finishing technology.

The present state of laboratory investigations shows that ion implantation nitriding is effective in carbon as well as in alloy steels. In particular our observations on low carbon steel indicate that nitrogen implantation forms ε-carbonitride precipitates, the kind of compound that plays such an important role on the improvement of the mechanical properties of steels when they are submitted to salt bath or gaseous carbonitriding. The amount of ε carbonitrides in the surface layers can be largely enhanced by simultaneous implantation of nitrogen and carbon. This aspect is now under investigation in our laboratory, where we are using a mixture of N_2 and CH_4 as the gas to be ionized in the ion source and accelerated into the target without mass analysis.

Another comparative study which should be encouraged is the lasting of the augmented wear resistance of steels nitrided by ion implantation and heat treatment. The model, originally proposed by the Harwell group, that nitrogen migrates during wear appears to be consistent with the experimental observations. However, it is necessary to quantify for how long this migration can be effective and how it compares with conventional nitriding performances.

To summarize our conclusions we say that large area - large current ion implantation machines can be competitively used as steel nitriding and carbonitriding facilities. Also the use of nitrogen implantation as a finishing step on the nitriding process performed under gaseous or salt bath heat treatments appears to be physically plausible and practically promising.

The development of adequate implantation equipment can make the costs accessible to a large number of applications. It is however necessary to connect these developments with further experimental work on the following still open questions:

i) optimum dose and optimum implantation parameters for each application and steel composition;

ii) optimum atomic species or combination of species that must be implanted in each application and steel composition;

iii) systematic study of synergistic effects of nitrogen implantation into conventionally treated cases;

iv) new mechanical properties that are also affected by nitrogen ion implantation.

References

1 G.Dearnaley and P.D.Goode, Nucl. Inst. Methods 189, 117 (1981)

2 B.J. Lightfoot and D.H. Jack: Heat Treatment'73, The Metals Society, London (1973), p. 248

3 D.B. Clayton and K. Sachs: Heat Treatment'76, The Metals Society, London (1976), p. 242

4 T. Bell, B.J. Birch, V. Korotchenko and S.P. Evans: Heat Treatment'73, The Metals Society, London (1973), p. 72

5 J.A. Riopelle: AFS Transactions, 83, 283 (1975)

6 M. Hudis: J. Appl. Phys. 44, 1489 (1973)

7 P.C. Jindal: J. Vac. Sci. Technol. 15, 313 (1978)

8 T. Bell: Heat Treatment of Metals 1975, The Metals Soc., London (1975) p. 39

9 K.H. Jack: Proceed. Roy. Soc. 195, 41 (1948)
10 E.Mitchell and C. Dawes: Metal Treatment and Drop Forging 31, 3 (1964)
11 N.E.W. Hartley, G. Dearnaley: J.F. Turner and J. Saunders: In Application of Ion Beams to Metals, Plenum Press, New York (1974), p. 123
12 N.E.W. Hartley: Thin Solid Films 64, 177 (1979)
13 P.D. Goode and I.J.R. Baumvol: Nucl. Instr. Meth. 189, 161 (1981)
14 G. Dearnaley, P.D. Goode: N.E.W. Hartley, G.W. Proctor, J.F. Turner and R.B.J. Watkins: In Ion Plating and Allied Techniques - 1979, Edinburgh (1979), p. 243
15 T. Varjoranta, J. Hirvonen and A. Anttila: Thin Sol. Films 75, 241 (1981)
16 M. Baron and R. Kossowsky, Nucl. Inst. Methods 182/183, 531 (1981)
17 H. Hermann: Nucl. Instr. Methods 182/183, 887 (1981)
18 C.A.dos Santos, B.A.S.de Barros,Jr., J.P.de Souza and I.J.R. Baumvol: Appl. Phys. Lett. 41, 237 (1982)
19 J.B. Pethica, Proceeding of the 3rd International Conference on Modifications of Surfaces Properties of Metals by Ion Implantation, Manchester (1981), p. 147
20 N. Dewey, H.M. Pollock and M.A. Wilkins, Idem p. 157
21 W. Hu, C.R. Clayton, H. Hermann and J.K. Hirvonen: Scrip. Mettal. 12, 697 (1978)
22 S.Lo Russo, P. Mazzoldi, I. Scotoni, C. Torello and S. Tosto: Appl. Phys. Lett. 36, 822 (1980)
23 J.K. Hirvonen: J. Vac. Sci. Technol. 15, 1662 (1978)
24 S.Lo Russo, P. Mazzoldi, I. Scotoni, C. Torello and S. Tosto: Appl. Phys. Lett. 34, 627 (1979)
25 G. Dearnaley: Private Communication.

Effect of Ion Mixing on the Wear Behaviour of Silver

L. Calliari[1], L. Guzman[1], S. Lo Russo[2], C. Tosello[1], G. Wolf[3], and G. Zobele[1]

Abstract

The effect of argon ion implantation on the mixing processes of the metal system Ag-Ni has been investigated. Silver electrodeposited copper bars, successively coated with a thin film of nickel evaporated under vacuum, were implanted with 100 keV argon ions at different doses and dose rates in order to obtain efficient Ag-Ni mixing. The effect of such surface treatment on the dry sliding wear behaviour of the metal system against ertalon has been tested.

Ion implantation on the bars induces surface modifications and mixing processes which can influence the wear behaviour. The results are discussed in the light of the information obtained by Rutherford backscattering (R.B.S.) and Auger electron spectroscopy (A.E.S.).

1. Introduction

Ion implantation provides a very general means of altering the surface behaviour of materials, but it is often difficult to obtain suitable ion beams of the elements which are useful to improve the surface properties. As an alternative treatment one may employ the ion mixing technique, which consists in ion bombarding - with an easily obtained gaseous beam - a thin coating of the appropriate material deposited on the substrate and allowing it to diffuse into the matrix [1,2].

It is well known that ion irradiation can give rise to atomic mixing even for systems where thermal alloying is not possible for any composition. A striking example are Ag and Ni which are almost immiscible also in the liquid state. The maximum equilibrium solid solubility is $\sim$ 0.1 at % Ni in Ag near 960°C and $\sim$ 2 at % Ag in Ni near 1435° C [3]. An extension of the solid solubilities up to 4.5 at % Ni in Ag and 16 at % Ag in Ni has been achieved by Tsaur and Mayer [4] bombarding a multilayer configuration with Xe ions at temperatures from -190°C to 250°C.

[1] Istituto per la Ricerca Scientifica e Tecnologica, I-38050 Povo (Trento), Italy

[2] Unità GNSM-CNR dell'Istituto di Fisica dell'Università di Padova, I-35100 Padova, Italy

[3] Facoltà di Scienze, Università di Trneto, I-38100 Trento, Italy

In the present paper we discuss some preliminary results obtained on the same Ag-Ni system by bombarding with Ar ions at two different dose rates a bilayer configuration consisting of a thin Ni film deposited on a Ag substrate.

This configuration was chosen in order to study the effect of ion mixing on the silver wear behaviour. With respect to this, one may take advantage of ion mixing processes to obtain silver hardening by at least three different mechanisms : (a) solid solution between Ag and Ni; (b) crystal grain refining, considering that two solid solutions, one silver-rich and the other nickel-rich, should be formed, and finally, if (a) and (b) were not efficient enough, (c) precipitation hardening by successive nickel segregation.

2. Experimental

2.1. Surface treatment

Silver electrodeposited copper bars, 50x5x5 mm^3 sized, were successively coated on two opposite faces with a thin nickel film (10 - 20 nm) by using an Edwards E206 evaporator. The base pressure was about 10^{-4} Pa. A calibrated quartz oscillator was used to monitor the deposited thickness. The deposition rate was of the order of 0.1 nm/s.

The implants were carried out in Trento with a 120 keV accelerator provided with an Ortec Duo-Plasmatron ion source suitable for high currents. The specimens, put in a vacuum chamber at 10^{-4} Pa, were implanted with 100 keV argon ions at nominal doses up to $7 \cdot 10^{16}$ Ar^+/cm^2, reproducible within 10%, and at current densities of 10 and 70 $\mu A/cm^2$. The specimens were polarized (+300V) to suppress secondary electron emission. The incident beam impinged over an area of 50x2 mm^2 and the specimen was moved back and forth under the beam with a velocity of 0.1 mm/s.

The sample temperature during implantation, which is dose-rate dependent, was measured in a dummy bar by a thermocouple.

2.2. Surface Microanalysis

Two different techniques have been used to characterize the near surface region of the implanted specimens. The first one was A.E.S. (Auger Electron Spectroscopy) combined with ion sputter etching. The measurements were performed with a Phys. El. Ind. model 590 S.A.M. (Scanning Auger Microprobe) at I.R.S.T. Laboratories in Trento.The second technique was Rutherford backscattering of 1.8 MeV helium ions performed at Laboratori Nazionali di Legnaro (I.N.F.N.). The backscattered ions were detected by a surface barrier solid state detector positioned at 160°C and a multichannel analyzer provided their energy spectrum. The information obtained by R.B.S. must be taken as an average over an area of approx. 1 mm^2 of analyzed surface, whereas the A.E.S. analyzed region was of the order of 1 μm^2.

2.3. Wear tests

Wear tests have been carried out with a reciprocal motion tribotester according to the scheme inserted in Fig. 3. The sliders were ertalon blocks of 10 x 5 x 3

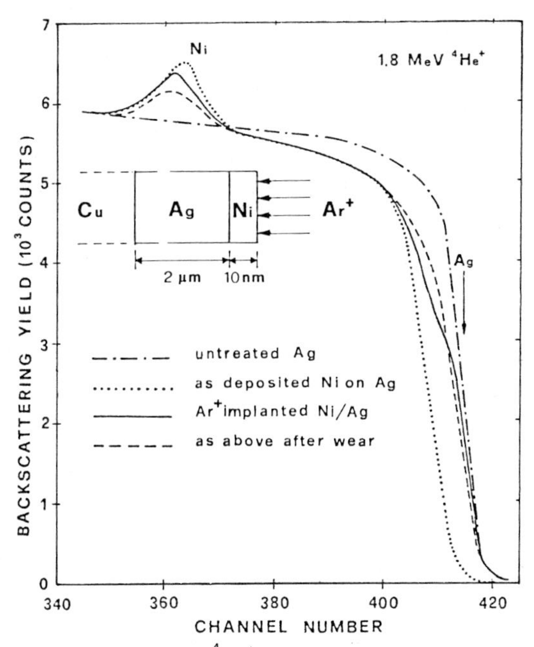

Fig. 1. 1.8 MeV $^4He^+$ RBS spectra of silver subjected to different surface treatments. The implantation conditions were : 100 keV Ar^+; 5.10^{16} ions/cm^2; 70 µA/cm^2.

mm^3. The choice of this material was made in order to obtain an optimal slider bar hardness ratio considering previous results [5] and the small thickness (2 µm) of the silver layer.

Total lowering of the arm, due to the wear, was continuously measured by a displacement transducer (10 mV/µm) put in front of the moving arm. Wear experiments were performed up to 80.000 cycles under 21 N load at a frequency of about 200 cycles/minute. The final weight loss of bars and sliders was evaluated by a Mettler balance (10^{-5} g of sensitivity).

3. Results

Figure 1 shows a comparison of the RBS spectra corresponding to different surface treatments of a silver electrodeposited copper bar. The spectra were taken over an area of 1 mm^2 in four different zones of the same bar, which correspond respectively to the following surface situations : untreated 2µm thick electrodeposited Ag; 10 nm thick Ni layer evaporated on Ag; the same situation after 100 keV Ar^+ bombardment at 5.10^{16} ions/cm^2 with the higher current density, 70 µA/cm^2, (the thermally isolated bars so irradiated reached during implantation the temperature of about 350 °C and will be called "hot" implanted in the present work); finally the implanted surface after the wear test against ertalon with a 21 N load and after 80.000 cycles.

The most interesting qualitative information resulting from the RBS spectra is provided by the evident Ag edge modification induced by the Ar^+implanta -

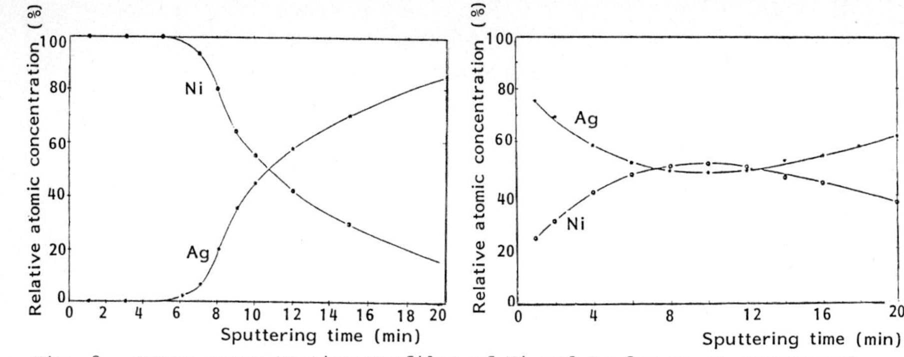

Fig. 2. Auger concentration profiles of Ni and Ag for an as-evaporated Ni-on-Ag sample (a) and for the same sample after Ar^+ bombardment (b). Irradiation conditions are reported in Fig.1

tion : this is striking evidence that Ag reemerges to the surface as a consequence of Ar^+ bombardment, resulting in the formation of a mixed zone of Ni and Ag. Preliminary and not yet satisfactory spectrum computer simulations indicate approximately a $Ag_{60}Ni_{40}$ composition.

From the analysis of the RBS spectra, by using the Harwell Bi^+ implanted Si as reference standard, we can obtain also some quantitative information : (i) the amount of evaporated nickel, 8.10^{16} Ni/cm^2, corresponds to a thickness of about 90 Å by assuming for the thin layer the Ni bulk density; (ii) the amount of sputtered Ni atoms by the Ar ions, $\sim 2.10^{16}$ Ni/cm^2, leads to a sputtering yield lower of an order of magnitude with respect to literature data [6] for pure Ni, this result is compatible with the formation of an Ag-rich surface;(iii) the amount of Ni atoms taken away by the wear process,$\sim 2 \cdot 10^{16}$ Ni/cm^2, is very low; this result is consistent with the very low weight loss of the "mixed" bar measured at the end of the wear test, as reported in Fig. 4, which will be discussed later.

To obtain complementary information on the mixing process occurring in the near surface region, also Auger spectroscopy has been employed.

Figure 2 shows the Auger concentration profiles of Ni and Ag for the "as evaporated" (a) and the "hot implanted" (b) samples. Before profiling, the samples were sputtered for 1 minute, the sputtering rate being about 1 nm/min, in order to eliminate surface contaminants as C and O. In evaluating these Auger profiles, the presence of implanted argon and the minor contributions of carbon and oxygen were not taken into account; only the Ag and the Ni signals were considered. The relative atomic concentrations of Ni and Ag were then calculated using the elemental sensitivity factors method and plotted as a function of the sputter time, which is proportional to the depth below the surface.

By comparing the profiles relative to the two different situations of Fig. 2 a and 2 b, one can clearly see the occurrence of mixing processes as a consequence of ion implantation. Fig. 2a shows indeed a Ni coating on a Ag substrate with a broadening of the interface, which is mainly due to artifacts associated with sputter depth profiling [7]. On the other hand Fig. 2b shows the presence of a large amount of Ag at the surface as a consequence of the Ni coating in-diffusion induced by the 100 keV Ar^+ bombardment. In Fig. 2b we can also see that the composition of the mixed zone is not constant as a function of depth.

The large difference between the profiles of implanted and unimplanted samples gives in any case striking evidence of the ion-induced mixing between Ni and Ag, in good agreement with the information provided by RBS analysis.

From the surface characterization we may expect rather different wear behaviour between unimplanted and ion-mixed bars. Figure 3 shows the wear curves relative to the couple ertalon slider-metallic bar for different surface treatments of the bars : (a) untreated Ag; (b) Ni coated Ag and (c) ion-mixed Ni-Ag surface. We can observe that the Ni coating alone (b) leads to the highest wear for the couple. Ar^+ implantation on the Ni coated bars (c',c'') reduces the wear approximately by a factor 2 with respect to (b) even though the amount of wear remains slightly higher with respect to the couple ertalon-untreated Ag (a',a'').

However we must outline that the arm displacement recorded by the transduced signal is representative of the total wear of both bar and slider. To have infor-

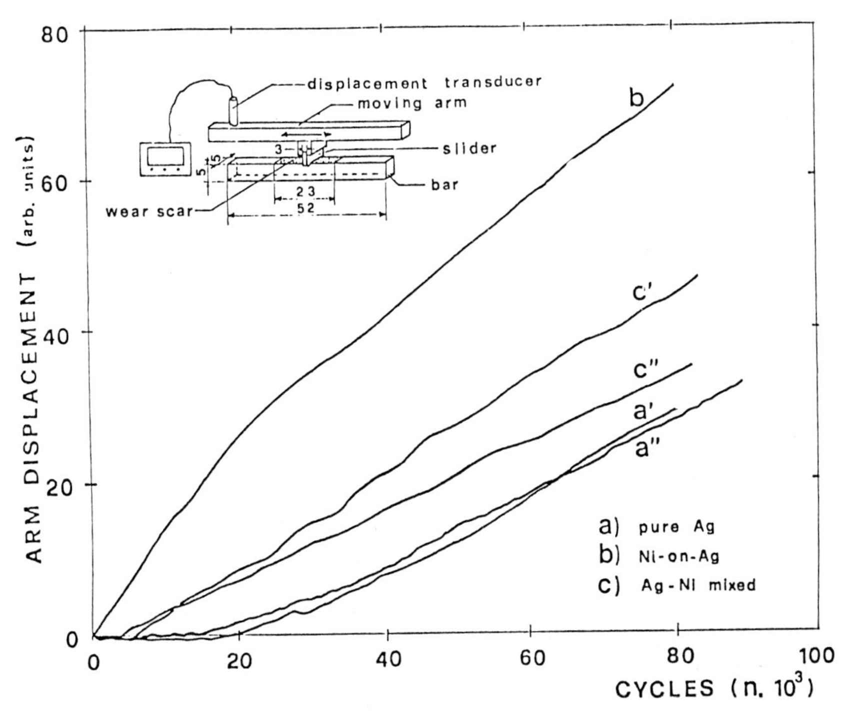

Fig. 3. Couple wear curves for ertalon sliding against : (a) electrodeposited Ag; (b) 10 nm coating Ni on Ag; (c) Ag-Ni mix as a consequence of Ar^+ implantation. A scheme of the wear tester is also reported

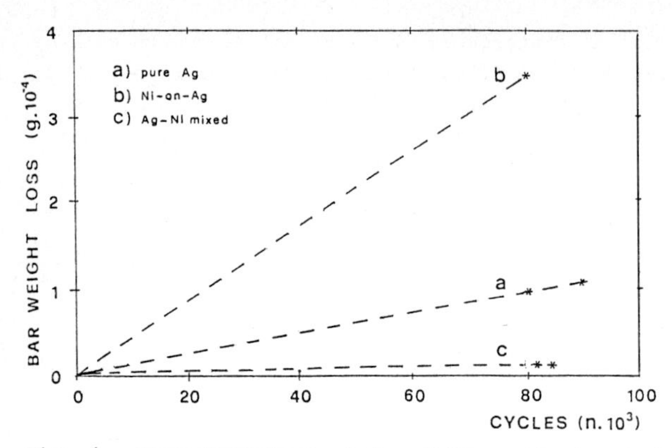

Fig. 4. Wear behaviour of the differently treated bars, as estimated from weight loss measurements at the end of the wear tests of Fig. 3

mation about the wear behaviour of the metallic bar we have performed weight loss measurements at the end of the wear tests to separate the contributions of bar and slider. These weight loss measurements have shown that in the case of ion-mixed bars practically there is no material loss, the total wear occurring at the expenses of the ertalon slider.

From these weight loss data we put in evidence in Fig. 4 the improvement obtained in the wear behaviour of the ion-mixed bars with respect to both Ni coated Ag and pure Ag. The very low weight loss of the ion-mixed bars is confirmed by the low amount of Ni atoms worn away, 2.10^{16} Ni/cm^2, as measured by R.B.S. and discussed before.

4. Discussion and Conclusions

A remarkable surface modification induced by Ar^+ bombardment of a thin nickel coating on a silver substrate has been found independently by two different microanalysis techniques : R.B.S. and A.E.S., both showing clear experimental evidence of the formation of a "mixed" layer of Ni and Ag.

Using R.B.S. or A.E.S. we are only able to determine the composition of the modified surface layer; to establish whether an interatomic mixing has occurred, resulting in the formation of new phases, other techniques like X-rays or electron-diffraction should be applied.

The results presented in this work have been obtained at a dose of 5.10^{16} Ar^+/cm^2 with a high current density, 70 μA/cm^2, leading to a temperature of ∿ 350°C during implantation. This hot implantation induces an indiffusion of the Ni coating into the Ag substrate in such a way that Ag comes to the surface, resulting in the formation of Ag-Ni alloys whose compositions range from Ag_{80} Ni_{20} to Ag_{50} Ni_{50}. However, we cannot exclude that the mixed zone is a two-phase mixture of two solid solutions, as found by Tsaur and Mayer [4] , or even Ag and Ni precipitates in the submicrometer range.

In terms of the current ion-mixing theories, it is difficult to establish to which mechanism is due the very large interdiffusion between Ag and Ni induced by the "hot" implantation. In addition to recoil implantation or cascade mixing, which are always present, it may be attributed also to temperature dependent radiation enhanced diffusion effects, as suggested recently by Dearnaley [8] and Marwick and Piller [9] .

The role of temperature as an important parameter to achieve an efficient Ag-Ni mixing is suggested by the results obtained on samples implanted at low dose rate : only a limited ion mixing was indeed observed for different doses by using a dose rate of 10 $\mu A/cm^2$, leading to a temperature slightly higher than room temperature. In all these cases the Ag surface concentration never exceeded 10% after the implantation.

With regard to the wear behaviour of the examined metal systems, we outline that electrodeposited Ag is already a wear resistant material currently used for electrotechnical applications. It is therefore difficult to improve further its wear behaviour. Following this objective we have verified that a superimposed Ni coating has a detrimental effect probably due to Ni wear debris acting in an abrasive way. On the contrary, the ion-induced mixing between Ag and Ni seems to result in a protective layer , free from interface problems, more wear resistant than electrodeposited silver.

The mechanism by which this wear behaviour improvement takes place, probably related to Ag hardening effects induced by ion mixing, should be clarified with further investigations.

Acknowledgements

The authors are indebted to Prof.F.Ferrari and Prof. I.Scotoni for encouragement and would like to acknowledge useful discussions with their colleagues as well as valid help from the technical staff at I.R.S.T.

References

1. G.Dearnaley, P.D.Goode, in Proc. of 3rd Intnal Conf. on Ion Implantation Equipment and Techniques - 1980, Nucl.Instr. and Methods, *189*, 126 (1981)
2. B.Y.Tsaur, S.S.Lau, L.S.Hung, J.W.Mayer, in Proc. of 2nd Intnal. Conf. on Ion Beam Modification of Materials - 1980, Nucl.Instr. and Methods, *182/183*,67 (1981)
3. M.Hansen, *Constitution of Binary Alloys* (Mc Graw-Hill, New York, 1958) p. 36
4. B.Y.Tsaur, J.W. Mayer, Appl . Phys. Lett. *37*, 389 (1980)
5. S.Lo Russo, G.Wolf, "*The dry wear of some steels of different hardness*", to be published.
6. H.H.Andersen, H.L.Bay, in "*Sputtering by Particle Bombardment I*", Ed. by R. Behrisch (Springer, Berlin, 1981) p. 175
7. S.Hofman, Surf. and Interf. Analysis *2*, 148 (1980)
8. G.Dearnaley, "*Bombardment Diffused Coatings and Ion Beam Mixing*", Harwell Report AERE-R10180, June 1981
9. A.D. Marwick, R.C.Piller, Nucl.Instr. and Methods, *182/183*, 121 (1981).

Methods to Control Target Heating During Ion Implantation

K.S. Grabowski and R.A. Kant

Naval Research Laboratory, Code 6671, Washington, DC 20375, USA

1. Introduction

The use of high-current ion implanters with beam powers in excess of 1kW requires improved methods of target cooling. This problem has already been addressed for ion implantation of Si wafers [1-3], but cooling of metallic targets needs further development. Compared to Si wafers, metallic targets typically have more awkward geometries, thicker cross sections, lower thermal conductivities, and in some cases (e.g., certain heat-treated steels) comparable temperature limitations during implantation ($T \lesssim 200^{\circ}C$). In addition, since metallic targets typically require higher implantation doses than Si wafers, use of high-current implanters is highly desirable. Heat conduction to a sink will generally be necessary for cooling of metallic targets.

This paper casts well-known mathematical solutions [4] to heat conduction problems in terms of ion-implantation parameters, and discusses the different regimes of conduction cooling. Examples illustrate that for most applications: (1) scanning of the ion beam and/or targets is necessary, (2) storing energy in target heat capacity is insufficient to limit target temperature rise, and (3) producing good sample contact with a heat sink is essential. Methods of producing adequate contacts are discussed, based on experimental measurements of the interface contact conductance, h, for various combinations of materials. Finally, as an example of successful target cooling by conduction techniques, the device used at the Naval Research Laboratory to cool tool-steel bearing races is briefly described.

2. Radiation Cooling

Radiation cooling of the target is only sufficient for those applications where a high equilibrium temperature or large radiating surface area is acceptable. As Fig.1 shows, to limit surface temperature to $500^{\circ}C$ for a rather typical effective total emissivity of 0.2 and an input power of 1kW, 0.25 m^2 of radiating surface area is needed. For lower temperatures, higher incident power densities, or lower effective emissivities, radiative heat transfer is clearly inadequate.

3. Conduction Cooling

The time-dependent temperature rise of a surface struck by a constant heat flux can be readily solved for the case of one-dimensional heat transfer [4]. Solutions expressed in dimensionless units are shown in Fig.2 for

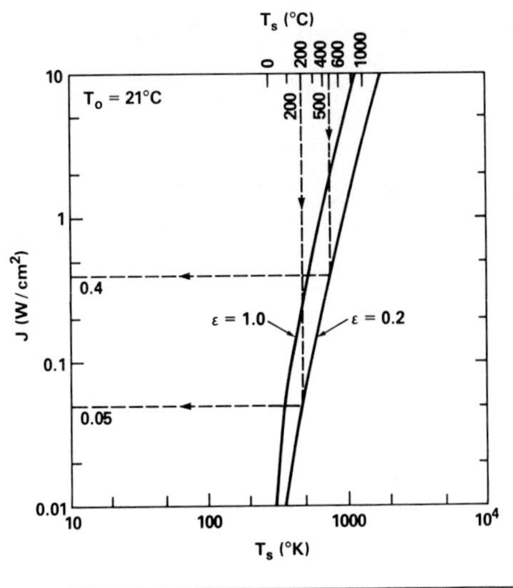

Fig.1. Power radiated per unit surface area as a function of surface temperature and effective total emissivity, ε, for surroundings at 21°C. Strictly, ε should include the influence of viewfactors and the emissivity of surrounding material

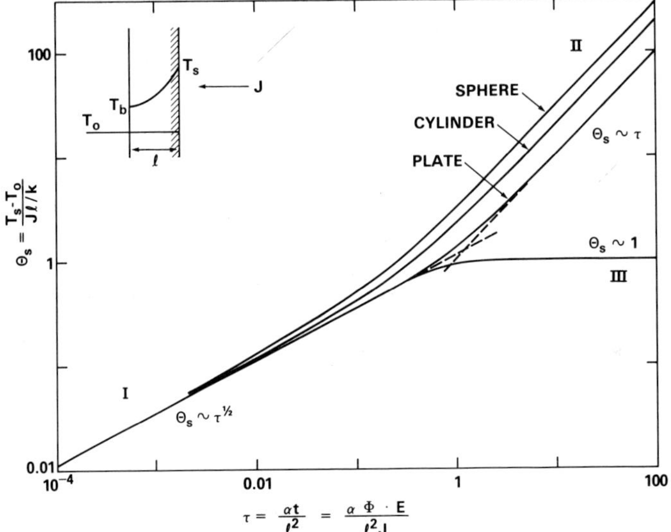

Fig.2. Dimensionless surface temperature rise, Θ_S, versus dimensionless time (or dose) τ, for incident power density J, assuming one-dimensional heat transfer. ℓ represents plate thickness, or cylinder or sphere radius; k, thermal conductivity; α, thermal diffusivity; ϕ, ion dose; and E, ion energy. Heat is withdrawn from the target in region III by a heat sink

plate, cylinder, and sphere geometries where Θ_S represents dimensionless surface temperature and τ represents dimensionless time (or implantation dose). As indicated in the figure inset: T_S represents the surface temperature, T_0 the initial temperature, and T_b the temperature either at the back of a plate of thickness ℓ or at the center of a sphere or cylinder of radius ℓ. J is the incident power density (W/cm^2). Other important variables include: k, thermal conductivity (W/(cm-K)); α, thermal diffusivity (cm^2/s) equal to $k/(\rho C)$ where ρ is density (g/cm^3) and C is heat capacity (Ws/(g-K)); and t, duration of exposure (s) equal to $\phi E/J$ where ϕ is implantation fluence ($ions/cm^2$) and E is ion energy (Ws/ion). Nominal values of α, k, and ρC for selected materials are listed in Table I as taken from [5]. Actual values depend strongly on exact alloy composition and specific heat treatment.

Table 1. Thermal Properties of Selected Materials

Material	α (cm^2/s)	k (W/(cmK))	ρC ($Ws/(cm^3K)$)
Cu	1.1	3.9	3.4
Al	0.95	2.3	2.4
Al (2024-T4)	0.50	1.2	2.4
Si	0.53	0.84	1.6
Brass (Cu - 30Zn)	0.38	1.2	3.2
Ta	0.24	0.54	2.3
Fe	0.23	0.80	3.5
Fe (0.10C)	0.18	0.65	3.5
Fe (M2 tool steel)	0.058	0.21	3.7
Fe (304 SS)	0.041	0.16	4.0
Ti	0.068	0.16	2.3
Ti (6Al - 4V)	0.026	0.068	2.6
Superalloy (IN 738)	0.035	0.12	3.4

Three different regimes of conduction heat transfer are indicated in Fig.2. In regions I and II all deposited heat is retained in the sample, whereas in region III a steady-state condition obtains where heat flow is constant through a plate sample to a heat sink. In region I the deposited energy has not yet diffused to the boundary of the sample (i.e., $\alpha t < \ell^2$ and $T_b = T_o$), so the surface temperature rise is that for heat diffusion in a semi-infinite medium and $\theta_s \propto \tau^{1/2}$. In region II most of the deposited energy is distributed throughout the sample (i.e., $\alpha t > \ell^2$, $T_b \simeq T_s$), so the temperature rise is limited by the heat capacity of the sample and $\theta_s \propto \tau$. In region III, for an ideal heat sink (i.e., $T_b = T_o$) $\theta_s = 1$, otherwise θ_s is constant but greater than 1.

The transition from region I to either II or III occurs quite sharply at $\tau \simeq 1$ for plate samples but more gradually for cylinder or sphere samples. The implantation conditions which produce $\tau = 1$ are identified in Fig.3. Examination of this figure reveals that for most metals implantations, τ exceeds 1. For a typical energy and fluence (100-keV ions, $1\times10^{17}/cm^2$), a nominally maximum power density (1-kW beam into 10 cm^2) and even a poorly conducting metal (Ti-6Al-4V, $\alpha = 0.026$ cm^2/s), τ will exceed 1 unless samples thicker than 0.5 cm are implanted. Use of thicker samples, highly focused unscanned beams, or low fluences are required to prevent τ from exceeding 1.

3.1 Region I (Heat-Diffusion Limited)

While this region is applicable for low doses of implantation, it is most relevant to cases of thick samples with low thermal diffusivity and/or for implantations conducted with high-current unscanned beams (see Fig.3). In these cases, large temperature increases may occur. In the low-dose limit, the temperature rise in region I can be expressed as:

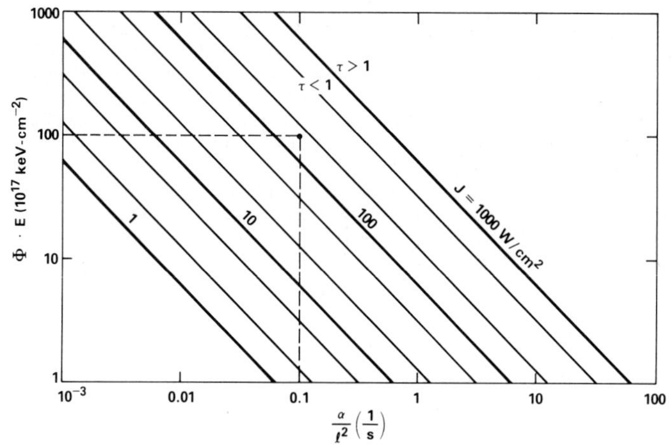

Fig.3. Ion implantation conditions for which $\tau=1$, with $\tau<1$ occurring below a given power-density line and $\tau>1$ above it

$$\theta_s = \frac{2}{\sqrt{\pi}} \tau^{\frac{1}{2}}, \quad \text{or} \tag{1}$$

$$T_s - T_o = \frac{2}{\sqrt{\pi}} \frac{(\phi E)^{\frac{1}{2}}}{\rho C} \left(\frac{J}{\alpha}\right)^{\frac{1}{2}} \tag{2}$$

Since for ion implantation into most metals ϕ, E and ρC are nearly invariant, the ratio of power density input to heat diffusion output determines the target temperature rise.

As an example, the implantation of 100-keV ions to a dose of 1×10^{17} cm^{-2} into 1-cm-thick plate of 0.1-%-C steel using an unscanned high-current beam (i.e., $J \gtrsim 300$ W/cm^2) maintains τ less than 1 and Eq.(2) predicts $T_s - T_o \gtrsim 530^oC$. To limit the temperature rise of this sample, the average incident power density must be reduced. Scanning the beam at an adequate rate can accomplish this.

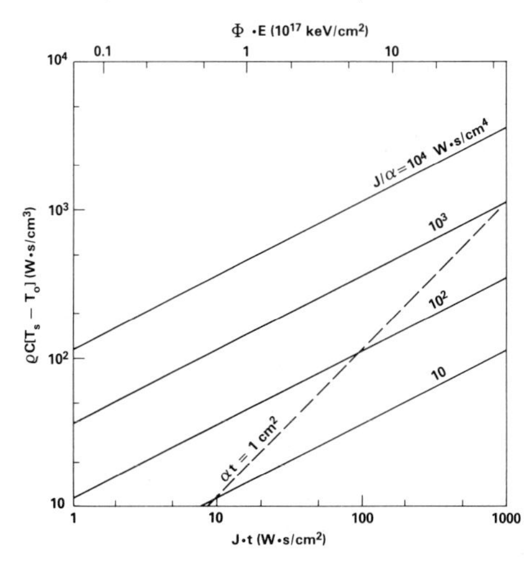

Fig.4. Pseudo-temperature rise, $\rho C(T_s - T_o)$, as a function of both abosorbed energy Jt (or ϕ E), and the ratio J/α. This figure is only valid when $\tau<1$, or to the left of the dashed line for a 1-cm-thick plate target. Dashed line for other target thicknesses can be drawn through other constant values of αt

Figure 4 graphically represents the square root dependence of (T_s-T_o) in Eq.(2) on both J/α and Jt (or ϕE). This figure can be used to determine the minimum necessary scan speed. Using the previous example; to limit the steel-plate temperature increase to 100^oC ($\rho C (T_s-T_o)$ = 350 Ws/cm^3) on a single pass of a 300 W/cm^2 ion beam (J/α = 1670 Ws/cm^4) the beam dwell time on a given spot must be less than 200 ms (Jt < 60 Ws/cm^2). For a 1.5-cm-wide beam this translates into a minimum scan speed of 7.5 cm/s or about 7 rpm for the edge of a rotating 20-cm-diameter disk. At this moderate scan rate, approximately 27 passes will be needed to complete the implantation, and input heat should be able to diffuse to a suitable heat sink between passes.

3.2 Region II (Heat-Capacity Limited)

This region applies to samples which are thermally isolated and for which $\tau > 1$. In the high dose-limit:

$$\theta_s = n\tau, \text{ or} \tag{3}$$

$$T_s - T_o = n \frac{\phi E}{\rho C \ell} . \tag{4}$$

The variables are the same used in Fig.2 except for the additional coefficient n, which equals 1, 2, or 3 for plate, cylinder, or sphere geometries, respectively. As before, ℓ represents either plate thickness, or cylinder or sphere radius.

For most implantation doses and typical target sizes, heat capacity alone is insufficient to cool the target. As a representative example, implantation of 100-keV ions to 1×10^{17} cm^{-2} into 0.1-%-C steel will produce a uniform temperature rise of about 460^oC in targets consisting of a 1-cm-thick plate, a 4-cm-diameter cylinder, or a 6-cm-diameter sphere. As this is a large temperature rise in these substantially sized samples it is clear that storage of implantation heat energy within many targets will not be acceptable. Heat storage could be augmented by attaching a small target to a massive heat sink, however, the heat sink would have to be cooled between subsequent implantations and heat diffusion throughout the large size would be limited.

3.3 Region III (Steady-State Conduction to Heat Sink)

The best method to limit target temperature rise is to secure the target to a good heat sink. For a plate target attached to an ideal heat sink $T_b=T_o$, so

$$T_s - T_o = \frac{J\ell}{k} . \tag{5}$$

Taking a 1-cm-thick plate of 0.1%-C steel as a representative implantation target, its temperature increase will exceed 200^oC only for incident power densities in excess of 130 W/cm^2. In other words, for a 1-kW ion beam scanned moderately well, an ideal heat sink would cool most targets adequately.

Unfortunately, ideal heat sinks cannot readily be attained in vacuum. In practice there are temperature drops across heat-conducting interfaces. These temperature drops can be expressed by

$$\Delta T = \frac{J}{h} , \tag{6}$$

where h (W/(cm^{2}K)) represents the interface contact conductance for contacting solids. Using h≈0.05 W/(cm^{2}K) as representative of steel contacting steel in vacuum, one readily finds that a heat flux of only 5 W/cm^2 will produce a 100°C temperature drop across the interface. Poor contact conductance is by far the greatest limitation to high incident power densities yet discussed.

Use of low incident power densities can help, but is not always practical. For example, to implant the inside groove of an outer race of a bearing (e.g., for corrosion resistance), only 1 or 2 bearings at a time can easily be implanted. For two 6-cm-diameter bearings with 1-cm-wide grooves, this means that only about 40 cm^2 are exposed to the beam, for an average incident power density of 25 W/cm^2 for a 1-kW ion beam. Each steel to steel contact interace would produce a temperature drop of about 500°C. Clearly, methods of improving interface contact conductance in vacuum are needed. Values of h near 1 W/(cm^2-K) would be desirable.

One further point on providing a good heat sink. Heat must ultimately be removed across the additional interface between metal and cooling fluid. Values of h for this interface typically range from about 0.01 to 1 W/(cm^{2}K) for a cooling medium of water. The value depends somewhat upon water temperature and cooling geometry, but mostly upon the flow velocity. Flow velocities in excess of about 200 cm/s will produce an h near 1. By providing adequate contact area between metal and cooling fluid it is possible to limit the temperature drop across the metal/fluid interface to a few tens of degrees C, even for 1-kW power inputs.

4. Interface Contact Conductance

4.1 Empirical Values

Many interface-contact-conductance measurements have been performed on various materials over the years (see references in [6]) and some have been collected in handbooks such as that of Rohsenow and Hartnett [7]. However, many of these measurements were performed on samples with carefully prepared surface finishes. Partly in an attempt to provide practical engineering values, we measured h at NRL for selected materials having machined surfaces.

Washers (0.16-cm thick, 2.54-cm OD, 1.27-cm ID) were machined from selected stock material and clamped between two Al-alloy cylinders, pressed together using calibrated springs. Heat was applied to one end in vacuum by a Joule-type heater and removed from the other end by water cooling. The total temperature drop across clamped washers was measured using four thermocouples attached to the Al-alloy cylinders. The interfacial temperature drop was determined by substracting the temperature drop expected from thermal conduction through the washers. Power levels up to 40 W were selected to produce interfacial temperature drops in excess of about 5°C.

Table II lists values of interface contact conductance h, measured using a contact pressure of 1.17 MPa (170 psi). The values listed with a "greater than" sign are lower-limit estimates due to the limited accuracy

Table 2. Interface Contact Conductance

INTERFACE	$h(W/(cm^2\text{-}K))$
SS/SS	0.04
SS/Al	0.19
SS/Al Foil/SS	> 0.3
SS/Indium/SS	> 0.6
SS/Silver Paint/SS	> 5
Al/Brass	0.5
Al/Cu	0.9
Al/OF-CU	1.5
Al/Al	1.6
Brass/Brass	0.1
Cu/Cu	0.6
OF-Cu/OF-Cu	1.5

SS: 304 Stainless Steel
Al: 6061, T6 Temper
Brass: Cu-30 Zn
Cu: Tough-pitch Cu
OF-Cu: Oxygen-free Cu

obtainable with a 40 W heater. For like materials the contact conductance improved about 40 fold going from SS/SS to Al/Al, with unacceptably low h values ($h<1\ W/cm^2$) occurring for SS/SS and Brass/Brass couples. For dissimilar washer materials the contact conductance was somewhat below the mean value of the like-washer pairs. These results mean that Al fixtures and 1.2 MPa clamping pressures can provide a nearly acceptablecontact conductance for clamping brass targets ($h{\sim}0.5$), but not SS targets ($h{\sim}0.2$). To clamp SS targets use of an interstitial material like indium or Ag paint may be necessary.

The semiconductor industry currently obtains poorer contact conductances for clamping Si wafers because wafer fragility limits the usable contact pressure to about 7kPa (1psi). Eaton/NOVA has obtained contact conductances of 0.018 - 0.024 $W/(cm^2K)$ using an elastomer-dome substrate and 0.020 - 0.050 using gaseous cooling [3]. More recently, Varian/Extrion has obtained $h{\simeq}0.06\ W/(cm^2\text{-}K)$ by introducing a small quantity of low-pressure gas to the interface between Si wafer and a computer-designed contoured Al dome [8].

4.2 Predicted Values

M.M. Yovanovich and V.W. Antonetti have recently found good correllation between the interface contact conductance measured in vacuum on samples with carefully controlled surface finishes, and specific physical parameters [6,9]. They found

$$h = 1.25\ \frac{mk}{\sigma} \left(\frac{P}{H}\right)^{0.95}, \tag{7}$$

where P is contact pressure, H is microhardness of the surface region deformed during contact, k is thermal conductivity, σ is the root-mean-square surface roughness, and m is the mean surface slope, a number directly obtainable from surface profilometry measurements. This correllation applies to vacuum ambients and for contact pressure greater than about 1 MPa (145 psi). The major point here is that contact conductance can be improved by (1)selecting materials with a large k/H ratio, (2) using large contact pressures P, and (3) carefully polishing the contacting surfaces.

Trends predicted by Eq.(7) were supported by the excellent improvement we observed in h when a thin foil of soft well-conducting metal was placed between two hard stainless steel washers. Even though an additional interface was produced by adding the foil, the net contact conductance was greatly improved. This technique is generally useful; however Yovanovich has shown [10] that using too thick a foil (i.e., $\gtrsim 0.1$ mm) can produce a temperature gradient in the foil sufficient to negate the improvement in h.

5. NRL Water-Cooled Heat Sink

The principles described in this paper were utilized in the design of a rotating water-cooled feedthrough presently in use at NRL. The water-cooled heat sink, viewed along the beam direction in Fig. 5, was designed to absorb 100 W of power while maintaining most rotating implantation targets at temperatures below 100°C. Attached to the heat sink is the outer race of a 22.5-cm-OD main-shaft ball-type bearing used in jet engines. The vacuum feedthrough can be tilted up to 22° and translated in and out of the vacuum chamber. It is typically rotated at 2 rpm, although speeds up to about 500 rpm are possible. Cooling water passes through the stainless-steel shaft into a Cu end plug. Samples are clamped onto an Al base plate bolted to the Cu plug, allowing considerably flexibility in target fixturing. With this design, a temperature difference of only 64°C was measured between the surface of an Al plate

Fig.5. Rotating water-cooled heat sink developed at NRL. The feed-through can be tilted up to 22°, translated in or out, and is typically rotated at 2 rpm

and the water supply temperature when a 105 W beam was directly incident on the Al plate.

Obviously, to remove 1 kW of power, improvements in this heat sink are needed. Directly cooling the Al baseplate would eliminate the thermal resistance between Cu plug and Al baseplate and more interface area for cooling water would be available. These two components probably contributed nearly two-thirds of the observed 64°C temperature drop at 105 W of power.

6. Summary & Conclusions

This work has shown that in many cases radiation cooling of targets is insufficient when a high-current ion implanter is used. Conduction cooling techniques must then be utilized. Three different regimes of conduction cooling were described: (I) heat-diffusion limited, (II) heat-capacity limited, and (III) steady-state conduction to a heat sink. The first two regimes apply when the target is thermally isolated. For most implantations into metals, doses are large enough and samples small enough that transition from region I into either region II or III occurs, especially if even a small amount of beam scanning is utilized. Furthermore, since few samples are large enough to completely store implanted energy without undergoing an unacceptable temperature rise, most metallic targets should be implanted under the conditions of region III.

This work has shown that with region III conduction cooling, substantial target heating can occur from interfacial temperature drops unless good interface contact conductance is obtained or beam scanning over a large area is possible. Engineering values of contact conductance h, as well as its expected dependence on contact pressure, surface microhardness and finish, and thermal conductivity were presented. In some cases use of a conductance-promoting interstitial foil may be necessary. Since beam scanning and water cooling are generally required, guidelines for their satisfactory application were also briefly described.

In conclusion, this work has shown that to prevent excessive heating of most metallic targets: (1) conduction cooling by a heat sink is necessary since radiation cooling and the target's heat capacity alone usually are inadequate, (2) some scanning of either beam or target is necessary (to limit interfacial temperature drops and to prevent localized target heating), and (3) producing good contact conductances is extremely important.

Acknowledgements

The authors wish to thank E.T. Tildon for her assistance in measuring interface contact conductances and M.M. Yovanovich for his insight on the theory of contact conductance.

References

1. P.D. Parry: J. Vac. Sci. Technol. 13, 622 (1976)

2. M. Bruel, B. Berthet, M. Floccari, and J.F. Michand: Rad. Eff. 44, 173 (1979)

3. M. King and P.H. Rose: Nucl. Instrum. Methods Phys. Res. 189, 169 (1981)

4. H.S. Carslaw and J.C. Jaeger: Conduction of Heat in Solids, (Oxford Univ. Press, London 1959)

5. American Society for Metals: Metals Handbook, 9th ed., Vol. 1, Properties and Selection: Irons and Steels (Amer. Soc. Met., Metals Park 1978); ibid, Vol. 2, Properties and Selection: Nonferrous Alloys and Pure Metals, 1979; ibid, Vol.3, Properties and Selection: Stainless Steels, Tool Materials and Special-Purpose Metals, 1980; Y.S. Touloukian and C.Y. Ho, ed.: Thermophysical Properties of Matter, 13 Vols (IFI/Plenum, New York 1970-1974)

6. M.M. Yovanovich: Prog. Astronautics Aeronautics 83, 83 (1982)

7. W.R. Rohsenow and J.P. Hartnett: Handbook of Heat Transfer, (McGraw-Hill, New York 1973)

8. S.C. Holden; N.L. Turner and R.B. Bramhall: private communications, data to be published

9. M.M. Yovanovich: private communication

10. M.M. Yovanovich: Prog. Astronautics Aeronautics 31, 227 (1973)

Part VIII

Implantation into Semiconductors

New Applications of Ion Implantation in Silicon Processing

T. Tokuyama

Central Research Laboratory, Hitachi Ltd. Kokubunji-shi, Tokyo 185, Japan

Abstract

Ion implantation is now recognized as an indispensable, matured technology for silicon-device fabrication. However, development of new implanters with specifications not available so far would facilitate sophisticated applications in several areas.

One example is the use of new ion species. Al^+ or Ga^+ implantation has come to be reevaluated as a means of obtaining deep-junction-layer devices. High-dose O^+ or N^+ implantation has been discussed as a candidate for realizing silicon-on-insulator (SOI) device structures. Another example is high-dose-rate implantation, a key technology for future low-cost solar-cell production. The problems of implanters and processing technologies which remain in these new areas will be discussed in this paper, in conjunction with our recent experimental results.

1. Introduction

More than ten years have passed since implantation technology was first implemented in a real semiconductor-production line. In the early days, use was limited to low-energy and low-dosage applications, because that is all the specifications of implanters at that time permitted. However, practical realization of this technology was a most fortunate occurrence, since threshold voltage control for MOS devices, the main application area at that time, was not easily attained by conventional diffusion processes. This was because of the lack of controllability of the doped-impurity concentration.

Because of developments such as implanters with specifications up to 200 keV energy and 10^{14}-10^{15} cm^{-2} practical dose, as well as pre-dep machines for 10^{16} cm^{-2} practical dose, implantation has now become recognized as an indispensable, matured technology for silicon processing. The highly accurate nature of profile and doping-concentration controllability for the technique, supported by the detailed characterization of the implanted layers and the development of sophisticated compatible-processing technologies, have put implantation in a position of importance never attained by other techniques in the past. Today's leading VLSI devices, 64kbit MOS RAMs, are now fabricated solely through use of implantation as a means of impurity doping.

Implantation technologies that are still under development include :

1) MeV-range high-energy implantation.

2) Simple, special-purpose implanters.
3) Application of new ion species other than the conventional B^+, As^+, and P^+.
4) Maskless implantation with a finely focused beam.

Not only the development of implanters, but also applications and process technologies, are still in the R & D stage for 1) and 4). Some years are required before these technologies can be used practically by industry, and thus they will not be discussed in this paper.

Ga^+ or Al^+ implantation for deep-junction formation of power and high-voltage semiconductor devices, and O^+ or N^+ implantation for making buried insulator structures, are representatives of the implantation of new ion species as indicated in item 3). In addition, simple low-cost implanters with considerable throughput capabilities are required for potentially numerous uses in the solar-cell industry. Fully automatic high-throughput implanters will no doubt be the key to the take-off of the solar-cell industry.

Topic areas 2) and 3) will be reviewed in this paper. Both state-of-the-art analyses and our own experiences will be presented.

2. Al^+ and Ga^+ Implantation

2.1 Features of Al and Ga in Si

The primary advantage of Al and Ga doping over B doping is the difference in diffusion constant. By means of this difference, deep-junction structures, hardly attainable by B diffusion, become economically feasible. A quartz-capsule closed-tube diffusion process has been conventionally used with Al diffusion for high-voltage and power silicon-device processes. However, the lack of controllability in carrier-concentration profiles, and a cost problem inherent to the capsule process have provided implantation with a second chance. Superiority in the diffusion constant not only results in reduced processing time, but also provides the possibility of lower temperature processing, even in shallow-junction device formation.

However, Al and Ga show a solid solubility that is an order of magnitude smaller, and have very small segregation constants when compared with B, as can be seen in Table 1 [1]. Therefore, a highly doped layer is essentially difficult to realize.

Table 1. Comparison of various material parameters of B, Al, and Ga impurity species in Si [1]

	Diffusion coeff. (1100°C) cm^2/s	Solid solubility (1150°C) cm^{-3}	Segregation coeff.
B	3.2×10^{-13}	4.5×10^{20}	0.80
Al	2.0×10^{-12}	2×10^{19}	0.002
Ga	6.7×10^{-13}	4×10^{19}	0.008

The complicated behavior reported so far for implanted Al^+ and Ga^+ [2,3], and lack of diffusion selectivity for Si and SiO_2 are other inconveniences with the use of these impurity species.

Various Al^+ and Ga^+ implantation features will be discussed below, based on our recent experiments in which we intend to obtain 10^{18} - 10^{19} cm^{-3} p-type layers 10 μm in depth, using implanted Al^+ and Ga^+ as a diffusion source.

2.2 Ion Source

Compounds such as $AlCl_3$ or $GaCl_3$ are conventionally used as a source material for Al and Ga ions. However, for simplicity in handling, we have inserted a small amount of Al or Ga metal into the cathode of a cold-cathode-type ion source and obtained Al and Ga ions with a BF_3 or BCl_3 gas discharge. Al and Ga ions are extracted from AlF_3 or GaF_3, obtained by the following reaction in the ion source :

$$Al + BF_3 \rightarrow B + AlF_3 , \quad Ga + BF_3 \rightarrow B + GaF_3 \quad .$$

2.3 Characteristics of Implanted Layers

It is known that the behavior of implanted Al and Ga atoms in silicon after annealing is rather complicated. In our Al^+ implantation experiments, this was similarly observed to be the case. Principally, the behavior has two aspects :

1) Most of the implanted atoms localize in a very thin substrate-surface layer, and tend to diffuse out from the surface.
2) Only a small portion of the implanted atoms substitute silicon lattice site to generate carriers.

Implanted atoms and carrier-distribution profiles are shown in Fig.1, for 1×10^{15} cm^{-2} implantation of 47 keV Al^+ (68 nm projected range) and 110 keV

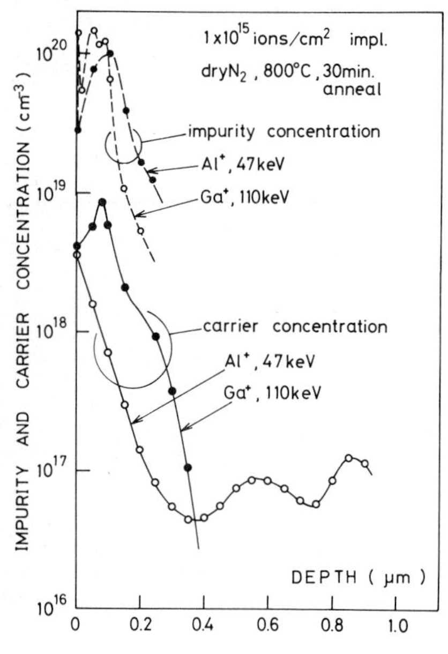

Fig.1. Distribution profiles for implanted atoms and electrical carriers after 800°C 30 min dry-N_2 annealing, for 1×10^{15} cm^{-2} 47 keV Al^+ and 110 keV Ga^+ implantation

Ga^+ (66 nm). About 60% of all the implanted Ga atoms remained in the substrate with a 10^{15} cm^{-2} dose. However, this ratio reduced to 1% with 10^{16} cm^{-2} Ga implantation. With Al^+ implantation, the ratio was similar for 10^{14} - 10^{16} cm^{-2}dose ($\approx$60%).

Localization of Ga and Al atoms in a surface layer after annealing is considered to be caused by the low solubility limit and low segregation constant of the impurities. Prevention of out-diffusion of surface-localized atoms seems necessary for effective utilization of implanted atoms, and thus appropriate capping-layer formation was explored.

One reason for the low carrier activation was assumed to be the interaction of implanted atoms with defects generated during annealing. The implantation results with various ion energies were compared. Carrier profiles obtained by an implantation of 300 keV Al^+, followed by annealing with SiO_2 capping are shown in Fig.2. Although the activation ratio was still as low as 10%, 10-μm-thick layers with a carrier concentration of 10^{18} cm^{-3} were obtained for 30 min annealing. Out-diffusion of Al atoms still occured through the SiO_2 capping layer when the annealing temperature was increased.

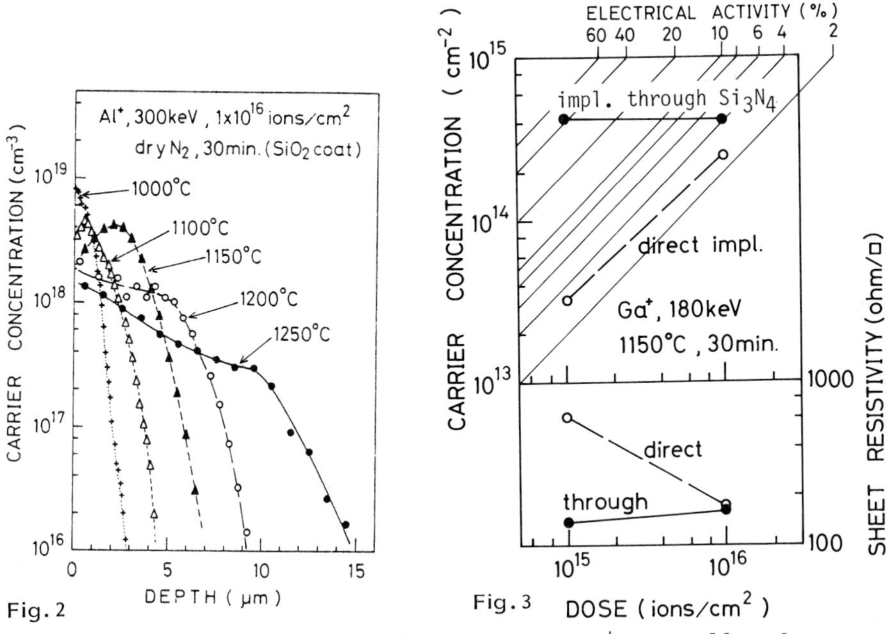

Fig.2. Carrier-distribution profiles for 300 keV Al^+, 1 x 10^{16} cm^{-2} implantation, after 30 min annealing in dry N_2 with a SiO_2 capping layer

Fig.3. Carrier concentrations and sheet resistivities for 180 keV Ga^+ implantation through 15 nm Si_3N_4 layers followed by annealing

Carrier concentrations and sheet resistivities obtained by Ga^+ implantation through a thin nitride layer (15 nm thick), followed by an annealing treatment, are shown in Fig.3. More than a 40% activation ratio was obtained for a Ga^+ dose of 10^{15} cm^{-2}.

In order to prevent defect generation in the silicon substrate during Ga^+ implantation, we implanted 80 keV Ga^+ into the 800-nm-thick surface oxide of the substrate. The implanted oxide layer, covered with a 20 nm Si_3N_4 layer, acted as a diffusion source during annealing treatment. Our results (Fig.4) show that the activation ratio increased up to 44% with 100 min annealing of a 10^{16} cm^{-2} dose. Carrier generation increased with annealing time, and this indicated the effectiveness of out-diffusion prevention.

Selective diffusion of Ga atoms has also been reported with an extension of implanted oxide and nitride capping structures [4].

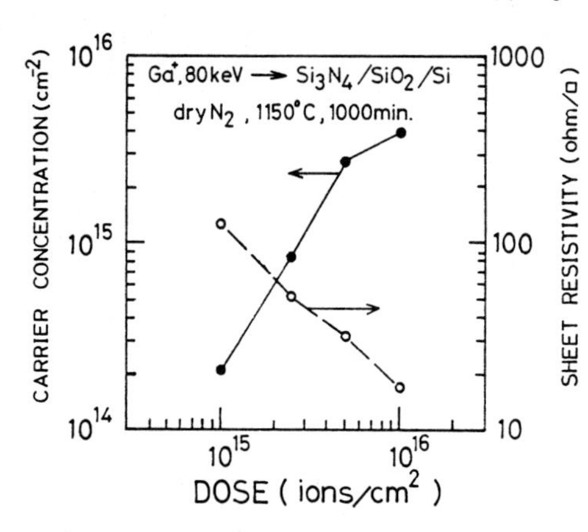

Fig.4. Carrier concentrations and sheet resistivities after annealing. Oxidized surface layer was implanted by 80 keV Ga^+, and was coated with Si_3N_4

3. Buried-Insulator Structures

3.1 High-Dose O^+ and N^+ Implantation

Various silicon-on-insulator (SOI) structures are being exploited in an attempt to develop new LSI isolation structures for sophisticated three-dimensional device structures. Great efforts in realizing SOI structures are directed towards the growth of silicon single-crystal layers on SiO_2 substrates. However, a buried-insulator structure which can be fabricated simply by a combination of ion implantation and conventional epitaxial growth has also attracted considerable interest.

Modification of a silicon surface layer into an oxide layer with high-dose O^+ implantation was first reported by Watanabe and Tooi in 1966 [5]. The concept of material modification is completely different from conventional implantation technologies, in which implanted atoms act only as minute amounts of the impurity species in the host crystal. First of all, an implantation dose in the order of 10^{18} cm^{-2} is necessary for material modification. For example, the implantation time for a 100-mm diameter wafer at a 10 μA/cm² dose rate (total ion-beam current at least 1 mA) is about 4 hours. Therefore, before this technique becomes practical, implanters providing dose rates of several hundred μA/cm² (total ion-beam current at least several dozen mA) must be developed.

As the following sub-section shows, in order to combine this technique with the epitaxial growth of single-crystal layers on the surface of an implanted substrate, ion energies of at least 150-200 keV are necessary in order for a single-crystalline surface layer to be present after implantation. Heating of the substrate during implantation by these 200keV several hundred μA/cm² beam must be kept within a reasonable temperature range by proper handling of the wafers.

As the characteristics of implanted layers are known to depend rather critically upon the temperature during implantation, it is difficult to predict whether the results reported so far will still be meaningful when practical high-dose-rate implanters are actually used.

3.2 The Process and its Problems

Applications of this process fall into two categories. In one, modification of a silicon surface layer into an insulator such as an oxide, nitride or carbide layer through implantation of O^+, N^+ or C^+ ions, makes fabrication of MOS structures, passivation layers, and various mask layers possible. In the other, implanted layers are confined in the bulk-silicon crystal, leaving the uppermost layer single crystalline. An epitaxial layer is then grown on this buried-insulator-implanted substrate. In both applications, it is necessary that the stoichiometry of the grown insulators be equal to tnat for SiO_2 or Si_3N_4, and that developed films be uniform and continuous in structural as well as electrical characteristics.

In an application of the first type, interface characteristics between the insulator layer and the semiconductor beneath the insulator are most important. The effect of ion implantation on the interface properties needs to be studied carefully.

In an application of the second type, on the other hand, the surface crystallinity of the substrate after implantation is most critical for the subsequent epitaxial growth process. Since the surface layer, which remains single crystal, becomes the seed crystal for epitaxial growth, defect density in this surface layer affects the grown crystal quality considerably. Processing conditions for realizing perfect buried-insulator layers, as well as for keeping the surface in a defect-free crystalline state, seems to depend rather critically on the implantation (energy, dose, dose rate, etc.) and annealing conditions.

Experimental conditions reported so far and their technological features are summarized in Tables 2, 3, and 4.

Table 2. Experimental conditions reported so far for high dose O^+ implanted Si

	Energy (keV)	Dose (cm^{-2})	Dose rate ($\mu A/cm^2$)	Annealing	Measurement
Watanabe, Tooi (1966) [5]	60	1.5×10^{18}	20		IR, MOS, Dielectric
Freeman et al. (1970) [6]	15 - 40	2×10^{18}	1000		IR, Dielectric, EM
Borders, Beezhold (1971) [7]	200	10^{17}	1	1000°C/15h	IR,
Dylewski, Joshi (1976) [8]	30(O_2^+)	10^{14}- 10^{18}	15	800°C/2h	IR, MOS, RHEED, Dielectric
Kirov et al. (1978) [9]	5 - 60	10^{15}- 10^{18}	1 - 70	500-1000°C	IR, MOS
Gill, Wilson (1978) [10]	40 - 60	3×10^{18}	10	800°C/2h	RBS
Hayashi et al. (1980) [11]	150	1.2×10^{18}	15	1150°C/2h	TEM, AES, XPS
Chiang et al. (1981) [12]	50	10^{17}	3	YAG Laser 2-2.5 J/cm²	TEM, SIMS, IR
Maeyama, Kajiyama (1982) [13]	150 70(O_2^+)	$0.6\text{-}3 \times 10^{18}$ $0.6\text{-}1.5 \times 10^{18}$	25 35	1150°C/2h	RBS, AES, XPS

Table 3. Experimental conditions reported so far for high dose N^+ implanted Si

	Energy (keV)	Dose (cm^{-2})	Dose rate ($\mu A/cm^2$)	Annealing	Measurement
Freeman et al. (1970) [6]	15, 25	$2x10^{18}$	1000		IR, EM, ED, Dielectric
Borders Beezhold (1971) [7]	200	$1x10^{17}$	1	1000°C/16h	IR
Edelman et al. (1976) [14]	40	10^{18}		600-1300°C/ 0.5h	TEM, IR
Bayerl et al. (1978) [15]	0.6-2.4M	$2x10^{17}$, 10^{19}		1000°C/ 2-16h	INR, RBS Dielectric
Bourguet et al. (1980) [16]	180	$2x10^{15}$-$2x10^{18}$	1.5	1200°C/2h	RBS, X-ray, EM IR, Dielectric
Maeyama, Kajiyama (1982) [13]	150 70(N_2^+)	$1.5x10^{18}$ $1.2x10^{18}$	28 40	1150°C/2h	RBS, AES, XPS
Chiu et al. (1982) [17]	1.75	10^{17}	100		IR, RBS, Optical
Hezel, Lieste (1982) [18]	0.5-5				AES, ELS

Table 4. Epilayer growth and device applications reported so far

	Buried insulator layer	Epilayer /Devices
Dexter et al. (1973) [19]	150 keV, $10^{17}/cm^2$ N^+, 1200°C/3h	$10^4/cm^2$ defect density, RBS
Itoh, Tsuchimoto (1975) [20]	85-400 keV, 10^{17}-$10^{18}/cm^2$ N^+ 1000°C/14h, 1200°C/3h	MOSFET
Izumi et al. (1978) [26]	SIMOX	19 stage CMOS ring osc.
Izumi et al. (1980) [21]	150 kev, $1.2x10^{18}/cm^2$ O^+(SIMOX)	SiH_4/1050°C, p-n junction 21 stage CMOS ring osc.
Ohwada et al. (1981) [22]	SIMOX	Buried channel MOSFET
Homma et al. (1982) [23]	150 keV, 0.1-$2.4x10^{18}/cm^2$ O^+, 1150°C/2h	SiH_4, TEM, $10^9/cm^2$ dislocation 10-15 % smaller mobility
Izumi et al. (1982) [24]	SIMOX	1.5 μm channel 1kb CMOS SRAM 400 GATE CMOS PLL
Akiya et al. (1982) [25]	SIMOX	High voltage MOSFET 180 V (n-ch), 250 V (p-ch)

O^+ Implantation : The oxygen concentration of an implanted layer has been reported to saturate at the stoichiometric SiO_2 composition level in an implanted layer. Further increase in $O^{\pm}$ dosage then results in a widening of the SiO_2 layer width [10]. AES and RBS measurement results were used to clarify this model [10,11]. O^+ implanted layers show amorphous SiO_2 formation even in an as-implanted state. Properties similar to those for thermal oxide were determined, using dielectric and IR measurements before and after high-temperature annealing [10]. However, if use as an active layer such as the region of a MOSFET is planned, the properties are not sufficient, even though no macroscopic defect structures remain [9]. An abrupt transition of the surface SiO_2 to the substrate Si was observed, and disorders found at the interface usually annealed out at lower temperatures when the implanted dose rate was high [10].

N^+ Implantation : On the other hand, N atoms implanted in excess of the stoichiometry usually remain in an implanted layer, and show Gaussian distribution [13,15]. With high-temperature annealing, the implanted layer becomes polycrystalline Si_3N_4 . When the implantation dose is in the order of 10^{17} cm^{-2} , the implanted and annealed layer becomes mixed polycrystal of Si and Si_3N_4 [16], which has imperfect insulator properties. Surface nitride layers generated by low-energy N^+ implantation are found to act as an oxygen-diffusion mask [17].

3.3 Epitaxial-Layer Growth

The idea of growing epitaxial layer on the surface of a buried-insulator substrate was first reported by Dexter et al. in 1973 [19]. Considerable progress was made in device applications of this epitaxial layer before detailed characterizations of the grown crystal were reported on by Homma et al. [23].

The essential condition for epilayer growth is that the surface of an implanted silicon substrate remains in a single-crystalline state after implantation. If this surface layer becomes amorphous due to high-dose implantation, no single-crystalline layer will result after annealing. This is different from the case for doping-impurity implantation. Polycrystalline material will result, as no single-crystalline seed will be found between the surface and buried-insulator layers.

In Fig.5, reported from Bourguet et al. [16], it can be seen that low-dose implantation results in a single-crystalline surface with an imperfect insulator layer, whereas high-dose implantation results in a perfect insulator layer with a polycrystalline surface.

Therefore, a perfect insulator with the single-crystalline surface necessary for epilayer growth can only be obtained under certain implantation

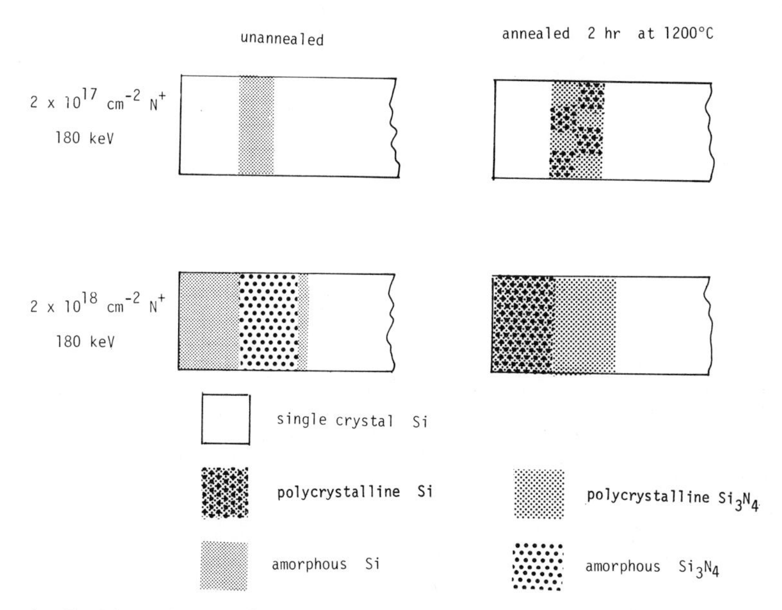

Fig.5. Diagrams of the composition and structure of silicon samples implanted with 180 keV nitrogen ions at doses of 2 x 10^{16} cm^{-2}, before and after 2 hr annealing at 1200°C. (Used with permission of Bourguet [16])

conditions, such as

1) high-energy, high-dose implantaion and
2) high-dose-rate or heated-substrate implantation.

Careful selection of implantation conditions has made it possible to clarify satisfactory insulator and surface-crystal characteristics. This has, for example, been done by RBS and dielectric measurement [16,19]. However, perfect crystallinity in a grown epilayer has not yet been reported. Dexter et al. reported on many defect structures in a grown epilayer as causing difficulties for the execution of a sufficient vapor-etching treatment before epi-growth [19]. Recent characterization by Homma et al. [23] of surface silicon layers after high-dose O^+ implantation illustrates the exsitence of many oxygen-related precipitates. Strain fields generated by these precipitates become the origin of defects found in the epilayer.

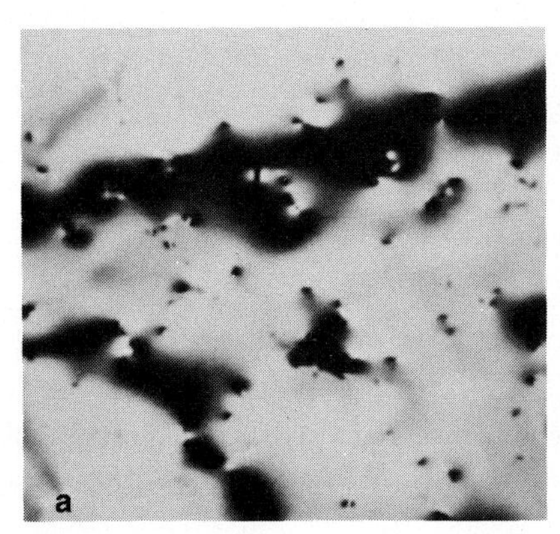

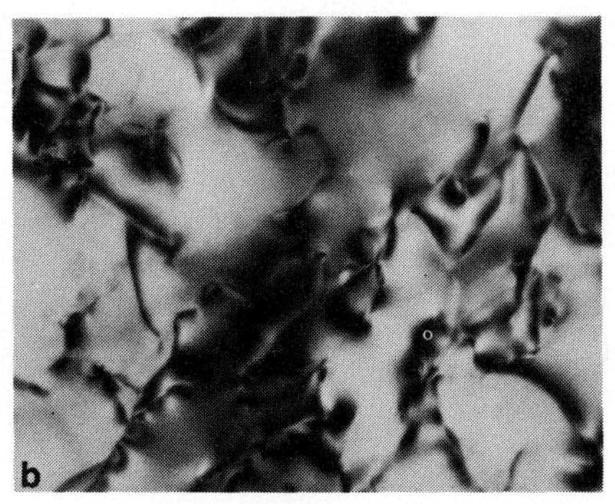

Fig.6. TEM photographs of (a) Si surface with 2×10^{18} cm^{-2} , 150 keV O^+ implantation followed by 1150°C, 2 hr annealing, and (b) epilayer surface grown on the substrate shown in (a). (Used with permission of Y.Homma [23])

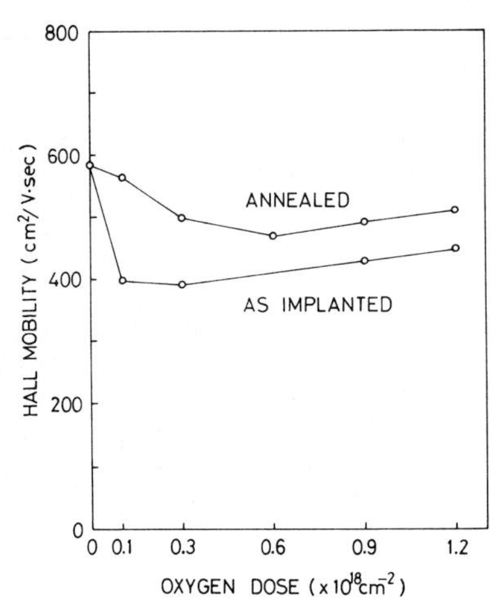

Fig.7. Electron Hall mobility in epilayers grown on various substrates implanted with different doses. Epilayers are 300 nm thick, with 5×10^{16} cm^{-3} phosphorus. (Used with permission of Y. Homma [23])

Dislocations in the order of 10^9 cm^{-2} were observed in an epilayer. Fig.6, from Homma et al. [23], shows TEM micrographs of silicon surfaces before and after epi-growth. They also reported that a decrease of the oxygen dose to 0.6×10^{18} cm^{-2} resulted in no etch pits in an epilayer. However, in this case, the buried SiO_2 layer is no longer a perfect insulator. Therefore, high-energy implantation is necessary for avoiding the presence of implanted oxygen atoms in the syrface layer of the substrate. Accordingly, development of high-energy, high-dose implanters is essential.

However, Fig.6 shows that no stacking faults were observed in an epilayer, different from SOS crystals. Carrier mobility in the epilayer was measured as being 10-15% lower than the bulk value, as shown in Fig.7 [23].

3.4 Device Applications

The first device application of an epilayer grown over a buried-insulator substrate was a MOSFET fabrication reported by Itoh and Tsuchimoyo in 1975 [20]. They described a nitrogen-implanted buried-insulator structure and a higher carrier mobility than that found in SOS-type structures.

An epilayer grown on an oxygen-implanted buried structure was named SIMOX (Separation by Implanted Oxygen) by a group at the Musashino Electrical Communication Laboratory, N.T.T., and device applications for this structure have been aggressively explored since 1978 [26].

Figure 8 shows the fundamental structure for a MOSFET on SIMOX. Through design of a 1-μm effective-channel FET, a 21-stage ring oscillator could be fabricated, and a minimum delay time of 95 ps with a power delay of 310 fJ was obtained [22]. Recent achievements include a 1k bit static RAM [24], 400-gate CMOS PLL [24] LSI's, and high-voltage (400 V) MOS IC's [25]. Local SOI structures not attained by SOS technology are properly utilized in this recent work.

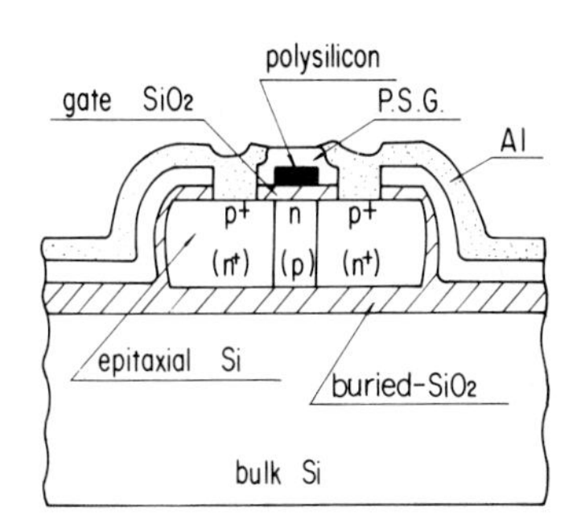

Fig.8. SIMOX-MOSFET structure. (Used with permission of K.Izumi [21])

4. Implantation for Solar-Cell Fabrication

Essential features for solar-photovoltaic energy-conversion systems have already been described. These include : a lack of moving parts, guaranteed long lifetime, a potential for scaling up from small to very large systems, and convenience of use as an on-site energy source.

Silicon crystalline cells are generally considered as primary photovoltaic devices because of the abundance and handling ease of their raw materials, as well as the establishment of their process and device technologies.

Although a great many efforts have been concentrated so far on the lowering of cell-manufacturing costs, the present module price still remains in the range of 10 $/W. If 10 $/W solar modules have a lifetime of 20 years, the cost of the generated electric power can be calculated as 36 ¢/kWh, which is several times higher than the present power price.

Total worldwide cell production in 1982 is estimated to be around 9 MW [27]. One of the main reasons for not reaching a reasonable cost is the small production volume. The generally agreed production volume necessary for maintaining the solar-cell industry is 10^4 MW/year, or about 10^3 times that at the present. Another reason is the need for a breakthrough in the development of low-cost production technologies.

A brief review based on our experience will be presented below on the usefulness of ion implantation.

4.1 Japanese National Project

An outline of the Japanese National Project for the development of solar-photovoltaic systems is shown in Fig.9. The project started in 1974, and in the first 7 years, basic breakthroughs in materials and processing technologies were attempted. Low-cost solar-grade silicon materials, ribbon, cast,and thin-film crystal technologies, as well as low-cost diffusion and implantation techniques, were the main subjects during that period. From 1980 to 1982, these results were consolidated for the development of a 500 kW/year experimental production line, which encompassed everything from raw materials to a panel-production plant. In this 500 kW/year line, 250 kW are to be fabricated by diffusion, and the other 250 kW by ion implantation for junction-formation processes. The 1983-84 term will be devoted to accumulating operation experience with these production lines, as well as data gathering for both production and field panel performance. A 10,000 kW/year plant is scheduled for construction from 1986 onwards.

The problem inherent in the diffusion process used so far in junction formation are difficulties in handling wafers automatically as well as a slow processing speed. We have developed a specific ion-implantation system for overcoming these weak points. The above-mentioned 250 kW/year production line is being constructed around a new implanter.

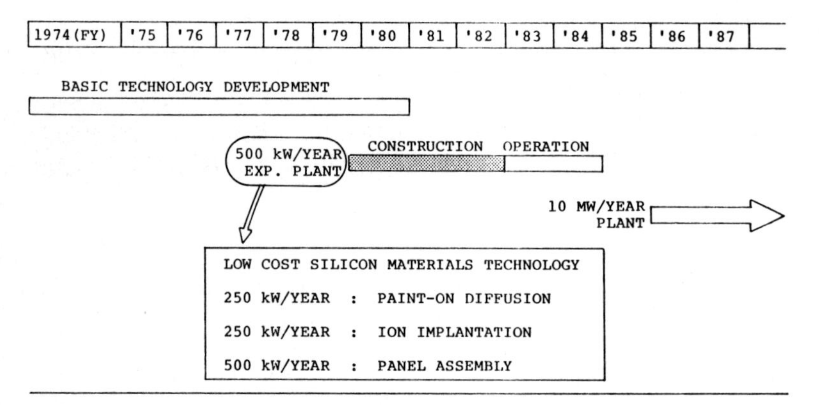

Fig.9. Outline of Japanese National Project for development of solar-photovoltaic energy-conversion systems

4.2 Throughput Considerations

Implanters presently in wide use in the semiconductor industry mostly have a nominal throughput of 200-300 100-mm wafers/hr at a $1 \sim 3 \times 10^{15}$ cm^{-2} dose. This throughput figure is generally not enough when one considers solar-cell production. From a cost-reduction viewpoint, the process should be perfectly automatic, and 24-hr continuous operation would generally be desirable.

For a 10^3 MW/year production facility for solar-cells, at least 4×10^6 100-mm wafers per day need to be handled. Reasonable throughput for an implanter is at least 2×10^4 100-mm wafers per day (200 such implanters for 10^3 MW/year production), or 1000 wafers/hr.

As a 3×10^{15} cm^{-2} dose can be implanted in 0.3 sec with an ion-beam intensity of 1 mA/cm^2 (or 3 sec at 100 $\mu A/cm^2$), a 1000 wafer/hr (3.6 sec per wafer) throughput can be attained at a several-hundred $\mu A/cm^2$ beam intensity. Temperature-rise considerations, however, tend to dictate that a low-dose-rate (or larger-diameter-ion-beam) implantation system be adopted, for the purpose of decreasing the energy-injection rate per unit area.

Fig.10. Photograph of implanter developed for solar-cell fabrication

4.3 Outline of our Implanter

As a first step towards obtaining a 1000 wafer/hr throughput, we have developed a machine that employs magnetic scanning of a large-diameter beam, combined with one-to-one mechanical wafer transport. 360 100-mm wafers per hour at a 3×10^{15} cm^{-2} P^+ dose can be processed. Details of the machine is reported by Tokiguchi et al. [28]. In Fig.10, photograph of the machine is shown.

We have used the newly developed microwave ion source with a magnetic analyzer, and obtained a beam diameter of 60-70 mm with a P^+ ion current of 10 - 20 mA at the wafer surface. Ion- beam deflection is ± 120 mm, and the average ion-beam intensity is in the order of 0.1 mA/cm^2 (average injected power 1 - 2 W/cm^2). Wafer-temperature rise was less than 200°C.

Wafers are automatically inserted into the machine, one by one, and transported across the scanned ion beam at a speed of 13.5 mm/s. A sinusoidal overscan is presently used in our system to obtain uniform beam intensity. However, by utilizing a triangular scan waveform with higher linearity and, for example, improving the wafer-transport-system configuration by setting up two parallel rows, a 1000 wafer/hr throughput can be achieved with little trouble.

4.4 Implanter Performance

When a large diameter beam is deflected by an analyzing magnet of high beam-transport efficiency, deterioration of mass resolution at the wafer surface usually occurs. For machine-simplicity and beam-transport-efficiency purposes, implanters without an analyzing magnet were reported on elsewhere [30,31,32]. In these machines, H^+, H_2^+, or O^+ and PO^+ impurity ions are implanted when PH_3 gas or solid phosphorus is used as the source material.

The characteristics of implanted layers with such impurities indicated some difficulties. In Fig.11, solar-cell conversion efficiencies (without anti-reflection coating) are compared for implanted ion species of P^+, PH^+, and $P^+ + H^+$. $P^+ + H^+$ show poor results. However, Itoh et al. [32] reported that cell efficiencies comparable to those obtained from mass-analyzed beam implantation were obtained when low-energy implantation (less than 10 keV) was employed.

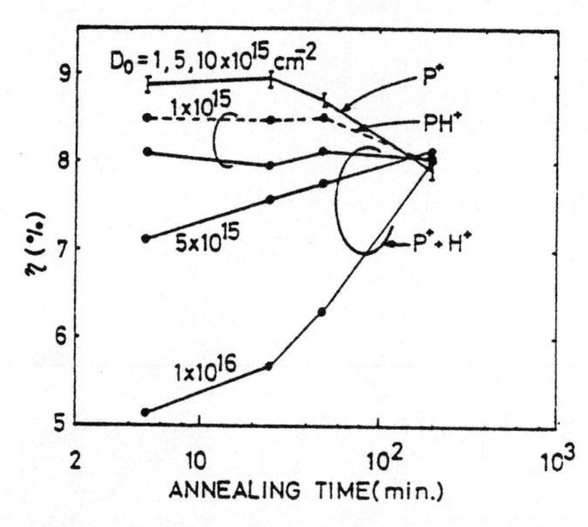

Fig.11. Effects of H^+ and PH^+ ion species on conversion efficiencies of implanted solar cells

The origin of lower cell efficiency with H^+ implantation is connected with the deep-lying defects generated by the implanted H^+. With PH^+ implantation, the implanted hydrogen does not generate defects in regions deeper than the junction depth formed by the implanted phosphorus. Thus, there is essentially no lowering of the efficiency.

In regard to the uniformity of implanted impurity distributions in a wafer, poor results were seen with deflection waveform nonlinearity, large-angle-deflection geometrical error, and variation in wafer-transportation speed, when compared with conventional implanter uniformity. Fig.12

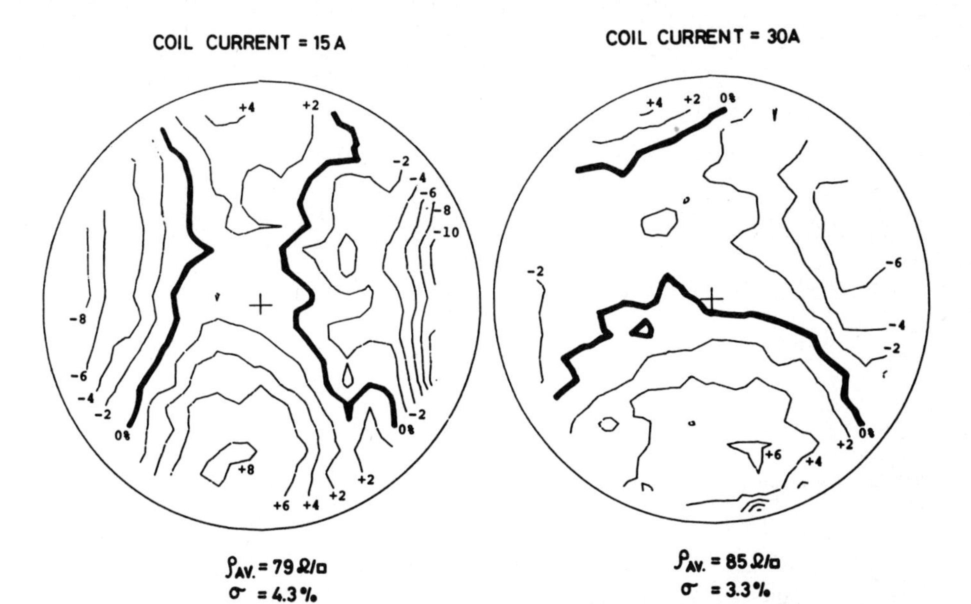

Fig.12. Uniformity of sheet resistivity in P^+ implanted and annealed wafers

shows resistivity-measurement results for an implanted wafer. An improvement with increasing deflection amplitude is indicated. A 3-4% standard deviation is, as a matter of fact, still smaller than the figures usually obtained with $POCl_3$ diffusion, and there are basically no harmful effects upon solar-cell characteristics.

Continuous implantation experiments with 1000 100-mm wafers at a 15 keV energy and a 3×10^{15} cm^{-2} dose resulted with only 15 wafers having edge chipping of less than 0.5 mm, and one wafer having chipping greater than 0.5 mm. Automatic wafer handling may be said to cause no major trouble.

4.5 Solar-Cell Performance

A low-cost cell-fabrication process employing the implanter in question is shown in Fig.13. After P^+ implantation into a p-type wafer, a BSF (back-surface-field) p^+ layer is formed by Al-paste printing. Anti-reflection coating, and plating of the electrode then follow.

Figure 14 shows a photograph of a completed solar panel. The potential capability of this implanter is at most 2 MW/year with the present design. The expected 1982 worldwide cell production of 9 MW could be obtained by 5 implanters having this design. The role of implanters in the future solar-cell industry should not be underestimated.

5. Conclusions

Several new applications of ion implantation in silicon processing have been reviewed, together with some of our recent experimental results. In con-

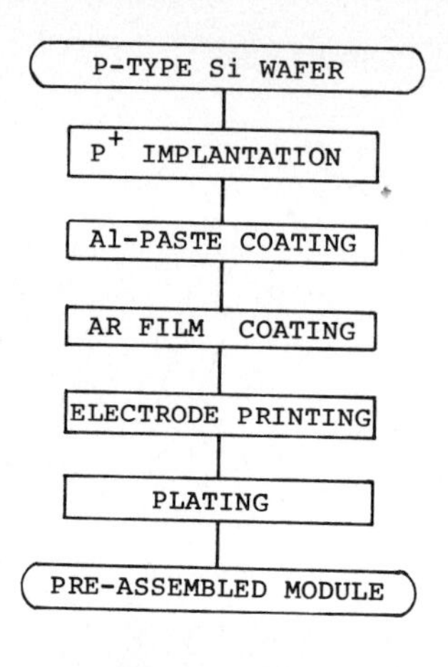

Fig.13. Tentative low-cost solar-cell-fabrication process using newly developed implanter

▼ Fig.14. Photograph of completed solar panel

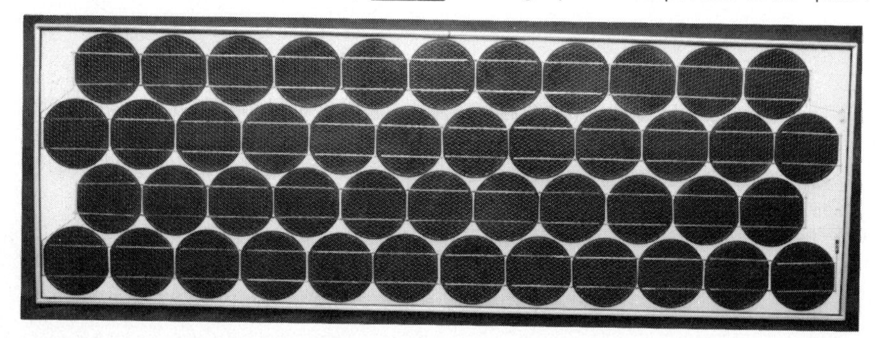

ventional impurity-doping applications, implantation has already risen to a position never attained in the past by other techniques. This is because of its doping-performance controllability as well as its compatibility with other VLSI processes. In the new areas, on the other hand, there are a great many problems still needing to be solved. Similar to development in the early days of implantation technology, numerous efforts must be continuously directed towards machine improvement and process optimization.

It should be noted that in the areas of compound semiconductors and non-semiconductors, implantation is now being favored by material scientists and process engineers. This is due to the fact that it shows a potential for realizing materials and device processes that have so far been difficult.

The success of implantation applications in the silicon-processing area is only a doorway leading to the vast and profound field of ion-solid-interaction engineering.

Acknowledgement

A part of this work has been contracted with the Agency of Industrial Science and Technology, MITI, Japan in connection with the National R & D Program, "Sunshine Project".

References

1. W.R.Runyan : *Silicon Semiconductor Technology* (McGraw Hill, New York, 1965),p.108, 156, 266
2. J.W.Mayer and O.J.Marsh : Ion Implantation in Semiconductors, *Applied Solid State Science,Vol. 1*, ed. R.Wolfe (Academic Press, New York,1969), p.318
3. N.G.Johanson and J.W.Mayer : Solid State Electronics 13, 123 (1970)
4. Y.Koshino, T.Ajima, J.Ohshima, K.Kirita and T.Yonezawa : 39th IEEE Device Res. Conf. IIIB-6 (Santa Barbara, June 1981)
5. M.Watanabe and A.Tooi : Japan. J. Appl. Phys. 5, 737 (1966)
6. J.H.Freeman, G.A.Gard, D.J.Mazey, J.H.Stephen and F.B.Whiting : *Proc. European Conf. Ion Implantation* (Reading, England, 1970), p.74
7. J.A.Borders and W.Beezhold : *Proc. 2nd International Conf. Ion Implantation in Semiconductors* (Springer-Verlag, New York,1971),p.241
8. J.Dylewski and M.C.Joshi : Thin Solid Films 35, 327 (1976), 37, 241 (1976), 42, 227 (1977)
9. K.I.Kirov, E.D.Atanasova, S.P.Alexandrova, B.G.Anov and A.E.Djakov : Thin Solid Films 48, 187 (1978)
10. S.S.Gill and I.H.Wilson : *Proc. IBMM 1978* (Budapest, 1978), p.1231
11. T.Hayashi, H.Okamoto and Y.Homma : Japan. J. Appl. Phys. 19, 1005 (1980)
12. S.W.Chiang, Y.S.Liu and R.F.Reihl : Appl. Phys. Lett. 39, 752 (1981)
13. S.Maeyama and K.Kajiyama : Japan. J. Appl. Phys. 21, 744 (1982)
14. F.L.Edelman, O.N.Kuznetsov, L.V.Lezheiko and E.V.Lubopytova : Radiation Effects 29, 13 (1976)
15. P.Bayerl, H.Ryssel and M.Ramin : *Proc. IBMM 1978* (Budapest 1978),p.1187
16. P.Bourguet, J.M.Dupart, E.Le Tiran, P.Auvray, A.Guivac'h, M.Salvi, G.Pelous and P.Henoc : J. Appl. Phys. 51, 6169 (1980)
17. Tzu-Yin Chiu, H.Bernt and I.Ruge : J. Electrochem. Soc. 129, 408 (1982)
18. R.Hezel and N.Lieske : ibid., 129, 379 (1982)
19. R.J.Dexter, S.B.Watelski and S.T.Picraux : Appl. Phys. Lett. 23, 455 (1973)
20. K.Itoh and T.Tsuchimoto : *6th Symp. Ion Implantation in Semicond.*, Inst. Phys. Chem. Res. (Saitama,Japan, Feb. 1975), p.43
21. K.Izumi, M.Doken and H.Ariyoshi : *Proc. 1979 International Conf. Solid State Devices,* Japan. J. Appl. Phys. 19-1 ,151 (1980)
22. K.Ohwada, Y.Ogura and E.Sano : IEEE Trans. ED-28, 1084 (1981)
23. Y.Homma, M.Oshima and T.Hayashi : Japan. J. Appl. Phys. 21, 890 (1982)
24. K.Izumi, Y.Omura, M.Ishikawa and E.Sano : 1982 Symposium on VLSI Technology (Oiso, Sept. 1982)
25. M.Akiya, S.Nakashima and K.Kato : 1982 International Conf. Solid State Devices (Tokyo, Aug. 1982)
26. K.Izumi, M.Doken and H.Ariyoshi : Electron. Lett. 14, 593 (1978)
27. P.D.Maycock : 3rd Photovoltaic Sci. and Eng. Conf. (Kyoto, May 1982)
28. K.Tokiguchi, N.Sakudo, H.Koike and I.Kanomata : *Proc. 4th Symp. Ion Source and Ion Application Tech.* (Tokyo, June 1980), p.28
29. K.Tokiguchi, H.Itoh, N.Sakudo, H.Koike, T.Warabisako, T.Saitoh, I.Kanomata and T.Tokuyama : this volume
30. J.C.Muller and P.Siffert : Nucl. Instr. Method 189, 205 (1981)
31. M.B.Spitzer and S.N.Bunker : Appl. Phys. Lett. 40, 976 (1982)
32. H.Itoh, K.Tokiguchi, T.Saitoh, M.Tamura and T.Tokuyama : *Proc. 3rd Photovoltaic Sci. and Eng. Conf. (1982),* to be published in Japan J. Appl. Phys. 21-2 (1982)

Limitations of Ion Implantation in MOS Technology

D. Widmann and U. Schwabe

Siemens AG ZFEME 4, Otto-Hahn-Ring 6, D-8000 München 83, Fed. Rep. of Germany

1. Introduction

Ion implantation has become a standard technique in advanced integrated circuit manufacturing. There are several unique features of ion implantation compared to thermal dopant deposition. Most important is the excellent doping profile control over a wide range of doses. Moreover, ion implantation is compatible with most of the manufacturing steps for integrated circuits, allowing applications which are not possible with thermal dopant deposition.

This paper reviews the limitations and problems of ion implantation if it is used for MOS integrated circuit fabrication. The emphasis is on standard ion implantation steps and their impact on MOS device performance.

2. Use of Ion Implantation in Advanced MOS Technology

Advanced MOS technology presently follows two main directions, namely scaled NMOS and CMOS. Scaled NMOS is the leading technology for dynamic memories and microprocessors, while CMOS has potential for low-power logic circuits and static memories.

The evolution of NMOS and CMOS technologies is characterized by a steady increase of the complexity of the integrated circuits,accompanied by scaling down of the minimum dimensions. This trend implies an increasing need for low defect densities and tight tolerances. Shallow doping profiles are required, and as a consequence, the processing temperatures must be lowered. Sophisticated vertical and lateral doping profiles, especially in the channel regions, are often provided in order to improve certain properties of the devices,such as the short-channel stability of the threshold voltage /1/, the punchthrough behaviour /2/, the hot carrier generation /3/, or the capacitance between gate and drain /4/.

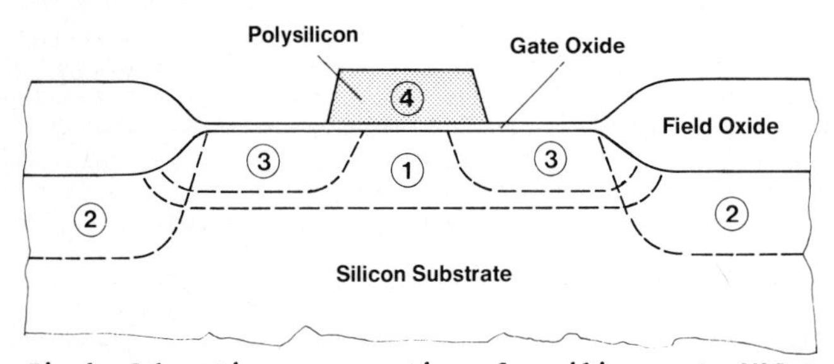

Fig.1. Schematic cross-section of a silicon-gate MOS transistor after source drain formation. The circled numbers indicate the doped regions. (1) Channel region. (2) Field isolation region. (3) Source and drain regions. (4) Polysilicon

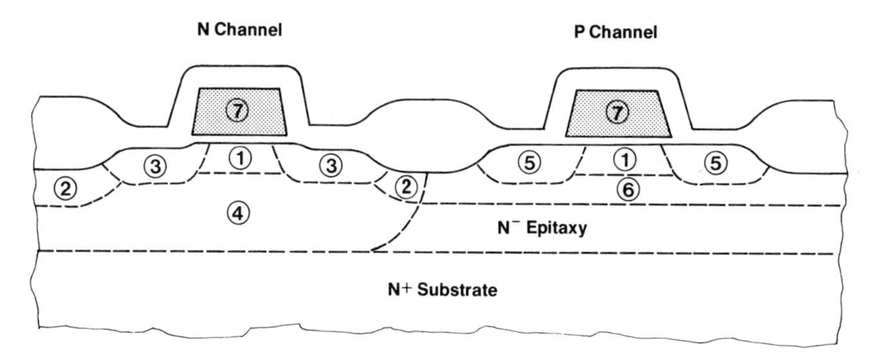

Fig.2. Schematic cross-section of the two complementary transistors of a silicon-gate CMOS integrated circuit with p and n wells in an epitaxial n^- layer. The circled numbers indicate the doped regions. (1) Channel regions. (2) P^+ field region. (3) N^+ source and drain regions. (4) P well. (5) P^+ source and drain regions. (6) N well. (7) Polysilicon

Due to these trends, ion implantation is used in advanced MOS technologies for nearly each of the required doping steps. Fig.1 shows schematically the different doped regions of an NMOS integrated circuit, while Fig.2 represents the corresponding cross section for a complex CMOS integrated circuit which uses p and n wells in an epitaxial n^- layer. This CMOS process needs 7 implantation steps. Only the heavy phosphorus doping of the polysilicon is sometimes carried out by standard thermal deposition techniques. The p and n wells are actually several microns deep. They are formed at an early stage of the CMOS process by near-surface implantation of boron and phosphorus for p wells and n wells, respectively, and by drive-in at elevated temperatures. On the contrary, advanced CMOS technologies require shallow p^+ and n^+ source and drain regions with a junction depth of only a few tenths of a micron.

3. Current Limitations of Ion Implantation in MOS Technology

3.1. Tradeoff Between Sheet Resistance and Junction Depth

Advanced MOS circuits need shallow n^+ and p^+ source and drain regions with a low sheet resistance. For a given junction depth there is, however, a lower limit for the sheet resistance, due to the solid solubility of the dopants in the silicon crystal /5,6/. Fig.3 shows the limiting curve for arsenic /5/, which is the preferred dopant for shallow n^+ sources and drains. Junction depth and sheet resistance values below the limiting curve are not accessible by varying the implantation and furnace-annealing parameters.

For boron p^+ source and drain regions, the limitation of the sheet resistance for a given junction depth is even more severe than for arsenic /7,8/. Moreover, shallow p^+ regions with junction depths below 0.4 µm preclude temperatures above 900 °C after ion implantation, except for very short times. As a consequence, well-established wafer processing steps such as the flow-glass technique must be modified /9,10/ or even replaced by other techniques /11/.

Similar to the trade off between the sheet resistance and the junction depth in single-crystal silicon, there is a lower limit of the sheet resistance of polysilicon films. For phosphorus doping, which yields the lowest polysilicon resistivities, the limiting curve is similar to that shown in Fig.3, if the polysilicon thickness is taken instead of the junction depth /12/.

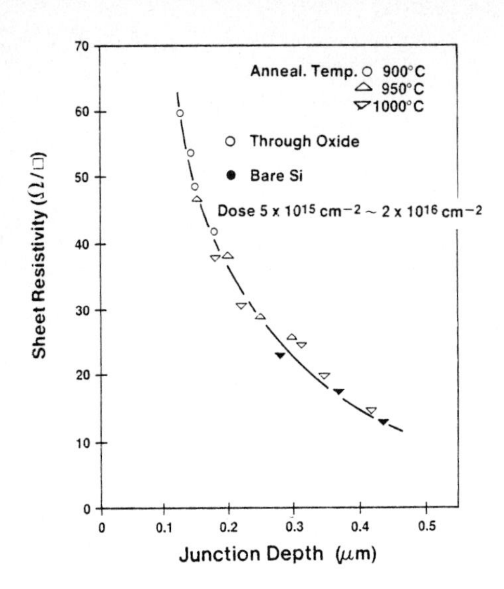

Fig.3. The lower limit of the sheet resistance for a given junction depth of arsenic-implanted and furnace-annealed regions (From Y.Wada and N. Hashimoto /5/)

Different solutions have been proposed to reduce the resistance of heavily doped single-crystal and polysilicon regions. N^+ or p^+ single-crystal regions may be overlaid by heavily doped polysilicon /13/. However, the polysilicon is not self-aligned to the n^+ or p^+ regions, if a silicon-gate technology is used. Metal silicide/polysilicon double layers may reduce the sheet resistance by an order of magnitude as compared to heavily doped polysilicon with the same thickness /14,15/. Recently, self-aligned deposition of silicides /16/ and refractory metals /17/ on source and drain regions has been used in NMOS and CMOS processes.

Although a low sheet resistance of the polysilicon is generally desired, polysilicon resistors with a high sheet resistance are sometimes integrated as load devices in logic circuits. Unlike heavily doped polysilicon, the resistivity of low doped polysilicon exhibits some anomalies caused by dopant segregation and carrier trapping at grain boundaries /18,19,20/. Two examples are shown in Figs.4 and 5.

In Fig. 4, the measured sheet resistance of polysilicon is plotted in terms of the implanted phosphorus dose. Before and after the polysilicon doping, the usual process steps which are necessary for a MOS logic circuit were carried out. A large effect on the polysilicon resistance is found if, after metallization, a plasma nitride passivation layer is deposited, as demonstrated in the figure. The resistivity reduction of up to 3 orders of magnitude in the case of plasma nitride passivation may be attributed to the action of hydrogen in the plasma nitride, which reduces the trap density at the grain boundaries /21/.

Fig. 5 shows an anomalous annealing behaviour of polysilicon doped with a phosphorus dose of 2.5×10^{15} cm^{-2} /22/. For a large dose of 2×10^{16} cm^{-2}, a continuous decrease of the sheet resistance with increasing annealing temperature is observed, as expected. If, however, the dose is about a factor of 10 lower, the sheet resistance increases until the annealing temperature reaches $900\,^{o}C$. Above $900\,^{o}C$, there is a rapid decrease of the sheet resistance. The anomalous annealing behaviour is assumed to be a complex function of the grain size, the phosphorus segregation and the carrier trapping at the grain boundaries.

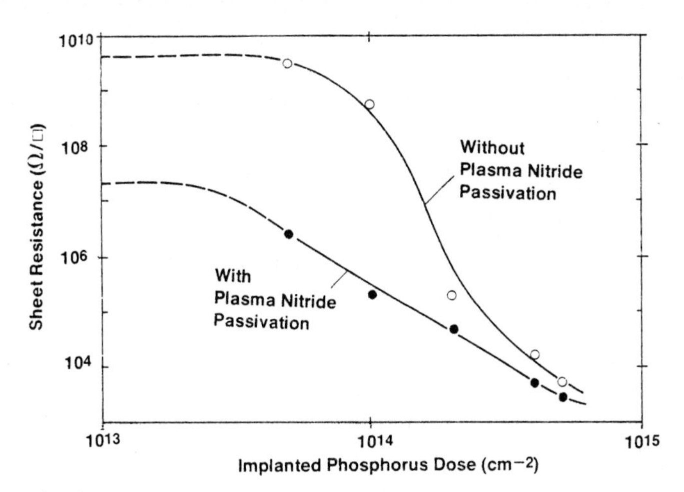

Fig.4. Measured sheet resistance of polysilicon as a function of implanted phosphorus dose, with and without a plasma nitride passivation after metallization

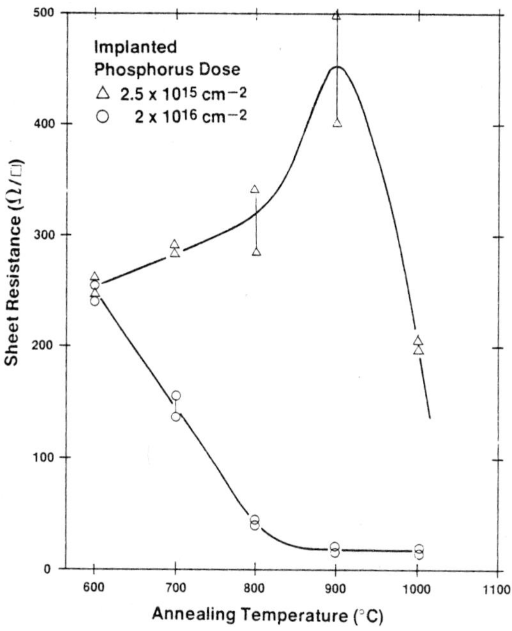

Fig.5. Measured sheet resistance of phosphorus-doped polysilicon (2.5×10^{15} cm^{-2} and 2×10^{16} cm^{-2}) after annealing at different temperatures. (From H. Oppolzer, R. Falckenberg and E. Doering /22/)

3.2. Lateral Spread of Implanted Dopants

It has been shown that implanted ions are scattered laterally by about the same distance as vertically /23, 24/. Fig.6 shows a calculated boron profile after $^{11}B^+$ ion implantation /24/. If this implantation is used for source and drain doping of a p-channel transistor, the gate-to-drain overlap is about 0.6 μm, even without any drive-in processing. Large gate-to-drain overlap regions are undesirable because a high capacitance between the gate and the drain degrades the switching speed of the transistor.

The lateral spread of implanted boron can be reduced by using lower acceleration voltages or heavier ions such as BF_2^+ as the implanting species.

In the case of arsenic sources and drains, the lateral spread of arsenic after ion implantation is not important in actual devices, since during annealing, the arsenic atoms generally diffuse over a distance which is larger than the range of the lateral spread. Again, the capacitance between gate and drain may be too high.

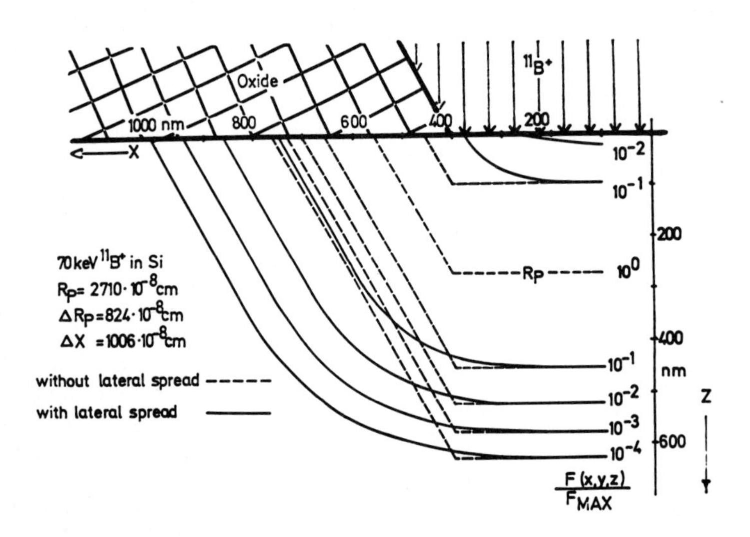

Fig. 6. Calculated boron-doping profile after ion implantation of 70 keV $^{11}B^+$. $F(x,y,z)/F_{MAX}$ denotes the relative boron concentration. The lateral spread of the boron atoms is similar to the spread in normal direction (From H. Runge /24/)

The gate-to-drain overlap region can be reduced by offsetting the implantation mask edge with respect to the gate edge. A possible method to accomplish this is the formation of a silicon-dioxide mask on top of the polysilicon, where the lateral dimensions of the oxide mask are slightly larger than the polysilicon dimensions /25/. In another approach, the screen oxide in the source and drain regions is thermally grown at a relatively low temperature between 800 and 900 °C before ion implantation /26/. If the polysilicon is heavily doped with phosphorus, the oxide on the polysilicon sidewalls may be more than four times thicker than the screen oxide. The sidewall oxide spacer can also be realized by conformally depositing silicon dioxide over the patterned polysilicon, followed by an anisotropic etch-back of the SiO_2 just down to the polysilicon surface /27/.

It should be noted that apart from the disadvantageous overlap effect, a laterally graded drain junction similar to the doping profile shown in Fig. 6 is desirable since it reduces the high electric field, and thus avalanche currents at the drain corner during transistor operation at high voltages. A graded drain junction together with an offset gate would therefore present a favorable configuration /28/.

3.3. Contamination Introduced by Ion Implantation

Under the term "contamination" we understand any material except the desired dopant which is implanted into or deposited on the wafer during the implantation process.

Three types of contamination must be considered if standard ion implantation equipment is used, namely, sputtered neutral species, organic contamination and particles. As will be pointed out below, the particle problem may be severe; while the effect of the other types of contamination, if present, can be minimized by adequate steps in wafer processing.

Metal atoms sputtered from metal parts within the implanter may reach the wafer surface, despite the elimination of the neutral beam by the generally used deflection of the ion beam. Also, polymers stemming from the pump oil may be deposited. Both types of contamination have been reduced in modern implanters by proper choice of the materials for the metal parts and pump oils. As a further precaution, a screen oxide film is generally provided on the regions to be implanted with high doses. Treatment of the wafers in an oxygen plasma removes the polymer contamination, if necessary, while a dip etch in diluted hydrofluoric acid strips off the screen oxide, or at least the upper portion of the screen oxide where the heavy metal contamination is localized. The dip etch procedure is not fully uncritical. Since wet etching is isotropic, polysilicon structures will be undercut, leading to undesirable effects such as residues in the cavities beneath the polysilicon edges and upbending of the polysilicon edges after thermal oxidation.

Particles falling on a wafer before ion implantation may locally prevent implantation. This effect sometimes presents a serious yield problem. Most critical are photoresist particles, which may blister off from the wafer surface due to mechanical damage caused by wafer clamping or by an improper automatic wafer-transport system in the implanter. Particles that don't fall on a wafer remain in the implanter and may be blown on other wafers during a later run. This effect is pronounced in those parts of the implanter where the gas flow is temporarily high, e.g. in the vicinity of load locks.

As an example, Fig.7 shows the result of particle detection before and after running a wafer through an ion implanter. Even more particles were found on the backside of the wafer. Of course, the design and operation of an implanter are not the only factors which influence particle contamination. Proper cleaning of the contaminated parts of the implanter and adequate photoresist processing are equally important.

Two other types of contamination should be mentioned. One of them is oxygen knock-on implantation, which will be discussed in the next paragraph on radiation damage. The other "contamination" effect is the dissociation of molecular

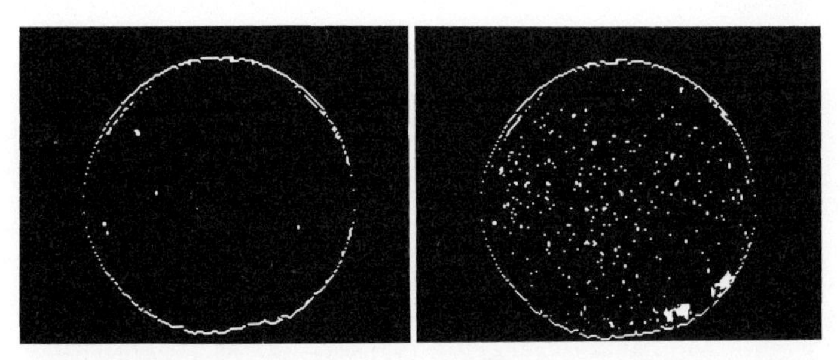

Fig.7. Particles detected on a wafer before (left picture) and after (right picture) running the wafer through an ion implanter. Ion implantation itself was omitted. The particle contamination is exaggerated on the pictures because the white spots which indicate the particles appear much larger than the particles

ions in certain ion-implanter types. An important example for this effect is the dissociation of BF_2^+ into B^+ and fluorine after mass analysis and prior to the final acceleration /29/. The B^+ ions are accelerated by the same acceleration voltage as the BF_2^+ ions and therefore reach a higher velocity and penetrate deeper into the wafers. In a CMOS process, where BF_2^+ implantation is used for shallow p^+ sources and drains, this effect is disastrous not only because the junction depth is larger than with BF_2^+ ions alone, but also because the oxide-mask thickness may not be thick enough to prevent penetration of the high-velocity boron ions into the n^+ source and drain regions (compare Fig. 11). The latter effect causes degradation of the breakdown behaviour of the n-channel transistors.

3.4. Damage Introduced in Materials by Ion Implantation

It is well known that high-dose ion implantations leave residual defects in silicon, even after high-temperature annealing /5,30-33/. Fig.8 shows the different stages of recrystallization of an amorphous zone produced by a high-energy high-dose arsenic implantation /33/.

It has been shown that the penetration of the residual dislocations corresponds to the penetration depth of knock-on oxygen /5/. For arsenic implanta-

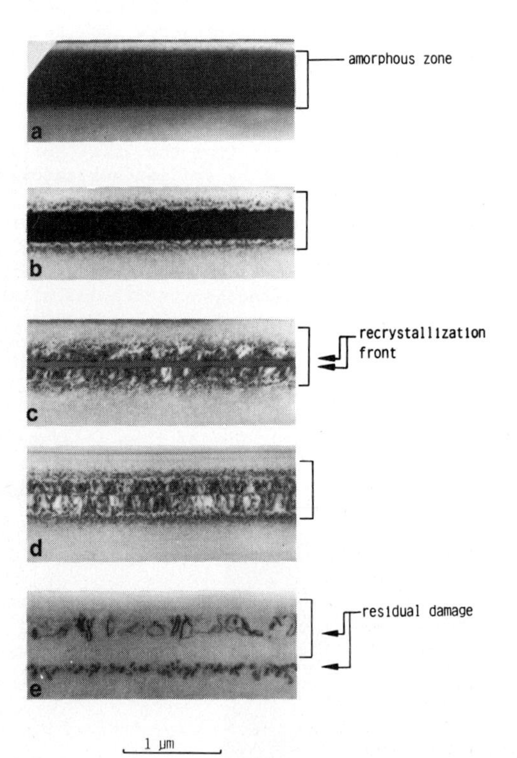

Fig.8. TEM micrographs of cross-sections through a silicon wafer implanted with a dose of 10^{15} cm^{-2} As^{++} at an energy of 760 keV. (a) As implanted. (b)-(d) Different stages of recrystallization during annealing by irradiating the backside of the wafer with a scanned electron beam. (e) Residual defects after a thermal furnace annealing at 930 ^{o}C for 30 minutes. (From E.F. Krimmel et al. /33/)

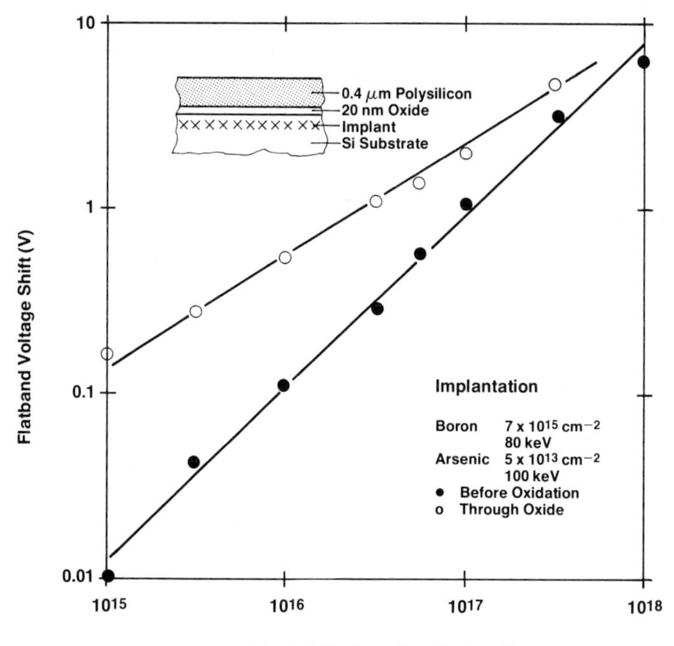

Fig.9. Measured flatband-voltage shifts of MOS structures after injection of electrons into the oxide. The upper curve corresponds to the case where the implantation indicated in the insert was carried out through the oxide followed by a 900 $^{\circ}$C anneal, while the lower curve corresponds to the case where the same implantation was carried out into bare silicon before oxidation at 900 $^{\circ}$C. The double implantation which was used for the experiment is of importance for so-called high- capacitance dynamic memory cells /34/. (From W. Müller, private communication)

tion energies below 100 keV the residual damage is within a surface layer of 0.1 μm.

It is important to know if there is any detrimental effect of the residual lattice damage on device performance. Several authors have demonstrated that the n^+p and p^+n junction leakage current is so small (< 50 nA/cm^2) that any influence of the damaged region can be neglected /5,31,32/, at least for junction depths down to 0.2 μm. This finding is explained by the fact that the junction depth in present devices is larger than the residual damage penetration.

Unlike the implantation damage in silicon, the damage introduced in SiO_2 films may have a deleterious effect on device performance. Figs. 9 and 10 show two examples.

In Fig. 9, the measured flatband voltage shift of a MOS structure with a polysilicon electrode is plotted in terms of the electron density injected into the 20 nm thick SiO_2 insulator at high electric fields. If all injected electrons travel through the oxide, the same flatband voltage will be measured before and after electron injection. If there are, however, traps in the oxide, part of the electrons will be trapped, thereby leading to a threshold-voltage shift. Fig.9 reveals a higher trap density for the case where the dopants were implanted through the SiO_2 film which acted as the insulator in the MOS structure. It is assumed from this result that ion implantation increases the trap density in the oxide.

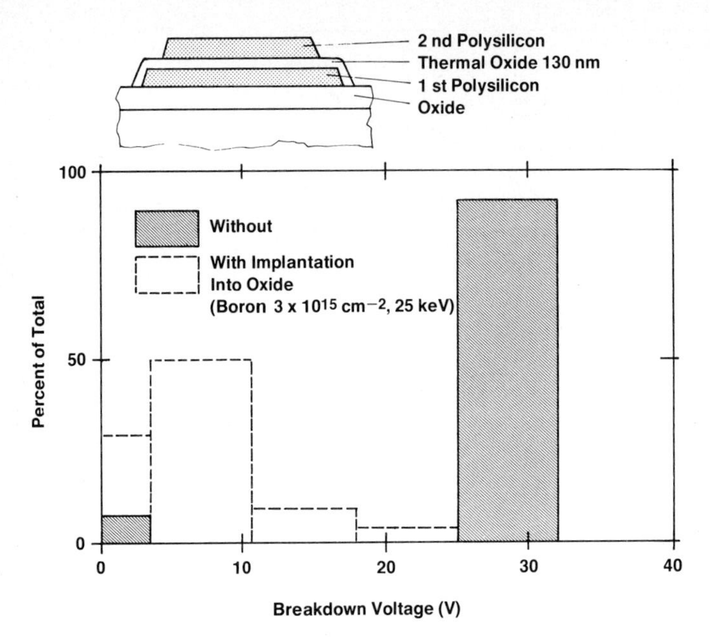

Fig.10. Distribution of the breakdown voltage of a polysilicon/oxide/polysilicon capacitor with and without implantation of boron into the oxide. The degraded breakdown behaviour of the boron-implanted oxide may be disastrous if so-called switched capacitors are integrated in a CMOS technology

As another example of oxide damage by ion implantation,Fig.10 demonstrates a severe degradation of the breakdown behaviour of a polysilicon/ thermal-oxide/polysilicon capacitor if a high boron dose was implanted into the oxide before the deposition of the upper polysilicon.

A further oxide-degradation effect has been found due to heavy arsenic implantation into the field oxide, which acts as a mask against source and drain implantation in MOS processes. If the upper portion of the field oxide which incorporates the implanted arsenic is left on the wafer, the threshold voltage of the field-oxide transistors is considerably reduced /35/. The effect has been attributed to charges in the oxide.

Advanced MOS integrated circuits with a polysilicon/metal-silicide double layer instead of polysilicon may have the metal silicide uncovered during source and drain implantation, and the question arises if there is any degradation of the silicide resistivity. For 0.2 μm tantalum disilicide on 0.3 μm doped polysilicon, it has been found that after arsenic source and drain implantation the sheet resistance increased from 2.5 Ω/□ to 7.5 Ω/□ , but full recovery was observed after a 900 °C anneal /36/.

3.5. Problems With Ion-Implantation Masks

In NMOS and CMOS processes, photoresist, SiO_2, and polysilicon are primarily used as implantation-mask materials.

While photoresist masking is uncritical at low doses, the resist mask may be degraded at high doses, and stripping of the resist may become difficult. If, however, the photoresist mask is stabilized prior to implantation, such as by a high-temperature bake (200 °C) or by plasma hardening /37/, and if the wafers are cooled during implantation, even high ion currents can be used.

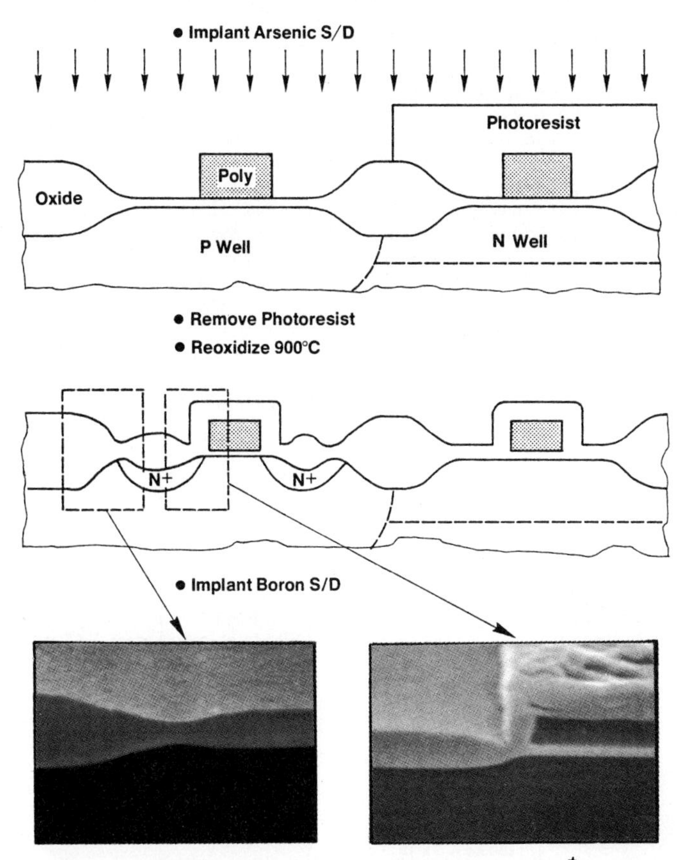

Fig.11. Oxide-thinning effect at the edges of n^+ regions during low-temperature (900 °C) CMOS processing. The thinned oxide portions may cause boron penetration into bulk silicon during the subsequent boron source and drain implantation

Care must be taken to avoid excessive sodium contamination of the SiO_2 beneath the photoresist, since some positive resists are known to contain small amounts of sodium, which can leave the resist and migrate into the SiO_2 during high-temperature baking or resist stripping in an oxygen plasma /38/.

A problem with SiO_2 masking against ion implantation can appear during low-temperature (900 °C) CMOS processing. As depicted in Fig.11, arsenic source and drain implantation is followed by a thermal reoxidation. Since highly doped regions oxidize faster, the oxide on top of the n^+ regions can be made thick enough to act as a mask during the subsequent boron source and drain implantation, while the oxide on the source and drain regions of the p-channel transistor is just thin enough to act as a screen oxide for the boron implantation.

Unfortunately, the oxide near to the edges of the n^+ regions tends to be thinner than in the interior of the n^+ regions. The thinner portions of the masking oxide may be too thin to provide sufficient masking against the boron implantation. As a consequence, the breakdown behaviour of the n-channel transistor may be degraded. The oxide-thinning effect can be explained by the lower arsenic concentration at the n^+ edges due to two-dimensional arsenic diffusion during oxidation.

In a silicon gate process, the polysilicon acts as a mask during source and drain implantation in order to prevent dopant penetration into the channel regions of transistors. Under certain conditions, improper masking has been observed /39,40/. Fig.12 shows our own results. $5x10^{15}$ cm^{-2} of arsenic ions were implanted into 0.4 μm thick polysilicon at different energies. The polysilicon was on top of a 50 nm thick gate oxide. If the grain size of the polysilicon is small compared to the polysilicon thickness - this is the case for undoped polysilicon - there is no indication of arsenic penetration into the bulk silicon even at ion energies of 180 keV. If the grain size is so large that the grains extend over the total polysilicon thickness - this is the case for heavily phosphorus doped and annealed polysilicon - the threshold voltage of transistors begins to be shifted for ion energies above about 100 keV. At 180 keV, the threshold-voltage shift corresponds to a penetrated arsenic dose of $3x10^{11}$ cm^{-2}. The effect has been explained by arsenic channeling through the polysilicon grains /39, 40/.

Cross Section TEMs of Polysilicon	Arsenic Implantation Data	Threshold Voltage Shift
	80... 180 keV $5 x 10^{15} cm^{-2}$	< 0.05 V
	80 keV, $5 x 10^{15} cm^{-2}$	< 0.05 V
	100 keV, $5 x 10^{15} cm^{-2}$	− 0.10 V
	180 keV, $5 x 10^{15} cm^2$	− 1.35 V

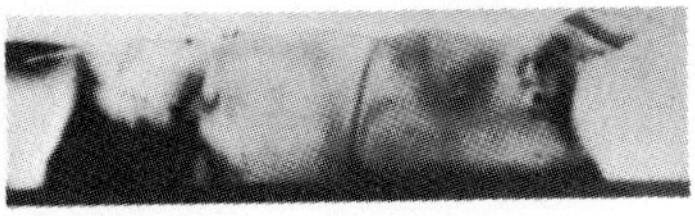

Fig.12. Threshold-voltage shift of a transistor after arsenic source and drain implantation at different ion energies. If the polysilicon grains are small (upper TEM micrograph), there is no indication of arsenic penetration through the polysilicon. Large grains (lower TEM micrograph) lead to large threshold-voltage shifts at high implantation energies. The effect has been explained by arsenic channeling through the polysilicon

3.6. Geometrical Limitations of Ion Implantation

In contrast to thermal dopant deposition, which exhibits uniform doping of surface elements independent on their orientation, ion implantation is a highly directional doping process. This special feature of ion implantation can be used for a controlled offset between the mask edge and the edge of the implanted region, for example in the case where the upper portion of the mask is overhanging /25/, or where an oblique angle of incidence is used together with steep mask sidewalls. In another approach, a very small transistor channel length is obtained by implanting boron and arsenic at different penetration depths through a tapered polysilicon sidewall /41/. There are, however, also some limitations of directional doping.

First, it must be taken into account that the backside of the wafers is not implanted, unless an extra implantation run is provided. Implantation of both sides of the wafers may be important, for example, in processes which use the gettering effect of heavily phosphorus doped regions by doping the total back surface of the wafers.

Regarding the front side of a wafer, the directional nature of ion implantation must be considered whenever the surface topography exhibits steep steps. If, for example, a polysilicon film conformally deposited over a stepped surface is doped by ion implantation, the non-horizontal portions of the polysilicon films will receive a smaller dose. The non-uniform dose distribution may have consequences for the etch-rate uniformity and for the resistance of polysilicon interconnections.

Another effect is illustrated in Fig.13, which shows a buried contact structure used in silicon-gate integrated circuits. Since, due to overlay errors, the contact area between the polysilicon and the bulk silicon must generally be smaller than the oxide opening, anisotropic etching of the polysilicon can lead to deep trenches in the bulk silicon, especially if excessive overetching is necessary for other reasons. As shown in Fig.13, subsequent source and drain implantation and drive-in may leave portions of the steep sidewalls undoped. The disconnection between the n^+ regions causes a high resistance between the polysilicon and the bulk n^+ region on the left-hand side of Fig. 13.

The geometrical effect of the generally used 7° tilting of the wafers with respect to the ion beam during ion implantation can be neglected in most

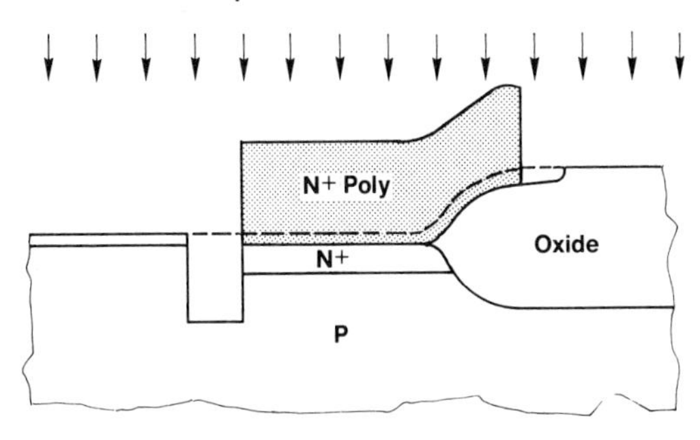

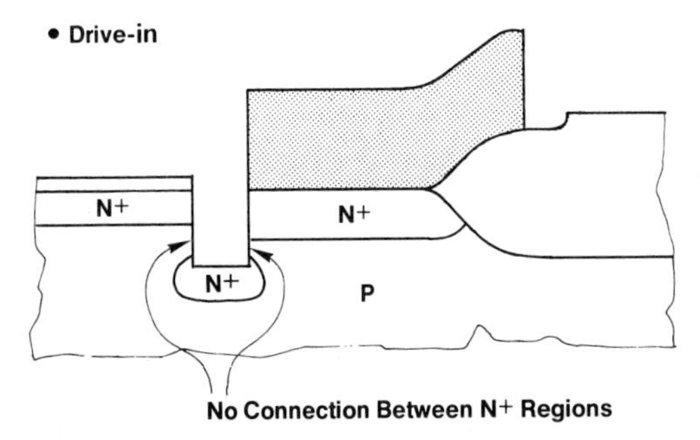

Fig.13. Schematical illustration of the effect of a possible disconnection between n^+ regions in a buried contact structure, if anisotropic etching of polysilicon is used with considerable overetching. Upper part: Cross-sectional view during ion implantation. Lower part: After drive-in

actual integrated circuits. With further down-scaling of the lateral dimensions accompanied by the trend towards vertical mask sidewalls, the effect will become more important. For example, the overlap between the gate and the source and drain regions of MOS transistors varies by 0.06 μm for arbitrarily oriented transistors, if 0.5 μm thick polysilicon with vertical sidewalls is used. For photoresist masks, which are usually 1 to 1.5 μm thick, the variation of the offset between the mask edge and the edge of the doped region would be correspondingly larger. If the mask sidewalls exhibit a negative slope angle of more than 7°, the offset variation would even be doubled. Similar limitations have to be considered for those approaches mentioned at the beginning of this paragraph which make use of the directional doping /25,41/, because the desired offset distances between different edges depend on the orientation of the mask edge with respect to the incident ion beam.

4. Conclusions

In advanced integrated circuit manufacturing, ion implantation has almost entirely replaced thermal dopant-deposition techniques, due to its well known benefits. A few effects must, however, be taken into account, which may present physical or technical limitations. They are summarized in this paper. The majority of the limitations is not critical, if proper process steps are provided before and after ion implantation.

Economical limitations have not been discussed in this paper. Another field which has been omitted is process modeling. Although much progress has been made to simulate implantation and drive-in processes, there is often disagreement between simulated and measured results.

In addition to the standard applications of ion implantation, actual developments offer new fields for this technique. Future integrated circuit manufacturing may make use of implanted buried isolating and conducting layers, implanted nitride-like layers as oxidation barriers, rapid annealing techniques, recrystallized polysilicon for three-dimensional integration, ion-implantation-induced contact and alloy formation, and other possibilities.

References

1 L. Risch, C. Werner, W. Müller, A.W. Wieder: IEEE Trans. Electron Dev. ED-29, 601 (1982)

2 H. Sunami, K. Shimohigashi, N. Hashimoto: IEEE Trans. Electron Dev. ED-29, 607 (1982)

3 S. Ogura, P.J. Tsang, W.W. Walker, D.L. Critchlow, J.F. Shepard: IEEE Trans. Electron Dev. ED-27, 1359 (1980)

4 P.J. Tsang, S. Ogura, W.W. Walker, J.F. Shepard, D.L. Critchlow: IEEE Trans. Electron Dev. ED-29, 590 (1982)

5 Y. Wada, N. Hashimoto: J. Electrochem. Soc. 127, 461 (1980)

6 T.M. Lin, W.G. Oldham: IEEE Electron Dev. Lett. EDL-2, 275 (1981)

7 R.B. Fair: Sol. State Technol., 220 (April 1982)

8 G. Fuse, T. Hirao, K. Inoue, S. Takayanagi, Y. Yaegashi: J. Appl. Phys. 53, 3650 (1982)

9 R.R. Razouk, L.N. Lie: Electrochem. Soc. Spring Meeting 1982, Abstract No. 85

10 M. Delfino, T.A. Reifsteck: IEEE Electron Dev. Lett. EDL-3, 116 (1982)

11 A.C. Adams, C.D. Capio: J. Electrochem. Soc. 126, 423 (1981)

12 M.M. Mandurah et al.: J. Electrochem. Soc. 126, 1019 (1979)

13 W.G. Oldham: Deutsche Offenlegungsschrift No. 2704626 (1977)

14 B.L. Crowder, S. Zirinsky: IEEE Trans. Electron Dev. ED-26, 369 (1979)

15 A.K. Sinha: J. Vac. Sci. Technol. 19, 778 (1981)

16 D.B. Scott, Y.C. See, C.K. Lau, R.D. Davies: IEDM Digest of Technical Papers, 538 (1981)

17 P.A. Gargini, I. Beinglass: IEDM Digest of Techn. Papers, 54 (1981)

18 T.I. Kamins: J. Electrochem. Soc. 126, 833 (1979)

19 A.K. Gosh et al.: J. Appl. Phys. 51, 446 (1980)

20 M.M. Mandurah et al.: Appl. Phys. Lett. 36, 683 (1980)

21 T. Makino, H. Nakamura: Appl. Phys. Lett. 35, 551 (1979)

22 H. Oppolzer, R. Falckenberg, E. Doering: In Institute of Physics Conf. Ser. 60, Sect. 6-1981, Proceedings 2nd Conf. on Microscopy of Semiconducting Materials, p. 283

23 H. Matsumura, S. Furukawa: Japan. J. Appl. Phys. 14, 1983 (1976)

24 H. Runge: Phys. Stat. Sol. (a) 39, 595 (1977)

25 R. Sigusch, K.H. Horninger, W.A. Müller, D. Widmann, W.G. Oldham: IEDM Digest of Technical Papers, 429 (1980)

26 H. Sunami, M. Koyanagi: Japan. J. Appl. Phys. 18, 255 (1979)

27 S. Ogura, P.J. Tsang, W.W. Walker, D.L. Critchlow, J.F. Shepard: IEDM Digest of Technical Papers, 651 (1981)

28 E. Takeda, H. Kume, T. Toyabe, S. Asai: IEEE Trans. Electron Dev. ED-29, 611 (1982)

29 T.W. Sigmon, V.R. Deline, C.A. Evans, W.M. Katz: J. Electrochem. Soc. 127, 981 (1980)

30 S. Mader, A.E. Michel: J. Vac. Sci. Technol. 13, 391 (1976)

31 H.J. Geipel, R.B. Shasteen: IBM J. Res. Develop. 24, 362 (1980)

32 W. Fichtner, R.M. Levin, T.T. Sheng, R.B. Marcus: Electrochem. Soc. Spring Meeting 1982, Abstract No. 182

33 E.F. Krimmel, H. Oppolzer, H. Runge, W. Wondrak: Phys. Stat. Sol. (a) 66, 565 (1981)

34 A.F. Tasch et al.: IEEE Trans. Electron. Dev. ED-25, 33 (1978)

35 W.R. Hunter, L. Ephrath, W.D. Grobman, C.M. Osburn, B.L. Crowder, A. Cramer, H.E. Luhn: IEEE Trans. Electron Dev. ED-26, 353 (1979)

36 D. Pawlik, E. Doering, H. Oppolzer: Electrochem. Soc. Spring Meeting 1982, Abstract No. 195

37 J.M.Moran, G.N. Taylor: J. Vac. Sci. Technol. 19, 1127 (Nov./Dec. 1981)

38 G. Bell, R. Stokan: Electrochem. Soc. Fall Meeting 1977, Abstract No. 139

39 Y. Wada, S. Nishimatsu, N. Hashimoto: J. Electrochem. Soc. 127, 206 (1980)

40 T.E. Seidel: Appl. Phys. Lett. 36, 447 (1980)

41 J. Tihanyi, D. Widmann: IEDM Digest of Technical Papers, 399 (1977)

Implant Processes for Bipolar Product Manufacturing and Their Effects on Device Yield

J.L. Forneris, G.B. Forney, R.A. Cavanagh, G. Hrebin, Jr., J.L. Blouse
IBM General Technology Division East Fishkill Facility, RT. 52,
Hopewell Junction, NY 12533, USA

I. Introduction

A major technology conversion is in progess at IBM's largest bipolar semiconductor manufacturing facility. Ion implantation is being implemented to replace the capsule diffusion process which for years was the most integral part of the IBM manufacturing technology. Implant processes are being used to fabricate subcollector and emitter device elements on IBM's most advanced logic and memory LSI chips. These products have been qualified with the implant processes and are being routinely manufactured and shipped to computer assembly facilities for applications in a broad series of IBM systems.

The technology conversion from capsule to ion implantation was not without difficulties. Problems stemmed from compatibility issues with the capsule process relative to process operations and product performance. Additionally, manufacturability had to be developed into the process as it was applied to larger and larger product volumes. Competing with a process (capsule) that had matured to a high level of manufacturing stability presented a significant challenge. In the first part of this paper we intend to describe the current implant processes in use and illustrate how some of the problems we encountered determined the final configuration of those processes.

The initial motivation for pursuing the technology conversion to implantation was based primarily on the technical advantages offered by the process: dose control, profile flexibility, process automation, safety, etc., and additionally, to serve as a bridge to the future.

Maintaining a competitive edge in semiconductors requires pursuit of state-of-the-art processes. The innovative talents of engineering are best applied to new processes where discovery and learning often lead to a lower cost, higher quality product. Through a highly motivated manufacturing engineering effort, a favorable cost advantage for implantation began to emerge. It stemmed from a variety of factors including: improved process yields, higher productivity and most importantly, significant increases in end of line product yield. During the entire experimental qualification period and in early phases of low level implementation, we consistently demonstrated the potential of the implant processes to reduce key semiconductor defects. This data provided the necessary justification and leverage to expand our plans of replacing the capsule process with implantation. We intend to discuss the effects of implantation on device defects and its interaction with the physical properties of the product.

II. Product Description

A cross section of an integrated N-P-N transistor Schottky-barrier diode structure, in which implanted emitter and subcollector processes are employed, is shown in Figure 1. The boron-doped p_+ substrate has a [100] orientation and a resistivity of 10-20 Ω-cm. The N^+ arsenic subcollector (buried layer) $7\Omega/\square$ and N^+ phosphorous-doped collector reach-through $25\Omega/\square$, provides a low ohmic path for emitter to collector current. This region serves the same purpose for Schottky barrier diode current flow. The arsenic-doped N^- epitaxy layer is 2μ thick with a resistivity of 0.2Ω-cm. The P boron base is diffused into the epitaxy to a depth of $0.75\mu m$ with a $400\Omega/\square$ sheet resistance. Completing the transistor structure is the N^+ arsenic emitter, $0.5\mu m$ in depth, with a $17.5\Omega/\square$ resistivity. Device elements are isolated from each other by a vertically integrated diffused junction-dielectric structure. The P^+ boron isolation diffusion into the substrate subsequently outdiffuses and intercepts the recessed oxide isolation (ROI), completing the electrical isolation of the device. Device passivation is achieved by a dual thermal oxide and CVD nitride layer. Metal to silicon contact is made through etched windows into which a Pt-Si alloy has been formed. Schottky-barrier diodes are formed in regions where the Pt-Si alloy forms over N^- epitaxy. The above-described device structure is interconnected with other device elements through three levels of interconnection metallurgy (not shown in Figure).

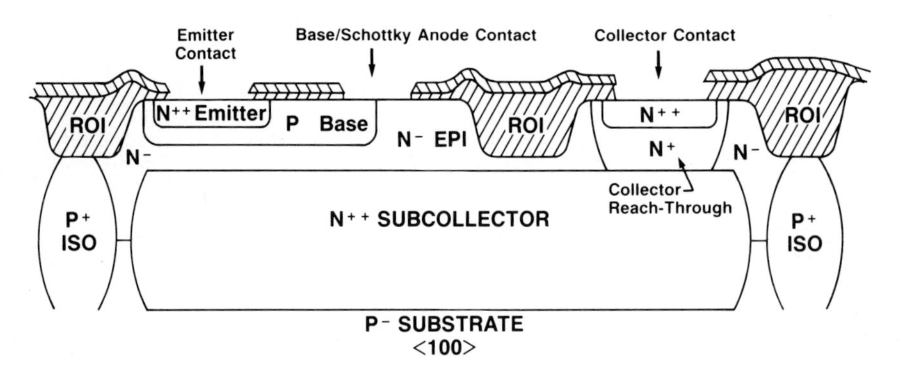

Fig. 1. NPN Schottky Clamped Transistor (not to scale)

III. Implanted Emitter Process Description

The processes used in fabricating the device structure in Figure 1 are identical through the etching of the contact holes through the nitride layer whether a capsule or implanted emitter process is subsequently used. However, from that point on, the process operations are significantly different. The description of the critical implant emitter operations follows with cross sections of process sequences shown in Figure 2a.

Emitter Oxide Etch. Etching of the oxides on those contacts that are to receive emitter implant is critical. The process must be tightly controlled in order to minimize the lateral etch of the oxide layer below the nitride

Fig. 2A. Implant Emitter Process Sequence

EMITTER OXIDE ETCH

COLLECTOR OXIDE ETCH

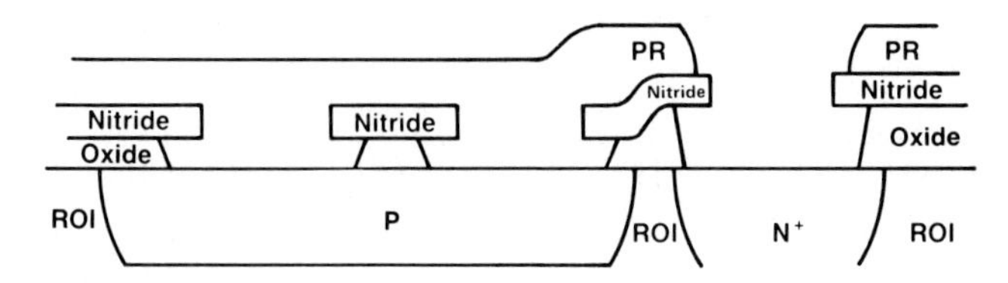

SCREEN OXIDE + IMPLANT MASK + IMPLANT

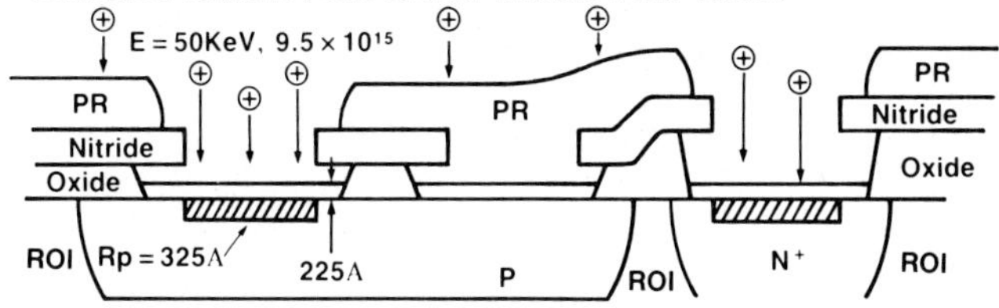

ANNEAL/REDISTRIBUTION + S/O ETCH

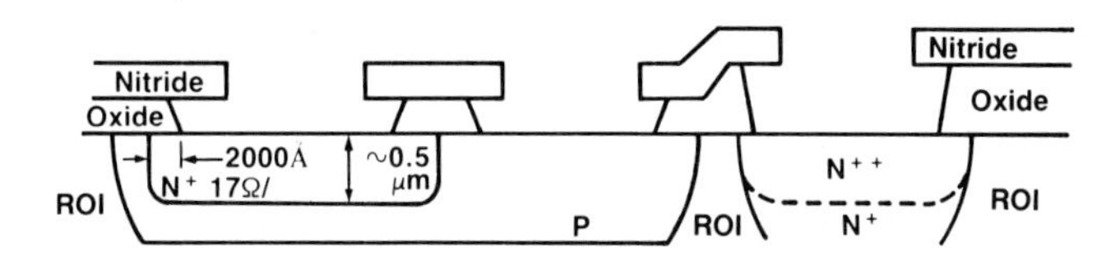

(undercut) while still guaranteeing total oxide removal to silicon. The undercutting is controlled to a nominal 1000A by means of a two-step etch process. First, a controlled etch is used to remove the thinner oxide in the emitter contact. This etch is defined by the same mask used in etching nitride contacts. A rather concentrated etch is used in this operation, contrary to the practice of using dilute etches for maximum time control. Practice has shown us that dilute etches are ineffective in uniformly removing oxides and residues from small contact holes (≤ 2.5 μm). It is necessary to guarantee that all oxide is totally removed from the contact holes. Otherwise, the proper As dose will not be implanted in the emitters. After this etch, a selective mask is applied to etch the remaining contacts. The emitter contacts are protected from additional etching, preserving the integrity of the nitride undercut, while the thicker collector oxide regions are etched to silicon. This precaution is taken to minimize undercutting because of the anisotropic nature of implantation. Since the nitride edges of the contact hole effectively define the implanted area, the larger the undercut, the greater the distance between the implanted region and the oxide silicon interface. If that distance is not kept to a minimum, the subsequent thermal annealing redistribution cycle will not be sufficient to laterally move the implanted arsenic under the oxide. Without adequate junction passivation (~ 2000A), surface leakage currents increase, current gain degrades, and metallurgical emitter-base shorts may occur.

Screen Oxide. The purpose of the screen oxide is twofold: to prevent loss of implanted arsenic during subsequent anneal-redistribution heat cycles and to prevent stress-induced defects from moving laterally from implanted areas to the junction causing high levels of emitter-collector leakage [1].

The silicon surfaces are specially prepared by a Huang clean to insure the absolute cleanliness necessary for uniform oxide growth. As an additional guarantee for uniformity, the initial layers are grown in an HCl ambient. The oxide layer is controlled to 225 ± 5A across a 100 wafer process. This is a fundamental requirement to insure the profile integrity of the implanted arsenic. Small deviations in oxide thickness produce wide variances in transistor device parameters when implanting at the energy of our process.

Implant Masking. The implant mask defines the emitter and collector contacts that are to receive the As implant. The masking material used is organic photoresist. The mask alignment is non-critical with sufficient tolerances for easy manufacturing control. The fundamental requirement of this mask is that it maintain its integrity during implantation, protecting those regions not intended to receive implant with minimum outgassing and particle flaking. This can cause neutral beam effects and high levels of particulate contamination during implantation, leading to overdose conditions and blocked contacts respectively. In order to maintain photoresist integrity, it is crosslinked in a oxygen plasma and vacuum baked at high temperatures. Photoresist prepared in this fashion is able to withstand the implantation conditions described below.

Implantation. The As^+ implantation is performed in an IBM designed system (TACONIC). It is a 50 kev implant to a dose of 9.5×10^{15} ion/cm^2. Wafers are placed in a slotted groove on an Al disc. The disc is aligned 7° off the normal axis with respect to the beamline, and rotates at 2,000 rpm while moving translationally through a stationary beam. The translational velocity is modulated to compensate for the angular velocity differential between inner and outer radii of the disc. The beam current is 4mA on the latest TACONIC models. Electron radiation of the wafers occurs coincident with As^+ implant to neutralize charge buildup on wafers. Target chamber vacuum pressures are maintained at 10^{-6} torr with wafer temperatures not exceeding 200°C. Latest model TACONIC systems implant up to 30 wafers in a single run, lasting 20 minutes.

Implant Anneal and Redistribution. After implantation, photoresist is removed from the wafers. A pre-anneal wafer cleaning is performed to insure that all residues and particulates are removed. The wafers are subjected to a 1000°C N_2 ambient for 90 minutes nominally. During this period, the implant damage is completely annealed and the As is redistributed to obtain a profile equivalent to capsule profiles ($Co = 2 \times 10^{20}$, $Xj = .5\mu m$). Precautions are taken during the anneal to raise and lower the wafers to process temperatures in a controlled (°C/min.) manner. This is done to reduce the susceptibility of wafers to plastic deformation and related defects. The process is carried out with batch sizes up to 100 wafers with resistivity control within ± 3% of the 17.5Ω/□ nominal, 30% tighter than the capsule process. After annealing, the screen oxide is etched from the contacts, and the wafers are now ready for device metallurgy.

IV. Implant Subcollector Process

The implant subcollector process is quite similar in design to the implant emitter process. However, it is less critical relative to manufacturing process operations control. The implant subcollector process sequence is shown in Figure 2b. A brief description of its unique features and key process comparisons follow.

SUBCOLLECTOR OXIDE ETCH + SCREEN OXIDE + IMPLANTATION

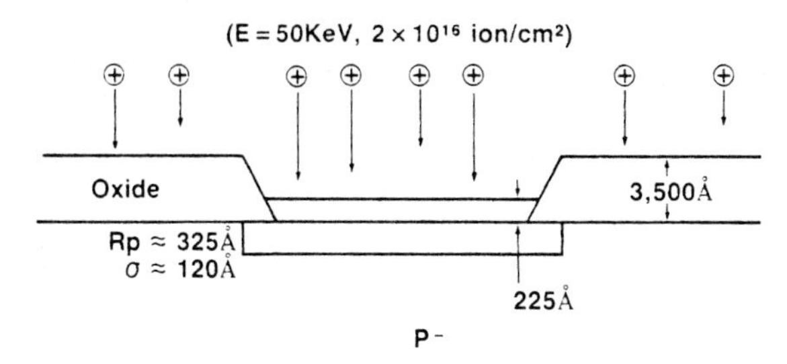

OXIDE ETCH + ANNEAL/REDISTRIBUTION

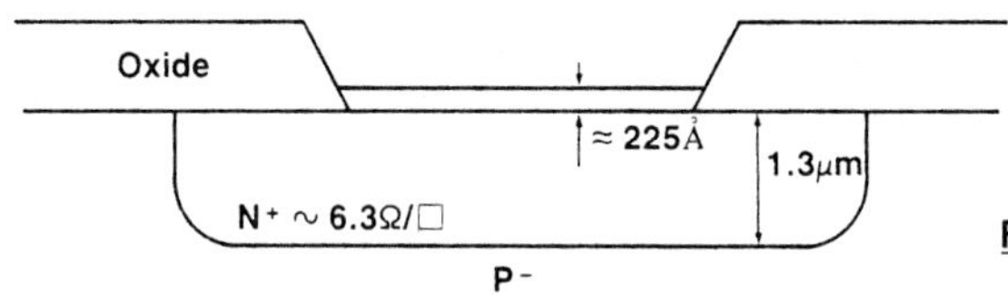

Fig. 2B. Implant Subcollector Process Sequence

The semiconductor process operations preceding either capsule or implanted subcollectors are identical through subcollector pattern etching with one exception. Capsule diffusion wafers require that oxides on the back of the wafers not be removed during subcollector oxide etch because of autodoping problems created at epi. This device side down procedure, which can contribute significantly to non-random defects, is not required for implanted subcollectors.

Subcollector Oxide Etch. This process is not as critical as the emitter oxide etch process due to the larger image sizes involved and the simplicity of the dielectric layer.

Screen Oxide. Wafers are prepared and screen oxide is grown in the subcollector regions in the same way as for the implant emitter. Its prime purpose is to prevent loss of As from vaporization during the subcollector anneal and redistribution heat cycles. The uniformity of the oxide is less critical for the subcollector due to the heavier As^+ doping, longer thermal cycle, and less sensitivity of dependent device parameters to Rs variations.

Implantation. Wafers are exposed directly to the implant beam without any masking material to delineate the subcollector regions. Masking is not required because the field oxide is sufficiently thick (3,500 Å) to prevent the penetration of 50 kev As^+. All implant processing parameters are identical to the emitter with the exception of dose (2.0×10^{16} ions/cm^2). After implantation, the screen oxide is partially etched in a dilute HF solution to remove any sputtered metallics that may have a deleterious effect on Epi quality.

Implant Anneal and Redistribution. The first portion of the implant subcollector anneal cycle exposes the wafers to an oxygen ambient at 780°C in order to preserve the thickness integrity of the screen oxide cap that had been previously etched. Oxide growth is limited to 100Å. The remainder of the heat cycle is performed at 1100°C in an Ar ambient for 90 minutes. Implant damage is annealed and the As redistributed to a depth of 1.3 $\pm$.2μm and a $Co \simeq 1\text{-}2 \times 10^{20}$ (S.R.).

No subsequent process operation is modified to accomodate implanted subcollectors except for epi. Due to the substantial decrease in arsenic pile-up at the silicon interface, relative to the capsule process, less autodoping occurs during epi growth. Consequently, the epi-layer is appropriately compensated to maintain device performance transparency with capsule product.

V. Measurement Strategy

The yield/defect characterization of the ion implant process was accomplished on product wafers containing the standard line monitoring diagnostic devices. In other words, we did not design special test vehicles for ion implant characterization. We relied on three sets of measurements for yield/defect monitoring. First, Si-probe leakage measurements made on a large Tx structure for early data feedback on process integrity and yield trends. Second, leakage measurements made on product test sites adjacent to product chips after device metal interconnections had been made. This provided the more detailed yield characterization necessary to delineate and understand process-device defect interactions. The product test site contains appropriate vehicles for monitoring both semiconductor and metallurgy-insulator yields. Included are multiple chains of parallel wired product transistors and Schottky diodes, with different active device areas. These device chains are of prime interest relative to yield characterization because of their high degree of sensitivity to both random and non-random device defects [2]. The third measurement is product test yields. Although less information is obtained relative to defect characterization than on test sites, this is the final measure of quality of a process and, ultimately, determines whether it will be implemented or rejected.

Data Base. The processes described above have been practiced in the manufacturing line with a high degree of stability since the first of the year. Prior to that, the processes and tools were undergoing changes to improve manufacturability and insure product performance transparency. Consequently, the data presented from the measurements described is generally restricted to the most recent time frame. Exceptions are identified. The control data or capsule diffusion data is from product runs, fabricated on the same manufacturing line and in the same time frame as the ion implant product. Thus we have an ideal manufacturing experiment for comparative analysis. Unfortunately, we are not able to control all the variables in the environment to facilitate data analysis (as in a lab experiment). However our measurement results are real and unequivocal.

VI. Leakage Limited Yield

Product yield is ultimately determined by a process' ability to center device parametric distributions to optimum yield and performance nominals while minimizing semiconductor defects. For the most part, semiconductor bipolar defects manifest themselves electrically as excessive junction leakages. These leakage currents prohibit the normal operation of a device and circuit, limiting product yields. As a consequence, bipolar process engineers are keyed to monitoring and improving the leakage limited yield (LLY) contribution of a process. The overall leakage limited yield of a transistor is a measure of the integrity of the leakage paths within a device: emitter to base, collector to base, and collector to emitter. The collector to emitter leakage path is the most significant detractor to LLY. The semiconductor defect that most often causes high collector to emitter leakages are referred to as "pipes". The control and reduction of pipes have been the object of intense engineering effort for many years in every bipolar manufacturing facility.

Parametrically, a pipe is detected with a BVceo test. Results of the test, to a minimum voltage criteria, are quoted in terms of BVceo or pipe yields. They manifest themselves electrically in an n-p-n transistor as a narrow, high resistance N-type conduction path between the emitter and collector regions as shown in Figure 3.

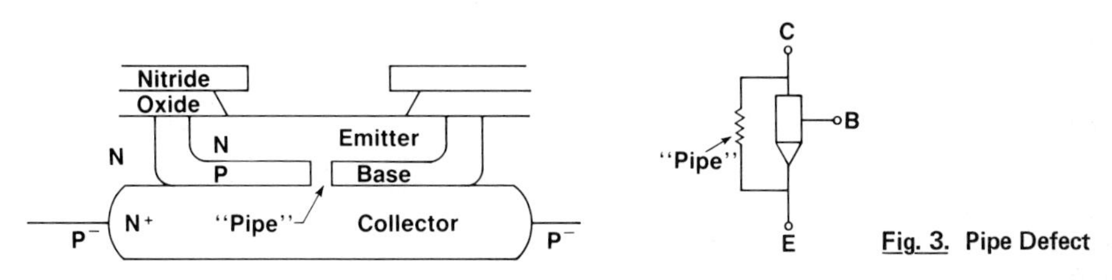

Fig. 3. Pipe Defect

Pipes can eminate from either the emitter or subcollector regions. They are caused and influenced by many factors: wafer stress, deleterious contaminants, crystallographic imperfections, etc. They are randomly distributed, and are in good agreement with Poisson's yield model:

$$Y = Yo \exp(-\lambda Ae)$$

where:

Yo = non-random defects
λ = pipe defect density
Ae = emitter area .

VII. Pipe Defect Improvements with Implanted Emitters

Data was collected on the data base described, on product test sites located on high density RAM product wafers, and plotted according to the model. Results are shown in Figure 4 for implant emitter and capsule emitter product. Both product types had capsule subcollectors. We observe that the Tx chain BV_{CEO} yields for implant emitter are higher than capsule primarily due to a reduction in pipe defect density, λ(110 defects/cm^2 vs. 132 defects/cm^2). The higher yield is also attributed, to a lesser degree, to non-random defects, indicative of an overall "cleaner" process.

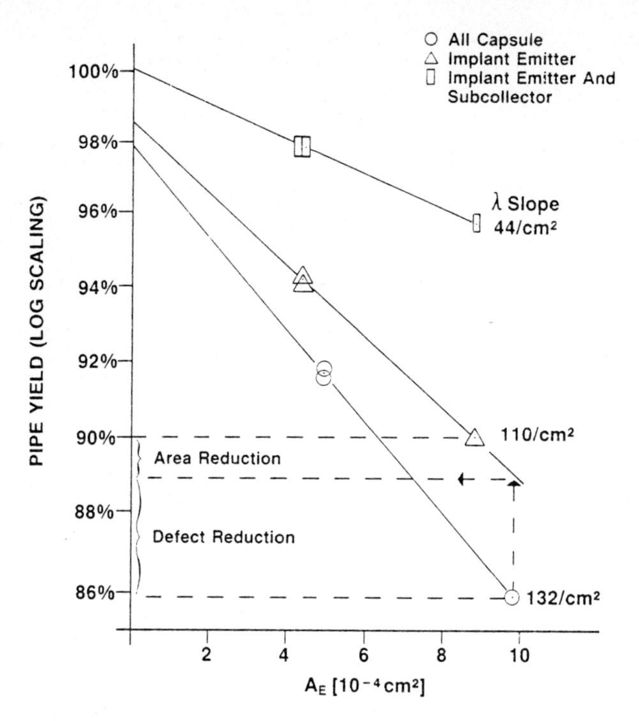

Fig. 4. **Pipe Yield (CEO) vs. Emitter Area**

We note that the yield points for implant, although derived from the same number of transistor chains, correspond to a smaller total emitter area. This is due to the anisotropic nature of implantation. Figure 5 shows an emitter contact and illustrates the junction formation for implant and diffused processes. The nitride openings are identical for both cases and are determined solely by photolithographic technology limitations. In the case of the capsule, the emitter size is ultimately determined by the oxide opening beneath the nitride because of the isotropic nature of diffusion, whereas for the implant, the emitter size is determined by the nitride opening because of the anisotropic nature of implantation. This effect

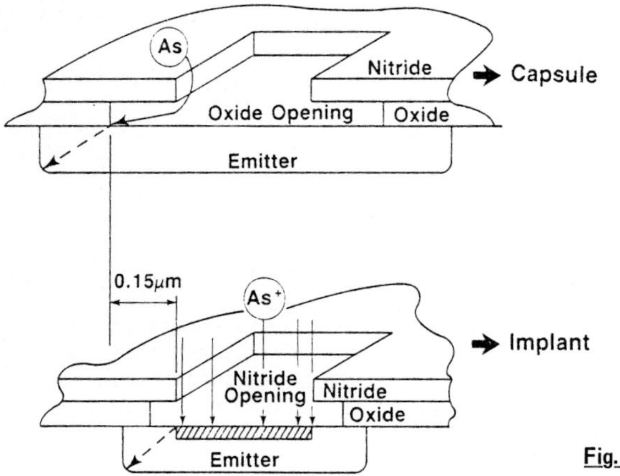

Fig. 5. **Implant Size Reduction**

produces a 0.15μm per edge reduction in emitter geometry for implant compared to capsule. Finally, we must consider an additional compensation for implant because of its narrower lateral diffusion. Considering both effects, there is an 11% net area reduction in the 3 x 5μm emitter transistors that make up the Tx chain. If the total emitter area of the Tx chain is not corrected, an error will result in calculating λ leading one to assume an overly optimistic reduction in defect density.

Although only a small part of the BV_{CEO} yield improvement on the 3 x 5μm emitter Tx chain was due to implant area reduction, it is obvious that the area reduction effects have greater impact on smaller geometries. Considering a 2.5μm diameter emitter, we would realize a 17% area reduction with implant over capsule. Phototechnology continues to push with exceeding difficulty towards smaller and smaller dimensions for reduction in emitter area for increased yield. With implant, an added "shrink" is provided designs without any phototechnology changes.

Having discussed the ramifications of area reduction, we turn our attention to the improvement realized in λ. We are aware that wafer stress plays a key role in the generation of pipe defects. Our observations support a position identifying the reduction of warpage as a contributing factor towards λ improvements.

Both thermal stress and bulk wafer properties play a key role in determining wafer tensile strength and resistance to plastic deformation. We know that the implant processes do not alter the key bulk wafer properties that affect warpage. The different warpage characteristics exhibited by implant wafers must therefore be related to differences in thermal stress. Figure 6 shows the differences in thermal profiles between the capsule diffusion process and the anneal/redistribution cycle of the implant process. The process operating temperature (1000°C) and ramp rates are the same for both. However, wafer insertion and withdrawal occurs at 950°C for capsule but 780°C for implant. The difference in insertion temperature is not as critical as the withdrawal temperature. As the edge of the wafer cools and contracts, the wafers bow in a concave direction. Typical wafer bows resulting from capsule processing are from .2 to 2 mils deviation from flat as measured optically. As the wafer bows, slip defects propagate through the wafer to emitter regions. Arsenic diffusion is enhanced along these

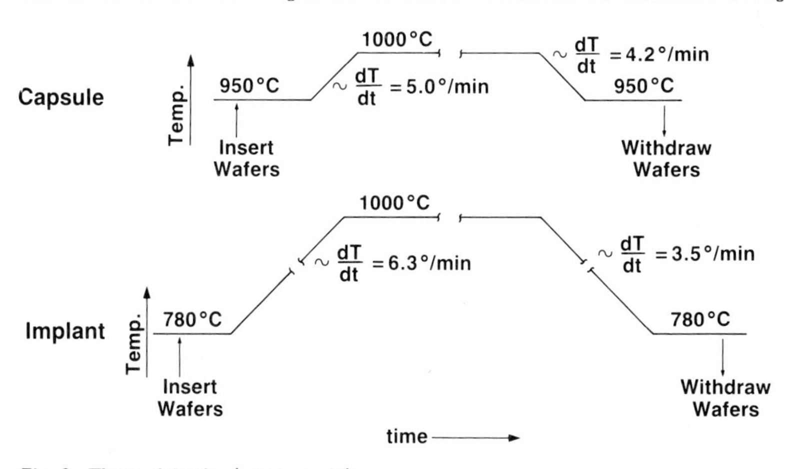

Fig. 6. Thermal Cycles (not to scale)

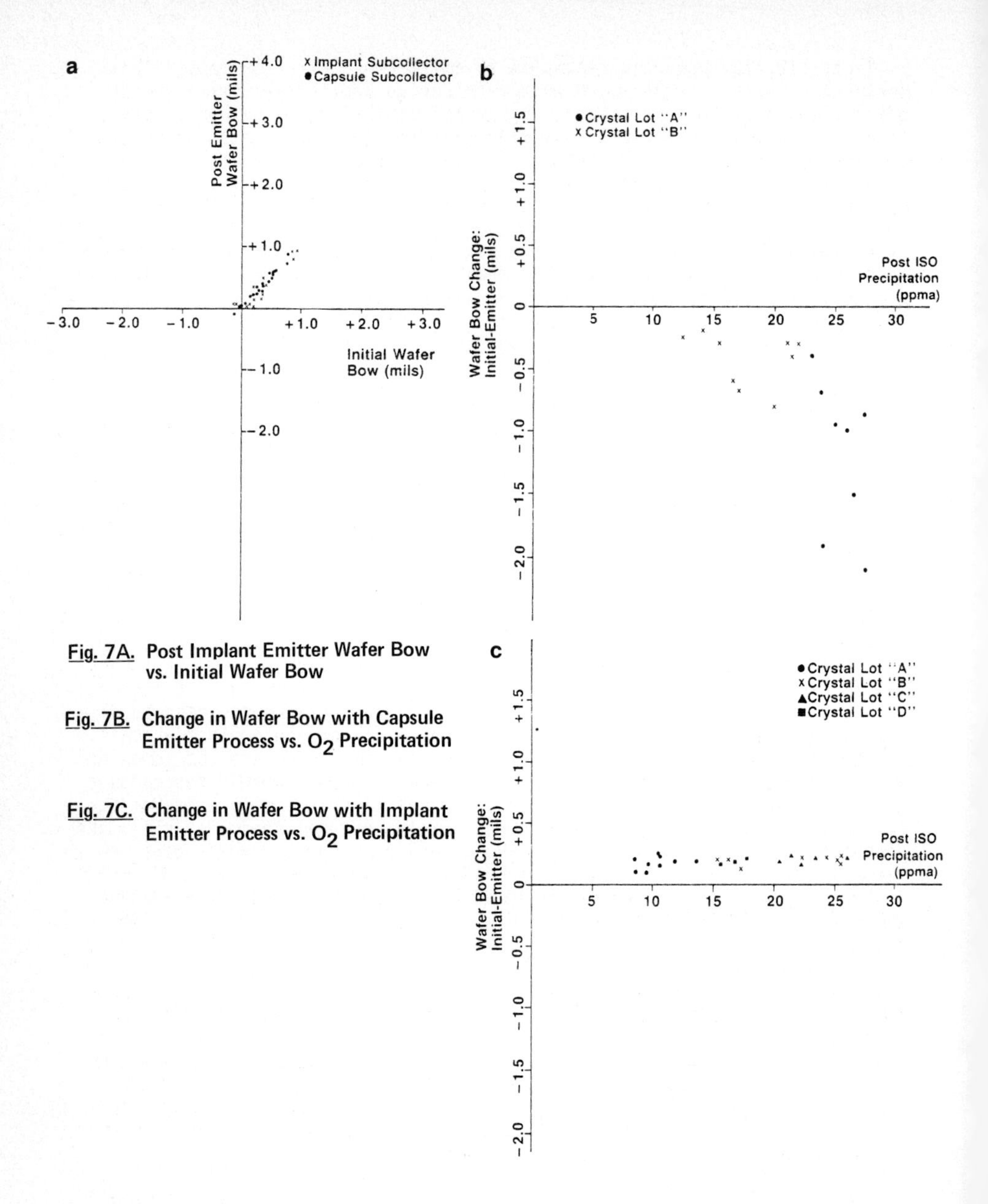

Fig. 7A. **Post Implant Emitter Wafer Bow vs. Initial Wafer Bow**

Fig. 7B. **Change in Wafer Bow with Capsule Emitter Process vs. O_2 Precipitation**

Fig. 7C. **Change in Wafer Bow with Implant Emitter Process vs. O_2 Precipitation**

defects, causing a leakage path from emitter to collector. The lower the withdrawal temperature, the less wafers will deform. But withdrawing at lower temperatures is not possible for capsule processing due to the excessive arsenic plating on the wafers, rendering them highly defective. This limitation does not exist with the implant cycle. As seen in the figure, wafers are slowly ramped to 780°C and removed to room temperature. Virtually no distortion exists on these wafers. Figure 7a shows measurements made after implant emitter processing and compared to initial wafer measurements.

Figure 7b and 7c show the results achieved in a controlled split lot experiment. They illustrate the difference in warpage between the ion implant emitter and capsule processes as a function of substrate oxygen precipitation - the key warpage sensitive material variable. We observe an implant emitter warpage of no more than 0.2 mil (considered to be within the measurement error of the optical technique) and constant for the full range of oxygen precipitation. Whereas, for the capsule process, we see warpages of up to 2 mils, with a very strong dependency on oxygen precipitation. The insensitivity of the implant emitter process to O_2 precipitation has significant impact on the wafer manufacturer who is otherwise forced to go through a costly sorting procedure in order to provide low oxygen wafers for capsule emitter processing to keep warpage at a minimum.

VIII. Pipe Defect Improvements with Implant Subcollector (Emitter)

Having discussed the improvement in pipe defect density with the ion implant emitter process, let us now examine results obtained when we combine this process with the implant subcollector process. This is shown in Figure 4, where we observe a marked shift in the BV_{CEO} curve due to a large reduction in pipe defect density. It must be noted, however, that this is limited data taken from lead product jobs. Nevertheless, there is confident optimism that the reduction in defect density from implant subcollector and emitter processing will be maintained on subsequent product runs and much improved over the capsule. It certainly represents an outstanding potential for the process. Our confidence is supported by earlier experimental data that showed significant yield improvements for the implant subcollector process with a "yield optimized dose level".

The objective of initial experiments with the implanted subcollector process was to define the exact As dose that would make the process identical to the capsule relative to Rs. Consequently, various dose levels were iterated about a nominal value calculated to be equivalent to capsule Rs. Unexpectedly, we found a strong LLY sensitivity to dose levels, with the lower dose levels giving very high yields. This is illustrated in Figure 8a showing yield results, as measured on a large Si-probable Tx structure, for various implant doses and the capsule. Additional experiments comparing capsule and implant doses, run with product test sites, showed lower dose implants resulting in the lowest pipe defect density with a substantial improvement over capsule (Figure 8b). We were not able to determine significant physical differences between high and low dose implant wafers. Etch pit density was somewhat higher on the highest dose samples, but not sufficient to explain yield and defect differences. Nevertheless, the direction for the implant subcollector process was clear. In order to increase the yield potential of the implanted subcollector the lowest possible dose level would be chosen. Unfortunately, from a yield perspective, we could only reduce our dose to $2x10^{16}$ ions/cm^2 in order to maintain a guarantee of performance transparency to capsule product.

SIMS profiles on the implant subcollector process were compared to the standard capsule subcollector process, both before and subsequent to a 5000A reoxidation. Both profiles showed a 50% decrease in As surface pile-up for implant compared to capsule. The profiles after reoxidation are shown in Figure 9. Spreading resistance measurements showed a surface Co of 1 to 2 x 10^{20}. Comparing this to the SIMS profiles implies a significantly larger amount of inactive arsenic for the capsule process. This suggests that inactive arsenic clustering may be contributing to the formation of crystallographic defects.

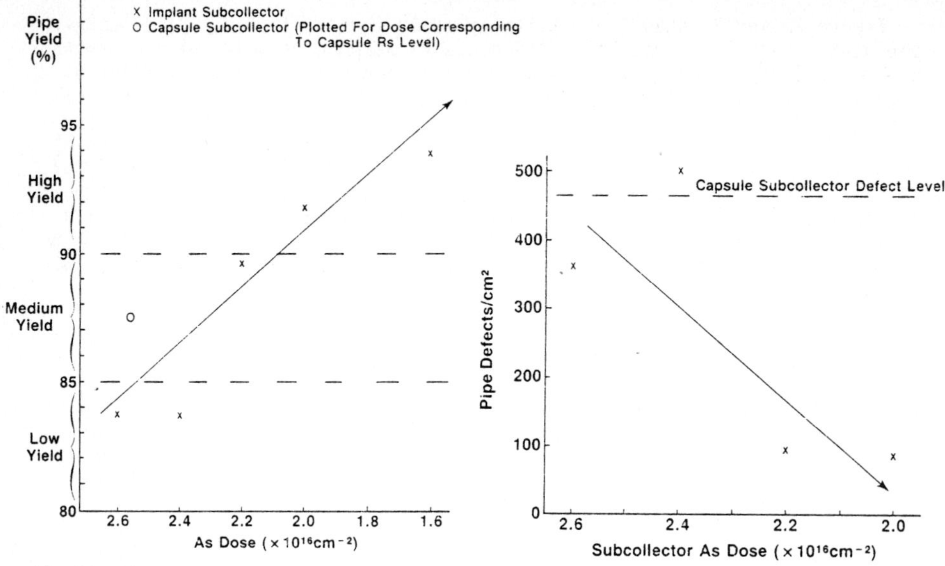

Fig. 8A. Pipe Yield vs. Implant Subcollector Dose

Fig. 8B. Pipe Defect Density Sensitivity to Subcollector Dose

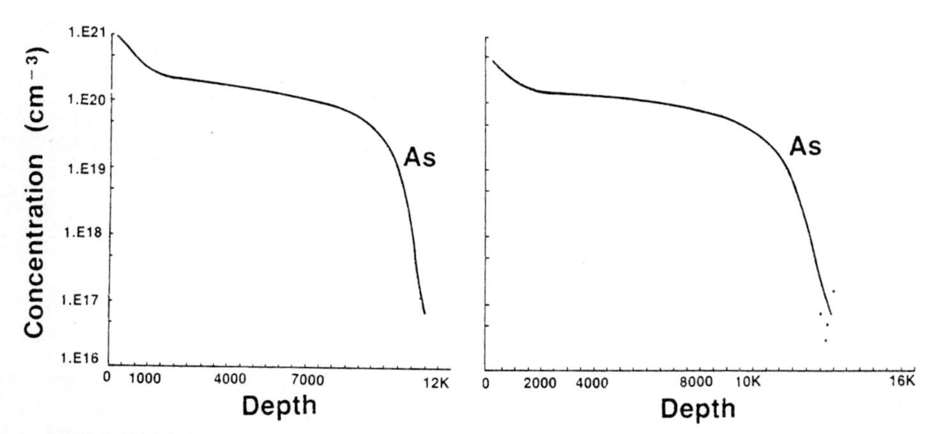

Fig. 9A. SIMS Profile of Capsule Subcollector, Post Reox

Fig. 9B. SIMS Profile of Implant Subcollector, Post Reox

A recent manufacturing experience tends to support the relationship between As pileup and device defects. Process control problems with the epi-prebake had caused a low temperature excursion on a significant number of runs. This resulted in a catastrophic increase in pipes for capsule product. The ion implant product was unaffected. It was proposed that with the capsule process, the low temperature excursion prevented the normal vaporization of As pileup, leading to clustering. But, the implant product is less sensitive to low temperature excursions since it has significantly less As and does not rely on As vaporization to reduce surface pileup.

The degree of arsenic clustering may be the basis for the explanation of yield differences between low and high dose subcollector implants. However, contradictions to this model arise from two observations; one, no detectable difference in etch analysis between low and high dose implant wafers, and two, high dose wafers generally show higher yield than capsule controls.

If the lower yield for the capsule process is an artifact of excessive As pileup at the silicon-oxide interface, an obvious alternative would be to lower the As concentration, increasing the capsule subcollector resistivity to the implant level. Results to date show a slight improvement for a lower source weight capsule process. However, the increase does not approach the levels attained by implant.

It was thought that perhaps differences in substrate interactions may be playing a key role in the yield advantages demonstrated by implant subcollector. It is well known that the amount and rate of O_2 precipitation in wafer substrates have a direct bearing on device leakage yield. A lack of precipitation results in a deficiency of defect gettering sites. Excessive precipitation is also a yield detractor, causing wafer warpage and a reduction of the defect free zone. Experiments were conducted to determine if there were differences in wafer precipitation behavior in ion implant subcollector processed wafers. Differences could arise from implantation damage effects and/or the uniqueness of the thermal cycle, i.e., ramping conditions, and the additional heat cycle required for screen oxidation. Oxygen precipitation and LLY results are shown in Figure 10. It is seen that the difference in precipitation between capsule and implant cells are insignificant, whereas the LLY for the implant subcollector was markedly higher than the capsule. We conclude that the yield differences seen for implant are not related to precipitation rate changes.

Additional work, at a more fundamental level, is required to understand fully the yield improvement and the sensitivities to defect reduction seen with the implant subcollector process. But it is real, substantial and open for manufacturing exploitation.

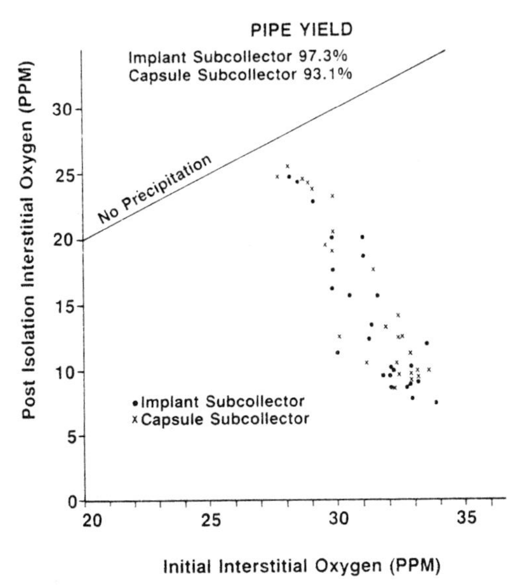

Fig. 10. **Post Isolation vs. Initial Interstitial Oxygen Concentration**

Prompted by concerns as to the impact on LLY and product yield, we conducted a series of experiments evaluating the impact of beam current on defect generation. LLY and final test results showed no negative impact up to 4mA. Further increases in beam current will be assessed in the future in an effort to improve the productivity of the implant process.

Finally, in closing our discussion of pipe defect density, let us consider it from a purely semiconductor manufacturers viewpoint. The odds of successfully fabricating an LSI chip that contains 30,000 3 x 5μm emitter transistors with the capsule process, due to pipe defects alone, would be 40%. With the implant emitter and subcollector process, it would be raised to 76% - quite a substantial difference in yield potential.

Now let us consider a VLSI chip with 300,000 transistors each with a smaller 2.5μm diameter emitter. Let us assume that the defect densities are identical to those calculated above for implant and capsule product, i.e., 44 defects/cm^2 and 132 defects/cm^2, respectively. This may be considered somewhat conservative since we would anticipate further λ reduction from other processes in moving a technology to VLSI. The maximum yield of such a product, considering pipe defects alone, would be 6% for the capsule process.

Products yielding this low are virtually unmanufacturable. The implant process would raise the yield potential to 44% - equivalent to capsule projections in the 3 x 5μm technology.

Thus, our projections show that the implant process has sufficiently reduced pipe density to allow manufacture of VLSI circuits with a higher probability for success. See Figure 11 for BV_{CEO} limited yield as a function of chip circuit density. Further improvements should be realized through reductions in subcollector dose. The improvements offered by implantation should be aggressively pursued and incorporated into current and future designs to the fullest extent allowable by the performance objectives defined for a product.

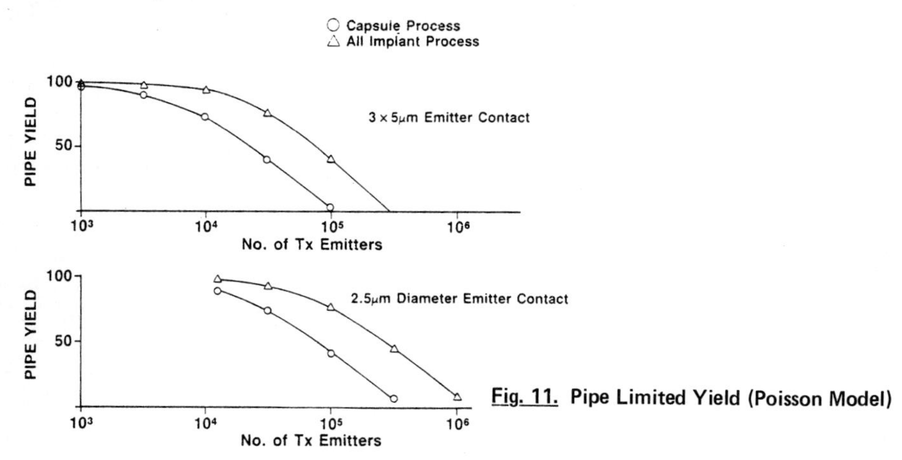

Fig. 11. Pipe Limited Yield (Poisson Model)

IX. Schottky-Barrier Diode Defect Reduction

Schottky-Barrier Diodes (SBD) are commonly used in our bipolar logic and array designs in a variety of applications - voltage level shifters, antisaturation clamps, and storage array elements. The formation technique involves the evaporation and annealing of Pt into contact regions defined over lightly doped N-type epitaxial silicon. The resulting metal-silicon junction (anode region) displays rectifying characteristics typical of the work function of the metal.

A defect can occur in this device if any part of the anode region is exposed to a high concentration of N-type dopant.

During capsule diffusion the anode is protected by thermal oxide in the order of 0.1μm thick. If a pinhole exists in the anode oxide, As will diffuse into it and form an N^+ pocket at that location. When the oxide is removed and metal is evaporated into the contact, the Schottky (metal to silicon) junction will be shunted by contact to the N^+ region. Thus instead of the expected rectifying characteristic, one will observe a leaky junction, characteristic of a diode in parallel with a resistor.

During emitter implantation, the anode area is protected by a layer of photoresist on the order of 1.5μm thick. The probability of a pinhole in a layer of this thickness is substantially reduced. Consequently, an improvement in SBD defects was anticipated.

A data base was obtained on SBD chains, on the same product test sites used for pipe defect characterization. The leakage yield data was interpreted through Poisson's model and plotted in Figure 12. As we see, the improvement in SBD defects is substantial - over a 33% density reduction. Although SBD devices generally occupy less area than transistor emitters, this reduction becomes particularly significant with high density ROS arrays that utilize Schottky diodes as storage array elements. In these products, the storage array can occupy up to 80% of the active chip area.

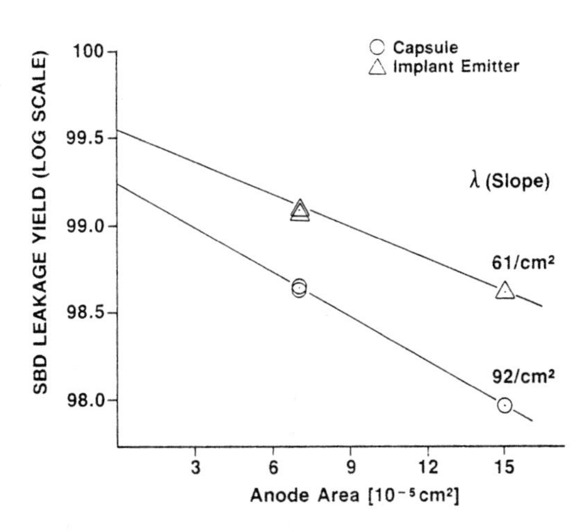

Fig. 12. SBD Yield vs. Anode Area

X. Emitter - Base Shorts

We have seen a high level of emitter-base (E-B) shorts with the ion implant emitter process. Shorts are detected by reverse biasing chains of transistors wired in parallel on product test sites and measuring them to minimum voltage specifications. From our diagnosis, we have concluded that the E-B shorts arise from two defect modes: wafer particulate contamination from processes prior to implant, and from mask defects. Both these defect modes are also common to the capsule emitter but can electrically manifest themselves differently. There are a variety of ways in which this can occur. Two examples are illustrated below.

Particle contamination from the implant masking operation can block the implant beam from the emitter contact, preventing emitter formation and causing an E-B short upon metallization. For the capsule process, photo contamination will prevent oxide removal from the contact. This not only blocks As from diffusing into emitter region but prevents metal from contacting the silicon, causing an open (Figure 13).

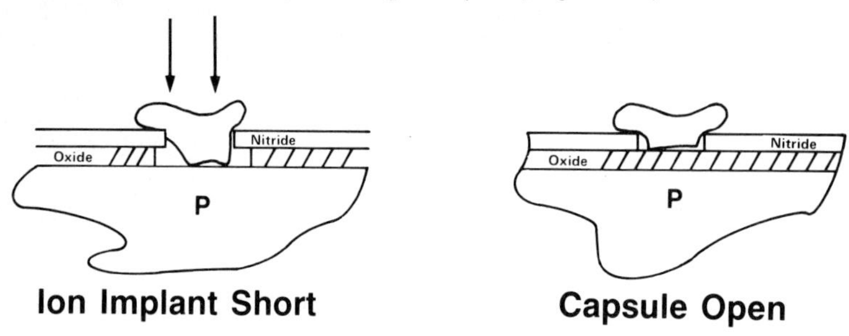

Fig. 13. Particle Contamination

Mask defects occurring with the implant process will cause an incomplete emitter formation in the contact region that subsequent metallization will cause to short to the base.

For the capsule process, this same defect will result in an undersized emitter that will lead to an area sensitive parameter fail or transistor burnout when powered at product test (Figure 14).

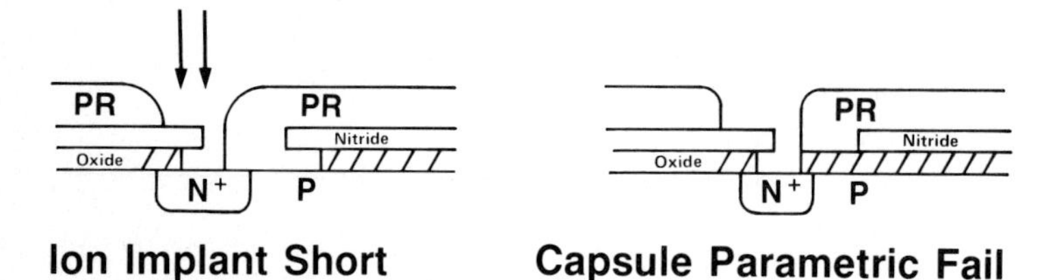

Fig. 14. Mask Defect

Seeing the same defect manifesting itself differently for the implant and capsule processes cautions us relative to the interpretation of E-B short yield. In other words, we know that the implant process will allow us to monitor electrically these defects with the E-B short test; the capsule process will not. The test, since it is applied to parallel Tx's, cannot detect opens or shifts in device parameters. Nevertheless, these most certainly will produce electrical fails at final product test.

Prompted by our diagnosis and model, a contamination reduction plan was put in place. We monitored the process improvements by tracking particle

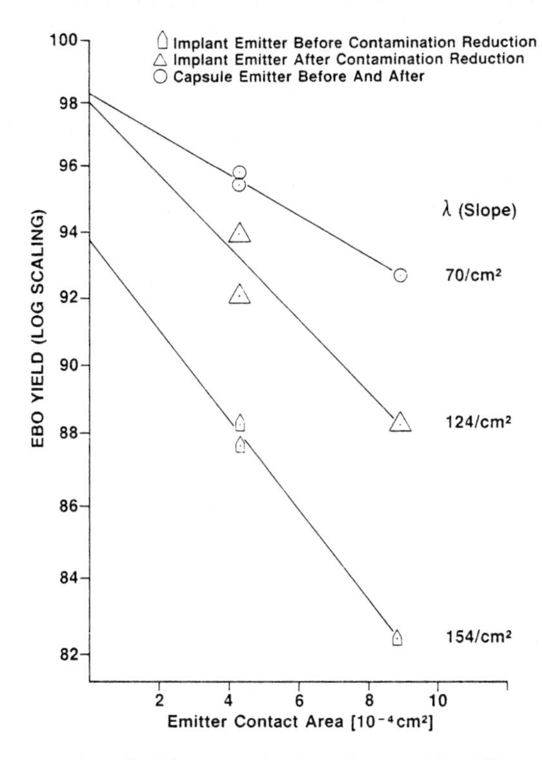

Fig. 15. Emitter Base Shorts vs. Emitter Area

count reductions on test wafers. Significant particle reductions were noticed with each change.

Although this contamination improvement plan is still in progress, the emitter-base yield results have already shown a 20% improvement in E-B short defect density (Figure 15). We also note a significant improvement in Yo, consistent with our observations that the defects tend to occur in clusters. Future photo-masking improvements are expected to result in further reductions in λ and Yo.

The E-B short yields measured on the capsule product are still higher than implant emitter product and show no change as a result of process improvements. This, we conclude from our model, is due to the insensitivity of the test to monitor effectively particulate contamination and mask defects on capsule wafers. The fact that these defects can be monitored by the implant process is a definite asset since process improvements can be accurately monitored. There is no doubt that additional emphasis must be applied to controlling these types of defects in order to realize the full yield potential of implant emitters.

XI. Product Test Yield

We have developed a substantial product yield history with the implant emitter process on a variety of logic and array products. One of these products is a high density, high performance, 256 x 10 RAM chip with a 13ns access time and 2.5W power dissipation. The chip employs minimum Tx dimensional groundrules, utilizes SBD's in its Harper memory cells, and is designed with high resistivity implanted resistors to optimize circuit density. This chip is the same product on which product test sites were used to classify the defect densities of pipes, SBD's, and E-B shorts discussed above.

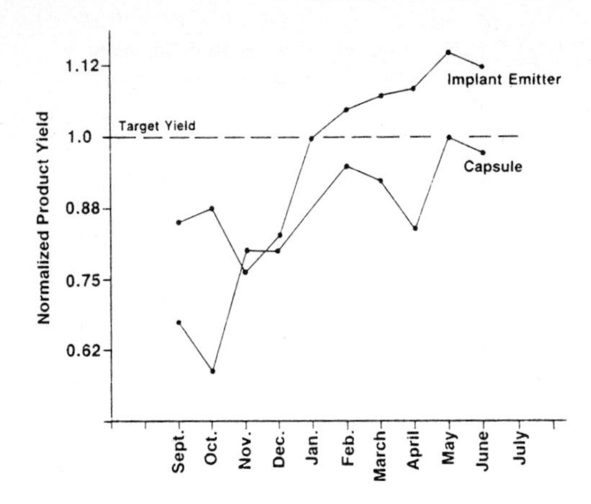

Fig. 16. Final Product Yields for 256 x 10 RAM

Product yields for the 256 x 10 RAM are plotted per month in figure 16. Yields for both capsule emitter and implant emitter are shown. A yield improvement trend is seen in capsule and implant emitter over the entire time period as a result of general process improvements made in the line. However, the implant emitter product shows a consistently higher yield than the capsule, typically a 15% improvement. This data shows, in perhaps the most dramatic fashion possible, the true definitive yield advantage of the ion-implanted emitter process. The higher product yields are realized as we have seen by the decreases in pipe and SBD defect density, and the improvements made relative to E-B short defects.

Our tool-driven implementation strategy called for first the implementation of the implanted emitter process and then the implementation of the implant subcollector process.

At the present time, implant subcollector (emitter) product volume is building up in the line and the data base at product final test is beginning to develop. Early indications support our optimism that the final product yield results will eclipse the excellent results seen with implant emitter product.

XII. Conclusions

The implant emitter process shows a distinct improvement in Tx pipe limited yield over capsule emitter product. This is due in part to emitter area reduction resulting from the anisotropic nature of implantation, but primarily due to a descrease in pipe defect density. Our observations support a position identifying the reduction in warpage as a contributing factor towards defect density improvements. Warpage reduction is explained by the optimization of the emitter thermal cycle. Implant emitter wafers show no O_2 precipitation dependency on warpage as do capsule wafers. They are virtually warpage free.

The implant subcollector (emitter) process shows even a more dramatic improvement on Tx pipe limited yield compared to capsule product. The pipe defect density was enhanced by optimizing the dose level which had shown a high degree of sensitivity to this defect. Profiles indicate a significant decrease in arsenic pileup for implanted subcollectors compared to capsule.

This suggests that there may be less arsenic clustering contributing to the formation of crystallographic defects. Experiments have shown that the defect density reduction cannot be explained by wafer O_2 precipitation changes. No yield degradation was shown with beam currents up to 4mA.

Schottky-barrier diode defect density shows 33% improvement with implant emitter processing. The process minimizes the probability of forming N^+ regions in the anode.

The implant emitter process shows a high sensitivity to emitter base shorts resulting from particulate contamination and mask defects. The capsule process manifests a different failure mode from these defects. Contamination reduction has caused a significant decrease in E-B short defect densities.

Product test yields for implanted emitter product show a dramatic improvement over capsule. Implanted subcollector (emitter) product yields are expected to better those of the implant emitter alone.

The implant process has made a timely and favorable entry into the manufacturing environment. As design densities approach VLSI proportions, we see the implant processes offering the type of leverage needed to manufacture successfully this new generation of product.

Acknowledgments

The authors would like to recognize the efforts of several people who contributed substantially to this paper. The oxygen precipitation and wafer warpage discussions were given great insight through the contributions of J. Stephansen and S. Case. The work done by D. Diddell on a low source weight capsule subcollector process provided supporting information as to the proposed pipe reduction model for the implant subcollector. The SIMS profiles documenting that discussion were performed by J. Webber. In addition, Final Test characterizations by J. H. Adams were instrumental to the qualification of these implant processes.

The implementation of these ion implant processes on bipolar product at East Fishkill would never have become a reality without the dedicated efforts and daily persistance of B. Callaghan, M. Haight and R. Knapp. Their contributions were of such a fundamental nature that none of the work and analysis described in this paper could have taken place without them.

Finally, the authors would like to thank Mr. L. F. Johnson, without whose continued management support and guidance this project would not have been possible.

References

1. S. Mader: Journal of Electronic Materials, Vol. 9, No. 6, 1980.

2. C. Scrivner: Microelectronics Measurements and Test Conference Procedings, March, 1982.

Buried Silicon-Nitride Layers Formed by Nitrogen-Ion Implantation and High-Temperature Annealing

G. Zimmer, W. Zetzmann, Z.L. Liu, and E. Neubert

Lehrstuhl Bauelemente der Elektrotechnik, Universität Dortmund, Postfach 50, D-4600 Dortmund, Fed. Rep. of Germany

1. Introduction

With growing interest in increasing the density of integrated circuits, isolation techniques have become more important. A dielectric or junction as an insulator is mostly used to prevent electrical interaction between the elements of IC´s. These methods consume a lot of space on the silicon crystal. The first attempt to use other techniques was SOS technology, but for normal VLSI-IC´s, SOS has been found to be too expensive. Another solution was to use buried dielectric layers formed by high-fluence implantation of O^+ of N^+ ions. Several papers have reported on buried oxide, using O^+ ion implantation with an epitaxial layer [1-6].

The use of buried silicon nitride has been suggested by Dexter et al. [7]. Because of the better properties of Si_3N_4, we decided to pursue this idea. Some papers [8,9] have reported on techniques to form such a buried-nitride layer. Thus, we first tried out the method reported by Bourget et al. [9].

2. Experimental

Single-crystal polished-silicon ⩽111⩾ wafers (20 Ωcm boron-doped) were first exposed to doses ranging from $5\cdot10^{10}$ N/cm^2 using N^+ and N_2^+ at an energy of 150 keV/N. Using our H.V. ion implanter we obtained ion currents from 30 $\mu A/cm^2$ to 60 $\mu A/cm^2$. In order to reduce implantation time in some experiments, N_2^+ ions were used. Using an aperture, the exposed area was kept to 1 cm^2 at the center of the wafer. After implantation the wafers were annealed at temperatures between 1000 °C and 1200 °C for 1 to 3h in dry N_2, or dry N_2 mixed with a small amount of O_2, in order to form, a thin layer of SiO_2. After this, some wafers were selectively etched to measure the thickness of the residual silicon layer and the buried silicon-nitride layer.

Other wafers were analyzed using Auger Energy Spectra (AES) depth analysis. After these experiments, we continued by realizing MOST elements for analysis of electrical parameters on the residual silicon layer. To investigate the crystallinity of the residual silicon layer, an epitaxial silicon layer of 3 µm thickness was grown using SiH_4 gas. Then, we determined whether it is possible to obtain thicker residual-silicon layers on top of the implanted nitride layer, with energies up to 300 keV. All samples were topologically investigated by optical and scanning electron microscopy.

3. Results

3.1 Structures of the Implanted Silicon-Nitride Layer

Our first goal was to form a continuous layer of silicon nitride. The projected range (R_p) and straggling (ΔR_p) for 150 keV are 0.344 µm and 0.077 µm, respectively [12]. Due to the compound data of SiN_4, we ought to have a top concentration of not less than $5 \cdot 10^{22}$ N/cm^2. The layer thickness of a continous layer of nitride was found to be 0.4 µm, using a dose of $1.5 \cdot 10^{18}$ N/cm^2 and an annealing time of 2h at 1200 °C, with a residual silicon layer of 0.2 µm. This was first measured by selective etching.

To obtain more information concerning the layer compounds, we analyzed these using AES, forming a depth profile. Two of these profiles are depicted in Fig. 1 for N^+ and Fig. 2 for N_2^+.

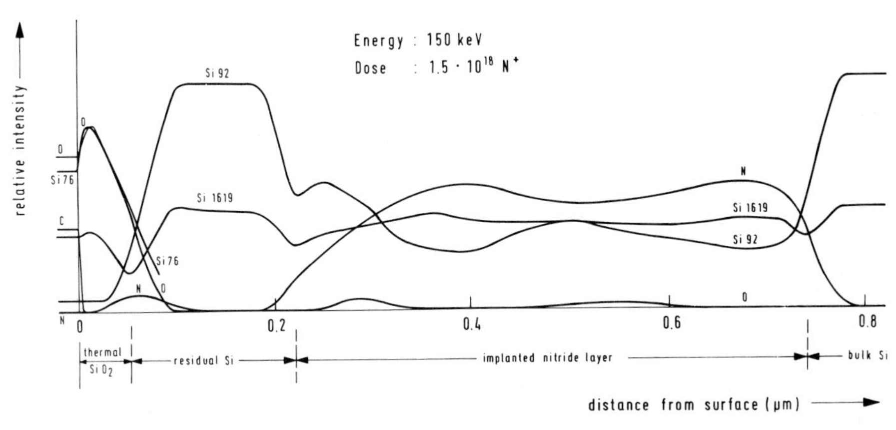

Fig. 1. AES Depth Profile of Implanted N^+ after anneal

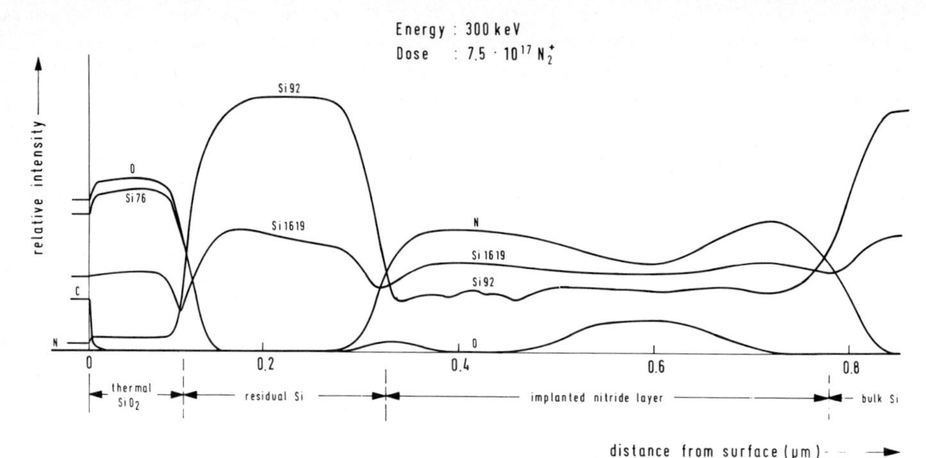

Fig. 2. AES Depth Profile of Implanted N_2^+ after anneal

3.2 Electrical Properties

Using the process parameters of $D = 1.5 \cdot 10^{18}$ N/cm^2, $E = 150$ keV for implantation, $\Theta = 1200$ °C, and $1h \leqslant t \leqslant 3h$ for annealing, we examined the electrical properties of the buried-nitride layer and the residual-silicon layer.

In order to measure the nitride layer, the residual-silicon layer was etched with $H_3C\text{-}COOH/HF/HNO_3$ etchant, and Al dots were distributed on top of the silicon-nitride layer. Thus, we obtained MNS capacitors, which made it possible to perform C-V and insulation measurements. C-V curves were measured with a voltage range from -50 V to +50 V, and no change in the capacitor value was found. The capacitor was measured at $1.5 \cdot 10^4$ pF/cm^2. This suggests a silicon nitride layer of 0.4 µm thickness and a dielectric constant of 7. The insulation current below the breakdown voltage was less than 100 nA/cm^2, and depended on annealing parameters. Breakdown also depended on annealing parameters, and took place between 70 V and 160 V, which means a breakdown field strength up to F = 3.5 MV/cm. Best results were obtained when the wafers were heated up slowly (2 °C/min) and annealed during 2 h at 1200 °C:

$$V_{BR} = 160 \text{ V} \qquad I_{is} \leqslant 10^{-9} \text{ at } V \approx 100 \text{ V}.$$

After measuring breakdown, irreversible ohmic contacts existed between the top layer and the bulk silicon. The same results were obtained using islands (n^+-doped) of residual silicon. Figure 3 shows these results.

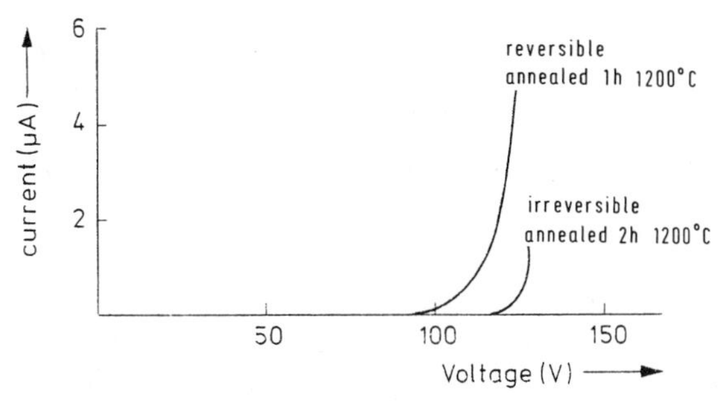

Fig. 3. Breakdown characteristics of Si_3N_4

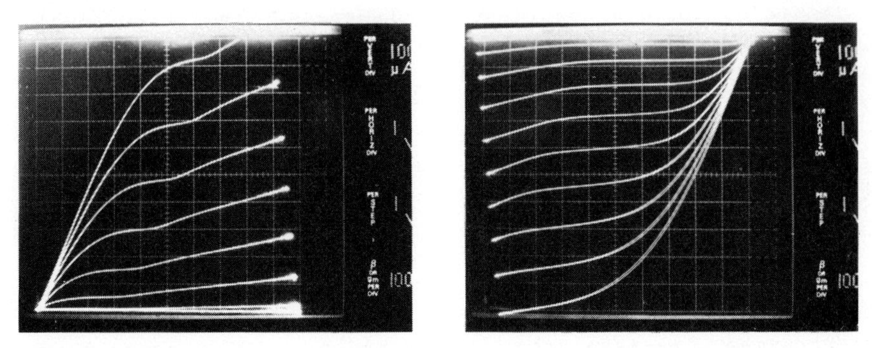

Fig. 4 and 5. Output characteristics of short channel CMOS transistors, left: NMOS, L_{eff} =2.5 μm, W = 10 μm right: PMOS, L_{eff} = 1.5 μm, W = 10 μm

In order to measure the electrical properties of the residual- silicon layer, we realized CMOS silicon-gate transistors in it. For transistor isolation islands were etched in the residual layer to form the active areas. Then a silicon gate CMOS process with 40 nm gate oxide was applied for transistor fabrication. Figures 4 and 5 show the output characteristics of a short channel NMOS and PMOS transistor on the same chip.

From these experiments, we learned that there is a small leakage current of $I \leqslant 10$ nA at V_{DS} = 10 V for a 2.5 μm n-channel-enhancement MOST or a 1.5 μm p-channel transistor on the same chip. The characteristics show the typical "kink effect" of SOS transistors with floating substrate. Carrier mobility measured by differential transconductance was found to be approximately half of that for bulk silicon ($\mu \simeq 360 cm^2/Vs$ for electrons and 140 cm^2/Vs for holes). Punch-through voltage was lower and threshold voltage higher, than for bulk silicon.

4. Discussion

First, we shall discuss the layer structure. The experiments showed that we were able to produce a continuous insulating layer with chemical and physical properties equal to those of a layer formed by LPCVD. Therefore, the layer is assumed to consist of large areas of crystalline Si_3N_4. Micrographs, as well as the formation of epitaxial silicon on the residual-silicon layer, indicate an almost totally recrystallized surface layer. These properties depend greatly on the implantation and annealing processes . With annealing temperatures below 1200 °C we also obtained a nitride layer, but it did not have a continuous structure. The electrical response is strongly correlated with the morphological appearance of the layers. Only layers with a continuous crystalline appearance resulted in good insulation quality and high breakdown voltages. Layers annealed below 1200 °C had high leakage currents and early breakdown (2V - 10V). The C-V characteristics could not be measured.

To interpret the MOST measurements, we should keep in mind that field implantation and S&D doping/diffusion were not modified at all. This results in a higher doping concentration, because the diffusion path was less than 0.2 µm. This is the reason for measurement of a higher threshold voltage. The leakage current of the MOST´s can be interpreted as representing a parasitic channel at the silicon/silicon nitride interface, since we can expect stress-induced surface states at this interface. This effect is already well known from the same technology. The silicon layer beneath the interface is often called the low-mobility layer (LML). This was also found for implanted buried oxides [1-6]. For this reason most investigators use epitaxy to realize MOST´s. Measured mobility of our silicon layer was better than in the case of SOS, for the same layer thickness [10]. To avoid a channel at the interface, we are planning to experiment with B^+ implantation, similarly to research already carried out with SOS devices [10].

5. Conclusion

Starting with data obtained from the literature, we investigated the possibility of forming a buried silicon-nitride layer by nitrogen-ion implantation. First, we determined the dose to obtain a continuous insulating layer, using an implantation energy of 150 keV/N. The dose should not be less than $1 \cdot 10^{18}$ N/cm^2. With a dose of $1.5 \cdot 10^{18}$ N/cm^2, we obtained the best results. To save implantation time, we also implanted N_2^+ ions at a 300 kV acceleration with D = $7.5 \cdot 10^{17}$ N_2/cm^2. The results of both implants have been compared.

In both cases, we obtained a nitride layer of 0.4 μm thickness with a 0.2 μm residual monocrystalline-silicon layer on top of it. The chemical and electrical properties of the nitride were equal to those of Si_3N_4 deposited by LPCVD. The residual silicon layer can be used to realize MOST´s in it. We realized CMOS-transistors with a slightly modified Si-Gate process. The leakage current was found to be very low, but independent of gate voltage or substrate voltage, due to a possible channel at the Si-Si_3N_4 interface. Mobility was measured to be half of that in bulk silicon.

Acknowledgements

The authors would like to thank Prof. H. Strack of the Technical University, Darmstadt, for providing epitaxial layers, Dr. Herion of KFA, Jülich, and Dr. K. Heidemann of the Physics Department, University of Dortmund, for sample analysis. The assistance of M. Obst and P. Staks during device preparation is gratefully acknowledged.

References

1 H. Mossadeg, R. J. Bennett and K. V. Anand: El. Lett. 18, 215 (1980)

2 K. Ohwada, Y. Omura and E. Sano: IEEE Trans. El. Dev. ED-28, 1081 (1981)

3 K. Ohwada, Y. Omura and E. Sano: IEEE Trans. El. Dev. ED-27, 2043 (1980)

4 T. Hayashi, H. Okamoto and Y. Homma: Jpn. J. Appl. Phys. 19, 1005 (1980)

5 K. Izumi, M. Doken and H. Ariyoshi: El. Lett. 14, 593 (1978)

6 H.W. Lam, R.F. Pinizzotto, H.T. Yuan and D.W. Bellavance: El. Lett. 17, 356 (1981)

7 R.J. Dexter, S.B. Watelski and S.T. Picraux: Appl. Phys. Lett. 23, 455 (1973)

8 T. Tsujide, M. Nojiri and H. Kitagawa: J. Appl. Phys. 51, 1605 (1980)

9 P. Bourget, J.M. Dupart, E. Le Tiran et al.: J. Appl. Phys. 51, 6169 (1980)

10 N. Sasaks and R. Togei: SSE 22, 417 (1979)

11 D.J. McGreivy: IEEE Trans. El. Dev. ED-24, 730 (1977)

12 J.F. Gibbons, W.S. Johnson and S.W. Mylroie: Projected Range Statistics (2nd ed., 1975), Dowden, Hutchingson & Ross, Stroudsburg Penn.

Combined Boron and Aluminum Implantation for High-Voltage Devices

J. Hilgarth and E. Schulz
AEG-Telefunken, Theresienstraße 2, D-7100 Heilbronn, Fed. Rep. of Germany

1. Introduction

Aluminum is a p-type dopant in silicon, similar to boron. Due to its fast diffusion, it is preferred when deep junctions in n-type silicon are required. Thyristors, high-power devices and high-voltage transistors are therefore the main applications. Al diffusion, however, suffers from some disadvantages because of its high reactivity with oxygen, moisture or silicon dioxide. Diffusion in sealed systems is complicated and expensive, and handling is difficult when reproducible results are desired /1/. Open-tube diffusion from coated Si wafers /2/ also requires an atmosphere in the tube which is totally free of oxygen and water vapor, in order to enable the transport of Al to the surface of the wafer to be doped. These conditions are difficult to realize in production.

Ion implantation seems to be the best method to insert Al into Si. The dose and the energy can be specified precisely, giving a defined starting condition for diffusion which will lead to reproducible results.

The aim of our investigations was to reduce the time and expenditure needed to fabricate high-voltage transistors by using Al implantation instead of boron diffusion. Additionally, we hoped to enhance the breakdown voltage by giving the base of the transistor a suitable doping profile. It will be shown that it is possible to realize these objectives by implantation of Al and B, followed by a single simultaneous drive-in diffusion.

For this purpose, it was necessary to study in more detail the behavior of Al diffusion into Si after implantation.

2. Experimental Procedures and Results

The implantations were carried out using a SCANIBAL 218 SCI implanter. The Al source was a vaporizer with a mixture of Al and AlF_3 powder: $2Al + AlF_3 = 3AlF$. The vapor pressure is reached at a temperature of about 650°C; argon was used as the carrier gas. A current of 2.5 mA could be obtained. An accelerator volge up to 200 kV can be used. Boron was implanted from BF_3 gas at a current of 1.7 mA.

The starting condition for Al diffusion after implantation is characterized by the fact that the transport of the Al from the source to the silicon surface, and the incorporation of the atoms in the Si just beneath the surface, have already taken place. Most of the atoms are electrically inactive, their distribution in depth is determined by the implantation energy, and we can assume a Gaussian distribution. At high temperatures, the atoms diffuse into

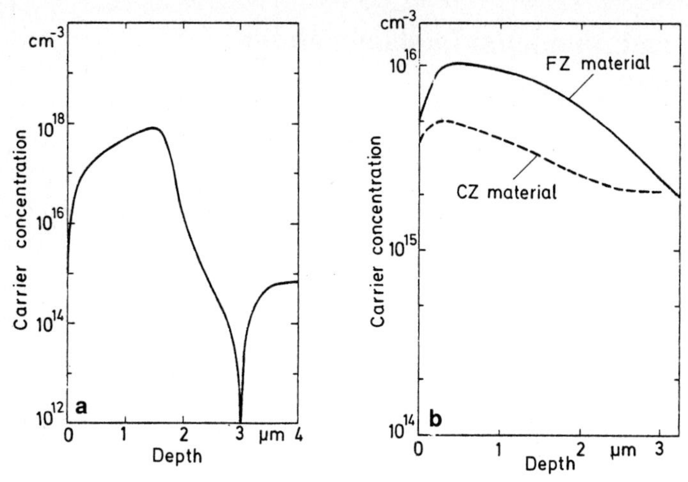

Fig. 1. SR profiles of Al implanted in Si: a. after 4 hours at 1000°C in Ar, FZ material, dose: $2x10^{15}$ cm^{-2}; b. FZ and CZ material, dose: $1x10^{14}$ cm^{-2}

the volume, but they also diffuse towards the surface. It will be shown that the surface region of the implented Si is a very good sink for the Al atoms.

A typical Al profile in Si after implantation and heat treatment, measured by the spreading resistance method (SR), is shown in Fig. 1a. This curve differs considerably from those usually known for B, P or As implantations. Remarkable above all is the absence of electrically active Al atoms near the surface. This is most clearly seen after long-time diffusion (about 10 h at 1250°C), but is also found after 1 hour of annealing at 1000°C.

Usually, drive-in diffusion takes place in atmospheres containing oxygen. Because of the high reactivity of Al with oxygen, we assumed that the diffusion of oxygen into the silicon surface during the drive-in process will cause the formation of Al_nO_m complexes which are electrically inactive and insoluble up to 1250°C. The fact that oxygen can compound with Al in Si is demonstrated in Fig. 1b: Al has been implanted into two samples with the same specifications ((100) oriented silicon, spec. resistivity 5-10 cm, boron doped). One crystal wafer was grown by the Czochralski technique (CZ), the other was float-zone material (FZ). The content of the oxygen in the CZ material was about $5x10^{17}$ cm^{-3}; that in FZ-Si, below $1x10^{16}$ cm^{-3}. It can be seen that the concentration of electrically active Al in the CZ material is much lower than in the FZ material. This result agrees with those found in the literature /3/. Obviously, reactions between Al and oxygen in Si are possible. To avoid diffusion of oxygen from the atmosphere into Si, we carried out annealing runs in pure Ar and pure N_2 gases. We found that there is no essential difference in the behavior of the Al atoms in Ar, N_2 or N_2+ O_2 gases (see eg. Fig. 1a). To locate the Al in the silicon, we made measurements using secondary-ion mass spectroscopy (SIMS). Applying SIMS, the total concentration of Al in Si is determined. Fig. 2a shows an Al profile obtained by means of SIMS, compared with the SR profile. In the region just below the surface where the SR curve decreases, the concentration of Al increases greatly to values much higher than the solubility limit $2x10^{19}$ cm^{-3}. The detailed reaction mechanism of the Al atoms in this zone is not yet fully understood, but it is certainly not oxygen which causes most of the Al to be inactive. On the other hand, diffusion does also take place in the surface re-

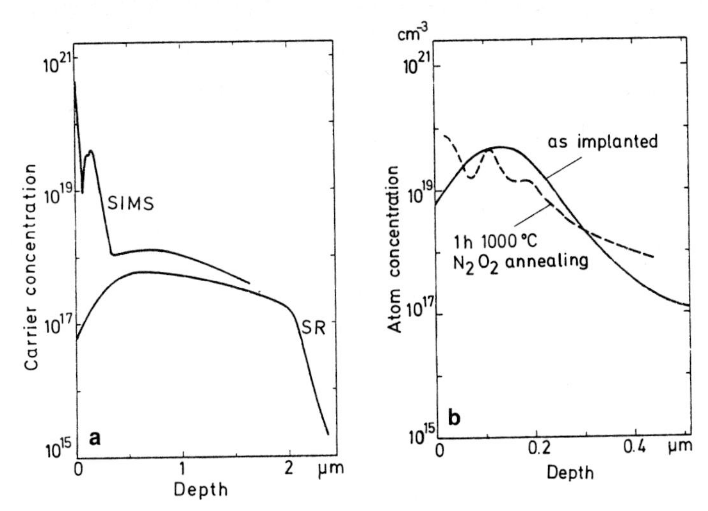

Fig. 2. SIMS profiles for Al implanted into Si: a. compared with the SR profile, dose: $1x10^{15}$, annealing: 4 hours at 1000°C in N_2; b. as implanted and after annealing

gion, as is shown in Fig. 2b, where an as-implanted SIMS profile is compared with the profile after 1 hour of annealing at 100°C. Most of the atoms have diffused towards the surface, but some atoms have remained in the implanted position. It seems possible that a non-semiconduction eutectic is formed here.

To determine which portion of the implanted Al atoms is not activated after drive-in diffusion, we made calculations using the computer program SUPREM II. As no specific model for Al diffusion exists, we used the boron model with modified parameters, such as the diffusion coefficient (from Ref. /4/) and the segregation coefficient. Because of the difference between CZ and FZ material, we made calculations only for FZ material. We obtained good agreement between the calculated results and SR measurements for deep junctions in the following way:

a) As there exists a zone of about 0.2 µm where all atoms will diffuse to the surface or are inactive, we assumed that 70 % of the implanted Al is absent. A dose of $1x10^{15}$ cm Al cm^{-2} means only $3x10^{14}$ Al cm^{-2}.

b) The implanted zone and the surface are sinks for the active Al atoms, and so the segregation coefficient S, defined by S= atoms in Si/atoms in SiO_2, must be very low. We applied a value of $S = 1x10^{-4}$.

It follows from these assumptions that only deep junctions can be calculated. Good agreement between calculations and SR measurements is obtained within the following limits: dose $1x10^{14}$ - $3x10^{15}$ cm^{-2}, energy 100 - 150 keV, temperature range from 1000 - 1250°C during drive-in diffusion in $H_2 + O_2$ atmosphere, time periods between 4 and 12 hours.

3. Application to High-Voltage Devices

Fig. 3a shows the cross section and the impurity profile of a high-voltage transistor using a well-known design. Three diffusions are necessary: reverse

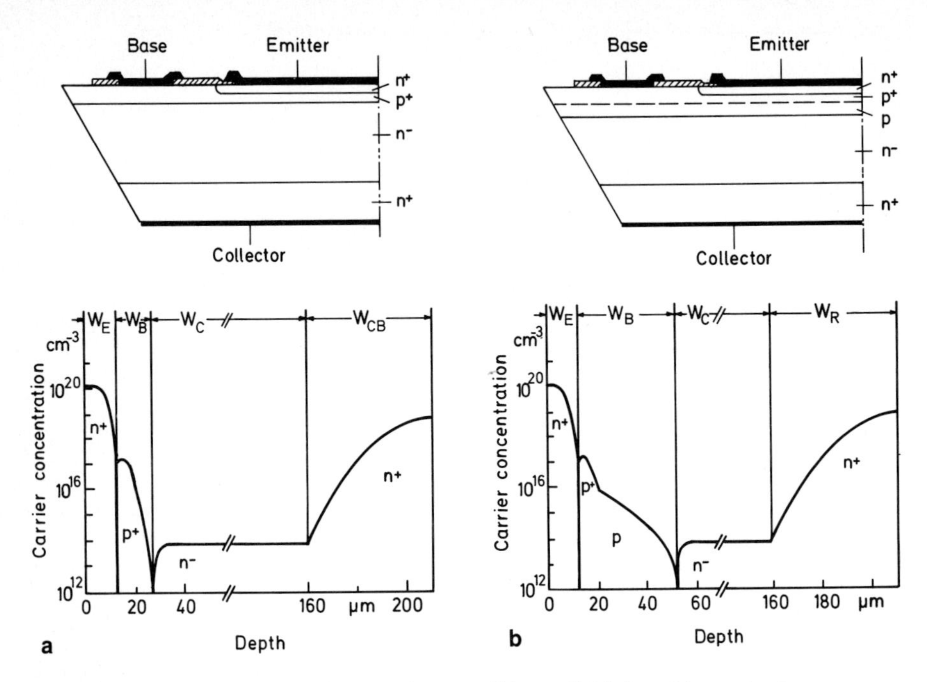

Fig. 3. Cross sections and impurity profiles of high-voltage devices: a. with p^+ base; b. with p^+p base

side contact n^+, base p^+ and emitter n^+. The substrate has a low carrier concentration (about 10^{14} P cm^{-3}). High reverse voltages are possible because of the wide collector zone W_c. Another limit in high-voltage application is represented by the profile of the base. The steep gradients in the doping concentration give rise to high field strength, with a premature breakdown most probably occurring at the mesa-etched flanks. We have tried to achieve a base impurity profile, as shown in Fig. 3b, with a reduction of the base impurity gradient in the region of the collector. The flat doping curve leads to a reduction of the field strength in comparison to a boron-doped base, since the depletion region can also extend into the base. This makes it possible to enhance the reverse voltage. If the reverse voltage is to be retained, we can reduce the low-doped collector zone W_c, thus minimizing the storage time of the collector. In this case, the switching behavior can be improved. In order to maintain a low contact resistance, the surface must be a p^+ zone. Using only one dopant, two base diffusions have to be carried out: a first one for forming a p zone, and a second one for forming the p^+-contact zone.

The experimental results concerning Al diffusion show that Al can be used to fabricate the p zone (Fig. 4a). For the base contact, Al is not suitable because of the absence of active ions in the surface region. This is remedied only by the diffusion of boron.

The best method is the implantation of boron and Al with a common drive-in step. Since Al has a higher diffusion coefficient than B (about four times higher at 1250°C), the two dopants diffuse at different rates. During the drive-in process, the faster Al atoms diffuse deeper into the Si. Implanted in a suitable dose, they will form the p zone. Boron, implanted in a higher dose, remains closer to the surface, forming the p^+ zone.

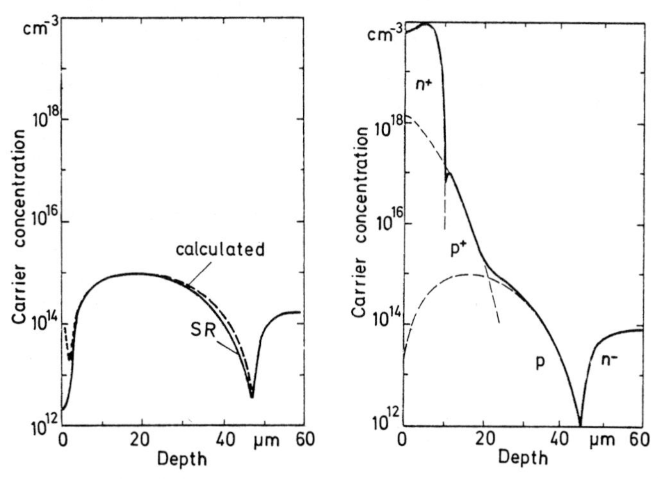

Fig. 4. SR impurity profiles: a. Al after 11 h annealing at 1250°C; b. a high-voltage device with B and Al base

We achieved the desired profile (Fig. 4b) with doses of 1×10^{15} Al cm^{-2} and 1.6×10^{15} B cm^{-2}, with a drive-in time of 11 hours at 1250°C. Within our limits of measurement error, we could not find any reaction between B and Al during diffusion. In Fig. 4b, calculated profiles are also presented. The agreement of the measured and calculated profiles shows that there is no reaction between B and Al in Si.

4. Conclusion

Al implantation has been studied as a tool for the fabrication of high-voltage devices. It was found that only a low quantity of the implanted Al becomes electrically active after diffusion. Most of the Al remains in the surface region, and remains electrically inactive. It was shown that boron and Al implanted into Si, applying only one simultaneous drive-in diffusion, eliminate the disadvantages of pure Al implantation. In this way, we obtain a means of easily fabricating deep junctions in a relatively short diffusion time, which also facilitates the fabrication of rather differing p-type profiles.

Acknowledgements

The authors gratefully acknowledge the contributions of Heike Haeberle who did the SR measurements, Dagmar-Karin Maier who did the SIMS measurements, Detlev Wallis for drawing the figures, and Dr. Guenter Goldbach for helpful discussions.

References

1 P. Rai-Choudhury, F.H. Selim, W.J. Takei: J. Electrochem. Soc. 124, 762 (1977)
2 M. Chang: J. Electrochem. Soc. 128, 1987 (1981)
3 S. Mizuo, H. Higuchi: Jpn. J. Appl. Phys. 21, 56 (1982)
4 H. Ryssel, I. Ruge: Ionenimplantation, Teubner, Stuttgart (1978), p. 87

Deep Implanted Layers of Boron in Silicon

S. Oosterhoff and J. Middelhoek

Solid-State Electronics Group, Twente University of Technology, P.O. Box 217, 7500 AE Enschede, The Netherlands

1. Introduction

Last year, the I.C. workshop of the Solid-State Electronics Group at our University obtained a 500 kV High Voltage Engineering ion implanter. The research with this machine will be concentrated on the deep implantation of Boron, Phosphorus and Arsenic, to process well-known transistor types in a different way. The electronic parameters of these transistors (such as emitter efficiency, frequency response, breakdown voltage, reverse operation) can be directly influenced by the shape of the concentration profiles obtained by implantation of double charged ions [1]. The penetration depths of 1000 keV ions are such that the resulting concentration profiles differ completely from those obtained with standard techniques.

2. Experimental method

The 500 kV ion implanter has been in full operation for about six months without a major breakdown. Our main critisism concerns the output of the ion sources. For the sake of convenience we use a Penning source. At present, this source allows a maximum current density of 5 nA/cm^2 on 2" wafers, in the case of double-charged boron ions. Double-charged phosphorus ions have a somewhat higher yield of 12-15 nA/cm^2. In cooperation with Dr. Cleff and co-workers from the University of Münster, some improvement in the source output was obtained, which resulted in the above-mentioned output. These current densities are rather low, so we are forced to use either long implantation times or limit our experiments to small implantation doses. Because small deep implanted doses also have many applications in IC technology, we started our study with high-energy, low-dose implantations. The use of deep implantations in device applications requires a thorough knowledge of the annealing behaviour. We therefore started with annealing experiments. Rutherford backscattering is not available at our University and because of the low concentrations we found out that measuring the resistance of the implanted layer with a specially designed Van der Pauw [2] structure (fig. 1) would provide an excellent method to monitor the annealing process.
To mask those parts of the wafer that do not have to be implanted, we started the processing by applying a 2 micron thick thermally grown silicon dioxide layer. This thickness of the silicon dioxide layer is required because of the great penetration depth of 1000 keV boron ions in silicon. Instead of the normally used aluminium bonding pads, we applied heavily boron-doped polysilicon interconnections. This had two advantages: In the first place the polysilicon interconnections can withstand any

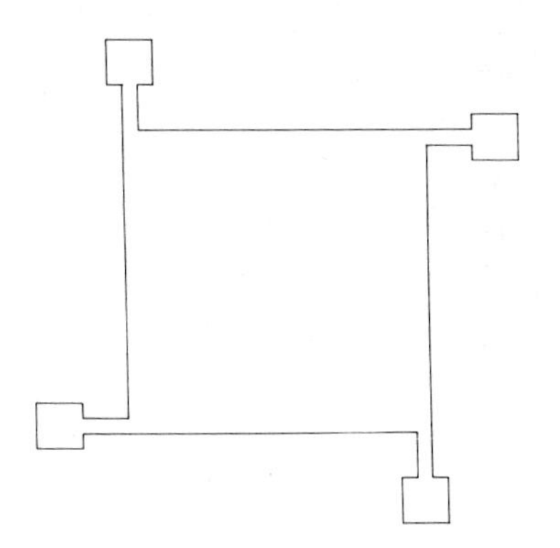

Fig. 1.Van der Pauw implantation area

annealing temperature up to 1400 ^{0}C, while the low meltingpoint of aluminium does not allow these high annealing temperatures. In the second place, the heavily doped polysilicon layer acts as a diffusion source. In this way, contact areas are made by diffusion (see fig. 2).

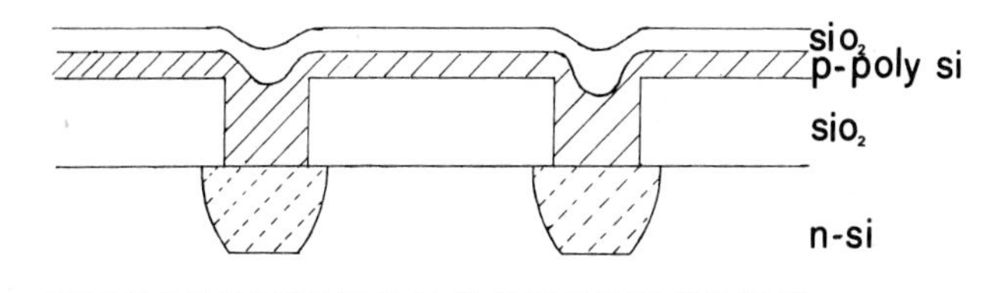

Fig. 2.Cross-section of the sample after diffusion of the contact areas

After the diffusion of the contact areas, the implantation window (see fig. 1) was opened by standard photolithography. Implantation was carried out, while the < 100 > oriented silicon surface was bare. The implantation dose amounted to 10^{13} double-charged boron ions per cm^2. This dose is far below the amorphization limit of $8 * 10^{16}/cm^2$ [3]. In order to avoid channeling, the wafers were mounted in such a way that the penetrating beam formed an angle of 7^{0} with the normal to the wafer surface (fig. 3).

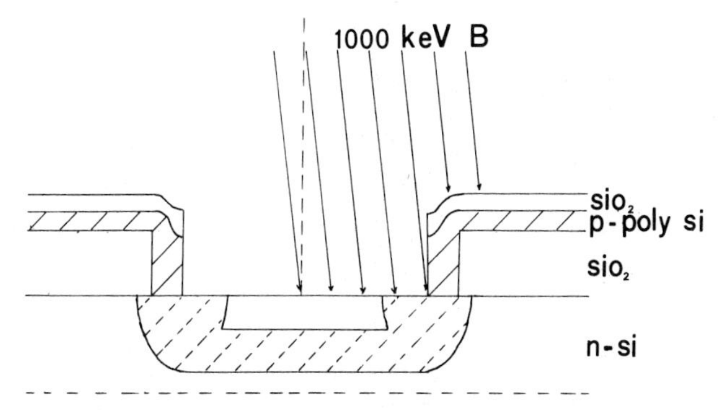

Fig. 3.Cross-section of the sample during implantation

After the implantation the wafer was coated with a 3000 Å thick CVD-grown silicon-dioxide layer, deposited at 350 °C during 7 minutes. A first short annealing already took place during this step.

3. Annealing results

The annealing experiments were carried out in an oxygen ambient in a standard oxidation furnace. The sheet resistance of 42 structures on one wafer was repeatedly measured after each 10 minutes annealing time. These isothermal experiments took place at four different temperatures: 400, 450, 500 and 550 °C and were extended up to three hours. At a first glance at fig. 4 it seems as if the curves all tend to a saturation value, but in fact this is only the case at 550 °C. At the other temperatures, the quick rise in conductance is followed by an increase at a slower rate. Moreover it is obvious that an initial annealing of 10 minutes has the same effect as an annealing for three hours at a temperature 50 °C lower.

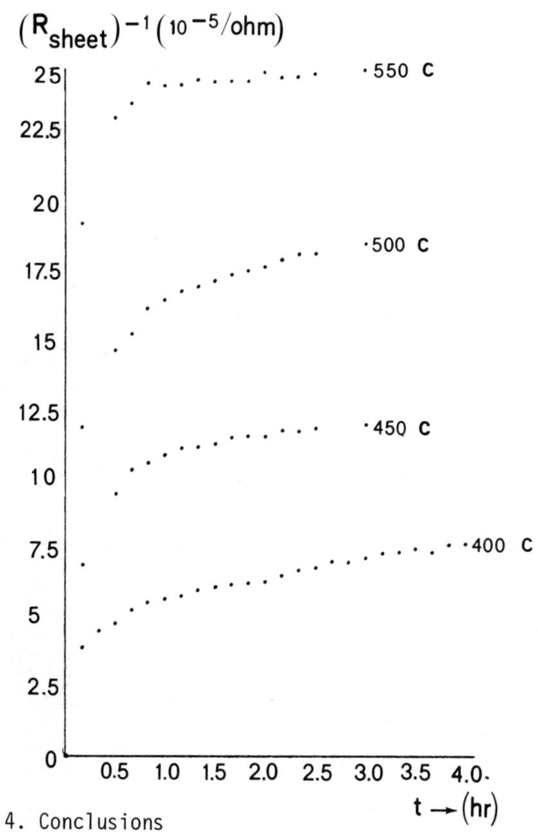

Fig. 4. Conduction of the implanted layers as a function of annealing time, at different temperatures

4. Conclusions

We assume the conductance to be dependent on two factors, viz. the concentration and the mobility of the charge carriers. The increase in the conductivity is either due to an improvement in the mobility, or to an enhancement in the activity of the implanted ions. Because of the low dose of the implantation, dramatic changes in the mobility are not expected. We therefore assume that the change in sheet-resistance values over two orders of magnitude during the first 10 minutes annealing is caused by an increase of the carrier concentration The annealing process brings the implanted impurities to substitutional lattice sites, where they become electrically active. Since the curves show different saturation values, we can conclude that different processes take place. Each of these processes has its own activation energy. These results therefore clearly show that it is incorrect to calculate one activation energy from isochronal experiments at different temperatures.

During our experiments we met with a serious problem concerning the concentration profile. From comparable experiments [4] concerning deep implantations, we expected a buried profile with a Pearson IV shape. All evidence obtained with the help of a hot-point probe, ball-grooving and staining pointed the fact that the implanted layer extended to the surface of the wafer. Only one junction was found instead of two as expected. This was in the case of boron implantations as well as for phosphorus implantations. The background concentration of the wafers was about $10^{15}/cm^3$, and the maximum of the implanted profile amounted to approximately $3 * 10^{17}/cm^3$. We tried to reveal the actual profile by carrying out an extra implantation of the opposite impurity type. After a 1000 keV boron implantation phosphorus was implanted at different energies and doses. The junction depths were determined with ball-grooving and staining, and the compensating concentrations were calculated for the phosphorus implantations.

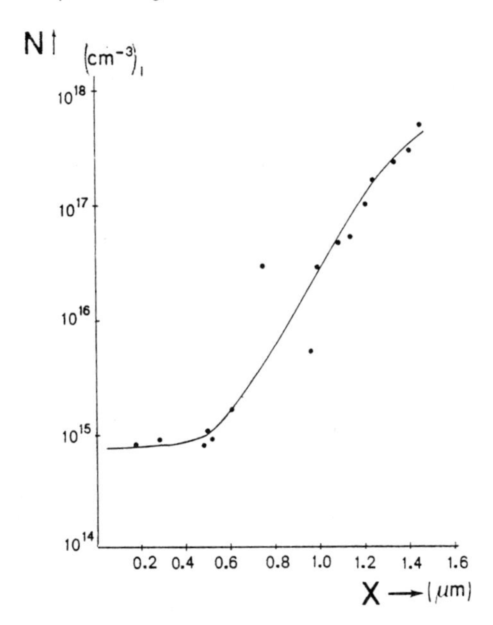

Fig. 5. 1000 keV boron profile made by means of compensating phosphorus implants

Assuming the concentrations of both impurities to be equal at the junction, a partial boron profile (1000 keV; $10^{13}/cm^2$) could be compiled (see fig. 5) under the assumption that the top of the phosphorus profile had a Gaussian shape.

From these results we can draw a prelimary conclusion that at these low concentrations and high energies, a concentration profile is found that deviates considerably from those reported by Hofker [4].

Acknowledgement

These investigations in the programme of the Foundation for Fundamental Research on Matter (FOM) have been supported by the Foundation for Technical Research (STW), future Technical Science Branch (Division of the Netherlands Organization for the Advancement of Pure Research (ZWO)).

References

[1] R.D. Dung, C.J. Delloca, L.G. Walker: IEEE Trans. on EL. Dev., Vol *28*, No. 10, 1981.

[2] L.J. v.d. Pauw: Philips Research Reports *13*, 1-9, 1958.

[3] H. Ryssel, I. Ruge: *Ionen implantation*, B.G. Teubner, Stuttgart, 1978.

[4] W.K. Hofker: Philips Research Reports Supplements No. *8*, 1975.

Planar Channeling of Si Implants in GaAs

R.T. Blunt, I.R. Sanders, and J.F. Singleton
Plessey Research (Caswell) Limited, Allen Clark Research Centre,
Caswell, Towcester, Northamptonshire, England

Abstract

Currently there is great interest in the use of ion implantation techniques to produce devices in GaAs, where well-defined profiles with steep back interfaces are considered essential for the production of low noise MESFETs and integrated circuits. Observations of abnormal profiles with deep tails resulting from implantation of 240 keV Si ions into (100) semi-insulating GaAs are reported in this paper. Both electrical profiles, as measured by differential Hall and strip assessment, and SIMS ion profiles will be presented to show the dependence of profile shape upon the precise orientation of the GaAs wafers during implantation. The results are demonstrated to be consistent with (110) planar channelling.

1. Introduction

The direct implantation of donor impurities, such as Si and Se, into semi-insulating GaAs substrates is an important process step in the manufacture of GaAs integrated circuits. The important advantage of ion implantation over epitaxial techniques in such applications are uniformity and reproducibility of doping level and thickness, high volume throughput of large area wafers (leading to a potentially low cost process) and the ability to selectively dope areas through masks to give planar devices. In addition a steep back interface on the carrier profile is considered to be necessary for the production of low noise GaAs MESFETs. Initial impetus to implement ion implantation for GaAs devices and circuits was frustrated by the dual problems associated with post implantation annealing at temperatures above the congruent decomposition temperature and procurement of high quality semi-insulating material. In this paper these problems will not be addressed but results of experiments to investigate the secondary problem concerning carrier profile shape will be presented.

During the evaluation of discrete GaAs MESFETs fabricated from annealed ion implanted layers, the run to run reproducibility of dc parameters was found to be considerably inferior to the uniformity of the same device parameters across each individual wafer. A possible explanation for this poor reproducibility was that the precise orientation of each wafer during implantation differed from one implant run to another. Indeed other workers have demonstrated that the carrier profile shape can be affected by wafer orientation and have demonstrated the existence of both axial [1,2] and planar ion channelling [3] of donor ion species in GaAs. This paper describes the results of an experimental programme to study the effects of wafer orientation during implantation on both the donor ion and carrier density depth profiles.

2. Experimental Procedure

Silicon ions were implanted at room temperature at 240 keV to a dose of $6x10^{12}$ cm^{-2} into (100) LEC grown undoped semi-insulating GaAs substrates (Metals Research). In all cases $^{29}Si^{++}$ ion species were implanted using the Harwell Mk.IV implanter. Prior to implantation all GaAs samples were polish-etched in 3:1:1 H_2SO_4:H_2O_2:H_2O for 15 minutes at 45°C; this treatment removing approximately 25 μm. Subsequent to etching samples were immediately washed in deionised water and dried in a stream of filtered nitrogen. All samples were misorientated 7° from <100> during implantation to avoid axial channelling.

Ideally for precise wafer orientation during implantation a goniometer stage is required. As such a stage was not available on the implanter used (nor indeed is available on any commercial implanter), an alternative approach was used to align samples in order to investigate the possible effects of planar channelling. GaAs samples were cleaved into approximately 2 cm squares, cleaned and mounted onto a series of 2" diameter Si wafers using small quantities of black wax as adhesive. Care was taken that no black wax was presented to the ion beam. Samples were aligned on the Si wafers, such that a <110> cleavage edge of the GaAs samples was rotated at angles (ϕ) of approximately 5°, 10°, 20° and 30° to the <110> reference flat of the Si wafer. On each Si wafer one GaAs sample was accurately positioned parallel to the reference flat as control $\phi = 0°$ samples. On one Si wafer a GaAs sample was accurately aligned with $\phi = 45°$. The actual angles were measured by photographing the loaded Si wafers and measuring the angles on an enlargement. The Si wafers were then placed in the implanter with the reference flats firmly pressed against the bottom edge of the implant holders. The sense of the 7° tilt to avoid axial channelling was about the vertical <110> axis perpendicular to the reference flats and such that, looking along the horizontal ion beam direction, the left-hand side of the wafers was down with respect to the right-hand side. The wafers were then mechanically scanned through the stationary beam in a horizontal direction perpendicular to the beam.

After implantation the GaAs samples were removed from the Si wafers by melting the black wax, solvent cleaned, dried and encapsulated in ~ 1200 Å of reactively sputtered Si_3N_4, sputtering from a Si target in a nitrogen/argon gas mixture. Nitride thickness and refractive index were checked by ellipsometry. The samples were then furnace annealed at 850°C for 15 minutes in flowing argon.

Carrier density and mobility depth profiles of the annealed implants were obtained by differential Hall effect measurements combined with anodic oxidation stripping. A semi-automated system for the repetitive anodisation, oxide stripping and Hall measurement was used. This system is based on a seven station carousel, the sample being automatically stepped from one station to another in the sequence: initial Hall measurement, anodisation, water wash, oxide strip, water wash, IPA rinse, air blow dry and repeat cycle. Individual samples, approximately 5mm square, were prepared for profiling by etching through the implanted layer into the substrate to leave a "clover-leaf" pattern. Contacts were made in the corners of the samples using Sn dots fired-in at approximately 300°C in forming gas. The samples were mounted on perspex holders and wires soldered to the dot contacts and to contact posts. Finally the contact posts, lead wires, contact dots and sample edges were coated with black wax to affix the sample firmly to the holder, to insulate the contacts electrically from the anodising solution and to delineate the area of the sample to be anodised.

Van der Pauw [4] Hall measurements involved four resistivity measurements (2 contact geometries, two current polarities) carried out at zero magnetic field followed by eight Hall effect measurements (two geometries, two current polarities, positive and negative magnetic fields). The current and magnetic field used were 100 μA and 0.22 T. All measurements were carried out at room temperature and in the dark. Anodisation was performed using a reacted ammonia-ethylene glycol-boric acid electrolyte with Pt foil cathode. The electrolyte was continuously agitated by air bubbling. Anodisation was carried out under strong white light illumination and at a constant current density of about 1 mA cm^{-2} up to a defined forming voltage. The amount of GaAs consumed was determined by step height measurement after repeated anodisation and oxide stripping cycles and found to be 13.1 ± 0.2 Å/V. An additional check on the GaAs removed per cycle was obtained by step height measurement of each sample after complete profiling and removal of the black wax anodisation mask. Anodic oxide was stripped in 25% ortho-phosphoric acid. The successive Hall data obtained was converted to carrier concentrations and Hall mobilities using the method described by Johansson et al. [5].

3. Results and Discussion

Carrier and mobility profiles of annealed implanted layers obtained by differential Hall and anodisation stripping are shown in Fig 1. This figure represents a summary of data from several separate implant runs, in which all samples were tilted 7° away from <100> during implantation. The angle of rotation with respect to beam direction and the sample cleavage edges was assumed to be close to 0° but the angle was not accurately determined. The profiles were divided into one of the two general shapes, (a) 'normal' or (b) 'deep'. The initial Hall measurements indicated that for both profile shapes the sheet carrier concentration, n_s was 4.2×10^{12} cm^{-2}, i.e. equivalent to 70% electrical activity and the sheet Hall mobility was 4100 cm^2/Vsec. With reference to the L.S.S. theoretical ion profile for 240 keV Si ions (also shown on Fig.1) it can be seen that the 'deep' profile extends well beyond the theoretical ion range.

A note of caution on the interpretation of the differential Hall profiles can be appreciated by inspection of the tail regions of the profiles. It was found difficult to obtain accurate van der Pauw measurements of points on the profile below about 5×10^{16} cm^{-3}. This is probably due to accumula-

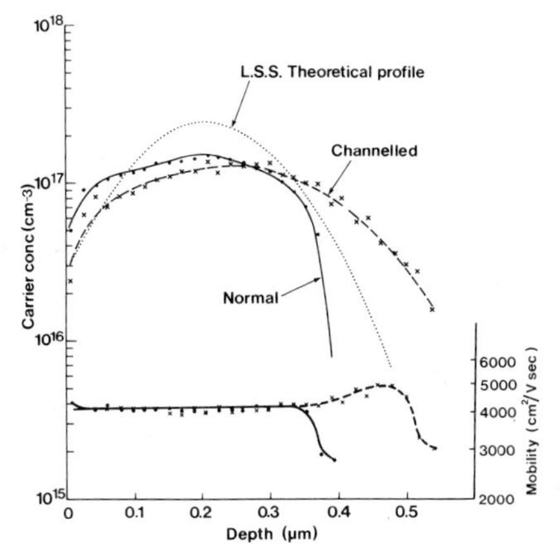

Figure 1. Analysis of Carrier Profiles (Run to Run)

(a) <100> Orientation → <100> Axial Channelling.

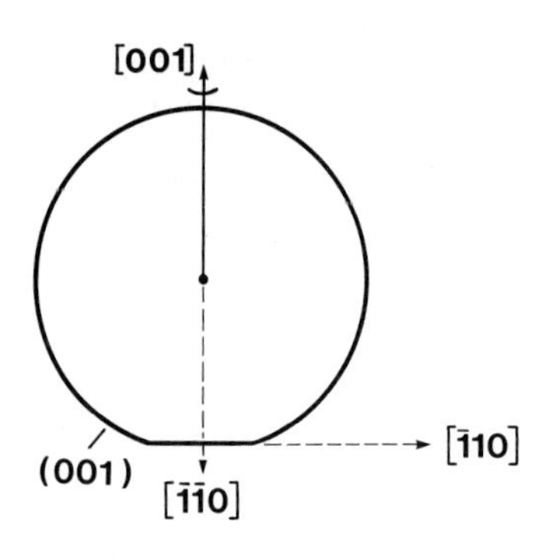

(b) 7° off <100> Misorientation → {110} Planar Channelling.

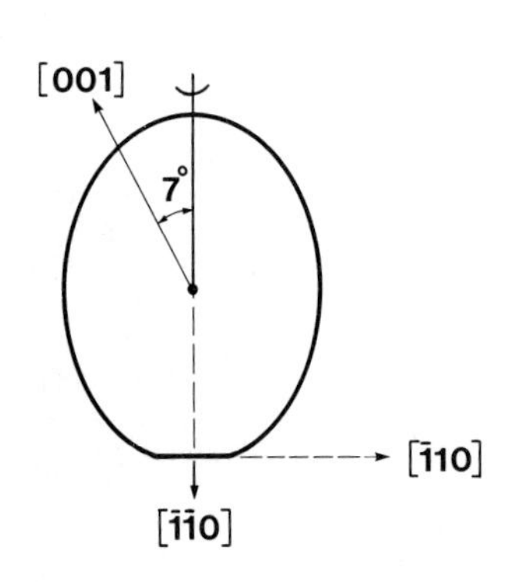

(c) ϕ Rotation → Reduced or No Channelling.

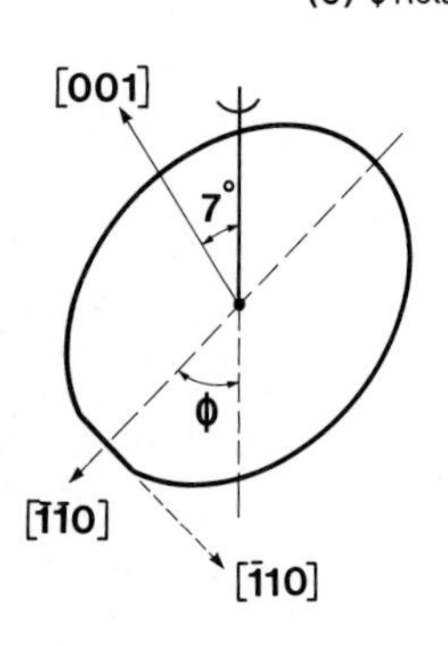

N.B. ⊥ denotes the ion beam direction (perpendicular to the paper)

---- denotes a line in the plane of the slice

Figure 2. Schematic Ball Model Representation of Channelling

tive non-uniformities in the anodic removal process which become more important as the conductivity of the thin remainder of the implanted layer decreases rapidly. In addition none of the points on the profiles is corrected for effects of surface depletion layers [6]. These effects will be small for the high concentration regions of the profile but near the tail this surface depletion layer will account for the majority of the remaining layer. This represents a major limitation of the technique; however, the 'deep' profiles extended much further than the normal profiles before these effects became marked and therefore the deeper and more graded profiles are not in doubt. The number of carriers contained in the tail region of the 'deep' profile represents ~ 10% of the implanted dose.

A possible explanation for this run-to-run reproducibility is that the exact orientation of the wafers actually varied from one implant run to another and that varying degrees of channelling occurred. Axial channelling is a well-known problem in ion implantation if the sample has an "open" low-order crystal direction parallel to the incoming beam [7]. This pattern is customarily avoided by tilting the sample with respect to the ion beam by ~ 7° from the sample normal. A comprehensive study of axial channelling of S, Si, Se and Te ions in GaAs [1] has recently been published and confirms this fact. Axial channelling can be appreciated with reference to the ball model of the GaAs lattice in Fig.2(a) which is oriented such that the beam direction (considered to be into the paper) is normal to one of the (100) cube faces of the unit cell.

However, even with the beam incident at 7° to <100> sample normal, it is possible for the incoming beam to line up with one set of {110} planes and planar channelling can then take place between these planes of atoms [3,8]. Fig.2(b) shows the same ball model tilted about the vertical <110> axis in the same sense as that used and outlined in Section 2. It can be seen that whereas the atoms in the vertical set of {110} planes have effectively closed off the channels, the horizontal set of {110} planes are as open as they were before tilting. This planar channelling can now be minimised by simply rotating the sample about the beam direction in the tilted plane (i.e. Fig.2(c)).

In order to prove whether planar channelling actually existed and was causing the deep profiles a controlled experiment was carried out to measure the carrier profiles as a function of the rotation angle in the tilted plane. These carrier profiles are shown in Fig.3. The GaAs samples were mounted on Si wafers as detailed in Section 2 and the geometry of the samples is schematically shown in the inset on Fig.3. It can be seen that the deep tail is only observed for a rotation angle (ϕ) of 0°. All the other profiles are not channelled and agree with each other within experimental error. These results agree with the findings of Tara and Inada [3] with the exception that they noted slight channelling at ϕ = 5° for silicon implants into Sn doped n-type LPE GaAs layers. It is surprising that channelling effects can be seen over such a large angular range as 5°, as if this did occur significant channelling effects would have been expected in all of our initial runs where care was not taken over the exact alignment of the samples. Channelling is also absent for the ϕ =45° sample, although planar channelling from {100} planes may be theoretically expected. This may reflect the accuracy at which this sample was mounted. However, more realistically and with reference to the ball model (see Fig.2(c), it can be seen that the {100} planar channels are much narrower than the {110} channels and therefore we conclude that {100} planar channelling either does not exist due to the finite size of the silicon ion or that the acceptance angle for such channelling is very small indeed.

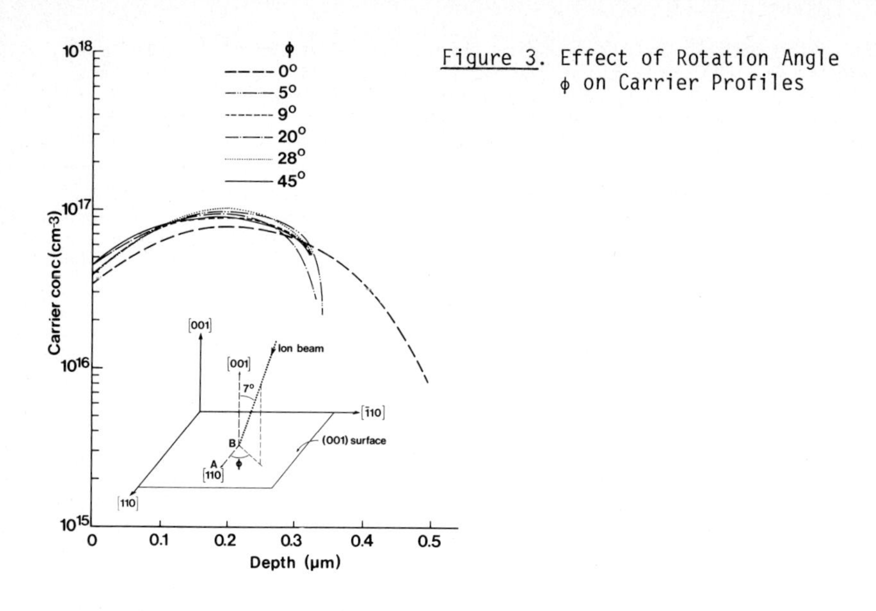

Figure 3. Effect of Rotation Angle ϕ on Carrier Profiles

Finally, in order to check further these channelling effects, a limited analysis of ^{29}Si ion profiles was carried by Secondary Ion Mass Spectroscopy. This SIMS analysis was carried out by Charles Evans and Associates using a Cameca IMS3F with a Cs^+ primary ion beam. Figure 4 (a) shows the results of three samples, (A) as implanted $\phi = 28°$, (B) implanted and annealed $\phi = 28°$ and (C) implanted and annealed $\phi = 0°$ on the same depth scale as the carrier profiles of Fig.3. Figure 4(b) shows the complete SIMS depth profiles into the substrate. The major problem with these data is the relatively small dynamic range of the SIMS profiles for Si in GaAs. However the profiles were all normalised to the dose of 6×10^{12} cm^{-2} after subtracting background (i.e. no dose loss is assumed on annealing). Crater depths were checked by step height measurement and interferometry. Confidence in the calibration can be gained by the good agreement between profile (A) and L.S.S. near the peak of the profile (see Fig.4(b)). By comparison of profiles

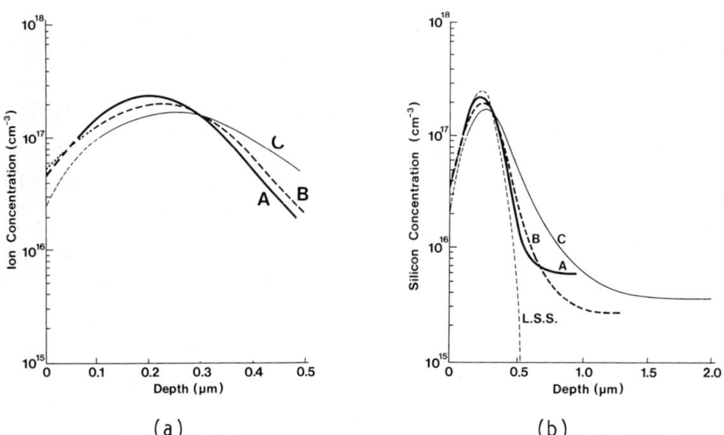

Figure 4. ^{29}Si SIMS Ion Profiles Normalised to 6×10^{12} cm^{-2} Dose

(A) and (B) it can be seen that there is no marked diffusion of Si during the anneal. Neither profile agrees well with L.S.S. near the tail even allowing for the respective background levels. This may be due to relative inaccuracies of the SIMS profiles or that the ion profile is not exactly Gaussian in the tail. It has been reported for a number of ion species and target combinations (and, indeed, for Se in GaAs) that higher moments of the normal distribution are required and better fits to tails of as-implanted profiles are obtained using Pearson IV type distributions [9]. In contrast profile (C) for $\phi = 0$ extends well beyond the expected ion range, thus providing further evidence for the existence of planar channelling.

5. Conclusions

Carrier depth profiles of annealed silicon implanted GaAs can exhibit tails which extend well beyond the theoretical ion range for truly amorphous targets. These tails have been confirmed on ion profiles obtained by SIMS and have been demonstrated to be consistent with {110} planar channelling. They can be avoided by appropriate misorientation and rotation of wafers during implantation.

Acknowledgments

This work has been supported, in part, by the Procurement Executive, U.K. Ministry of Defence, sponsored by D.C.V.D. and is published with the permission of the Directors of Plessey Research (Caswell) Limited. The authors are indebted to D.J. Chivers, A.E.R.E., Harwell for the ion implantation and to Charles Evans and Associates for the SIMS analysis.

References

1 R.G. Wilson and V.R. Deline: Appl. Phys. Lett., 37, 793 (1980)

2 T.J. Harris, B.J. Sealy and R.K. Surridge: Elect. Lett., 12, 664 (1976)

3 T. Tara and T. Inada: Solid State Tech., 22, 69, (1979)

4 L.J. van der Pauw: Philips Research Reports, 13, 1 (1958)

5 N.G.E. Johansson, J.W, Mayer and O.J. Marsh: Solid State Electronics, 13, 317 (1970)

6 H.M. Hobgood, G.W. Eldridge, D.L. Barrett and R.N. Thomas: IEEE Trans. Elect. Devices, ED-28, 140 (1981)

7 V.G.K. Reddi and J.D. Sansbury: J. Appl. Phys. 44, 2951 (1973)

8 P. Blood: Phys. Stat. Sol. (a), 25, K151 (1974)

9 A. Lidow, J.F. Gibbons, V.R. Deline and C.A. Evans: Appl. Phys. Lett. 32, 15 (1978)

Application of High-Current Ion-Implantation Systems in Semiconductor-Device Technology

B. Raicu

Applied Implant Technology, 2940 Kifer Road, Santa Clara, CA 95051, USA

1. Introduction

With the third generation of high-current implanters, a clear trend is developing towards processes requiring high doses at high throughputs. High-current, high-energy predeposition implanters can only be used at full power by providing good wafer cooling during the implantation process. Adequate wafer cooling permits good crystal quality after annealing, as well as making high-dose-rate processes with photoresist masks feasible.

LSI and VLSI processes require oxide integrity after high-dose-rate implants. A high-current electron flood gun, capable of neutralizing surface-charge build-up during $2x10^{16}$ As/cm^2 implants allows the implementation of a yield-enhancement process using high-dose ion implantation for poly-Si doping (AIT patent applied for).

A fast, very efficient annealing technique developed by AG Associates was used for low-resistance poly-Si formation, employing high-dose ion implantation and heat-pulse annealing (AIT and AG Associates patent applied for).

2. Wafer-Cooling Effects on Crystal Quality and Photoresist-Mask Integrity: Process Results with AIT III-X Ion Implanters

During high-dose implant processes with high beam power, proper wafer cooling avoids in situ annealing and photoresist-mask damage. Uniform wafer cooling during implantation permits the formation of a continuous amorphous layer in the implanted region. During annealing, the amorphous layer regrows epitaxially and defect-free, thus leading to an efficient doping activation and fewer residual defects [1] [2] [3].

Beam heating effects with AIT III-X implanters are controlled by [4]:

- large-area beam;
- large batch size;
- optimized scanning system and duty cycle;
- excellent heat transfer and uniform wafer cooling with wafer-plate model 154/2 [5].

The AIT III-X predeposition implanters provide the highest beam current available today, with the highest energy and the lowest power density:

- Maximum beam current: 12.5 mA
- Maximum energy: 120 keV
- Beam area: 6x6 cm^2
- Maximum beam power density: 41.6 W/cm^2 .

Because of the AIT III-X's lower power densities, only simple passive cooling is required. Table 1 shows wafer temperatures for the most usual process applications in MOS and bipolar integrated circuit technology. The data on the dose rate's effects on the quality of the implanted layer after annealing, including sheet resistance, maximum carrier concentration, junction depth, and doping uniformity, are summarized in Table 2. The doping effect is not dose rate dependent due to the excellent wafer cooling provided by the wafer holder of model 154/2, depicted in Fig. 1. Using model 154/2, the throughput of a source and drain process is 180 4" wafers/ hour. An emitter process of $1x10^{16}As/cm^2$ has a throughput of 108 4" wafers/hour.

Table 1. Wafer temperature during implant processes on model 154/2 heat sink wafer plates for most characteristic applications using AIT III-X implanter

Process	Dopant	Dose (i/cm^2)	I_B (mA)	Energy (keV)	Proc. Time (min)	Wafer temperature (°C) with different masks Resist	Oxide	Poly
Interconnect (Poly-doping)	As	2E16	12.5	100	24	104	100	100
Bipolar IC emitters	P	1E16	12.5	40 60	12	41 52	40 50	41 51
MOS IC source and drain or buried layers	As	5E15	12.5	60 110	6	48 54	46 49	46 52
High dose processes at max. beam power	P	1E16	12.5	120	12	80	74	81

Table 2. Dose-rate effects on activation efficiency in a standard ion-implantation process for source and drain, using the AIT III-X implanter

Beam Current (mA)	Beam Power (W)	Beam Power Density (W/cm^2)	Dose/Scan (i/cm^2)	Process Time (min)	Junction Depth (μm)	Maximum Carrier Concentration (cm^{-3})	Sheet Resistance ($\Omega/\square$)	Doping Uniformity $\frac{\sigma}{\overline{R_s}}$ %
2.085	250.2	7.0	4.17E14	36	0.35	1.2E20	31	0.36
4.165	499.8	14.0	8.33E14	18	0.37	1.3E20	30	0.26
6.0	720.0	21.4	1.2E15	12	0.375	1.2E20	31	0.44
8.3	996.0	29.7	1.66E15	9	0.38	1.25E20	31	0.31
2.5	1500.0	39.2	2.5E15	6	0.33	1.5E20	30	0.5

Implant conditions: Dopant:As; total dose:$5x10^{15}i/cm^2$; energy: 120 keV.
Annealing conditions: Temperature:1000°C; time:30 min; ambient:dry N_2

Figure 1. Model 154/2 Wafer Plate

The ability to use photoresist masks with ion-implantation predeposition processes offers unique advantages, and allows cost-effective ion implantation for high doping concentrations in LSI and VLSI applications.

During the ion-implantation process, special care for wafer cooling and preimplant photoresist treatment by hard baking makes the technique effective. The photoresist material is modified during the irradiation process. The main effect is a graphitization of the base polymer, producing H, O_2, and simultaneous diazide decomposition, producing N_2 [6][7][8].

Effects:
- Optical transmission decreases.
- The mask becomes thinner.
- Under some conditions, the photoresist flows or shrinks. Predictable shrinkage is preferable to flow on the registering mask.
- Bubble formation can occur with poor heat transfer.

Effective heat transfer from wafer to wafer holder provides feature size control and good photoresist strippability up to maximum beam power of 1500 W. Calculated photoresist temperature does not exceed 5.2°C over the wafer temperature in ion implant process at maximum beam power [9]. See

HPR-204 As IMPLANT

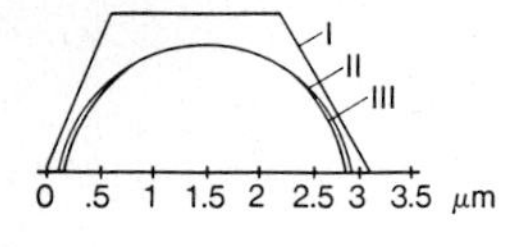

Implant Conditions:
ϕ =5E15 icm^{-2}
I_b=12.5mA
E =120KeV
Implant Time – 6 min.

1a

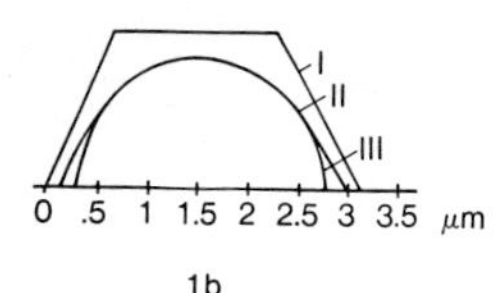

ϕ = 1E16 icm^{-2}
I_b = 12.5mA
E = 80KeV
Implant Time – 12 min.

1b

Figure 2. Photoresist-line modification during high-dose HPR-204 As implantation.
2a: source-and-drain process or buried-layer process;
2b: emitter process.

I = Line shape before hard bake
II = Line shape after hard bake
III= Line shape after implant

Hard bake process: 30 min, vac; T = 120°C

Table 1 for experimental results. Feature size modification is predictable and within the limits of .25μm for a 2μm line. Figure 2 exemplifies photoresist line modification during high dose implant.

After high-dose implant the photoresist is only strippable in O_2 plasma. The stripping time is longer for higher-energy implants; high dose rate implanted photoresist is stripped faster and the stripping time is related to the ion species.

3. Oxide Integrity During High Dose Implants: Electron Flood Gun Effect

Processing with high beam currents can deteriorate the exposed SiO_2 surface due to surface charging, and can reduce breakdown voltage of thin and thick oxide in MOS devices. With the introduction of dielectric isolated bipolar devices, the importance of avoiding surface charging increases.

A high current electron flood gun, capable of neutralizing surface charge, is used. In Figure 3 the AIT III-X process chamber with flood gun is shown.

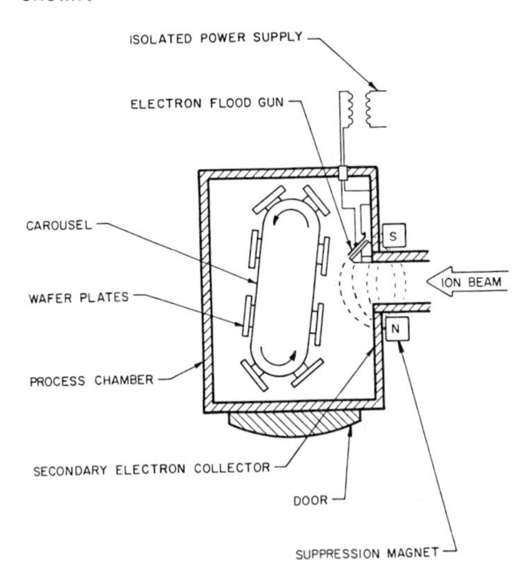

Figure 3. AIT III-X process chamber with flood gun

Preliminary results demonstrate the high process efficiency of AIT III-X with electron flood gun during implants up to a beam current of 12.5mA.

1. A 63% improvement of V_{BD} [thin oxide] is achieved by using flood gun during the following source and drain process: Implant As, $\emptyset=5\times10^{15}$i/cm^2, I_b=12.5mA, E=120 keV (throughput 180 4" wafers/hour).

2. High-Dose Poly Doping by ion implantation can successfully replace As spin deposition. Implant Process: As, $\emptyset=2\times10^{16}$i/cm^2, I_b =12.5mA.

   Effect: 20% improvement in poly-Si sheet resistance
   20-25% increase in V_{BD} [thick oxide]
   13% increase in V_{BD} [thin oxide]
   20% increase in device yield .

Additionally, the excellent results obtained by high-dose poly doping seen during the flood-gun characterization encourages us to study the effect of the annealing technique on poly-Si sheet resistance.

4. High-Dose Ion Implantation and Heat-Pulse Annealing of Poly-Si for Low Resistivity Applications

Efficient doping of poly-Si by high-dose ion implantation and appropriate annealing techniques can increase process yield and functional density.

Doped poly-Si Applications:
- Gate electrodes
- Buried contacts
- Interconnects
- Emitters and diffusion sources for shallow emitters .

High-dose ion implantation with high-current predep systems can replace successful phosphorus doping from $POCl_3$ and arsenic doping from As spin on. The effect is a process for low resistivity poly-Si which is highly efficient, clean, and particle free.

The annealing technique is extremely important due to the impurity effect on the grain size formation during different time/temperature conditions. Recently, a new annealing technique using halogen lamps was developed by AG Associates [10]. Using this technique with high-dose, high dose rate implants in poly-Si, and working jointly with AG Associates, a research

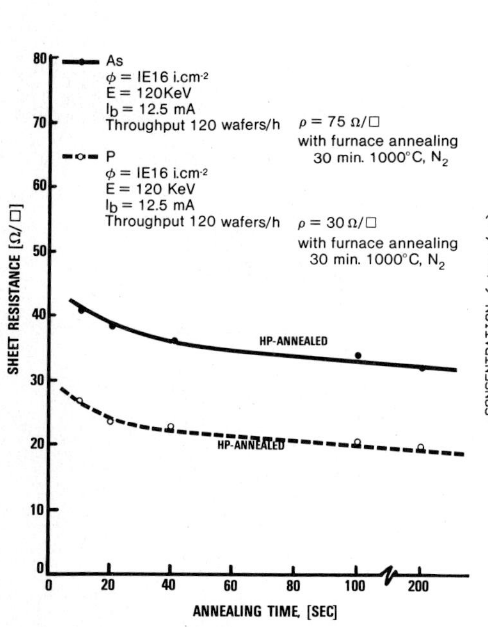

Figure 4. Poly sheet resistance versus annealing time after high-dose ion implantation and heat-pulse annealing

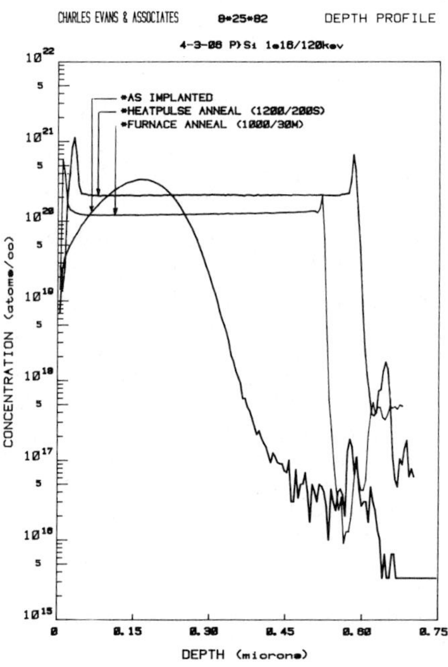

Figure 5. SIMS measurements on as implanted, furnace annealed and heat-pulse annealed poly-Si

program was developed to study heat-pulse effects on high-dose implants in poly-Si. The results will be disclosed in an extended paper prepared with A. Gat and S. Shatas. However, some results pertaining to P-implanted poly are given below. Implant conditions: $\emptyset=1\times10^{16}$ i/cm^2; E=120 keV; I_b=12.5mA.

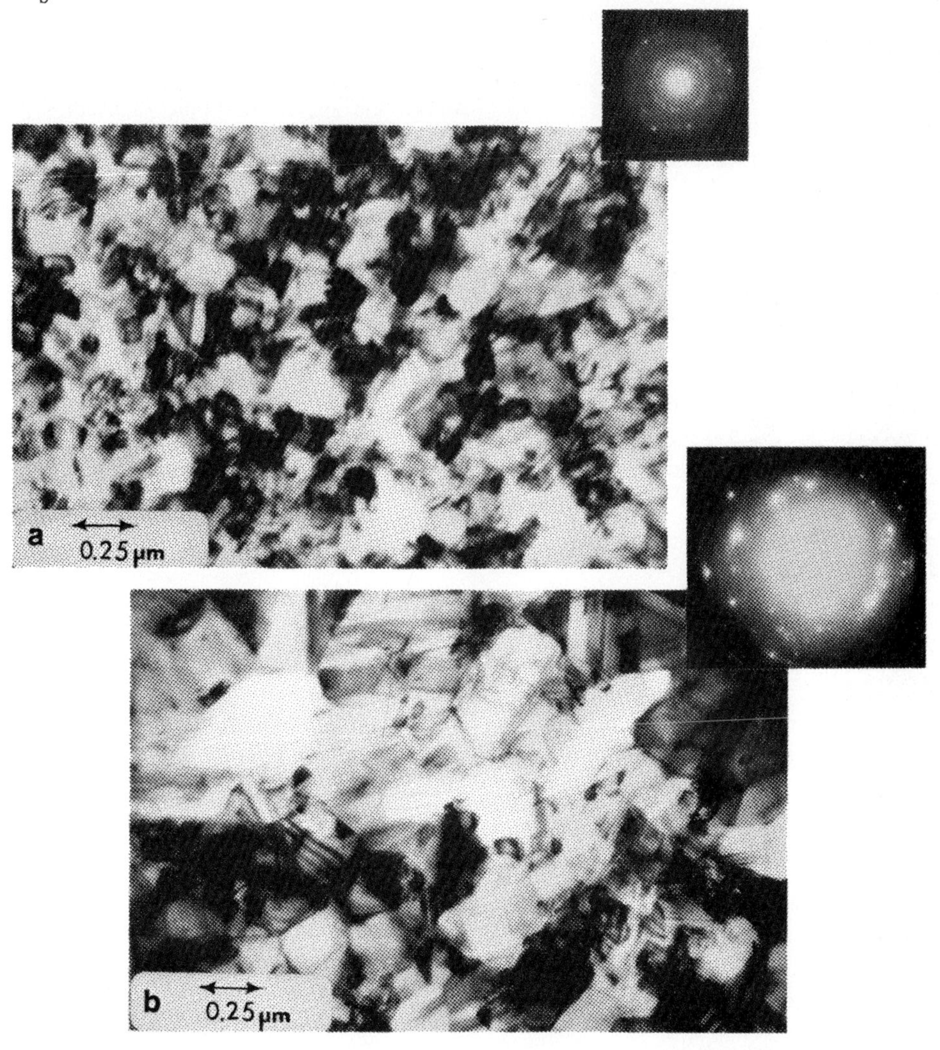

Figure 6A. TEM on poly-Si structure after high-dose implant and furnace annealing.

Implant: P, $\emptyset=1\times10^{16}$ i/cm^2
I_b=12.5 mA, E=120 keV
annealing: furnace,
1000°C 30 min, N_2
Sheet resistivity: 30 Ω/□
Average grain size: 2,000 A ± 1,000 A

Figure 6B. TEM on poly-Si structure after high-dose implant and heat-pulse annealing.

Implant: P, $\emptyset=1\times10^{16}$ i/cm^2
I_b=12.5 mA, E=120 keV
Annealing: Heat pulse,
1200°C, 200 sec, air
Sheet resistivity: 20 Ω/□
Average grain size: 10,000Å ± 5,000Å

Isothermal and isochronal heat-pulse annealing was performed and compared with standard furnace annealing. The Heat-Pulse conditions (t_a, T_a) can be used to tailor the poly conductivity and grain size. Poly sheet resistance measurements after isochronal heat-pulse annealing at 1200°C demonstrate high activation efficiency [See Figure 4]. SIMS measurements show a very uniform distribution of P in the poly layer after heat-pulse annealing [See Figure 5]. TEM on heat-pulse and thermal annealed samples shows that heat pulse causes large overlapping grains. The heat-pulsed annealed sample has an average grain size five times greater than the furnace-annealed sample [See Figure 6]. Better implant activation, together with increased poly grains, explain the formation of low resistance poly at implanted doses lower than usual.

5. Conclusions

This paper demonstrates the feasibility of high-current predep processes for high doping concentration in LSI and VLSI circuits with high throughputs using the AIT III-X ion implanter. In this connection:

- Photoresist masks can be used up to the maximum beam power for high dose rate processes.

- Good doping uniformity and high electrical efficiency of implant processes are achieved with thermal annealing and heat-pulse annealing.

- By using heat-pulse annealing the doping efficiency is dramatically increased.

- Insulator integrity can be maintained in advanced devices by using an electron flood gun during high-dose processes. This avoids surface damage and increases oxide breakdown voltage.

ACKNOWLEDGEMENTS

Many thanks are due to J. Kingsley, D. Aitken, A. Noeth, L. Steen, and M. Wauk for useful discussions and encouragement during this work. Special thanks are expressed to S. Adkins for his help during the research.

The work on heat-pulse annealing was done with A. Gat and S. Shatas (AG Associates); a detailed paper will follow in this regard.

During our research, we used special measurement techniques in the following laboratories:

Aracor for TEM
Charles Evans and Associates for SIMS
Solecon Laboratories for spreading resistance measurements.

I would like to express my appreciation for the high-quality work provided by these laboratories.

REFERENCES

1. B. L. Crowder: J. Electrochem. Soc. 117 671 (1970)
2. L.A. Christel, J.F. Gibbons, T.W. Sigmon: J. Appl. Phys. 52 7143 (1981)
3. B. Raicu: In Applied Materials 1982 Spring Technical Seminars, May, (1982)
4. D. Aitken: "The series III-X predeposition machine", this volume
5. J. Kingsley: AIT Internal Report (1982)
6. Y. Okuyama, T. Hashimoto, T. Koguchi: J. Electrochem. Soc. 125, (8), 1293 (1978)
7. T.C. Smith: "Wafer cooling and photoresist masking problems", this volume
8. B. Raicu, L. Steen: "Feasibility of photoresist as an ion implant mask", AIT Applications Report, June, (1981)
9. M. Wauk: "Surface heating of photoresist", AIT Internal Report, May (1982)
10. A. Gat, S. Shatas: Introduction to Heat Pulse Processing Technology, AG Associates (1982)

Implantation Doping of Germanium with Be, Mg, Zn, and B Ions

M. Metzger, Z. Zhang*, B. Schmiedt, and H. Ryssel

Fraunhofer-Institut für Festkörpertechnologie, Paul-Gerhardt-Allee 42,
D-8000 München 60, Fed. Rep. of Germany

Abstract

Germanium avalanche photodiodes were fabricated by implanting B, Be, Mg, and Zn. The best results were obtained by using B for the active area and Be for the guard ring. The reverse currents are as low as 100 nA at 95% of the breakdown voltage, for a diode with an area of 9.6×10^{-4} cm^2. Multiplication factors in excess of 100 are easily obtained.

1. Introduction

In an optical fiber communication link, photodiodes are used as detectors for converting the received optical power into an electrical output signal. In the case of an optical fiber on the basis of quartz, there are three transmission regions suitable for optical communication. The transmission regions between 1.0 and 1.3 µm as well as between 1.5 and 1.8 µm offer an especially low attenuation and dispersion. In addition, the eye is impervious to wavelengths above 1.4 µm. This means that in the longer wavelength region there is no danger for the eye at the usual irradiation intensities. With a maximum of the spectral sensitivity at 1.55 µm, germanium photodiodes seem to be well suited for the required wavelength regions. The fabrication process is very similar to that employed in silicon technology; therefore, the use of germanium offers better conditions for mass production than the use of III-V compound semiconductors does.

The reverse current of germanium diodes is much higher than that of silicon diodes. It is strongly affected by process temperatures during fabrication; therefore, the use of ion implantation as a low-temperature doping technique seems to be advantageous for high-performance devices. Recently, it was shown that it is in fact possible to fabricate very good avalanche photodiodes in germanium through ion implantation [3].

Optical-fiber communication poses the following requirements for an infrared photodetector. The signal-to-noise ratio of the detection system has to be optimized. This means that the reverse currents of the photodiodes must be as small as possible, the quantum efficiency high, and the multiplication factor sufficiently high to enable fitting on the following circuit. For the detection of high bit rates, a short rise time and a minimal prolongation of the optical pulses are necessary.

The lifetime of the photogenerated minority carriers in the implanted part of the photodiode is very small, so that the quantum efficiency

---

*) Permanent address: Institute for Semiconductor Research, Peking

decreases with the depth of the implanted region. High quantum efficiency therefore requires a shallow junction. The implantation has to take place at a low energy; and the dopant should have a small diffusion coefficient in germanium, in order to avoid diffusion during thermal annealing.

In avalanche photodiodes, current gain or multiplication is obtained when the photogenerated carriers gain sufficient energy from the electrical field to generate additional carriers by impact ionization. In a standard implanted planar diode, the lateral doping profile is pronouncedly curved at the periphery of the implanted region. Therefore, for a given reverse bias, the electrical field reaches its highest value at the diode periphery. In consequence, avalanche multiplication and breakdown will only take place at the peripherical junction, as can be seen from Fig. 1.

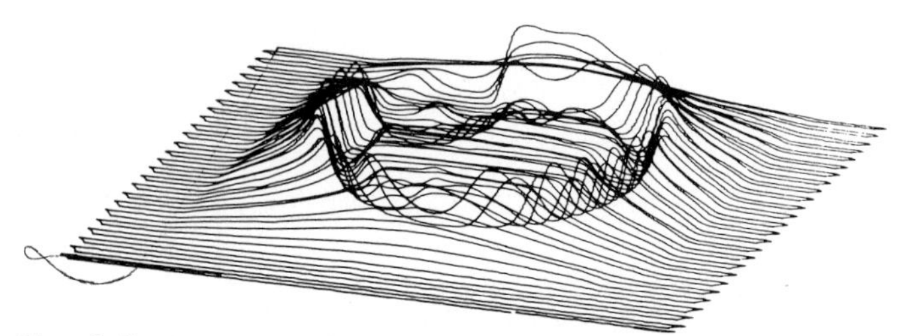

Fig. 1. Raster scan of the photocurrent of a reverse-biased Ge-APD. The signal in the center of the plot corresponds to the photosensitive area; the surrounding ring corresponds to the metallization which covers the junction periphery. Outside of it is the bulk material. A comparison of the photocurrent in the active area to that at the periphery shows that the multiplication takes place at the latter. (The diode structure is shown in Fig. 2)

To avoid this, a guard ring has to be employed, overlapping the periphery of the first junction. If its p-n junction is linearly graded and deep enough, the peripheral breakdown voltage can be increased to values higher than that of the abrupt photosensitive junction. The breakdown voltage for such a junction is nearly independent of the curvature, and becomes a function of the impurity gradient only [1]. Because the impurity gradient of an implanted profile is not sufficiently low for the required breakdown voltage, an additional drive-in diffusion step has to be performed. As stated above, the diffusion temperature has to be kept very low in order to avoid high dark currents.

The pulse response of photodiodes is mainly affected by the carrier-collection time, by the junction capacitance in connection with the series resistance and the load resistance, and by multiplication effects. For fast diodes, the depth of the depletion region should be in the order of the penetration depth of the incident light, since the minority carriers behind the depletion region are collected by diffusion which is a much slower process than carrier collection with an electrical field.

In this study, the activation behavior of implanted B, Be, Mg, and Zn was investigated, and photodiodes were produced.

2. Experimental Techniques

Our investigations of the doping behavior of B, Be, Mg, and Zn concentrated on their suitability for the fabrication of Ge-APD's. For measurement of the profiles, activation analysis and the SIMS technique were utilized. The annealing behavior of the elements was investigated using the van der Pauw method. To measure the breakdown voltages of a guard ring, or of the abrupt photosensitive junction, the diode structure shown in Fig. 2 was used. The guard ring should have a greater avalanche breakdown voltage (ABV) than the photosensitive junction, so that one measures the ABV of the active junction. The ABV of the guard ring can be measured at the outer guard ring.

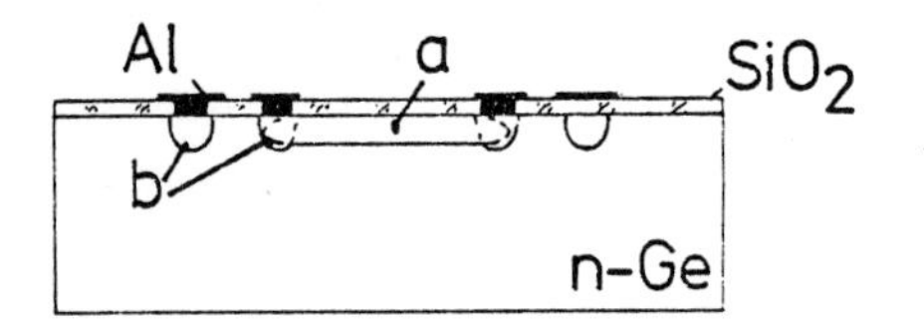

Fig. 2 Cross-section through a Ge-APD test structure
a) active area
b) guard rings

Very important factors are the homogeneities of the photosensitivity as well as the multiplication. To measure these a laser scanner was employed through which it is possible to measure both factors in a locally resolved manner (see Fig. 1).

For the fabrication of the photosensitive area, a boron implantation promised good results in respect to the above requirements. The advantage of boron is its very low diffusion coefficient in Ge, resulting in the fact that no modification of the implanted profile was observed during the following thermal processes, thus ensuring that shallow junctions are obtainable even after thermal annealing. As doping elements for the guard ring, beryllium, magnesium, and zinc were chosen. Beryllium and magnesium are distinguished by high diffusion coefficients in germanium, whereas zinc was investigated because it had been reported upon as being suitable for deep guard rings [2].

The implanted doses chosen for this investigation ranged from $1 \times 10^{14} cm^{-2}$ to $5 \times 10^{15} cm^{-2}$; the annealing or drive-in temperatures ranged from room temperature to 450°C.

3. Results

Boron implantation into germanium causes less damage than implantation of other elements belonging to the third group, such as aluminum or indium. Because of its low stopping power in SiO_2, boron can be implanted through the passivation layer, so that the technology can be reduced by one step in comparison to an aluminum or indium implantation. For an implantation energy of 90 keV, nearly complete electrical activation was found for doses up to $5 \times 10^{15} cm^{-2}$. The necessary annealing conditions are about 350°C for one hour. Figure 3 shows a comparison of the theoretical implantation profile to an experimental profile for a boron-doped germanium sample, as measured by the (n,α) method under the above conditions. It can be seen that no profile change is brought about by thermal annealing.

Capacitance-voltage measurements indicated a linear relationship between the applied bias voltage and $1/C^2$ (C junction capacitance). This makes it certain that an abrupt junction was formed.

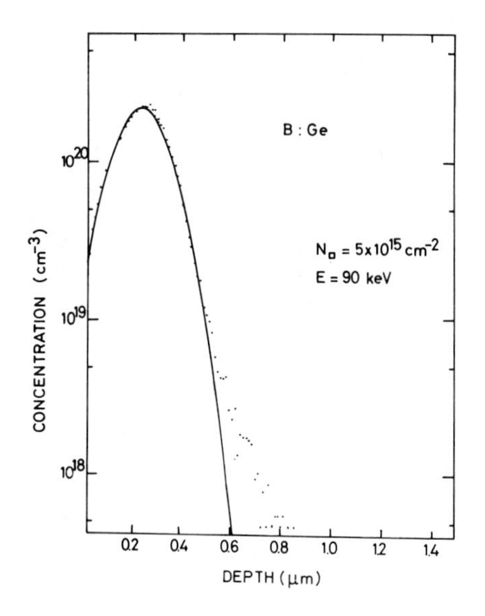

Fig. 3. Impurity profile of a boron-implanted germanium sample.
-: theoretical profile,
: measured profile

To form the guard ring, diffusion has to be performed at temperatures lower than 650°C, since it was found that at higher temperatures, as well as in the case of diffusion times significantly longer than one hour, a considerable amount of GeO_2 is formed at the interface between the germanium and the SiO_2 passivation layer. This leads to an increase in the surface leakage current. Therefore, the elements for the guard ring should have high diffusion coefficients as well as good annealing properties at low temperatures.

In order to obtain deep p-n junctions all other elements were implanted at an energy of 200 keV. For beryllium, at all applied doses, annealing starts at a temperature of 200°C. Annealing at 300°C for one hour results in a saturation of the electrical activation, while in the case of the lower dose only, the electrical activation amounts to one hundred percent.

In the case of Mg, an annealing effect is obtained for implantation doses of $1 \times 10^{15} cm^{-2}$ and higher. This sample was fully annealed after a one-hour treatment at a temperature of 400°C. At higher doses, as well as at lower doses, the electrical activation was lower.

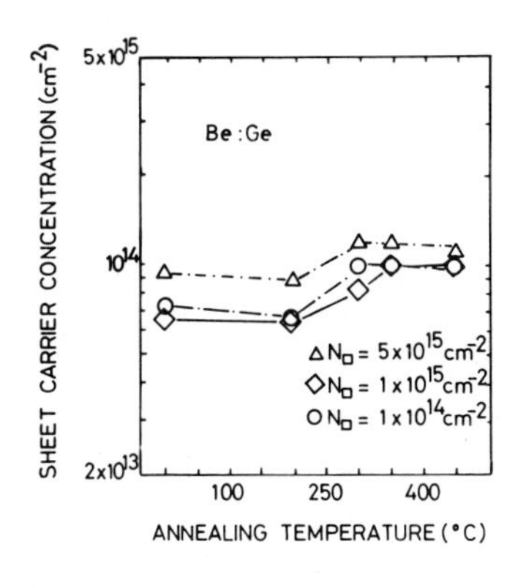

Fig. 4. Sheet carrier concentration of Be-implanted Ge as a function of annealing temperature (annealing time 1 h)

To obtain information on the profiles, SIMS measurements were made. In this connection, the implantation parameters were the same for all elements investigated, namely, a dose of 5 x $10^{15}cm^{-2}$ and with an energy of 200 keV. Except for Zn, the profiles indicated a long tail towards the bulk of the sample. However the accuracy of the measurement was not precise enough to allow the profile to be followed to the p-n junction. Therefore, the avalanche breakdown voltages (ABV) for the different junctions were measured, as indicated in Table 1.

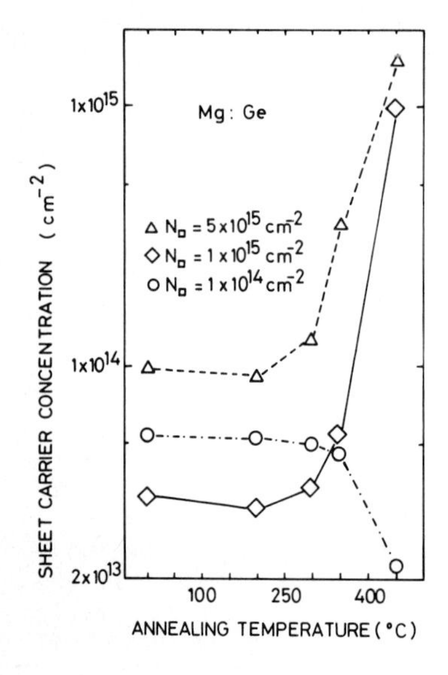

Fig. 5. Sheet carrier concentration of Mg-implanted Ge as a function of annealing temperature (annealing time 1 h)

Table 1. Comparison of avalanche breakdown voltages for various diodes. The given value of the boron-doped diode is that for the planar part of the junction

SUBSTRATE RESISTANCE (Ωcm)	ELEMENT	IMPLANTATION DOSE (cm^{-2})	ENERGY (keV)	ANNEALING (°C / h)	ABV (V)
0.1 - 0.5	B	$5x10^{15}$	90	650 / 1	30 - 35
"	Be	$1x10^{14}$	250	"	50 - 55
2.4 - 3.0	B	$5x10^{15}$	90	"	140 - 160
"	Be	$1x10^{14}$	250	"	160 - 180
"	Zn	$5x10^{15}$	200	"	110 - 120
"	Mg	$5x10^{15}$	200	"	160 - 170

In this investigation, Zn did not fulfill the already stated requirements for a guard ring. The magnesium-formed guard ring led to a high reverse current. The best results were obtained with a Be-doped guard ring. The reverse currents of a B-Be diode with an active area of $9x10^{-2}$ mm^2 are below 1 μA; for some devices they are even below 100 nA at 95% of the ABV. The volume component of the reverse current was measured at 60 nA for this diode.

Figure 6 shows measurements of such a diode's photocurrent, for zero bias as well as for high reverse bias. It can be seen clearly that the multiplication takes place at the active area in the center of the device. The multiplication factors obtained are in the order of about 100. In some devices, however, factors up to ca. 1000 were measured.

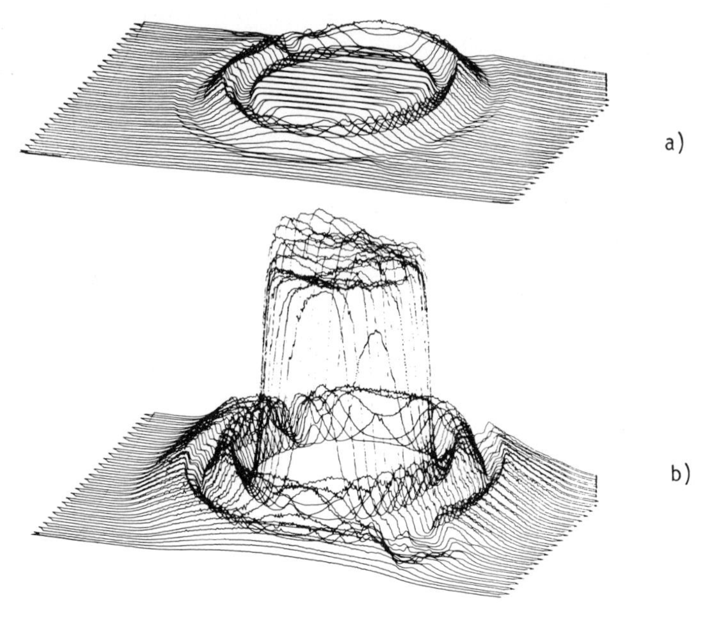

Fig. 6 . Photocurrent of a Ge-APD.
a) at zero bias
b) near the avalanche breakdown voltage

Finally, the pulse response of the diode was investigated. Figure 7 shows the response to the incident light pulse of a mode-locked Nd:YAG laser. The rise time is between 50 and 80 psec, with a full-width-half-maximum of about 150 psec.

For germanium avalanche photodiodes, a combination of boron and beryllium in the manner described gives the best results. Because all process

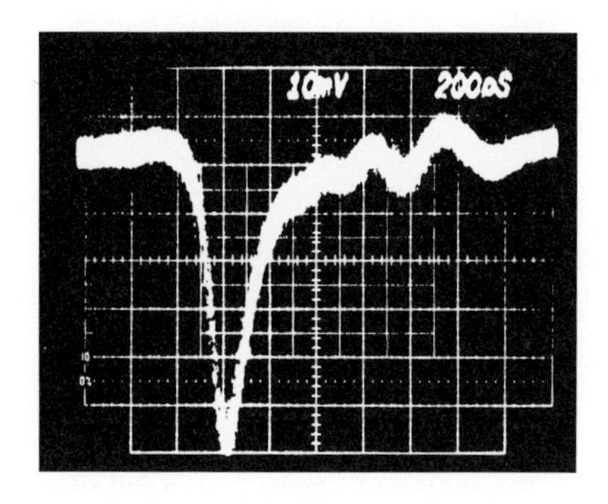

Fig. 7. Pulse response of a Ge-APD

temperatures are kept very low, the breakdown characteristics are very sharp in comparison to those reported by Kagawa et al. [3], who used an annealing temperature of 650°C.

References

1. S.M. Sze, Physics of Semiconducter Devices, John Wiley & Sons, New York (1969)

2. T. Kaneda, H. Fukuda, T. Mikawa, Y. Banba, and Y. Toyama, Appl. Phys. Lett. 34, 12 (1979)

3. S. Kagawa, T. Kaneda, T. Mikawa, Y. Banba, Y. Toyama, and O. Mikami, Appl. Phys. Lett. 38, 429 (1981)

Low Energy Implantation of Nitrogen and Ammonia into Silicon

T.Y. Chiu, W.G. Oldham

Department of Electrical Engineering and Computer Sciences and the Electronics Research Laboratory, University of California, Berkeley, CA 94720, USA

C. Hovland

Perkin-Elmer, Physical Electronics Division, 6509 Flying Cloud Drive, Eden Prairie, MN 55344, USA

Introduction

Thin dielectrics have recently attracted increasing attention. New methods to form thin silicon nitride films have been studied [1,2]. This paper reports on silicon nitride formation by low energy implantation of nitrogen or ammonia into silicon. Extensive material investigation on nitrogen implanted films using various analytical methods, including ellipsometry, chemical etching, transmission electron microscopy (TEM), X-ray photoelectron microscopy (XPS), infrared transmission spectroscopy (IR), and Rutherford backscattering spectroscopy (RBS) is discussed. An improved local oxidation scheme using the implanted layer as part of the oxidation mask is reviewed [3]. The film's electrical properties are also reported [4]. The potential of low energy implantation to form thin gate dielectrics is examined.

Experiments

The experiments employed (100) oriented silicon wafers. The native oxide was removed before loading into an ion milling machine (Veeco Microetch System). The system was first pumped down to below 2×10^{-6} torr and then the implantation was carried out with nitrogen or ammonia pressure at 8×10^{-5} torr. The total dose of the implant was always greater than 0.3 C/cm^2. The samples were then annealed in dry nitrogen or oxidized in wet oxygen.

Results

Ellipsometry Measurement.- The data are taken using He-Ne laser (632.8 nm). Figure 1 shows the ellipsometric parameter Δ versus the implantation energy. The data indicate that film thickness increases with higher implant voltage. Figure 2 shows Δ as a function of annealing time at the temperature of 950°C. The data indicate that the film reaches a steady-state condition within 5 minutes of heat treatment. No nitridation due to the nitrogen annealing ambient is observed. However, a difference in annealing transient between the N_2 implanted and the NH_3 implanted layers is observed.

Since the refractive index of the film is unknown, the absolute thickness of the N_2 implanted layer is determined by cross-sectional TEM (Fig.3). An amorphous region of 9 ± 1 nm is found. The film is apparently divided into two parts by a layer of small features (~2-3 nm in size). The physical nature of these features is unknown. The 9 nm thickness yields an effective refractive index of 1.57 for the N_2 implanted samples. Assuming an equal refractive index, the NH_3 implant produces a film of 11.5 ± 1 nm after annealing.

Chemical Etching - Figure 4 shows the etching characteristics of the unannealed films. The etch rate is much higher for the ammonia-implanted layer than the nitrogen-implanted film. Figure 5 and 6 show the etching data of the annealed and oxidized films respectively. The nitrogen annealed layers are more resistant to the attack of diluted hydrofluoric acid. In addition, the etch-

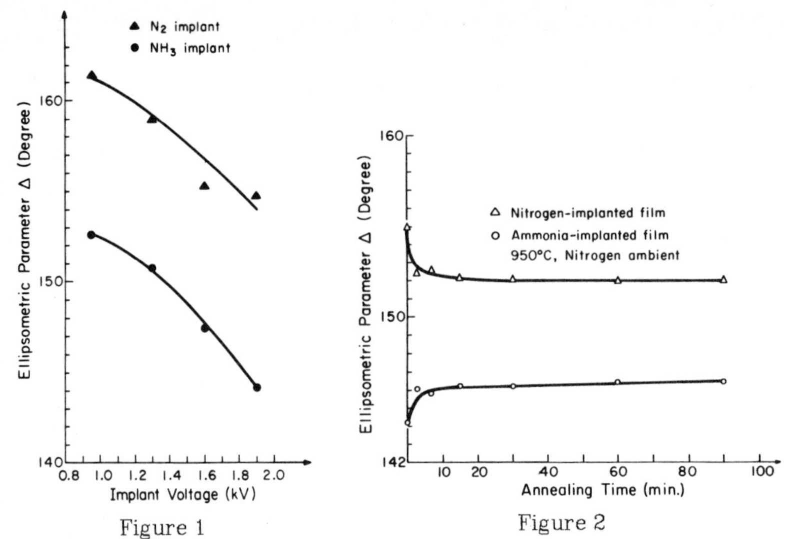

Fig.1. The ellipsometer parameter, Δ, versus the implantation energy. The data are taken on the as-implanted samples

Fig.2. The ellipsometric parameter, Δ, versus the annealing time. Note that Δ reaches a steady state within 5 minutes

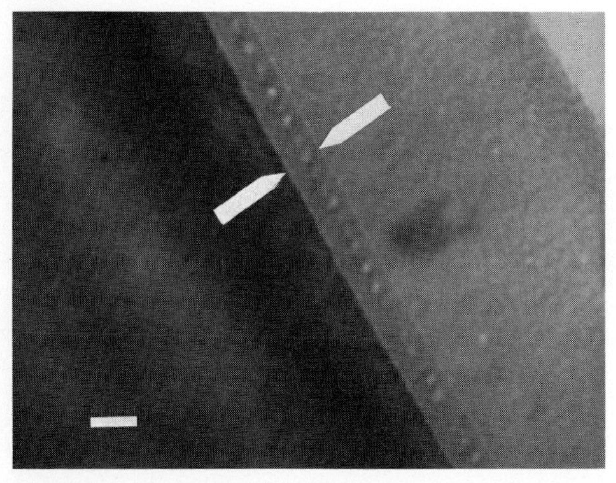

Fig.3. The cross-sectional TEM picture of the nitrogen-implanted layer. The amorphous layer is marked by the two arrows. The bar in the lower left indicates 10 nm. The implanted layer is found to be 9±1 nm thick. (Courtesy of Dr. Ken Ritz of Signetic Co. and Dr. William Stacy of Phillips Research Lab.)

ing behavior is almost identical. A three-layers structure appears to have formed. The XPS result shows that the top surface of the nitrogen annealed films is partially oxidized.

The etching study indicates that, prior to the heat treatment, the products of N_2 implant and NH_3 implant have very different chemical properties. How-

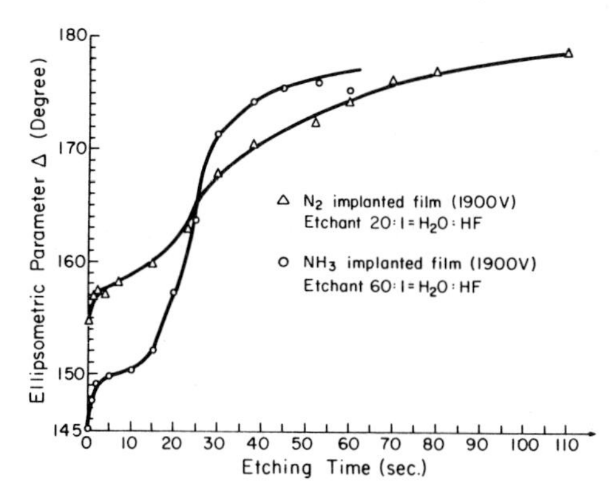

Fig.4. The ellipsometer parameter, Δ, of the as-implanted sample versus the etching time. Note that the etching solutions had different hydrofluoric acid concentration

ever, the chemical properties become similar after annealing. Since one sample is prepared for etch data point,and the consistent results show that the etching is very reproducible.

XPS.- The XPS technique is used for compositional analysis as well as chemical state identification. Since chemical etching is well controlled, one can utilize this method to probe the film at the region of interest. To establish references, measurement on three CVD nitride samples after brief 20:1 HF etch were made. The average nitrogen to silicon ratio (N/Si) was 1.39.

An XPS analysis was also done on the N_2 implanted samples. The nitrogen annealed film was found to be partially oxidized on the surface. During the composition analysis, care was taken to etch through this oxynitride layer. Overetching so that Si substrate contribution could significantly distort the N/Si ratio was also avoided. Therefore the measurement was confined between $171>\Delta>159$.

Four measurements on nitrogen-implanted layer were carried out on both unannealed and annealed film types. The data showed that the N/Si ratio was 1.18 for the as-implanted layer and 1.26 for the annealed film. It should be noted that both ratios were lower than the CVD standard.

Table 1
Binding Energy, Auger Electron Energy and Auger Parameter (eV)

	N1s	N KLL	α_N^*	Si2p	Si KLL	α_{Si}^*
Standard	399.1	378.2	777.3	103.3	1610.9	1714.2
As-implanted	397.5	380.0	777.5	101.7	1612.6	1714.3
Annealed	397.5	379.6	777.1	101.7	1612.3	1714.0

Chemical State Identification.- Table 1 lists the binding energy of N1s, Si2p peaks and the kinetic energy of N KLL and Si KLL peaks. The Si KLL peak is excited by the Bremsstrahlung portion of the incident X ray. Because of charging on the thick CVD nitride standard, modified Auger parameters, α_N^* and α_{Si}^*, are calculated for comparison [5]. It is clear from Table 1 that the chemical state of the as-implanted and the annealed films are very close to that of standard CVD nitride. However, a difference of 0.3 to 0.4 eV in the Auger parameter

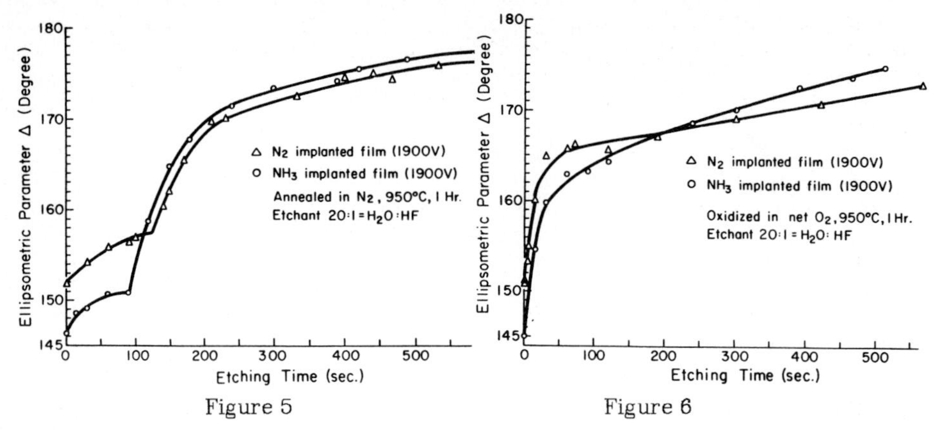

Figure 5 Figure 6

Fig.5. The ellipsometer parameter, Δ, of the nitrogen annealed samples versus the etching time. The surface appears to have a different etching characteristic in comparison to the bulk. An XPS analysis reveals that the surface has a high oxygen content and is probably partially oxidized by the residual oxidant in the nitrogen ambient

Fig.6. The ellipsometer parameter, Δ, of the oxidized sample versus the etching time. The two films showed very similar etching behavior

between the as-implanted and the annealed samples is observed. It is interesting that the annealed film has consistently lower modified Auger parameters than the unannealed layer. IR and RBS results are summarized below [2].

Transmission Infrared Spectroscopy.- The results show the existence of N-Si bonding in both the as-implanted and the annealed samples. However, the transmission minimum shifts from about 850 cm^{-1} to 800 cm^{-1} after heat treatment.

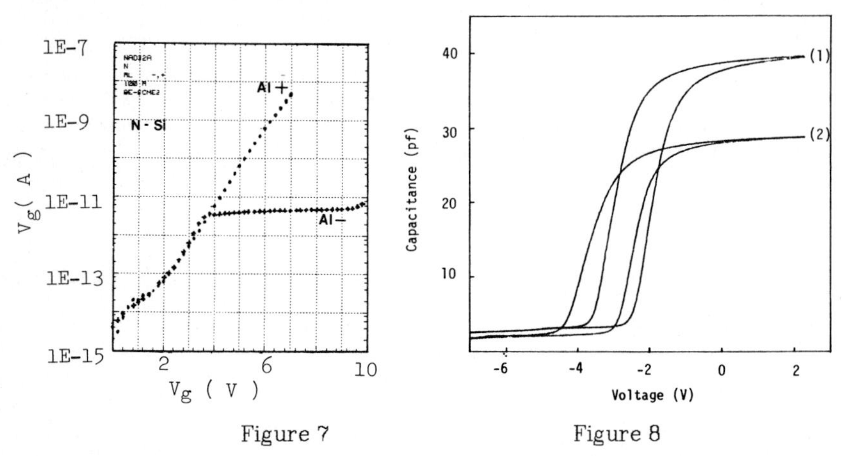

Figure 7 Figure 8

Fig.7. Typical I-V relationship of the annealed samples. The substrate is N type, (100) oriented Si

Fig.8. The C-V curves of the nitride films, (a) after 4 hours of N_2 anneal at 950°C, (b) with an additional 1 hr. anneal in steam at 950°C. The substrate is N type, (100) oriented Si

Rutherford Backscattering Spectroscopy.- The R.B.S. measurement shows that the total nitrogen atoms incorporated in the Si are about $3.5\times10^{16}/cm^2$. The as-implanted layer has a N/Si ratio of 1. Substantial damage is also observed. After thermal treatment, the ratio approaches the stoichiometric nitride value of 1.3. The damage to the Si substrate is reduced but not totally removed after annealing at 900°C for 1/2 hour.

Electrical Properties.- The as-implanted film exhibits non-linear ohmic characteristics. After annealing, the layer becomes an insulator. Figure 7 is a typical I-V relationship of the annealed film on N type Si substrate. The current has a near exponential dependence on the voltage. While the duration of the heat treatment does not change this dependence significantly, the pre-exponential constant decreases with increasing annealing time. Figure 8 is a typical high frequency (1 MHz) C-V curve of an annealed film. The dielectric exhibits prominent hysteresis and a shift of 3 V in flat band voltage. The study indicates so far that the C-V behavior is not altered by either the duration of the nitrogen annealing or an additional heat treatment (<600°C) in forming gas. The ammonia-implanted films display very similar C-V behavior. From the accumulation capacitance and assuming $\varepsilon=6$, the dielectric thickness for N_2 and NH_3 implantation at 1.9 KeV is determined to be 10.6 nm and 11.6 nm respectively.

Even though nitrogen and forming gas annealing do not remove the cause of hysteresis and flat band shift, major changes occur after the dielectrics are exposed to a wet oxidation ambient. The breakdown field increases from 6-7 MV/cm to 10 Mv/cm. The breakdown distribution is found to be very tight as shown in Fig.9. The C-V curves are shown in Fig.10 as a function of oxidation time. As this figure indicates, oxidation of the ammonia implanted film reduces the fixed charges and the trapping centers in the dielectric significantly.

Oxidation Resistance.- The wet oxidation kinetics of the N_2 implanted layer were investigated. A composite dielectric is formed, and the thickness of oxide on the nitride increases approximately linearly in time [3]. Depending on the

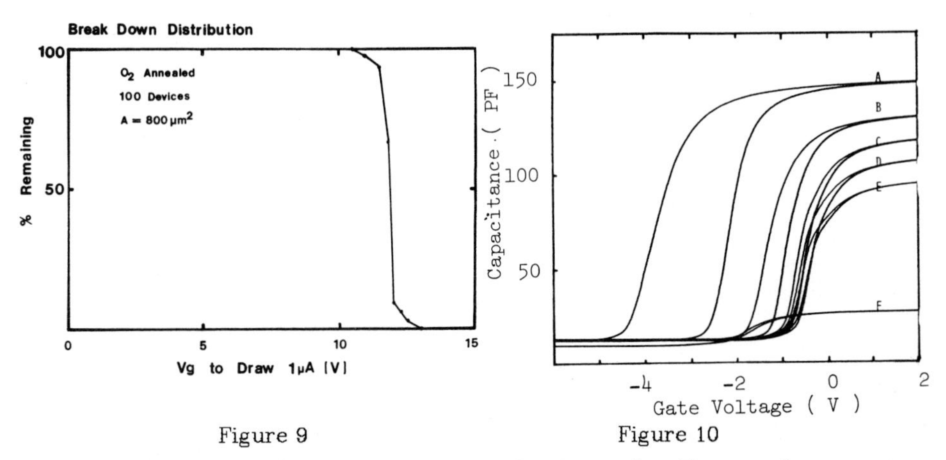

Figure 9 Figure 10

Fig.9. The breakdown distribution of the oxidized samples. The samples are oxidized in steam ambient for 1 hr. at 950°C. A 1 μA current is injected into each capacitor and the maximum voltage recorded

Fig.10. The C-V curves as a function of wet oxidation at 950°C for: (A) 1 hr., (B) 2 hr., (C) 3 hr., (D) 3 hr. 20 min., (E) 3 hr. 40 min., (F) 4 hr. Note that the flat band voltage shift decreases due to the oxidation. The accumulation capacitance also decreases indicating that the nitride is converted into oxide

oxidation temperature, about 700 nm to 900 nm of oxide can be masked by the implanted nitride. An oxidation rate activation energy of 2.03 eV is found for both the implanted film and plasma enhanced nitride.

The oxidation resistance may be utilized for selective oxidation technology. Using the implanted nitride as an oxidation mask, the length of the bird's beak is reduced by half as compared to the conventional LOCOS technology. Further improved scheme is drawn in Fig.11. The thin nitride serves to seal off oxidant which diffuses laterally in the pad oxide. (It is therefore called Sealed Interface Local Oxidation, or SILO). In addition, the stress of the CVD nitride also inhibits the oxide growth at the edge. SILO technology shows a promising potential and is being actively pursued at U.C. Berkeley.

Discussion and Conclusion

Recent studies of low energy implantation showed that LSS theory underestimates the projectile range. An improved model has been successful in overcoming the discrepancy [6]. Assuming that each atom retains its incident energy after dissociation at the Si surface, the range of our implant is calculated using the improved model. The calculation agrees fairly well with the experimentally observed value listed in Table 2.

Table 2
Thickness of the As-implanted Films Derived by Various Methods (nm)

	N_2 Implant	NH_3 Implant
T.E.M.	9±1	-
Ellipsometer (n=1.57)	9	10.9
Electrical (C-V)	10.6	11.6
Projected Range in Si (Theoretical)	10.7	13.8

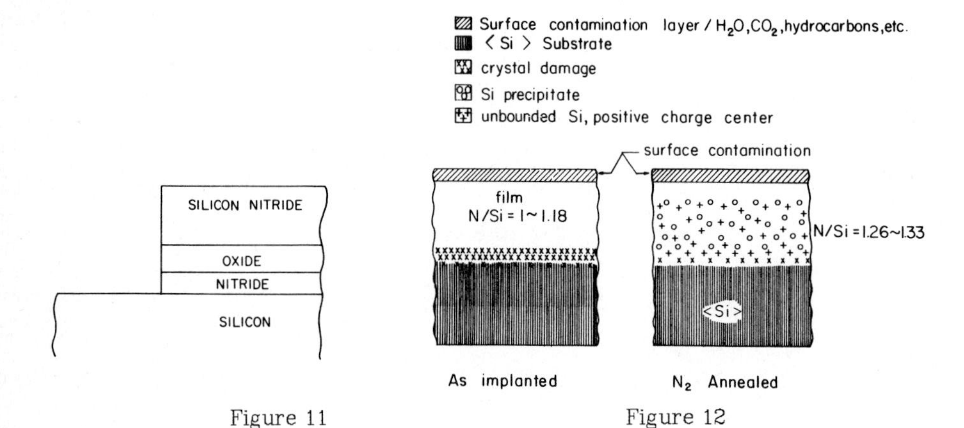

Figure 11

Figure 12

Fig.11. The geometry of the SILO technology. The top nitride and the pad oxide are both CVD deposited. The bottom nitride seals the oxidant which diffuses laterally in the pad oxide from the Si substrate

Fig.12. The present understanding of the implanted nitride. The as-implanted nitride has high N/Si ratio and substrate damage. After heat treatment, the damage is partially annealed, the N/Si ratio increases, and Si precipitates may possibly form

Table 3
The Material Characteristics of the N_2 Implanted Film

	As-implanted	Annealed
Etch Rate	~0.2 nm/s	~0.04nm/s
R.B.S.:		
Compositional	N/Si=1±10%	N/Si=1.3±10%
Damages	very high	reduced
X.P.S.:		
Compositional	N/Si=1.18±10%	N/Si=1.26±10%
Auger	α_N^*=777.5	α_N^*=777.1
Parameters	α_{Si}^*=1714.3	α_{Si}^*=1714.0
I.R. Transmission		
Minimum	800 cm^{-1}	850 cm^{-1}
Electrical:		
I-V	non-linear ohmic	insulator
C-V	...	positive fixed charge $< 1\times10^{13}$ /cm^2

Table 3 summarizes all the material characteristics of the N_2 implanted layers examined thus far. The data for the as-implanted and the annealed films are listed in the left and the right column respectively. It should be pointed out that the change with annealing detected by XPS method is very close to the resolution limit of the instrument (energy resolution is 0.2 eV). However, when all the data are considered together, a consistent picture emerges. From the etch rate, one can conclude that the Si-N bonding is stablized as a result of heat treatment. IR and XPS Auger parameter data indicates that the atomic environment undergoes a subtle change as a result of heat treatment. The XPS data provide the evidence that the change is a loss of the polarizability around the binding Si and N [7]. The conductivity change of the dielectric also supports the above assertions. The RBS and the XPS composition analysis indicates that the N/Si ratio increased after heat treatment. Both results show that the as-implanted layer is a sub-stoichiometric silicon nitride compound with excess silicon. The annealed film is also likely to be silicon rich, yet with higher N/Si ratio. The state of the excess silicon is still unclear. Some XPS data show that, after annealing, some could be in the elemental state. This evidence points to the possibility of Si precipitates in the nearly stoichiometric nitride film. RBS data indicate that a highly damaged region exists below the implanted layer. The damage is reduced but not completely removed as a result of heat treatment.

Figure 12 illustrates the present understanding of the N_2 implanted layer by putting the numerical data into a pictorial form. Because of its impact on the electrical behavior, it is very important to understand the material properties of the implanted layer. For example, since unsaturated excess Si acts as a positive charge center in SiO_2 and nitrogen has been known to be a donor in Si, the flat band shift could be due to either one or both of these factors. Figure 10 shows that by converting the nitride film into oxide without oxidizing the Si substrate, the fixed charge in the dielectric can be removed. This strongly suggest the existence of fixed charge such as unsaturated excess Si in the annealed dielectric. The evidence of the material analysis clearly supports this model.

The implanted nitride has been considered as a potential gate dielectric. However, the film has to be rid of trapping centers and the fixed charges in order to be a viable candidate. One possible approach is to oxidize the nitrided area as well as the field oxide area simultaneously. Other potential applications, such as the SILO technology, are also being pursued.

Acknowledgement

This research is sponsored by the Philips Research Laboratory, and by DARPA under Grant N00039-81-K-0251.

References

1. T. Ito, I. Kato, T. Nozaki, T. Nakamura and H. Ishikawa: Appl. Phys. Lett. 38, 370, (1980)
2. T. Y. Chiu, H. Bernt, and I. Ruge: J. Electrochem. Soc. 129, 488,(1982)
3. J. Hui, T. Y. Chiu, S. Wong and W. G. Oldham: IEEE Elec. Dev. 29, 554, (1982)
4. T. Y. Chiu, and W. G. Oldham: Electrochem. Soc. Proceeding, 81-2, 918, (1981)
5. J. A. Taylor: Appl. of Surf. Sci. 7, 168 (1980)
6. S. Kalbitzer and H. Oetzmann, Rad. Effects 48, 57 (1980)
7. C. D. Wagner: Farady Discussion of the Chemical Society 60, 291 (1975)

Doping Behavior of Implanted Magnesium in Silicon

H. Sigmund and D. Weiß

Fraunhofer-Institut für Festkörpertechnologie, Paul-Gerhardt-Allee 42, D-8000 München 60, Fed. Rep. of Germany

Abstract

Mg-implanted layers (5×10^{14} to 5×10^{15} cm^{-2}) which are annealed at low temperatures (500°C to 600°C) show high n-type conductivity. Contrary to the usual doping elements in silicon, the sheet carrier concentration shows a sharp decrease with increasing annealing temperatures; minimum sheet resistivities of 800 Ω/□ were obtained after a "thermal" annealing step at 550°C for 30 min. From profile measurements (Hall effect and SIMS), it is concluded that the interstitial solubility for Mg at 500°C in these samples is as high as 1×10^{18} cm^{-3}. At temperatures above 700°C the electrically active Mg concentration is rapidly gettered by the damage layer and Mg precipitates, and becomes electrically inactive. A model for the segregation behavior of Mg in silicon is discussed briefly.

1. Introduction

It is known, based on absorption and ESR measurements made on Mg-diffused silicon samples, that interstitially dissolved Mg in silicon forms a double donor with the donor levels E_{D1} = 0.11 eV and E_{D2} = 0.25 eV [1,2]. The preparation of these samples was accomplished by sandwich diffusion at 1200°C. The samples showed a very low interstitial solubility (≈ 10^{15} cm^{-3}), as revealed by resistivity measurements [1]. Measurements of the totally dissolved Mg were not made in these experiments. Recently performed investigations on the segregation and solubility of Mg in silicon at high temperatures (950°C to 1200°C), by atomic-absorption spectroscopy (AAS) as well as by secondary-ion mass spectroscopy (SIMS), have revealed a high solubility of Mg (4×10^{18} to 1.5×10^{19}cm^{-3}) [3]. The samples were prepared by special liquid-phase epitaxy; the epi-layers showed conductivity values similar to the diffused samples. In order to investigate the segregation and doping behavior of Mg in silicon at lower temperatures, these experiments with implanted Mg were performed. The isothermal annealing and diffusion behavior in the temperature range between 450°C and 950°C was investigated through SIMS and Hall-effect measurements.

2. Experimental Procedure

Samples with patterns of the van-der-Pauw type [4] were made using the planar technique (Fig. 1). An important aspect of the van-der-Pauw structure is represented by the As-implanted contacts, which ensure ohmic beha-

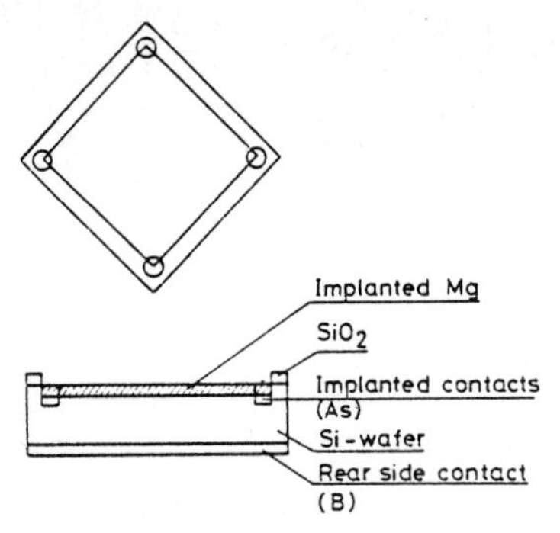

Fig. 1. Van-der-Pauw pattern

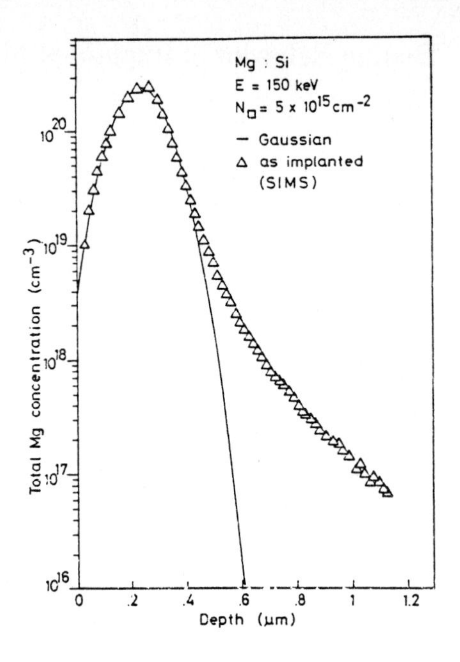

Fig. 2. Theoretical (continous line) and measured (SIMS) Mg distribution of a 150 keV implantation. It can be seen that the Mg penetrates more deeply into the crystal than would be expected from the gaussian distribution with R_p and ΔR_p values according to Biersack [9] ►

vior even at high annealing temperatures. Boron implantation into the back surface (unpolished) improved the contact on the reverse side, which is useful for the anodic stripping technique and measurement of current-voltage characteristics. The implanted contacts were annealed for 30 min at 900°C. Samples prepared in this manner were implanted with Mg into the polished surface at room temperature. Data on starting material and the implantation parameters are listed in Table 1. To avoid channeling, the angle of incidence was 7° relative to the (111) crystal direction. Figure 2 shows the theoretical and measured (SIMS) distribution of a 150 keV Mg implantation into Si. A dose of 5×10^{15} cm^{-2} is assumed to reach the amorphous dose, while 5×10^{14} cm^{-2} is below this dose [5]. After implantation, the slices were cut into quadratic wafers containing one van-der-Pauw pattern each (Fig. 1). Isothermal annealing between 400°C and 800°C was carried out in a nitrogen atmosphere. Time intervals from 7.5 to 90 min were used; continous 6 h isothermal annealing was applied to some samples. The effective carrier density $N_{S,eff}$ and the effective mobility μ_{eff} is given by $N_{S,eff} = r/(e \cdot R_{H,S})$ and $\mu_{eff} = R_{H,S}/(r \cdot \rho_S)$, where $R_{H,S}$ is the measured sheet Hall coefficient and ρ_S the sheet resistivity. Following the usual practice, the scattering factor r is approximated by unity. Interpretation of the effective values are discussed in detail by Baron et al. [6]. The measurements were carried out at room temperature. To avoid errors due to magnetoelectric effects (Nernst, Ettinghausen, Righi-Leduc, etc.), current and voltage probes were cyclically exchanged [7]. Therefo-

Table 1: Material and implantation data

Si wafers, Wacker Fz-Si	Doses 5×10^{14} and $5 \times 10^{15} cm^{-2}$
Orientation (111)	Energy 80 and 150 keV
Resistivity 50 Ωcm, p-type	R_p 0.139 and 0.238 µm
one side polished	ΔR_p 0.053 and 0.0829 µm

re, ρ_S and $R_{H,S}$ are average values extracted from these current and voltage measurements. Anodic stripping technique [8] was used for determination of the number of carriers as a function of depth. The applied electrolyte was NMA (0.025g KNO_3 dissolved in 10 ml H_2O + 500 ml N-methylacetamide); the forming voltage was 120 V. The thickness of the removed layer was determined mechanically, the average of one step was 26 ± 2nm.

3. Experimental Results

The isothermal annealing experiments showed that Mg-implanted samples display a quite different doping behavior than that for implantation with the ordinary doping elements. The results are shown in Fig. 3, where the effective carrier density $N_{S,eff}$ is plotted against the annealing time. All samples with a dose of 5×10^{15} cm^{-2} showed a decreasing sheet carrier concentration with increasing annealing time (≥ 7.5 min), until they reached a nearly constant value for a certain temperature. In samples with a dose of 5×10^{14} cm^{-2}, the sheet carrier concentration at low temperatures (500°C, 550°C) first increases, then reaches a maximum, and finally drops to nearly the same value as in the amorphous sample. Figure 3 shows that a temperature-dependent, quasi-equilibrium sheet carrier concentration is established, the level of which drops drastically with increasing annealing time. A good example of this characteristic is represented by the 600°C isothermal curves, where the equilibrium $N_{S,eff}$ value is reached after annealing for ca. 3 h. The 800°C isotherms show a nearly constant sheet carrier density value over the whole investigated range - the $N_{S,eff}$ decrease obviously occurs so quickly that it cannot be observed in these

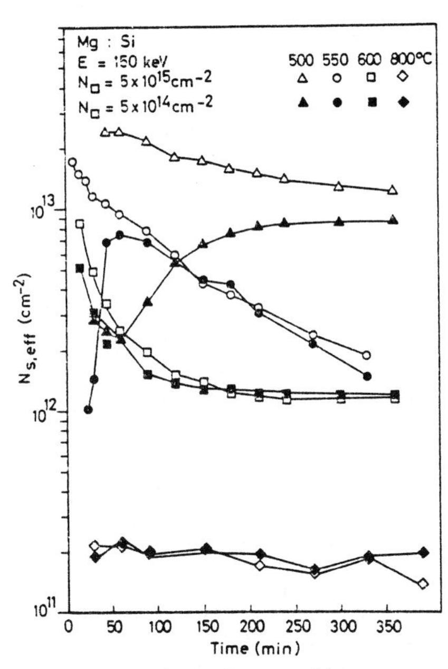

Fig. 3. Isothermal annealing curves for four different temperatures

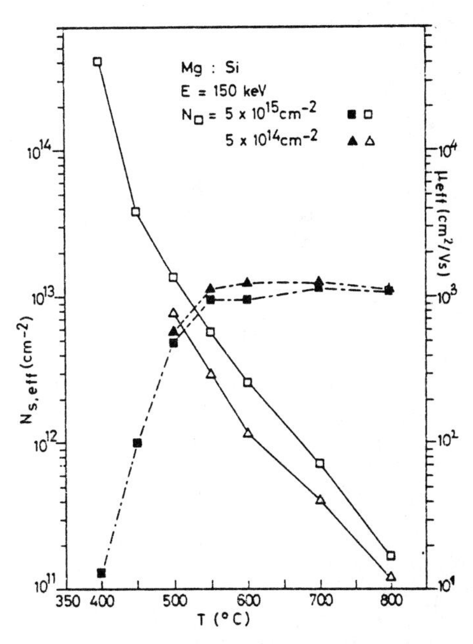

Fig. 4. Effective carrier concentration ($N_{S,eff}$) and effective mobility (μ_{eff}) after 6 h isothermal annealing

measurements. The non-constant behavior of the 550°C isotherms is assumed to result from a measurement error due to non-ohmic contacts, which can cause $N_{S,eff}$ values which are to low. Figure 4 shows the effective carrier density $N_{S,eff}$ and the effective mobility versus annealing temperature after 6 h isothermal annealing for a temperature range from 400°C up to 800°C. Samples implanted with a dose of 5 x 10^{15} cm^{-2} could only be measured at an annealing temperature of 500°C and above, due to poor recrystallization at lower temperatures. Implants with 5 x 10^{15} cm^{-2} already showed a high effective sheet carrier density (about 10% electrically active) at an annealing temperature of 400°C. Figure 5 shows current-voltage characteristics under reverse bias, whereby the annealing temperatures are the variable parameter. The plotted curves show a steep reduction of leakage current between 450°C and 500°C annealing temperature, while at higher annealing temperatures the drop occurs much more gradually. The temperature range from 400°C up to 550°C is characterized by a steep increase in the effective mobilities μ_{eff}, due to the recrystallization with increasing annealing temperature in this range. At temperatures higher than 550°C, the mobility values are almost in agreement with Irvin's data [10]. Mobilities in layers with a dose of 5 x 10^{15} cm^{-2} lie below the values of samples implanted with a dose of 5 x 10^{14} cm^{-2}. The effective sheet carrier concentrations decrease almost exponentially over the entire investigated range. The measured $N_{S,eff}$ value is only slightly dependent on the implantation dose. It should be mentioned that in our experiments the effective carrier density is not reversible. This means that an established value of $N_{S,eff}$ for an annealed sample cannot be increased again by annealing it at a lower temperature.

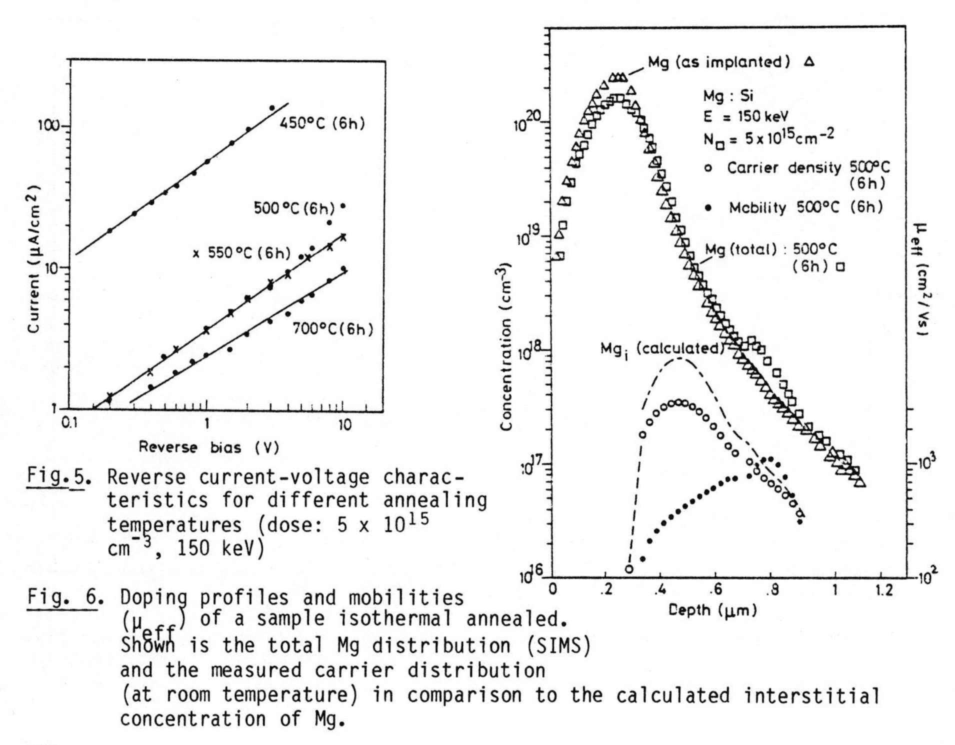

Fig. 5. Reverse current-voltage characteristics for different annealing temperatures (dose: 5 x 10^{15} cm^{-3}, 150 keV)

Fig. 6. Doping profiles and mobilities (μ_{eff}) of a sample isothermal annealed. Shown is the total Mg distribution (SIMS) and the measured carrier distribution (at room temperature) in comparison to the calculated interstitial concentration of Mg.

Distributions of carriers, determined by Hall-effect and sheet-resistitivity measurements combined with anodic stripping, are compared to SIMS profiles. With the SIMS technique the total amount of Mg in the sample can be determined. In Fig. 6, the total Mg distribution in a sample - implanted with a dose of 5×10^{15} cm^{-2} (150 keV) - before and after a 6 h annealing at 500°C is plotted. An important finding is that after annealing the Mg remains in the sample to a large extent (75%). The other 25% of the Mg is assumed to be at the surface probably as MgO. The small peak at a concentration of 1.5×10^{15} cm^{-2} suggests a slight diffusion into the crystal. Figure 6 also shows the number of carriers and the mobility as a function of depth. All data were obtained after 6 h annealing at 500°C. It is seen clearly that only a small percentage of the total Mg atoms is electrically active. Brooks [11] has shown that the average number (f) of electrons occupying a double donor is given by:

$$f = \frac{2}{1+\left[1+4\exp(E_{D2}-E_F)/kT\right]/1+4\exp(E_F-E_{D1})/kT\right]} , \qquad (1)$$

where E_{D1} and E_{D2} are the first and second donor levels, respectively. The Fermi level E_F can be obtained (if E_F is several kT below the bottom edge of the conduction band E_c) from $n = N_c \exp((E_F-E_c)/kT)$ with N_c being the effective density of states in the conduction band. Thus, the concentration of Mg interstitials (Mg_i) can be calculated from Eq (1) and the expression: $Mg_i = n/(2-f)$. In Fig. 7, the average number of electrons per Mg_i atom transferred to the conduction band is plotted versus the Mg_i concentration for several temperatures. It should be noted that temperature-dependent Hall-effect and sheet-resistivity measurements indicate increasing carrier densitiy with increasing temperature (Fig. 8).

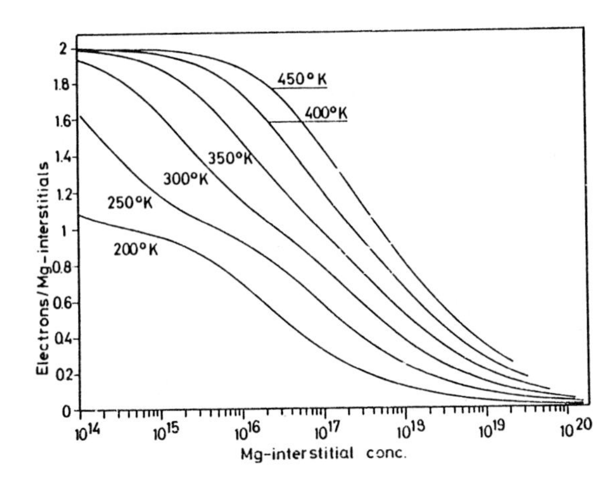

Fig. 7. Probability of ionization of interstitial Mg in dependence of the Mg doping level

The concentration of interstitial Mg atoms, determined by Eq. (1) from the measured electron density is plotted in Fig. 6 (dashed line). The total Mg concentration is greater than the interstitial concentration by factor of 6 in the tail and by a factor of 17 at the maximum of the Mg - interstitial distribution. The ratio increases sharply as one comes closer to the surface. The carrier profile could only be determined at a depth of 0.25 µm and above, where the concentration increases rapidly. Increase of the

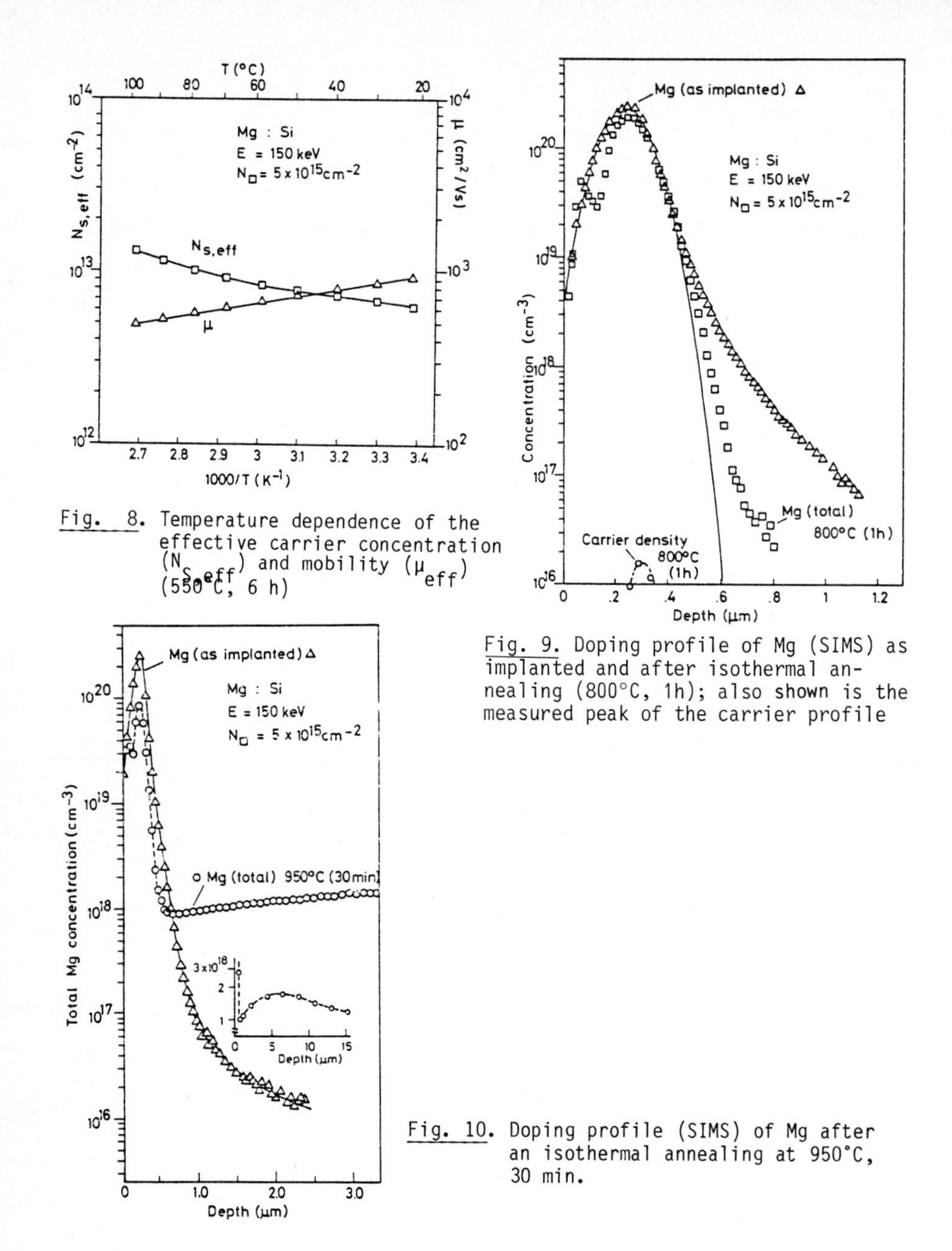

Fig. 8. Temperature dependence of the effective carrier concentration ($N_{s,eff}$) and mobility (μ_{eff}) (550°C, 6 h)

Fig. 9. Doping profile of Mg (SIMS) as implanted and after isothermal annealing (800°C, 1h); also shown is the measured peak of the carrier profile

Fig. 10. Doping profile (SIMS) of Mg after an isothermal annealing at 950°C, 30 min.

carrier concentration is accompanied by increasing mobilities. In Fig.9 the total Mg concentration and measured electron concentration after 1 h annealing at 800°C is shown. Also in this case, 75% of the implanted Mg remains in the sample. At this annealing temperature, Mg does not diffuse into the crystal, but approaches the Gaussian implantation distribution. It can therefore be concluded that the Mg is gettered by the damage region or by Mg precipitates. This peak in carrier concentration lies closer to the surface (0.29 µm) than the maximum of the carrier distribution after a 6h annealing at 500°C. This suggests that the damage layer becomes thinner and that the crystal recrystallizes from the bulk. The maximum of the electron density now has a value of about 2×10^{16} cm^{-3}. An interesting phenomenon is observed when the annealing temperature is increased to 950°C. Figure 10 shows SIMS profiles before and after a 30 min annealing at 950°C, a temperature which lies slightly above the eutectic point. Mg diffuses fast into the crystal at a concentration of about 2×10^{18} cm^{-3}, and could be measured even at a depth of 15 µm. Hall measurements on samples annealed at temperatures higher than 800°C could not be performed.

4. Discussion

In order to explain the annealing and doping behavior of implanted Mg in silicon, the following segregation model is proposed. According to this model, the implanted depth is divided into two regions (A and B) as depicted in Fig. 11. Region A can be characterized by low carrier concentration (≈ 5×10^{15} cm^{-3}) low Hall mobilities, whereas the total Mg concentration in this region is several orders of magnitude above the measured electron concentration. Region B shows high electron concentrations with high mobility values (close to bulk mobilities); a high fraction of the total Mg concentration is electrically active. Because substitutional Mg (Mg_s) in silicon probably forms a deep acceptor level (preliminary DLTS measurements have revealed a level at 0.55 eV), a strong compensation should occur if the number of substitutional Mg atoms exceeds the concentration of interstitial Mg atoms. The implanted samples showed n-type conductivity in all cases. It is therefore very likely that at lower annealing temperatures, Mg_i atoms react with Mg_s atoms and form neutral complexes: $Mg_i + Mg_s = (Mg_s \cdot Mg_i)$.

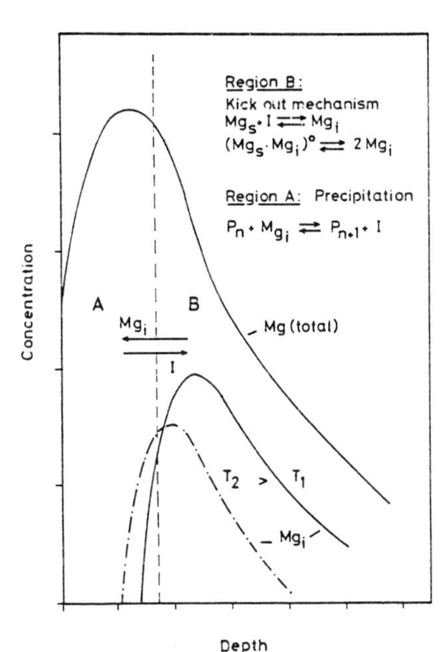

Fig. 11. Model for the annealing behavior of implanted Mg in silicon

The complexes ($Mg_s \cdot Mg_i$) are isoelectronic, so they should have no influence on the electron concentration. At higher temperatures, the complexes in region B dissociate. Furthermore, the substitutional Mg atoms react with Si interstitials (I) according to the "Kick-out" mechanism [12]: $Mg_s + I = Mg_i$. The total reaction between Si interstitials and the complexes would then be:

$$(Mg_s \cdot Mg_i) + I = 2\, Mg_i. \qquad (2)$$

Between regions A and B, there is a sharp gradient in the interstitial Mg concentration (s. Fig. 11). This concentration gradient is much steeper then the gradient into the bulk. Thus, at higher temperatures, Mg_i atoms diffuse rapidly into region A, and the Mg concentration is increased . It seems very probable that Mg silicide clusters are formed in region A. A suitable reaction may be given in the following form: $P_n + Mg_i = P_{n+1} + I$, where P_n is a Mg-silicide precipitation with n Mg atoms. Based on this assumption, the experimentally observed annealing kinetics of Fig. 3 may be described analytically [3]. At temperatures between 900°C and 950°C, the equilibrium point of the precipitation reaction is shifted to the left side of Eq.(2), and Mg atoms diffuse into the bulk rapidly. This drastic change in the behavior of region A occurs in a very small temperature interval, so that is very probable that the structure of the precipitates is changed between 900°C and 950°C.

We are indebted to Mr. Kranz/IFT for performing the implantation of the samples.

References

1. R.K. Franks, J.B. Robertson: Sol. State Comm. 5, 479 (1967)
2. L.T. Ho, A.K. Ramadas: Phys. Rev. 35, 462 (1972)
3. H. Sigmund, R. Braungart. Ch. Höpfl, D. Weiß: Research Report NT 846 (1981) FRG
4. L.J. van der Pauw: Philips Res. Repts. 13, 1 (1958)
5. H. Ryssel, I. Ruge: Ionenimplantation, Stuttgart (1978), p. 33
6. R. Baron, G.A. Shifrin, O.J. Marsh, J.W. Mayer: J. Appl. Phys. 40, 3702 (1969)
7. H.H. Wieder, Characterisation of Epitaxial Semiconductor Films, ed. by H. Kressel, N.Y. (1976)
8. A. Manara, A. Ostidich, G. Pedroli, G. Restelli: Thin Solid Films 8, 359 (1971)
9. J.P. Biersack: Hahn-Meitner-Report, HMI-B334 (1980): projected ranges of the most common ion-target combinations are published in [5].
10. S.M. Sze, J.C. Irvin: Solid-State Electronics 11, 599 (1968)
11. H. Brooks: Advances in Electronics and Electron Physics, Vol 7. N.Y. (1955)
12. A. Seeger: phys. stat. sol.(a) 61, 521 (1980)

Part IX

Transient Annealing

Beam Annealing of Ion-Implanted Silicon

J.F. Gibbons

Solid-State Electronics Laboratory, Stanford University,
Stanford, CA 94305, USA

1. Introduction

Extensive research has been performed over the past several years on the use of lasers, electron beams and arc sources for annealing damage created in silicon by ion implantation. This field, originally identified as "beam annealing" because its focus was on the removal of defects introduced by ion implantation, has rapidly broadened to encompass much more diverse situations, many of which do not involve ion implantation and may not even involve defect removal. In particular, lasers and electron beams have been used to recrystallize thin films of vapor-deposited polysilicon with substantial improvements in its electronic properties [1]; to facilitate the formation of metal silicides [2]; and to perform a number of other processing functions that are of increasing importance in the fabrication of fine geometry integrated circuits and high speed devices. In this paper we will concern ourselves entirely with the annealing process; specifically, the mechanisms by which laser, electron beam and arc source annealing proceeds and the basic metallurgical and electronic properties of beam annealed material.

2. Basic Beam Annealing Mechanisms

Two distinctly different beam annealing mechanisms have been identified, depending on the duration of the beam exposure. For Q-switched lasers or pulsed electron beams, exposure times are typically in the range of 5 ns - 500 ns and the annealing process then involves the formation of a thin molten layer of silicon that recrystallizes on the underlying substrate when the radiation is removed. If the irradiated sample is an ion-implanted single crystal and the depth of the molten layer is sufficient to envelop the implantation damaged region, the molten layer regrows by a very high speed liquid phase epitaxial process on the crystalline substrate, producing material with a very high degree of structural perfection and very superior electronic properties.

For cw systems, on the other hand, the silicon surface is typically exposed to the beam for 0.1-10 ms and in some cases for durations of several seconds. The annealing of ion—implanted material can then proceed by a process similar to that which occurs in conventional furnace annealing; i.e., a solid phase epitaxial regrowth process at temperatures that are well below the melting point. As in the pulsed beam case, a very high degree of crystalline perfection and very superior electronic properties can be obtained under appropriate annealing conditions. However, the absence of melting proves to be of interest since no redistribution of the implanted impurity profile then occurs during the annealing process, whereas significant impurity redistribution occurs when annealing is effected by a pulsed laser or electron beam. These and other differences in the two annealing processes make it convenient to discuss them separately. In what follows we first consider the pulsed beam annealing process and then take up the cw alternative. Conventional furnace annealing will be seen to be a special case of cw beam annealing.

3. Central Features of Pulsed Beam Annealing of Ion-Implanted Silicon

We will begin with a brief review of experimental data that characterize the annealing of ion-implanted silicon using a Q-switched laser pulse.

Pulsed laser annealing has been demonstrated using a variety of sources and pulse durations. In most of the experiments reported so far, implanted samples have been annealed directly in the laboratory ambient; i.e., no special precautions have been taken to immerse the wafer in an inert environment during annealing. The area irradiated by the beam is in most cases large compared to both the diffusion length for heat in the solid and the thickness of the wafer, so the process can be treated as being basically one-dimensional.

Experimental results from various laboratories are now reasonably consistent and are summarized in Table 1. For convenience, the data are selected to illustrate the annealing of As^+-implanted silicon with the As^+ implantation conditions chosen to provide amorphous regions of differing thicknesses at the sample surface. In the cases reported in Table 1, the beam intensities employed were in the range of ~40-60 MW/cm^2.

The principal features of the data are as follows. For pulses of 50-100 ns duration (typical of a Q-switched laser):

1. Surface melting occurs at a threshold energy of 0.2-3.5 J/cm^2, depending on the laser wavelength and the thickness of the amorphous layers [3].

Table 1. Pulse Energies for Annealing As^+-implanted Silicon

Laser Pulse Length (ns)	As^+ Impl. Par. Dose (cm^{-2}) Energy (keV)	Amorphous Layer Thickness, X_d (Å)	Melt Initiated (J/cm^2)	Fully Annealed (J/cm^2)
Ruby, 50	5×10^{15}, 400	4300	0.6	2
Ruby, 150	1.4×10^{16}, 100	1700	0.64	1.4
Nd:YAG, 110	8×10^{15}, 100	~1500		6.0
40	10^{15}, 130	468	3.5	4.5
Nd:YAG, Doubled 40	10^{15}, 30	468	0.2	0.85

2. Full annealing of an ion implanted layer (as judged by crystal recovery and electrical activity) requires additional energy in an amount that also depends on both the laser wavelength and the thickness of the amorphous layer.

3.1 Impurity Profiles in Pulse Annealed Silicon

Clear insight into the basic device implications of pulsed laser (or electron beam) processing is provided by the extensive early work of White and co-workers [4].

Figure 1 shows B profiles in as-implanted and laser annealed silicon samples taken from their early work. The measurements were made by secondary ion mass spectroscopy (SIMS) and therefore yield the total concentration of boron without regard for lattice location. The samples were implanted at 35 keV to a dose of 1 x $10^{16}/cm^2$. The as-implanted profile is approximately Gaussian as expected, and is only marginally changed by conventional furnace thermal annealing at 900°C for 30 minutes. In contrast, the profile measured after laser annealing (1.6 J/cm^2, 60 ns pulse duration) exhibits a substantial redistribution of boron. In particular, after the pulsed laser annealing cycle, the impurity profile becomes almost uniform from the surface down to a depth of approximately 0.2μm in the crystal, and significant quantities of boron are observed at depths of approximately 0.5μm.

The redistribution of the implanted boron is found to be both pulse energy density and pulse number dependent. Figure 2 shows experimental results measured after laser annealing with different pulse energy densities in the range 0.64 J/cm^2 to 3.1 J/cm^2. At a laser energy density of approximately 0.6 J/cm^2, only surface melting is initiated and the boron profile is indistinguishable from that of the as-implanted sample. Hall effect

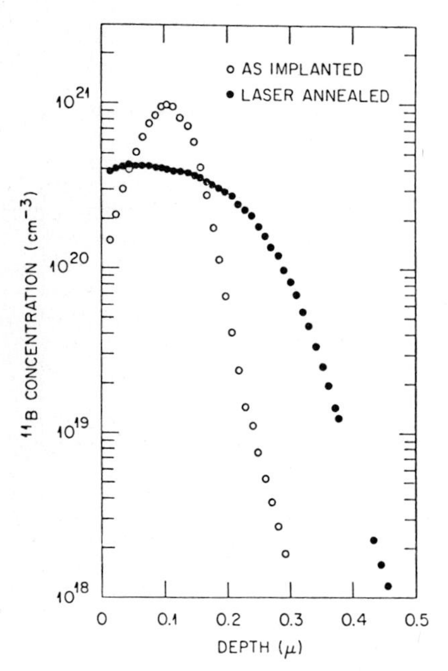

Fig.1. Boron redistribution produced by pulsed laser anneal (after White, et al. [4])

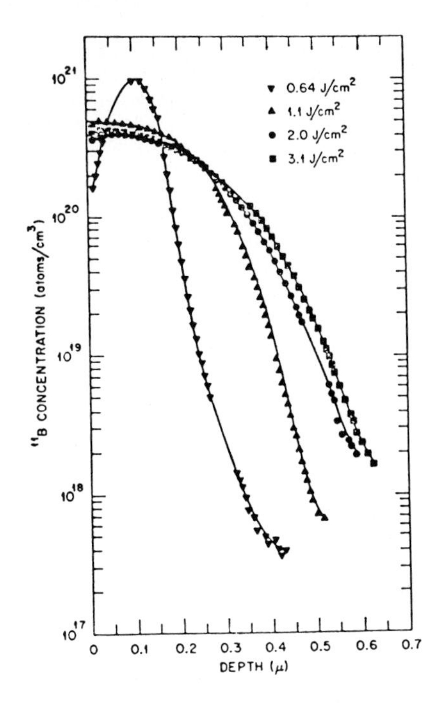

Fig.2. Boron profiles after pulsed laser annealing with increasing pulse energy (after White et al. [4])

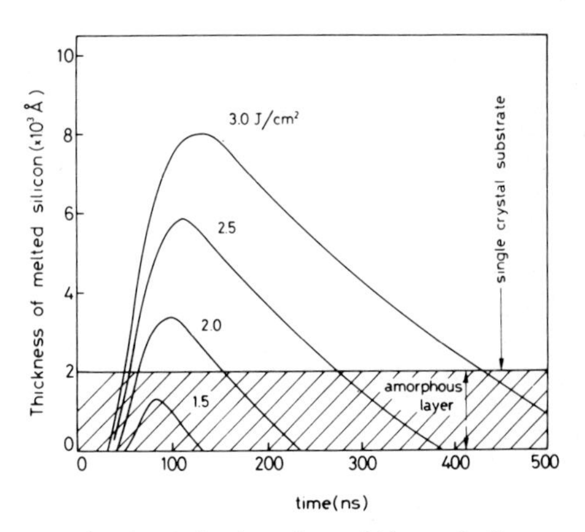

Fig.3. Calculated position of the melt front as a function of time (after Baeri et al. [5])

measurements and transmission electron microscopy show about 30% of the expected electrical activity and significant damage remaining in the form of dislocation loops under this pulse energy. At 1.1 J/cm^2 and greater, the impurity profiles are almost flat topped in the surface region, and the boron spreads deeper in the sample as the energy density is increased.

The substantial redistribution of boron induced by pulsed laser annealing cannot be explained by thermal diffusion in the solid phase because the time duration is too short. However, theoretical calculations using a one-dimensional heat conduction equation show that a region several thousand angstroms deep can be melted for pulse energies greater than about 1 J/cm^2 [5]. Calculations of the melt front position as a function of time for silicon irradiated with a 60 nanosecond pulse from a ruby laser are shown in Fig. 3. The melt front is seen to reach a maximum penetration of approximately 0.8μm for a pulse energy of 3 J/cm^2. The melt front then sweeps back toward the surface, recrystallizing the material epitaxially as it proceeds. While the crystal is molten, the dopant atoms have a very high diffusion coefficient and the implanted profile can change markedly. For boron in silicon, the experimental data can be fit by using a liquid diffusion coefficient of $2.4 \pm 0.7 \times 10^4$ cm^2/sec [8] and a diffusion time of 180 ns. These parameters provide the calculated fit shown in Fig. 4 and adequately justify the conclusion that normal diffusion processes in the molten state account for the spreading of the implanted profile during pulsed laser annealing.

Hall effect and transmission electron microscopy measurements made on implanted material annealed in this way show 100% electrical activity and no defects to a resolution of at least 50 Å, provided that the amorphous layer is sufficiently thin. However, it should be mentioned that since the reflection coefficient R at the surface of an irradiated sample

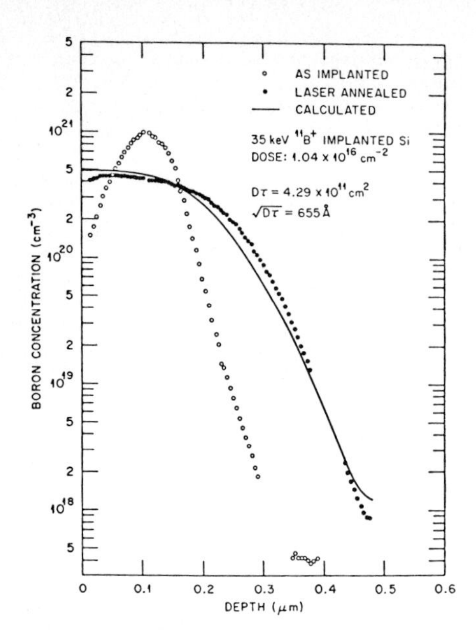

Fig.4. Comparison of experimental and calculated B profiles in pulse laser annealed Si assuming liquid phase diffusion of B during re-recrystallization (after White et al. [4])

changes from energy 0.35 to 0.7 when the surface becomes molten, only 30% of the pulse over and above the melting threshold is absorbed by the silicon. The result is that it is difficult to melt layers that are in excess of approximately 1μm without heating the surface to the boiling point, which leads to very poor surface morphology. As a result, pulsed laser annealing is generally useful only for the annealing of relatively shallow layers.

3.2 Summary

To summarize, the mechanism of annealing for Q-switched laser pulses involves melting of a surface layer followed by a liquid phase epitaxial regrowth on the underlying substrate. The critical parameter for this process is the pulse energy density. The principal electrical characteristics of the annealed layer are:

1. 100% substitutionality of the implanted dopant, even for concentrations that exceed the solid solubility.

2. No residual defects in TEM to 50 Å resolution.

3. Redistribution of the implanted dopant via diffusion in a liquid layer during the recrystallization process.

4. Residual point defects below the recrystallized layer that require a subsequent low temperature (800°C, 30 min) anneal for their removal. These defects may be thought of as arising from the fact that silicon vacancies and other crystalline defects diffuse rapidly from the high temperature portion of the crystal toward the cooler interior where they form point defects. These defects have been shown to reduce the lifetime of minority carriers in the bulk of the silicon substantially, though this reduction can be largely removed by an appropriate thermal anneal.

4. CW Beam Processing

In contrast to the pulse annealing process, a scanning laser or electron beam provides an extremely convenient and highly controllable means for heating the surface of a semiconductor to a given temperature while holding the body of the material at a convenient low temperature (typically 350-500°C). Recognition of this fact leads naturally to a comparison of the annealing mechanism with the annealing process for furnace annealing.

4.1 Furnace Annealing Process

Conventional furnace annealing of implantation-amorphized silicon proceeds by a solid-phase epitaxial (SPE) recrystallization process. Atoms at the amorphous-crystalline interface rearrange themselves into crystalline locations by a process that appears to involve vacancy diffusion in both the crystalline and disordered layers. The process is described quantitatively by an activation energy E_a and proceeds at a rate

$$r(t) = r_o \exp(-E_a/kT) \quad , \tag{1}$$

where r(t) is normally measured in Å/second. Measurements of r(t) made by Csepregi et al. [6] in the temperature range 400-600°C on undoped <100> silicon (amorphized by the implantation of Si^+) show an activation energy of $E_a = 2.35$ eV and a pre-exponential multiplier of 3.22×10^{14} Å/sec. Using these values at a temperature of 800°C gives a furnace regrowth rate of about 0.3 μm/sec for <100> undoped Si. In other words, a 0.5 μm thick amorphized layer can recrystallize by the solid phase epitaxial process on the underlying substrate in less than two seconds if the layer is held at a temperature of 800°C.

The implanted dopants are normally incorporated into substitutional sites during this recrystallization process, leading to high electrical activity. However, point defects and trapping centers form during the recrystallization process (related to the vacancy motion by which the process proceeds), and these defects must be annealed out to obtain good pn junction characteristics, i.e., high carrier mobilities and reasonable carrier lifetimes.

The motion and agglomeration of defects during the annealing is especially troublesome if the implant dose and energy are not sufficient to produce an amorphous layer that envelops the implanted dopant. Such a condition is most often obtained when B is implanted into Si, a case which has been thoroughly studied. A 30 minute anneal in the temperature range 800°C-1000°C then produces a combination of dislocation loops, rods and precipitates that are nearly immune to further furnace annealing [10,11].

Partly as a result of these problems it is customary to use a so-called two-stage annealing process [7]. The first stage is carried out at ~600°C for 1/2 hour and is intended only to recrystallize the implanted region. A number of point and line defects remain after this stage, which lead to low electrical activity and poor carrier mobility and lifetime. The low temperature anneal is then typically followed by a 1000°C, 10 min. anneal to remove point defects, increase carrier mobility and lifetime, and provide for some impurity diffusion so that pn junctions formed by the process are located outside the region of residual damage. Such a process is especially important in the annealing of implanted <111> Si, i.e., for most bipolar applications. In contrast a single stage anneal can be sufficient for less demanding applications in <100> Si.

4.2 Basic CW Laser Annealing Systems

The basic cw laser annealing process is identical to the furnace annealing process just described, except that the sample is maintained at the annealing temperature for such a short time that only the fastest thermal processes, including solid-phase epitaxy, can be carried to completion. Dopant precipitation and the formation of dislocation loops and rods are generally not observed since there is insufficient time for them to form.

The basic system used for scanned cw laser annealing is shown in Fig. 5 and consists of an Ar cw laser that is passed through a lens and deflected by X and Y mirrors onto a sample that is mounted in the focal plane of the lens [8]. The X mirror is mounted on a galvonometer that is driven with a triangular waveform and the Y mirror is mounted on a galvonometer that is driven by a staircase waveform. This arrangement permits the beam to be scanned across the target in the X direction, stepped by a controlled Y increment and then scanned back across the target in reverse X direction. Individual scan lines can be overlapped or not by appropriate adjustments of the Y step. As an alternative the sample can be mounted on an XY table and mechanically scanned underneath a stationary laser beam.

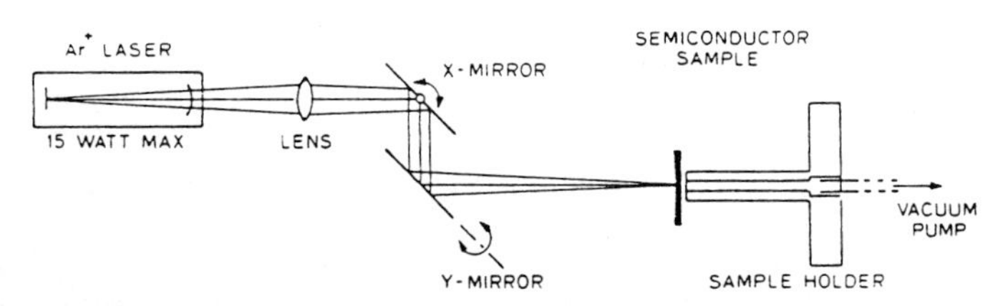

Fig.5. A general schematic of the annealing apparatus, including Ar^+ laser, lens, perpendicular X and Y mirrors, and a vacuum sample holder

The samples are mounted on a sample holder that can be heated to about 500°C. Control of the annealing ambient can be obtained by placing a cylindrical quartz jacket around the sample holder and pumping appropriate gases into this jacket. A variety of lenses, laser powers, scan rates, and sample temperatures have been found to produce essentially perfect annealing of ion-implanted semiconductors. If the samples are held at room temperature, a typical set of annealing conditions consists of a laser output (Ar, multi-line mode) of 7 W focused through a 79 mm lens into a 38 micron spot on the target. The spot is typically scanned across the target at a rate of approximately 2.5 cm per second. Adjacent scan lines are overlapped by approximately 30% to produce full annealing in the overlapped areas. The laser power for full annealing can be reduced (and the width of the annealed line increased) by increasing the sample temperature.

4.3 Surface Temperature Profiles

The beam geometry and scanning conditions listed above lead to a spot dwell time on the order of 1 ms. This is to be compared to a thermal time constant (for a 40 µm cube of Si) of approximately 10 µs, from which it follows that the semiconductor surface has adequate time to come to thermal equilibrium with the scanning heat source. It is therefore possible to calculate exactly the surface temperature that will be produced at the center of the spot by simply solving the steady-state equation for heat flow. Calculations of this type have been carried out for both circular and elliptical scanning beams [9]; the results for a cylindrical beam irradiating a silicon substrate are shown in Fig. 6. The calculations presented there account for the temperature dependence of the thermal conductivity and specific heat, and have proven to give very accurate estimates of the surface temperatures achieved with the laser beam.

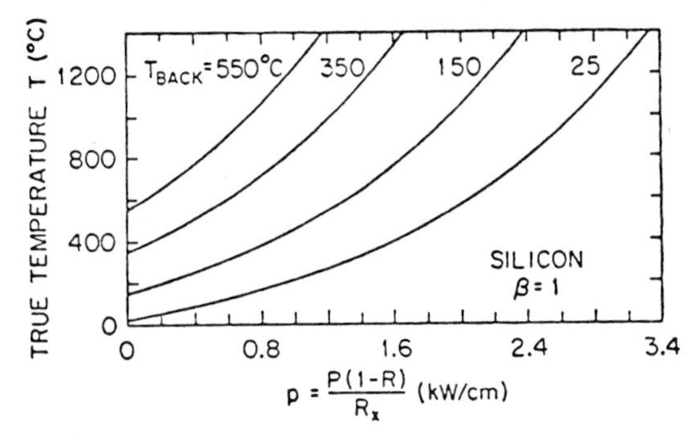

Fig.6. The true maximum temperature (X=Y=Z=V=0) in Si is plotted versus the normalized power p ($p=P(1-R)/R_X$) for different substrate backsurface temperatures. P = laser power; R = reflection coefficient; and R_X = beam radius at $1/E^2$ intensity

Two features of these curves are worth particular attention. First, the horizontal axis is in units of power per unit radius of the beam, this being due to the fact that the heat-flow problem has essentially hemispherical symmetry. As a result the surface temperature is a function of power divided by spot radius rather than power per unit area of the beam. Secondly, the sizeable decease of thermal conductivity of Si with temperature leads to a situation in which the temperature at the irradiated surface is a very sensitive function of the backsurface temperature. For example, a surface temperature at the center of a 40 micron spot of 1000°C can be obtained with a 5 watt laser output if the backsurface temperature (or thermal bias) is 350°C. If the backsurface temperature is reduced to 150°C, the temperature in the center of the irradiated area drops by nearly 500°C. Hence it is very important to control the backsurface temperature accurately, and it is also possible to use relatively low laser powers if substantial thermal bias can be employed.

4.4 Basic Mechanism of CW Beam Annealing

As mentioned earlier, the basic mechanism of cw beam annealing is solid-phase epitaxy. The most convincing illustration of this fact is provided by the work of Roth et al. [10] and illustrated in Fig. 7. Here the regrowth rate of both implantation-amorphized and UHV deposited Si layers on a <100> Si substrate is plotted as a function of the surface temperature produced by the laser. The data show exactly the form expected for a process described by Eq. 1, and in fact the growth rate at 800°C is found to be 0.3 μm/sec, in excellent agreement with the furnace annealing result. Hence the regrowth process is quantitatively identified as solid-phase recrystallization.

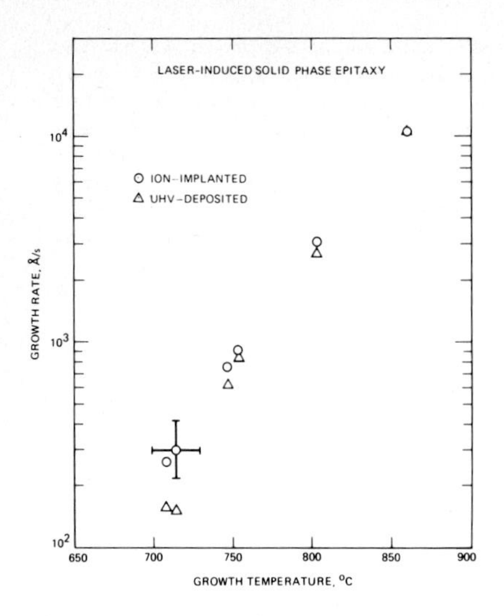

Fig.7. SPE growth rates for amorphous Si layers formed by ion implantation and UHV evaporation, determined from time-resolved reflectivity measurements

4.5 Impurity Profile

Figure 8 shows the impurity profiles obtained by SIMS under as-implanted, laser annealed and thermally annealed conditions for As^+ implanted into <100> Si under typical conditions. The most striking feature of this figure is that the laser annealed profile is identical to the as-implanted profile. In other words, there has been no diffusion of the implanted species during the laser anneal. Furthermore, the as-implanted impurity distribution is matched exactly by the Pearson type IV distribution function using LSS moments [11], so the experimental and theoretical profiles

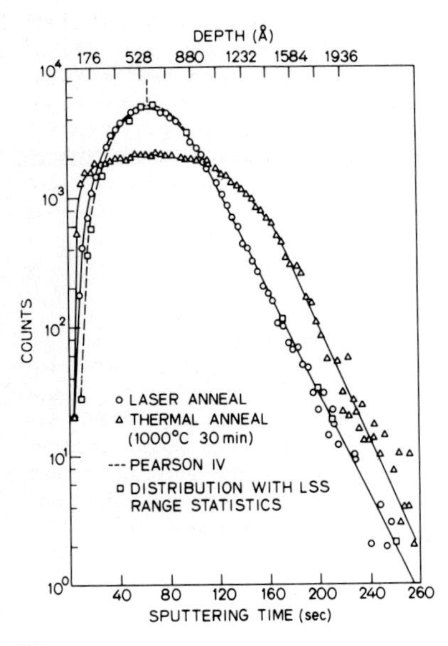

Fig.8. Carrier concentration and mobility profiles obtained on As-implanted samples annealed with a scanning Ar cw laser beam

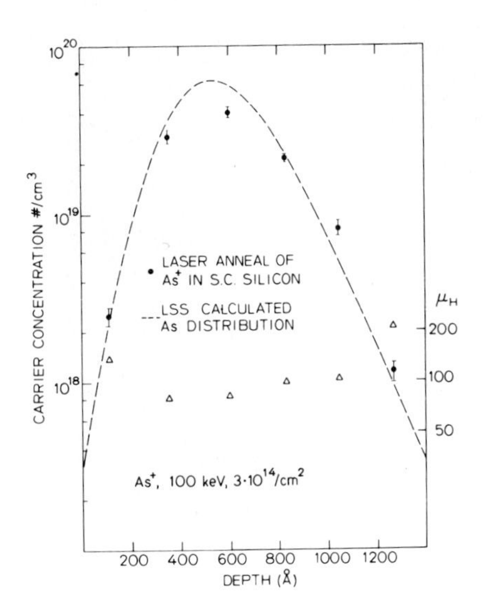

Fig.9. As concentration profile in As-implanted silicon after laser anneal and thermal anneal

are in excellent agreement. The thermal anneal shows the well-catalogued impurity redistribution given by the open triangles in Fig. 8.

Majority carrier profiles and carrier mobilities were obtained by sheet resistance and Hall effect measurements and are shown in Fig. 9. As can be seen the carrier concentration profile also fits the Pearson type IV distribution quite well. Under very high dose conditions (> $10^{16}/cm^2$), As precipitation can occur near the peak of the profile, leading to a residual, nonsubstitutional As content of approximately 5% [12].

4.6 Transmission Electron Microscopy

Typical results of TEM performed on thermally annealed and laser annealed samples are shown in Fig. 10. The thermally annealed sample (Fig. 10a) shows a single crystal diffraction pattern with a bright field micrograph containing the usual variety of ~200Å diameter defect clusters and dislocation loops. The laser annealed sample shown in Fig. 10b is essentially free of any defect observable in TEM except near the boundary between crystallized and amoprhous regions. It should be emphasized also that no defects are observed in TEM in the region where adjacent scan lines overlap.

4.7 B-implanted Single Crystal Si

A similar set of experiments has been performed in B-implanted Si. The central results, reported in Ref. 13, are identical to those described above for As-implanted Si. In particular, 100% electrical activity can be obtained with no diffusion of the implanted species from its as-implanted profile. Recrystallization is also perfect as judged by TEM to a resolution of ~ 20 Å. These results are independent of whether the B is implanted into pre-amorphized Si or directly into single crystal material.

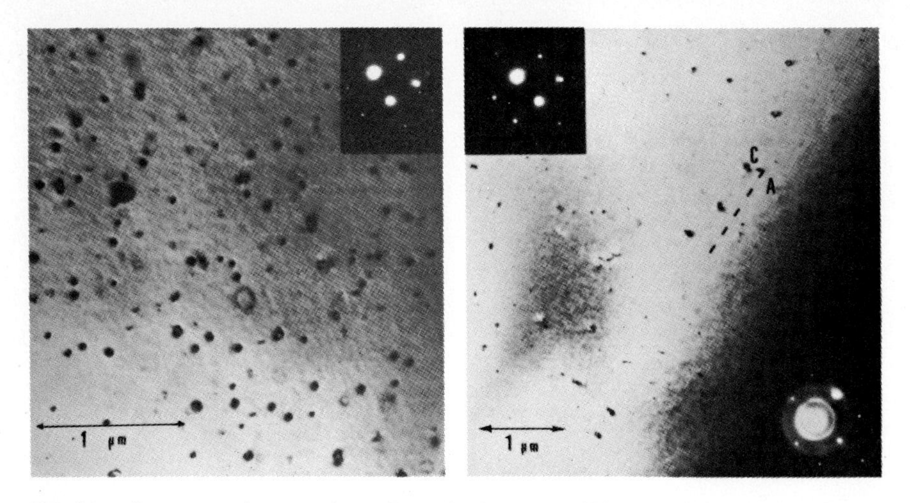

Fig.10. Electron micrographs of As-implanted silicon subjected to thermal anneal of 1000°C 30 min (a) and laser annealing; (b) inserts show diffraction patterns which are typical to their regions

5.3 Summary

To summarize the foregoing, laser cw annealing proceeds by solid phase epitaxial recrystallization. For "small" irradiated areas (40 μm spot), the critical parameter is the beam power per unit radius. The principal results of the annealing are:

1. 100% substitutionality of the implanted dopant even for concentrations that exceed the solid solubility.

2. No residual defects in TEM to 50 Å resolution.

3. No dopant redistribution during annealing.

4. Residual point defects remaining below the recrystallized layer that require a subsequent low temperature anneal for their removal (800°C for 10 minutes).

For VLSI applications, the absence of dopant redistribution may be a significant feature of this annealing process. In any case it is an ideal companion for the implantation process because the dopants are annealed into their as-implanted sites. Since the implanted impurity profile can be calculated with considerable accuracy, this process provides a means of assuring that computer simulations of impurity profiles based on the implantation process can be realized with precision.

5.Annealing With Large Diameter CW Sources

A very attractive alternative for cw laser annealing is the use of cw arc sources. Arc sources can be configured to produce both large diameter annealing spots and ribbon-shaped beams. These beams are scanned at speeds that produce dwell times on the order of seconds, which substantially reduces the severity of the thermal shock that is often obtained with a cw laser. Such an annealing time is, however, still short enough to prevent excessive dopant redistribution during annealing of ion-implanted semiconductors. Furthermore, the throughput of an arc lamp or ribbon electron beam annealing system can also be very high (hundreds of 4" wafers per hour) and, in addition, both of these annealing techniques are insensitive to anti-reflective dielectric coatings, unlike their laser counterpart.

Both arc lamps and electron beams can be used for annealing in two possible modes, an isothermal mode and a heat sink mode. In the isothermal mode the entire wafer reaches the annealing temperature. The dominant heat loss mechanism in this case is radiation; the time required to reach a given temperature is typically on the order of 0.5-5 seconds. This method has the advantage of requiring only low beam power. However, in certain cases it is desirable to reach annealing temperature more rapidly or to confine the heating to the sample surface. The heat sink mode must then be employed [14], in which the backsurface of the sample is kept at a specified temperature T_0. The principal heat loss mechanism under these conditions is conduction through the wafer.

5.1 Stationary Arc Source Irradiating a Thermally Isolated Wafer

A convenient geometry for an analysis of this form of annealing is obtained by imagining a source of radiant energy (e.g., an arc source or simply quartz halogen lamps) within an enclosure, the sample to be annealed being supported by thermal insulators near the center of this volume (Fig. 11). In practice, several lamps can be arranged above and below the wafer to assure uniform illumination. Two distinct modes of operation exist, depending on the reflectivity of the inner walls of the cavity. In one mode, the reflector oven mode, the walls of the enclosure are made highly reflecting. This insures that energy from the source is efficiently coupled from source to sample, with the heating of the cavity walls kept to a minimum. In the second mode, the black-body mode, the walls are made highly absorbing. In this case, the light from the source is first absorbed by the walls and then reradiated back to the wafer. The walls and wafer are at approximately the same temperature in this mode. In this section we will present the results of numerical calculations which show the temperature versus time behavior of systems operating in these two modes.

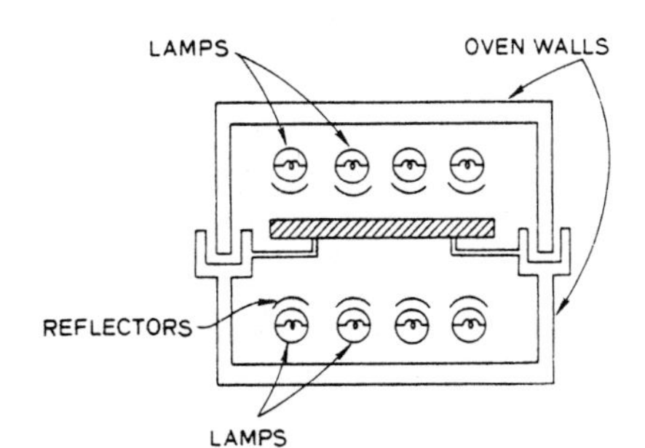

Fig.11. Basic annealing system using cw arc lamps

In Fig. 12 we show wafer and cavity temperatures vs time for a reflector oven system driven with an initial power of 12 kW. The power is reduced to the value required to maintain a steady-state temperature of 1000°C when that temperature is reached. As can be seen, a 4" Si wafer, 400μm thick,

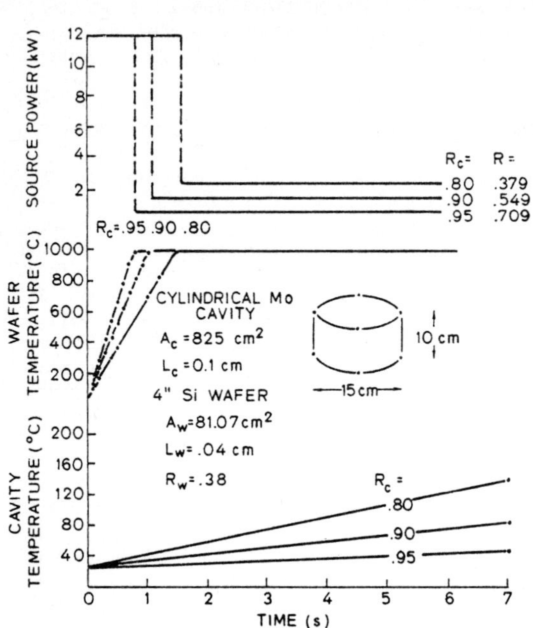

Fig.12. Source power, wafer temperature and cavity temperature versus time for isothermal annealing in the reflector oven mode with an initial power of 12 kW. The subscript 'c' refers to cavity and the subscript 'w' refers to wafer

can be heated to 1000°C in roughly one second. Full annealing of an implanted layer can occur if the temperature is maintained at 1000°C for a time interval in the range of 1-10 seconds.

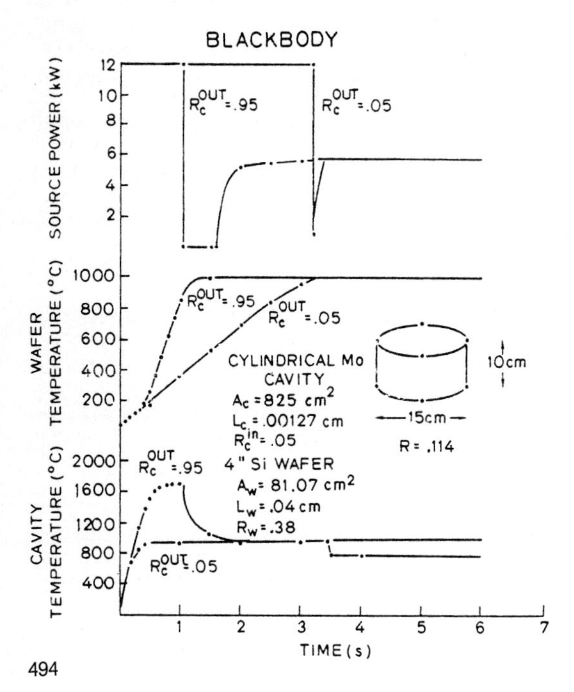

Fig.13. Source power, wafer temperature and cavity temperature versus time for isothermal annealing in the blackbody mode with an initial power of 12 kW. R_c^{out} is the reflectivity of a cavity that surrounds the heat that is radiated away from the blackbody enclosure

Similar analysis of a blackbody cavity is shown in Fig. 13, where it is seen that the temperature behavior is similar except for the fact that somewhat longer time is required to reach a given annealing temperature.

The electrical and metallurgical properties of material annealed in this way are similar to those obtained with cw laser or electron beam processing insofar as measurements have been made. Both of these types of annealing systems are easily made and have great promise for future applications.

5.2 Rapid Annealing of Silicon With a Scanning CW Hg Lamp

An extremely practical form for a scanned annealing system has been built using a 3" long mercury arc lamp with an elliptical reflector. A variety of arc sources can be used, though a mercury lamp is recommended because the spectral distribution of this lamp is most heavily weighted in the uv range.

The light from the lamp is focused into a narrow (< 5mm wide) ribbon by a 4" long reflector with an elliptical cross section. By using this shape of reflector to collect and focus the light, an intense linear heat source can be created while still maintaining a reasonable working distance between the sample and the lamp. The reflector has major and minor axes of 10 cm and 8.6 cm, respectively. This configuration gives a magnification factor of about 3.2 and a working distance of about 26 mm between the edge of the reflector and the focal plane.

The wafers are placed on a heated sample stage, which can be translated beneath the lamp at speeds up to 10cm/s. A schematic representation of the arc lamp annealing system is shown in Fig. 14.

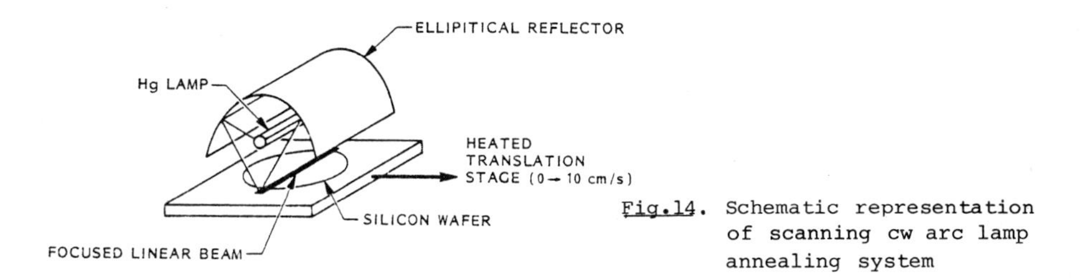

Fig.14. Schematic representation of scanning cw arc lamp annealing system

Annealing experiments were carried out using 2 and 3 inch 1-8Ω-cm p-type (100) silicon wafers which were implanted with $^{75}As^+$ at 100keV to $1x10^{15} cm^{-2}$. Several combinations of arc lamp power, scan rate and substrate temperature can be used to achieve a wafer temperature sufficient for good annealing, ~ 1000°C. In general, scan rates from 5mm/s to 1 cm/s, substrate temperatures of 400° C to 600° C and arc lamp input power of 1Kw/inch to 1.5Kw/inch gave good results.

Because of the length of the arc lamp, an entire 3" wafer can be annealed in a single scan. Transmission electron microscope (TEM) diffraction patterns made from samples taken from the unannealed and annealed regions clearly indicate the amorphous and the completely recrystallized nature of these regions, respectively.

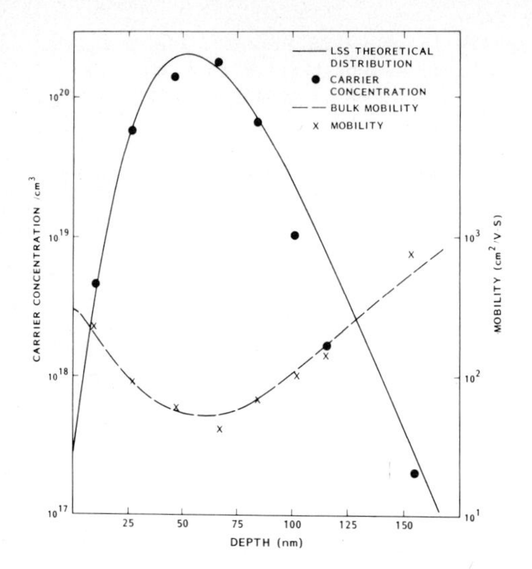

Fig.15. Carrier concentration and mobility versus depth from an arc lamp annealed sample

Carrier concentration and mobility of the scanning arc lamp annealed material as a function of depth were determined by means of differential sheet resistivity and Hall effect together with an anodic oxidation stripping technique. These results are shown shown in Fig. 15, along with the as-implanted profile calculated using LSS theory and published bulk silicon mobilities for the respective impurity concentrations. As shown, no measurable dopant redistribution occured during the annealing process and the free carrier mobility in the annealed region is as good as found in bulk silicon.

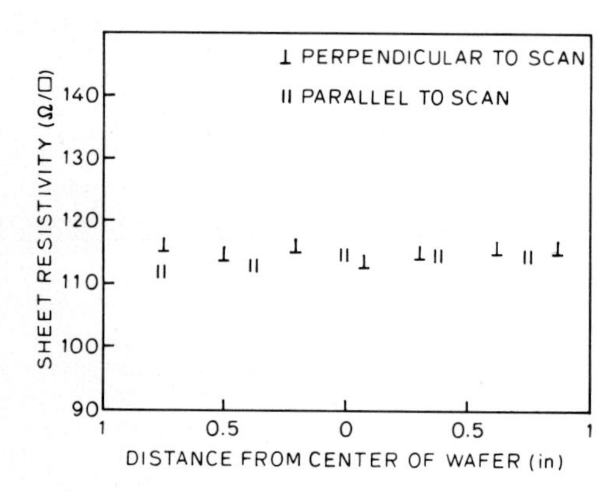

Fig.16. Sheet resistivity profiles across an arc lamp annealed wafer

Finally, to assess the uniformity of the anneal, four point probe sheet resistivity measurements were made on a wafer which was completely annealed in a single scan. The variation across the wafer from side to side and top to bottom (with respect to the scanning beam) showed no significant variation in either direction, indicating a very uniform annealing of the implanted wafer. These data are shown in Fig. 16.

4.8 Summary

Arc lamp annealing systems can readily provide the power necessary to anneal ion-implanted silicon under annealing conditions that are physically similar to those obtained with cw laser or electron beam sources. The high throughput capability of the arc source systems gives them an advantage for practical semiconductor processing applications.

Acknowledgments

The author would like to thank the members of the Stanford Beam Annealing Group for much of the material from which this paper is drawn and DARPA (S. Roosild and R. Reynolds) for the financial support and encouragement which made the work possible.

References

1 J.F. Gibbons: In Laser and Electron Beam Solid Interactions and Materials Processing - 1981, ed. by J.F. Gibbons, L.D. Hess and T.W. Sigmon (North Holland, New York, 1981).
2 T. Shibata, J.F. Gibbons and T.W. Sigmon, Appl. Phys. Lett. 36, 7 (1980).
3 D.H. Auston, C.M. Surko, T.N.C. Venkatesan, R.E. Slusher, and J.A. Golovchenko, Appl. Phys. Lett. 33, 5, 437 (1978).
4 C.W. White, W.H. Christie, B.R. Appleton, S.R. Wilson, P.P. Pronko, and T.W. Magee, Appl. Phys. Lett. 33, 7, 662 (1978).
5 P. Baeri, S.V. Campisano, G. Foti, and E. Rimini, J. Appl. Phys. 50, 2, 788 (1979).
6 L. Csepregi, J.W. Mayer and T.W. Sigmon, Phys. Lett. 54A, 157 (1975).
7 J.F. Gibbons, Proc. IEEE 60, 9, 1062 (1972).
8 A. Gat and J.F. Gibbons, Appl. Phys. Lett. 32, 3, 142 (1978).
9 Y.I. Nissim, A. Lietoila, R.B. Gold and J.F. Gibbons, J. Appl. Phys. 51, 1 (1980).
10 J.A. Roth, G.L. Olson, S.A. Kokorowski, and L.D. Hess: In Laser and Electron Beam Solid Interactions and Materials Processing, ed. by J.F. Gibbons, L.D. Hess and T.W. Sigmon, (North-Holland, 1981), pp. 413-426.
11 J.F. Gibbons, W.S. Johnson and S.W. Mylroie, Projected Range Statistics in Semiconductors (Dowden, Hutchinson and Ross, 1975).
12 W. Brown: In Laser Effects in Ion Implanted Semiconductors, ed. by E. Rimini, Inst. di Struttura della Materia, Universita di Catania, Corso, Italy (1978).
13 A. Gat, J.F. Gibbons, T.J. Magee, J. Peng, V.R. Deline, P. Williams, and C.A. Evans, Jr., Appl. Phys. Lett. 32, 2767 (1978)
14 H.S. Carslaw and J.C. Jaeger, Conduction of Heat in Solide, 2nd Edition (Clarendon Press, 1959), p. 11.

Radiation Annealing of Silicon-Implanted GaAs with a CW Xe Arc Lamp

M.S. Lin, B.C. Hsieh, C.H. Peng, and J.C. Lou

Institute of Electrical Engineering, National Tsing Hua University,
855, Kuang Fu Road, Hsinchu, Taiwan 300, Rep. of China

Abstract

Xe-lamp light was used to anneal radiation damage and activate the dopant in silicon multi-implanted SI-GaAs. The recovery of damage appeared to take place from the interior via a solid-phase epitaxial process, with a 0.3 eV activation energy. Electrical activity and carrier mobility of samples annealed by 1.7-14 W/cm² Xe light are higher than those obtained by thermal annealing in the temperature region of 700-850°C. The activity of 93% may be the highest value that has been reported up to now in the laser or electron-beam annealing literature.

1. Introduction

In order to anneal lattice damage introduced by implantation and to increase the activity of dopants, high-temperature annealing is needed. However, diffusion of the dopants into the substrate cannot be avoided and, consequently, the desired profiles of the layer may not be attainable. Therefore, during the last few years, there has been growing interest in energy-pulse annealing techniques, either with a laser or with an electron beam. Many reports have since been published [1-8].

Laser radiation, either pulsed or CW, can be successfully employed in annealing the ion-implanted region in Si without redistribution of the implanted ions. In contrast to the successful cases with Si, other studies have revealed that laser annealing of GaAs is more difficult, because surface degradation occurs as a result of evaporation of the arsenic at a relatively low temperature [1], or due to the formation of defects [2,3]. In this paper, we report on a low-temperature process using a low-cost Xe-lamp light system. It covers a large irradiation area, and many samples can be handled simultaneously without the problem of the scanning-rate effect. The effects of power density, substrate temperature, and light-irradiation time on the characteristics of room-temperature silicon-multi-implanted SI-GaAs are systematically studied, and are compared to those in the case of annealing by a thermal process.

2. Experimental Procedure

Silicon was multi-implanted into SI-GaAs with energies of 25, 75 and 180 keV to achieve a 0.3 μm flat active layer for microwave devices. Implantations were performed at room temperature, with wafers tilted 8° to the <100> axis to reduce channeling effects. Following implantation, samples were coated with a ca. 200 nm thick SiO_2 layer deposited by electron-gun evaporation, and annealed in pure H_2 gas or in air by 1.7-14 W/cm² Xe light. The profiles were obtained by means of successive chemical etching with a solution of H_2SO_4:30% H_2O_2:H_2O in proportions of 4:1:5.

Ellipsometry and Hall-effect measurements were performed to characterize the residual damage and the electrical properties.

3. Results and Discussion

Figure 1 shows changes in substrate temperature for wafers held at 400°C and irradiated by different power densities of Xe light. The Xe lamp and substrate heater were turned off after 5 minutes of light irradiation. A slower temperature rise, compared to laser annealing, assured that the temperature monitored in this way was nearly equal to the true wafer temperature. Also, the temperature rise and fall curves were sufficiently reproducible. For the highest power density of 14 W/cm², a heating time of 5 min always increased the temperature to 760°C and saturation. In this system, the peak temperature was determined only by the time of light irradiation and the substrate heating temperature.

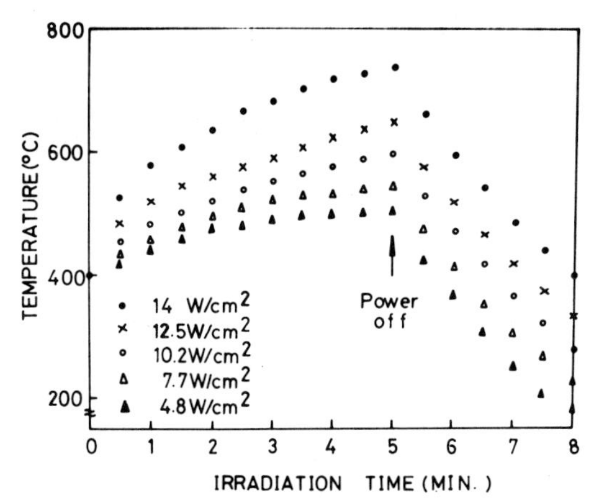

Fig. 1. Substrate-temperature curves for wafers held at 400°C and irradiated by different power densities of Xe light

In order to study the residual damage in the implanted region after thermal or Xe-light annealing, successive layers were stripped off chemically, and the value of the extinction coefficient (K) was measured. Since K is indicative of the damage present, a damage profile is obtained, as shown in Fig. 2. For comparison, damage profiles resulting from thermal annealing have also been investigated and plotted. The results indicate that damage recovery appears to take place from the interior, via a solid-phase epitaxial mechanism, in both the Xe-light and the thermal-annealing processes. Even though the implanted layer has been annealed by a low power density of the Xe light, 1.7 W/cm², the residual damage is less than that in the case of thermal annealing for the temperature range of 700-850°C. This fact is also reflected in the electrical properties to be discussed in the following paragraphs.

From the damage profiles, one can also easily calculate the recrystallization rate of the implanted layer. Figure 3 shows the substrate temperature's effect on the damage profile, for 2 min irradiation with 14 W/cm² Xe light. The Si ion-implantation energy and the dose are 150 keV and 2×10^{14} /cm², respectively. It can be seen that the damage decreases as the substrate temperature increases, and that the damage recovery appears to take place from the

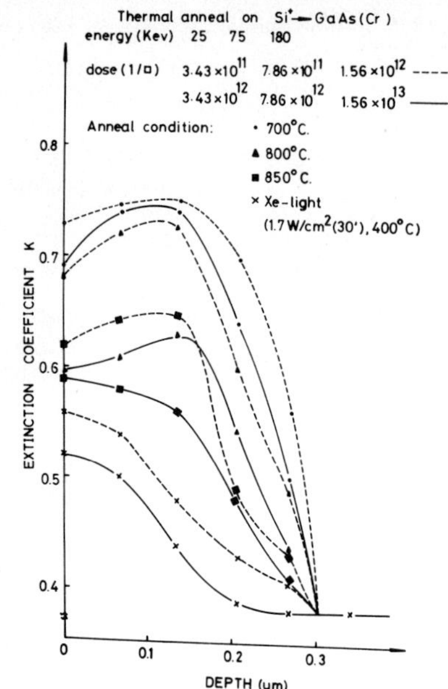

Fig. 2. Damage profiles of Si^+-multi-implanted SI-GaAs after thermal or Xe-light annealing.

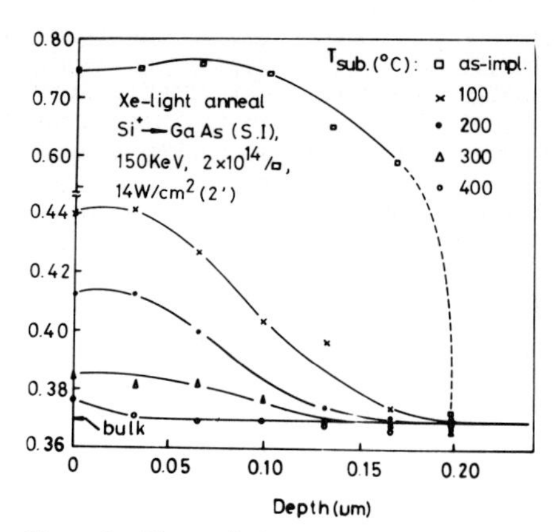

Fig. 3. The substrate temperature effect on the damage profile, for 2 min irradiation with 14 W/cm² Xe light

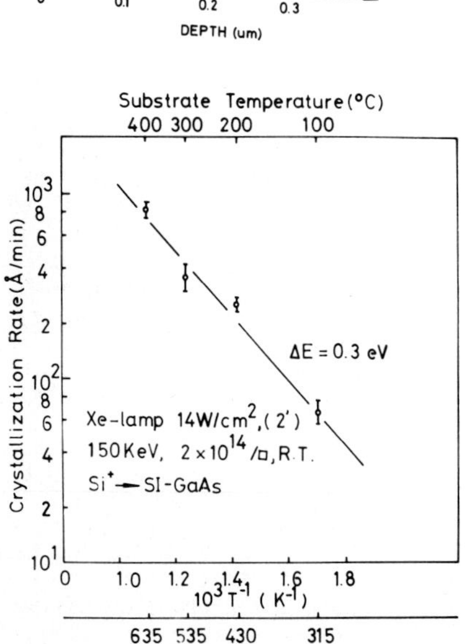

Fig. 4. Recrystallization rates calculated from Fig.3 vs reciprocal peak temperature

interior crystalline-damage interface to the surface. From the intersection of the tangent of the profiles with the bulk line, the recrystallization rates are calculated from the interval divided by the irradiation time. These calculated recrystallization rates are plotted in Fig. 4 as the reciprocal peak temperature; an 0.3 eV activation energy for Xe-light annealing is obtained. This value is consistent with that of our previous photoluminescence studies [9] as well as of Kato's electrical-conductivity studies [10].

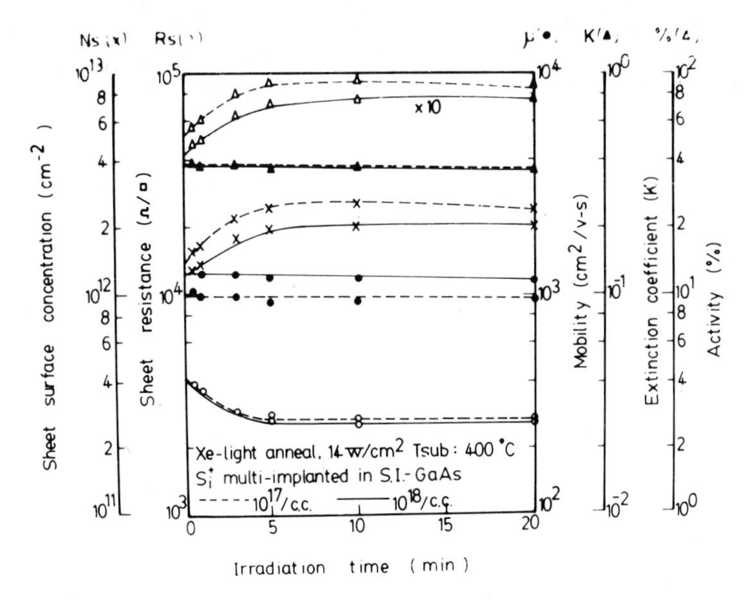

Fig. 5. Hall-effect data, activity and extinction coefficient for Si^+ multi-implantation into SI-GaAs vs light irradiation time

The effects of power density, substrate temperature and irradiation time in Xe-light annealing upon the electrical characteristics of room-temperature silicon-implanted SI-GaAs were systematically studied, and were compared to values for annealing by a thermal process. Figure 5 shows the effects of the light-irradiation time on the Hall-effect data, the activity and the extinction coefficient for Si multi-implanted SI-GaAs. The power density and the substrate temperature are 14 W/cm^2 and 400°C, respectively. A 5-minute Xe-light annealing was found sufficient to completely anneal the ion-implantation-induced damage, and to activate most of the Si implanted into the GaAs. It can be seen that Xe-light annealing for a longer period does not activate additional Si ions. In the case of low-dose implantation to achieve a $10^{17}/cm^3$ flat concentration, the activity increases from 57% to 93% with an increase in the irradiation time from 0.5 to 5 minutes, and then saturates. This shows that a very high activity of the implanted layer can be achieved by 14 W/cm^2 Xe-light annealing. To our knowledge, the 93% activity may be the highest value that has been reported to date in the laser or electron-beam annealing literature.

The power density's effects on the electrical and optical properties of the implanted layer are shown in Fig. 6. It can be seen the sheet carrier concentration and the activity increase gradually, and saturate in the power-density region above 12 W/cm^2. This is also confirmed in our photoluminescence and transmission-electron-microscope studies. The prismatic-dislocation-loop density decreases, and the ratio of the Si donor-emission intensity to that of the Si acceptor increases, with an increase in the Xe-light power density; and eventually both saturate.

Figure 7 shows the effect of substrate temperature in the case of Xe-light irradiation. The extinction coefficients for substrate temperatures of both 300 and 400°C approach those of unimplanted SI-GaAs; however, a higher activity value is obtained when the GaAs is heated to 400°C. The substrate-temperature effect may be attributed to the increase in the optical absorption band of the material as the band gap of GaAs narrows. At the same temperature or above, using the furnace-annealing process, the same high activity cannot be achieved.

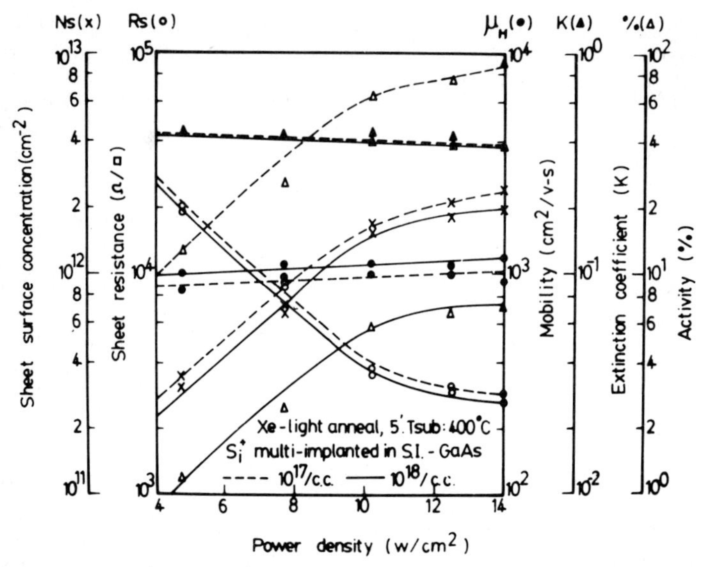

Fig. 6. Hall-effect data, activity and extinction coefficient for Si^+ multi-implantation into SI-GaAs vs power density of Xe light

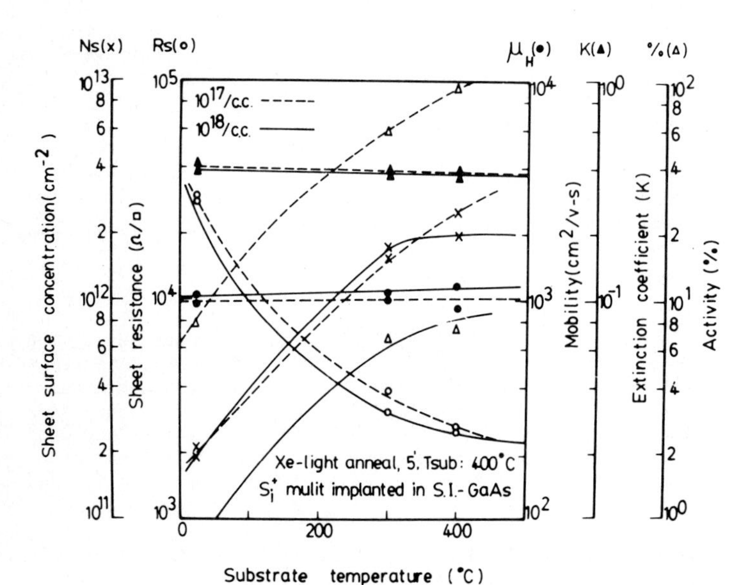

Fig. 7. Hall-effect data, activity and extinction coefficient for Si^+ multi-implantation into SI-GaAs vs substrate temperature with Xe-light irradiation

The low mobilities (~ 1000 cm^2/Vs) obtained in the implanted-annealed layers are influenced by the high-concentration Cr-doped substrate in the range of $2\text{-}4 \times 10^{17}/\text{cm}^3$ [11]. However, the mobility of Xe-light annealing is always greater than that of thermal annealing; the ratio is about 1.5-2.0.

In summary, Xe light can be used to anneal implanted damage completely and to activate the dopants in GaAs to 93%. To our knowledge, the activity of 93% may be the highest value that has been reported as yet in the laser or electron-beam annealing literature. The annealing of damage appears to take place from the interior via a solid-phase epitaxial process, with a 0.3 eV activation energy.

References

1. S.S. Kular and B.J. Sealy: Electron. Lett. 15, 413 (1979)
2. S. Nojima: J. Appl. Phys. 52, 7445 (1981)
3. D.E. Davies, J.P. Lorenzo, and T.G. Ryan: Appl. Phys. Lett. 37, 612 (1980), and IEEE Elec. Device Lett. 3, 102 (1982)
4. N.J. Shah, H. Ahmed, I.R. Sanders, and J.F. Singleton: Electron. Lett. 16, 433 (1980)
5. R.L. Mozzi, W. Fabian, and F.J. Peikarski: Appl. Phys. Lett. 35, 337 (1979)
6. C.L. Anderson, H.L. Dunlap, L.D. Hess, and K.V. Vaidyanathan: in Laser-Solid Interactions and Laser Processing-1978, ed. by S.D. Ferris, H.J. Leamy, J.H. Poate (Am. Inst. Phys., New York, 1979), p. 585
7. S.G. Liu, C.P. Wu, and C.N. Magee: in Ref. 6, p. 603
8. J.L. Tandon and F.H. Eisen: in Ref. 6, p. 616
9. M.S.Lin: in Proc. 6th Symposium on Electronic Materials and Devices-1980, ed. by C.Y. Wu (Taiwan; 1980), p. 78
10. Y. Kato, T. Shinada, Y. Shiraki,and K.F. Komatsubara: J. Appl. Phys. 45, 1044 (1974)
11. B.T. Debney and P.R. Jay: Solid State Electronics 23, 773 (1980)

Pulse-Laser-Induced Epitaxial Regrowth of Ion-Implanted Semiconductors

G. Götz, W. Andrä, H.-D. Geiler, and M. Wagner

Sektion Physik, Friedrich-Schiller-Universität Jena, Max Wien Platz 1, DDR-6900 Jena, German Democratic Republik

Abstract

The work presented is focused on two possible techniques to anneal radiation damage arising during implantation, by the use of a laser treatment. By using a pulsed laser, this annealing process will be either a solid-phase or a liquid-phase regrowth. Which kind of regrowth occurs depends on the time duration of the laser pulse. In the present work, the employment of two different high-power lasers for the annealing of ion-implanted silicon is demonstrated. A review is given with respect to some laser-operation parameters and annealing results.

Liquid-phase epitaxy is achieved by an irradiation of the implanted wafers with a Q-switched Nd-glass laser. The ultrafast recrystallization process generated by the laser pulse makes it possible to achieve supersaturation of implanted species. This effect is demonstrated for high-dose implantations of arsenic and antimony in silicon. The different behaviour of these two dopants with respect to their electrical activation under laser irradiation is discussed.

A free-running high-power Nd-glass laser, connected with an in situ diagnostic system on the basis of time-resolved reflectivity measurements, is described; this is employed in the solid-phase annealing. The real-time analysis of the effects of laser irradiation upon the regrowth kinetics allows an automatic control of the laser irradiation, to avoid wafer destruction and out diffusion of dopants.

1. Introduction

Following the initial studies of Kachurin et al. [1] and Khaibullin et al. [2], extensive research has been performed using laser, electron, or ion beams for the annealing of damage in semiconductors caused by ion implantation [3-5]. There are two principal processes which can be used for this purpose: liquid-phase epitaxy (LPE) and solid-phase epitaxy (SPE). In the case of laser annealing, LPE can be carried out using nanosecond pulses (10-100 ns), and SPE using millisecond pulses (1-10 ms) [6,7].

For the application of laser annealing to technological processes, it is of great importance to know the limits of this method, especially for the activation of electrical carriers and defect-free recrystallization of damaged layers. In this paper, these topics will be discussed for laser annealing (LPE and SPE processes) of As- and Sb-implanted silicon layers.

2. Experimental Techniques

Silicon wafers of <100> or <111> orientation were implanted at room temperature with 100 keV As ions and 65 keV Sb ions, in the dose range between $1 \times 10^{15} cm^{-2}$ and $5 \times 10^{16} cm^{-2}$.

For the annealing, the following types of lasers were used:

LPE: - Q-switched ruby laser (wavelength 694 nm, pulse length 30 ns, energy density 0.1-1.5 $J\,cm^{-2}$).

- Q-switched Nd-glass laser, shown in Fig. 1 (wavelength 1.06 μm, pulse length 30-70 ns, TEM_{00} mode, energy density up to 4 $J cm^{-2}$, beam diameter 1.5 cm, homogeneity in the central beam region better than 95 %).

SPE: - free-running Nd-glass laser, shown in Fig. 2 (wavelength 1.06 μm, pulse length 1.5 ms, maximum output power 1 MW).

The beam of a He-Ne laser (wavelength 633 nm) was focused to a 100 μm-diameter spot (1/e) onto the center of the sample at nearly normal incidence, and the reflected part of this test beam was detected by a Si photodiode. In addition, the intensity of the laser pulse was monitored by another Si photodiode.

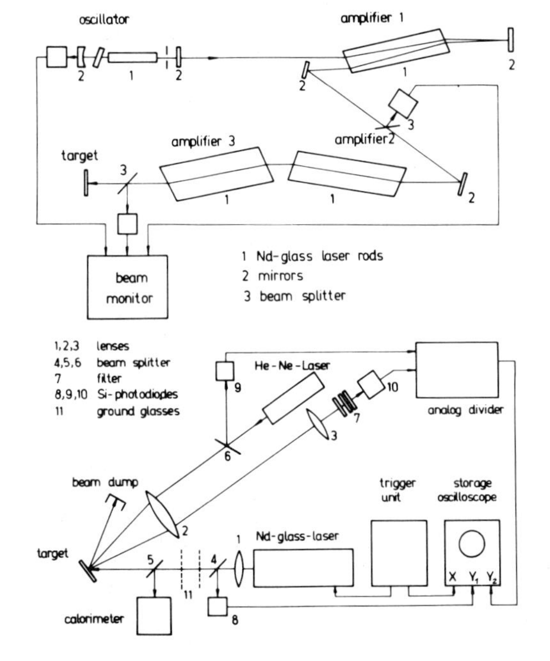

Fig. 1. Equipment for liquid-phase annealing

Fig. 2. Equipment for solid-phase annealing (combined with in-situ analysis system)

Following irradiation, the results of the annealing process were investigated by the following methods:

- four-point-probe resistance and Hall-effect measurements, combined with anodic sectioning, provided the total electrical carrier concentration as well as the carrier concentration profile.

- The Rutherford backscattering technique (RBS), combined with channeling, determined concentration profiles of dopants and their incorporation on lattice sites. 1.4 MeV He ions were used in an optimized scattering geometry, improving the resolution in depth.

3. Results and Discussion

3.1 Liquid-Phase Epitaxy (LPE)

A comparison of the concentration profiles of electrical carriers and dopants on lattice sites is given by Fig. 3 (As implantation) and Fig. 4 (Sb implantation). In both cases, it is well established that all impurity atoms on lattice sites also become electrically active.

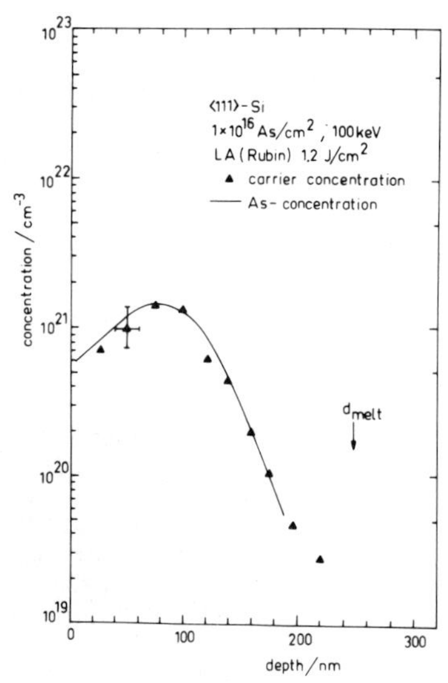

Fig. 3. Comparison of concentration profiles of electrical carriers and As atoms on lattice sites after pulsed-laser annealing

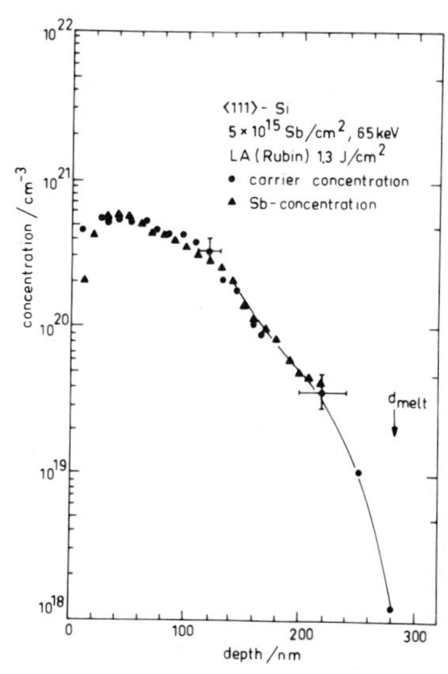

Fig. 4. Comparison of concentration profiles of electrical carriers and Sb atoms on lattice sites after pulsed-laser annealing

The concentration profiles of the implanted ions and the electrical carriers after laser annealing are compared in Fig. 5 (As implantation) and Fig. 6 (Sb implantation), for different dose values. Depending on the diffusion of the implanted ions in the liquid layer melted by the laser irradiation, the profiles are broadened. The depth of the p-n junction corresponds to the maximum depth of the solid-liquid interface, d_{melt}. Consequently, it should be possible to adjust the depth of the p-n junction by changing the energy density of the laser beam. In Fig. 5 and Fig. 6, the solid solubility limits (C^{0}_{max}) of the dopants are marked by arrows. The carrier concentration profiles indicate that a significant fraction of the implanted ions is incorporated on lattice sites, exceeding the solid solubility limit.

An important question for the application of laser annealing is that of the laser energy which is necessary to obtain complete activation of the

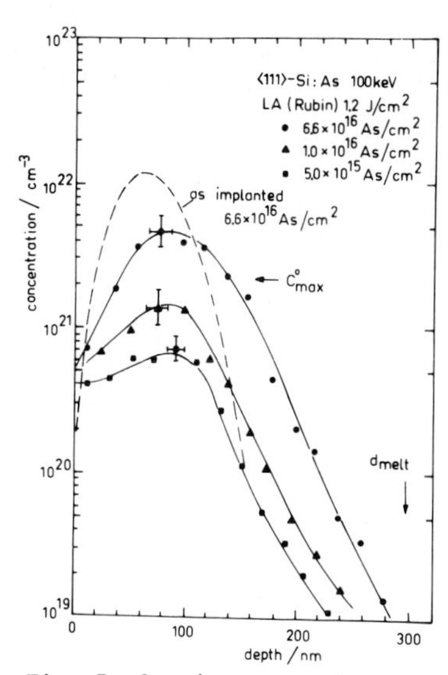

Fig. 5. Carrier concentration profiles after pulsed-laser annealing (for various doses of As ions)

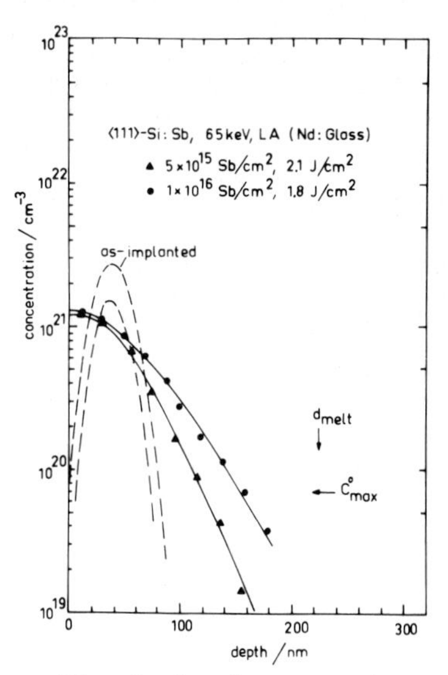

Fig. 6. Carrier concentration profiles after pulsed-laser annealing (for various doses of Sb ions)

implanted ions. It is well known that the thickness of the molten layer (d_{melt}) has to be somewhat greater than the depth of the damaged (for high doses, the amorphized) layer (d_{amorph}), to guarantee good recrystallization [6]. This is demonstrated in Fig. 7, where the sheet carrier concentration and the total concentration of impurities within the molten layer are represented as a function of the thickness d_{melt}(related to the projected ion range, Rp). The thickness of the molten layer is clearly determined by the irradiation conditions [8,9]. For both dopants, complete activation is achieved under the condition $d_{melt} \geq d_{amorph}$.

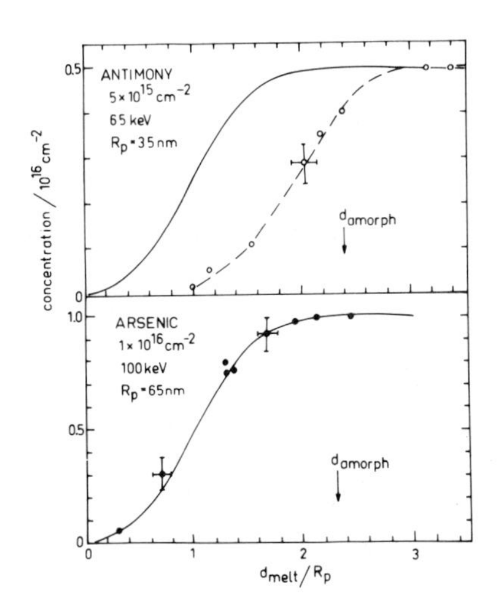

Fig. 7. Comparison between sheet carrier concentration and total atomic concentration within the molten layer, as a function of melting depth

However, there are differences under the condition $d_{melt} < d_{amorph}$. Whereas in the case of As implantation all atoms in the molten layer are activated, in the case of Sb implantation only a partion of the Sb atoms within the molten layer become electrically active. The latter is caused by segregation effects. The equilibrium segregation coefficient for Sb atoms in silicon is much smaller ($K_o = 0.023$) than that for As atoms ($K_o = 0.3$). It seems that for very thin molten layers, the effective segregation coefficient (taking into account the influence of moving liquid-solid interfaces) is nearer the equilibrium value than would be expected for the very high interface velocities in thick layers [10].

For the application of laser annealing, it is additionally important to obtain information about the total dopant concentration which can be electrically activated. The results for As and Sb implantation are summarized in Fig. 8, which shows the peak values of the carrier concentration profiles as a function of the implanted dose. Over a wide dose range, all implanted impurity atoms can be activated by laser annealing. Although the solid solubility limit can be exceeded by about 3.3 times for As atoms, and 18 times for Sb atoms, there are definite saturation values, depending on the atomic species:

As atoms: $C_{max} = 5 \times 10^{21}\ cm^{-3}$, and

Sb atoms: $C_{max} = 1.5 \times 10^{21}\ cm^{-3}$.

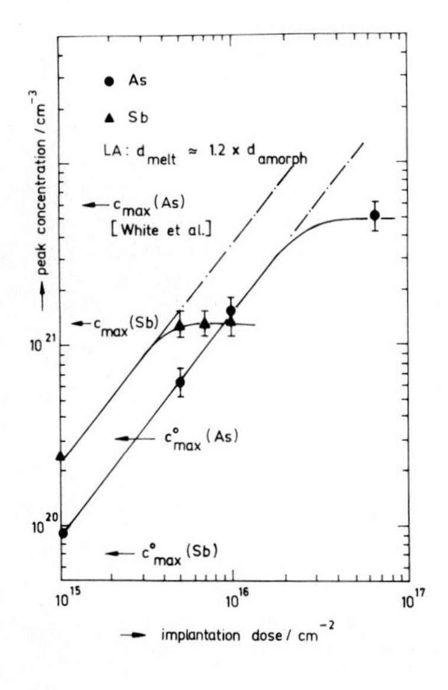

Fig. 8. Peak values of carrier concentration profiles versus implantation dose.

C^o_{max}: solid solubility limit

C_{max}: maximum solubility after laser annealing [11]

d_{melt}: melting depth

d_{amorph}: thickness of amorphous layer

3.2 Solid-Phase Epitaxy (SPE)

The equipment shown in Fig. 2 allows in situ study of annealing behaviour by time-resolved reflectivity measurements [12 13]. A typical oscillogram is represented in Fig. 9 (10^{15}As/cm^2, <100> Si). The annealing process can be divided into three stages: The first is the heating of the sample, starting with the laser pulse. Then, if the temperature is high enough, the movement of the crystalline-amorphous interface will start. This movement can be tracked due to periodic changes in the reflection signal. The figure displays an annealing process which has ended just before the sample reaches its maxi-

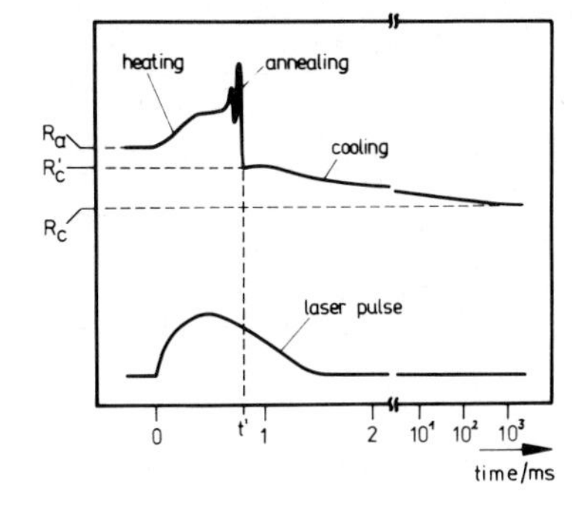

Fig. 9. Typical oscillogram for laser-induced high-temperature solid-phase annealing.

R_a: reflectivity of amorphous Si

R_c: reflectivity of crystalline Si

R_c': reflectivity after the end of the annealing process

mum temperature. After a time of 1 ms, the maximum temperature of the sample surface region is reached; within another ms, the stored heat energy dissipates to the bulk. R_c' marks the reflectivity of the sample immediately after the annealing process has ended at time t'. From the oscillogram, conclusions can be drawn on the velocity of the interface, nucleation processes, and the movement of dopants.

Reflectivity oscillograms and RBS spectra measured from silicon samples implanted with 1×10^{15}As/cm^2 (a, circles) and 5×10^{15}As/cm^2 (b, triangles) are shown in Fig. 10. It can be seen that perfect regrowth can be achieved, in which case more than 95 % of the implanted As atoms occupy substitutional lattice sites.

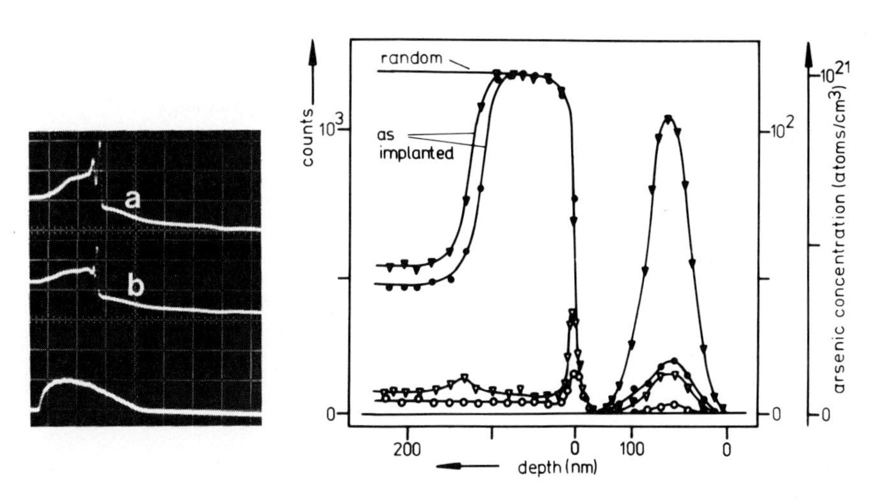

Fig. 10. Reflectivity oscillograms and RBS spectra measured from Si samples implanted with:

1×10^{15} As/cm^2 (oscillogr.a, circles) and

5×10^{15} As/cm^2 (oscillogr.b, triangles).

Filled symbols: aligned spectra before annealing
open symbols: aligned spectra after annealing (62 J/cm^2)
horizontal scaling (oscillogr.): 50 µs/div.

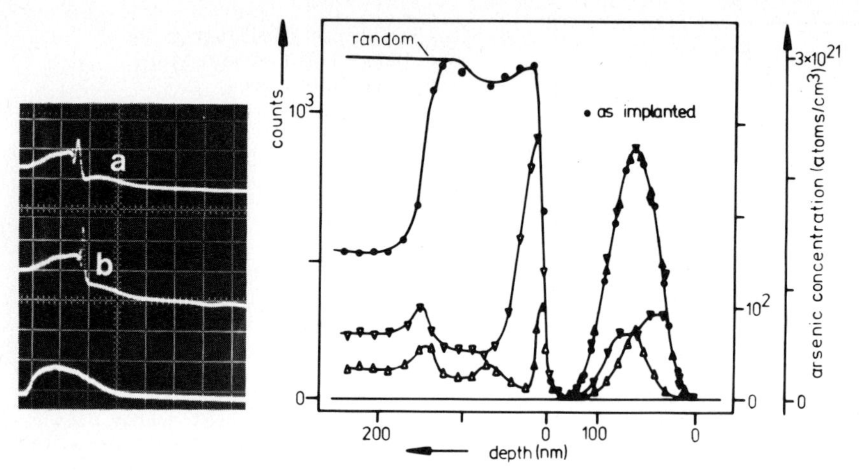

Fig. 11. Reflectivity oscillograms and RBS spectra measured from Si samples implanted with 1×10^{16} As/cm^2.

● aligned   as-implanted
▼ random, ▽ aligned after 60 J/cm^2 (oscillogr. a)
▲ random, △ aligned after 58 J/cm^2 (oscillogr. b)

At an implantation dose of 1×10^{16} As/cm^2 (Fig. 11), for which the maximum As concentration exceeds the solid solubility limit, the annealing process results either in a complete recrystallization of the amorphous layer (with residual defects, however, at depths corresponding to those of the initial crystalline-amorphous interface and the maximum As concentration), or in the formation of a heavily damaged surface layer. The maximum concentration of As atoms on substitutional lattice sites has a value of 1.8×10^{21}As/cm^3 , which corresponds to the maximum solid solubility of arsenic in silicon.

To obtain a better understanding of the recrystallization process, the movement of the crystalline-amorphous interface was investigated by time-resolved reflectivity measurements. Fig. 12 displays the velocity of the interface versus its depth. The shapes of the curves exhibit, on the one hand, an acceleration of epitaxial regrowth due to the influence of the implanted

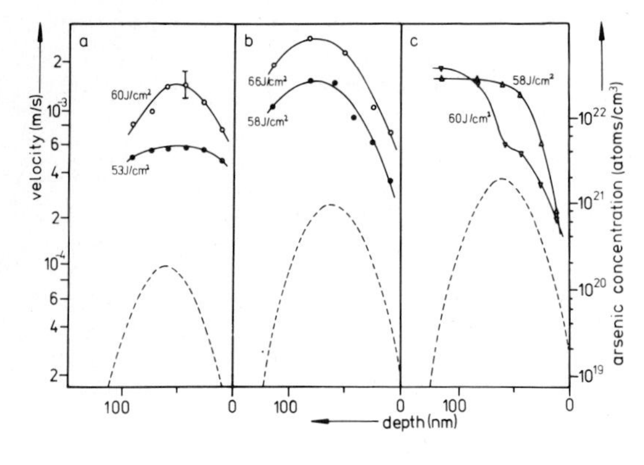

Fig. 12. Crystallization velocity versus depth. The dashed lines represent the As concentration calculated from theoretical data.

a: 1×10^{15} As/cm^2
b: 5×10^{15} As/cm^2
c: 1×10^{16} As/cm^2

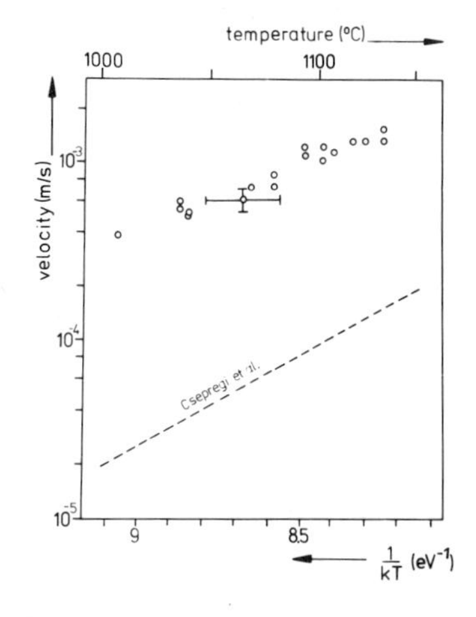

Fig. 13. Velocity of the crystalline-amorphous interface versus temperature. The dashed line represents, values calculated on the basis of data given in Ref. [14]

As atoms, and on the other, a retardation of the regrowth process towards the surface, caused by the effects of nucleation processes.

Fig. 13 shows the dependence of the crystalline-amorphous interface velocity on the temperature during regrowth, calculated from the reflectivity R'_c (see Fig. 9). Over the temperature range investigated, the regrowth rate is well characterized by an Arrhenius-type equation with an activation energy of 1.6eV.

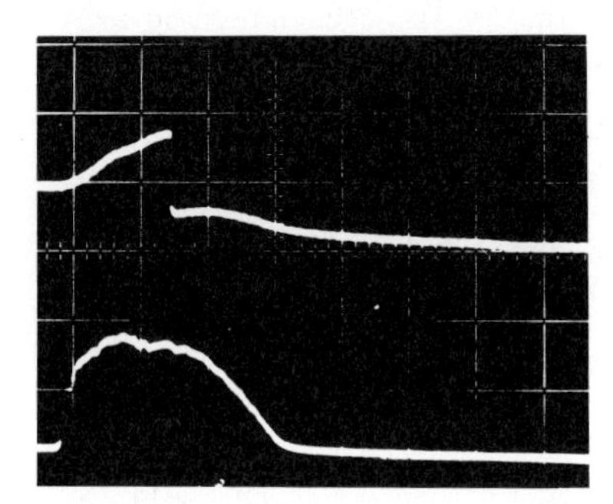

Fig. 14. Reflectivity oscillogram for laser-induced explosive crystallization. Horizontal scaling: 500 μm/div.

Fig. 15. High-energy TEM micrograph (1 MeV) of a silicon layer after laser-induced explosive crystallization

In some cases, laser irradiation of amorphous silicon layers with thicknesses greater than 200 nm results in a very fast crystallization process [15]. The oscillogram shown in Fig. 14 illustrates that under laser irradiation of amorphous silicon layers (480 nm thick, 7×10^{14} P/cm^2 , 200 keV, 80 K), the reflectivity signal drops abruptly within a time duration of about 10 μs. A TEM analysis (Fig. 15) reveals laminated single-crystalline structures. The velocity of the crystallization process was estimated from the results to be in the order of 10 m/s. This leads to the conclusion that an explosive liquid-phase recrystallization process, with a laterally-moving crystallization front, has taken place.

4. Conclusions

Silicon layers implanted with high concentrations of As or Sb ions can be annealed by laser pulses through LPE or SPE processes, respectively.

LPE yields complete activation of the implanted ions if the depth of the molten layer exceeds the depth of the amorphous layer in the order of 20 %. The maximum carrier concentrations obtained are $C^{As}_{max} = 5 \times 10^{21} cm^{-3}$ and $C^{Sb}_{max} = 1.5 \times 10^{21} cm^{-3}$. All impurity atoms on lattice positions are electrically active. The depth of the p-n junction can be adjusted by varying the laser-pulse energy.

In the case of SPE, complete activation of As atoms was possible up to the solid solubility limit ($C^{As}_{max} = 1.8 \times 10^{21} cm^{-3}$). The shapes of the concentration profiles after the annealing process were identical to those for the implanted ions. In situ time-resolved measurement of the reflection signal allows a direct study of the crystallization process, as well as of impurity migration.

References

1. G.A. Kachurin, N.B. Pridachin, L.S. Smirnov: Fiz. Tekh. Polup. 9, 1428 (1975).
2. E.I. Shtyrkov, I.B. Khaibullin, M.M. Zaripov, M.F. Galjatutinov, G.M. Bajasikov: Fiz. Tekh. Polup. 9, 2000 (1975).
3. Proc. Int. Conf. on Laser Solid Interactions and Laser Processing - 1978, ed. by S.D. Ferris, H.J. Leamy, J.H. Poate (Am. Inst. Phys., New York, 1979).
4. Proc. Mat. Res. Soc. Meeting, Boston (1980).
5. J.E.E. Baglin, R.T. Hodgson, W.K. Chu, J.M. Neri, D.A. Hammer, L.J. Chen: Nucl. Instr. Meth. 191, 169 (1981).
6. J.S. Williams: in Laser and Electron Beam Processing of Electronic Materials - 1979, ed. by C.L. Anderson, G.K. Celler, G.A. Rozgonyi (Electrochem. Soc., Princeton, 1980), p.249.
7. E. Rimini: in Laser and Electron Beam Processing of Electronic Materials - 1979, ed. by C.L. Anderson, G.K. Celler, G.A. Rozgonyi (Electrochem. Soc., Princeton, 1980), p. 270.
8. K.H. Heinig, H. Woittennek, M.U. Jäger: in Proc. Int. Conf. Ion Implant. in Semicond., Reinhardsbrunn (1977), ZfK - 360, p. 111.
9. P. Baeri, S.U. Campisano, G. Foti, E. Rimini: J. Appl. Phys. 50, 788 (1979).
10. P. Baeri, S.U. Campisano, M.G. Grimaldi, E. Rimini: in Proc. "Laser and Electron Beam Processing of Materials", Cambridge, MA (1979).
11. C.W. White, P.P. Pronko, S.R. Wilson, B.R. Appleton, J. Narayan, R.T. Young: J. Appl. Phys. 50, 3261 (1979).
12. G.L. Olson, S.A. Kokorowski, R.A. Mc Farlane, J.W. Mayer: Appl. Phys. Lett. 37, 1019 (1980).
13. G. Götz, H.-D. Geiler, M. Wagner: Phys. Stat. Sol. (a) (to be published).
14. L. Csepregi, E.F. Kennedy, J.W. Mayer, T.W. Sigmon: J. Appl. Phys. 49, 3906 (1978).
15. H.-D. Geiler, G. Götz, M. Wagner, E. Glaser: Phys. Stat. Sol. (to be published).

CO_2 Laser Annealing of Ion-Implanted Silicon: Relaxation Characteristics of Metastable Concentrations

J. Götzlich, P.H. Tsien, G. Henghuber, and H. Ryssel

Fraunhofer-Institut für Festkörpertechnologie, Paul-Gerhardt-Allee 42, D-8000 München 60, Fed. Rep. of Germany

Abstract

The relaxation behavior of supersaturated concentrations resulting from CO_2 laser annealing of high-dose arsenic, phosphorus, and boron-implanted silicon was investigated by thermal post-treatment at different temperatures ranging between 700 and 1100°C. Depending on ion species and post-treatment temperature, a different time constant for the relaxation was found. By measuring carrier-concentration profiles, the equilibrium carrier concentration at different temperatures was obtained.

1. Introduction

Laser annealing is a relatively new alternative process to thermal annealing of ion implanted semiconductors. The advantages of laser annealing are perfect recrystallization without any remaining crystalline defects and the high speed of the recrystallization process, avoiding any excess diffusion in the wafer outside the irradiated area.

There are two types of recrystallization mechanisms. One mechanism is the solid-state epitaxial regrowth of the damaged layer by irradiation with cw lasers; the other mechanism is the liquid-phase regrowth usually done by irradiation with pulsed lasers. The times applied for these two mechanisms are some ms to s in the case of cw laser annealing, and only several dozen in the case of pulsed-laser annealing. The velocity of the interface during the regrowth can reach several µm/sec during cw laser annealing, and up to several m/sec during pulsed-laser annealing.

Due to this high recrystallization velocity, the dopant atoms cannot achieve thermal equilibrium. For high implantation doses, therefore, the solid solubility of the implanted atoms can be exceeded appreciably [1-5]. If the solid solubility of dopant atoms is exceeded, the high concentrations are thermally metastable, and relax by thermal post-treatment [6-11]. These metastable supersaturated layers are one of the most interesting phenomena of laser annealing. Therefore, we studied the relaxation behavior of such supersaturated concentrations at different temperatures.

2. Experimental Procedure

The experimental procedure to create supersatured layers was as follows: First, arsenic, phosphorus, or boron ions were implanted into <100> silicon wafers. The ion energy and dose were 150 keV and 1×10^{16} cm^{-2} for the arsenic, 80 keV and 2×10^{16} cm^{-2} for the phosphorus and 50 keV and 1.5 x

10^{16} cm^{-2} for the boron implantations, respectively. All implantations were performed at room temperature. After implantation, the samples were annealed by CO_2 laser irradiation at 1200°C for 10 sec. After this high-temperature activation, the samples were annealed at lower temperatures in the range between 700 and 1100°C for different times. The annealing for periods up to 1000 sec was performed by heating the samples with a CO_2 laser to the desired temperature. By this heating method, the rise time of the temperature can be reduced to 1 - 2 sec, instead of some minutes in a conventional diffusion furnace. During the CO_2 laser irradiation the temperature was monitored by an IR thermometer. For prolonged heating times above 1000 sec, a conventional furnace was used. To avoid oxidation, these samples were annealed in a flowing nitrogen atmosphere.

To determine the effective sheet carrier concentration, sheet resistivity and mobility, Hall-effect and sheet-resistivity measurements were made using the van-der-Pauw method. Carrier-concentration profiles were obtained by using anodic oxidation and etching the oxide layer.

3. Results and Discussion

After the 10 sec activation of the implanted atoms, the effective sheet carrier concentration was measured to be 0.95, 1.85 and 2.05 × 10^{16} cm^{-2} for the arsenic-, boron-, and phosphorus-implanted samples, respectively. This means that for the phosphorus and boron implantations, the active dose is higher than the implanted dose. This phenomenon has been observed by other groups [12,13], but also in other experiments by our group [3,14]. The reason for this effect is not yet understood, but we suggest that a correction of the Hall factor r (r is the scattering factor and gives the ratio of Hall-to-drift mobility) could give an explanation for this anomalous impurity concentration [15].

The results obtained with arsenic-implanted samples are shown in Fig. 1. Here, the effective sheet carrier concentration as a function of the annealing time after the activation is given. At each temperature, the sheet carrier concentration decreases to a minimum, followed by a slight increase. The reduction is caused by the relaxation of the activated metastable arsenic atoms. The following increase is due to the diffusion broa-

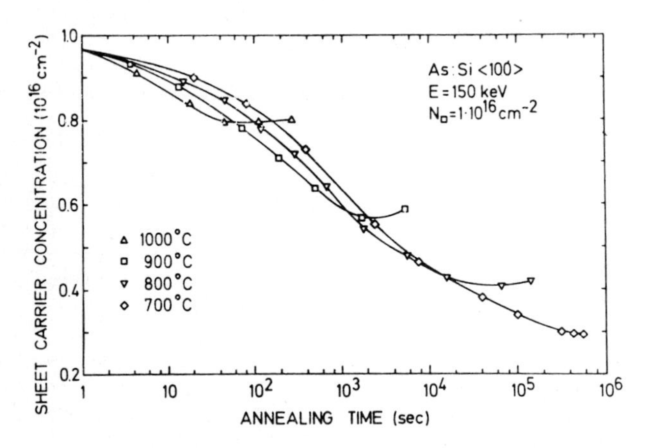

Fig. 1. Dependence of sheet carrier concentration of arsenic-implanted silicon on the annealing time for temperatures from 700-1000°C

dening of the implanted profile with increasing annealing time. It is obvious that the integral activation will increase if the profile is broadened by diffusion. By measuring the relaxation-time constant at each annealing temperature, it was possible to obtain the activation energy of the relaxation process. For arsenic-implanted silicon, we measured an activation energy of 3.4 eV.

In Fig. 2, carrier concentration profiles of arsenic are shown. The dotted profile is the arsenic profile after laser activation. The other curves given are the profiles for annealing times at different temperatures, for the lowest sheet carrier concentration shown in the previous figure. This means that the measured maximum concentration at each temperature corresponds to the maximum electrical activation which is thermally stable. The fact that only a slight diffusion broadening of the profiles can be seen demonstrates that the reduction of the carrier concentration is mainly due to the relaxation of metastable arsenic concentrations.

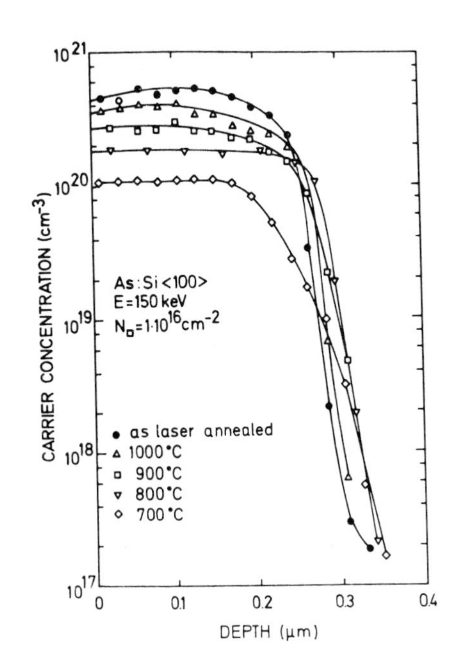

Fig. 2.
Carrier concentration profiles of arsenic-implanted silicon after annealing to maximum stable electrically active concentration at temperatures from 700 to 1000°C

Similar experiments with arsenic-implanted silicon were made by Lietoila et al.[5]. They measured an activation energy of 2.0 eV at temperatures of about 400°C. In this temperature range, they observed arsenic precipitations; at 900°C, however, no precipitation were found, indicating another relaxation mechanism at this temperature. Since we determined the activation energy at high temperatures (700-1000°C), we assume that the discrepancy between their and our measurements is due to different relaxation mechanisms. Our maximum electrically active concentrations are slightly higher than given by Lietoila et al., but they confirm that their values might be slightly too low.

Another annealing behavior can be seen for phosphorus-implanted silicon in Fig. 3. The sheet carrier concentration decreases with increasing annealing time at each temperature, but the curves for constant temperature do not intersect one another as those for the arsenic-implanted samples do. The decrease rate of the sheet carrier concentration increases with decreasing annealing temperature. The arsenic-implanted silicon showed contrary behavior (see Fig. 1).

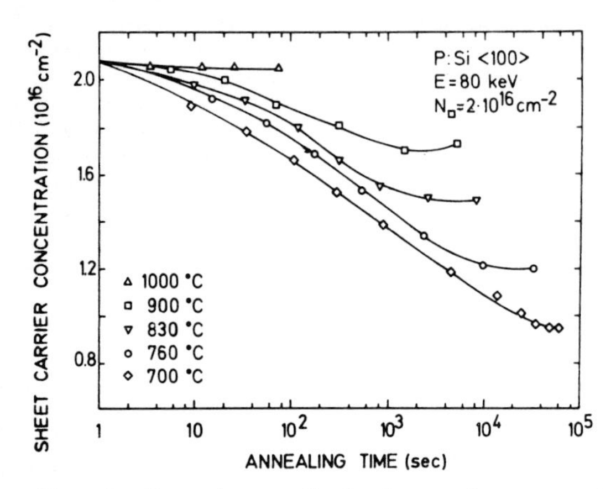

Fig. 3. Dependence of sheet carrier concentration of phosphorus-implanted silicon on the annealing time, for temperatures from 700-1000°C

Because of the shorter periods needed to reach minimum sheet carrier concentration, the activation energy for phosphorus is lower than for arsenic. We obtained an activation energy for phosphorus of 1.9 eV.

In Fig. 4, phosphorus carrier concentration profiles are given which were obtained after annealing the samples for periods corresponding to the minimum sheet carrier concentration. Again, only a slight diffusion of the dopant atoms took place. Therefore, the decrease of the carrier concentration is dominated by the relaxation process.

The last dopant species investigated was boron. The dependence of the sheet carrier concentration of the laser annealed samples on the postannealing-temperature-treatment time is shown in Fig. 5. Again, the lower the temperature, the longer the time to reach minimum sheet carrier concentration, and the lower the value of this concentration. The time behavior is similar, but not as pronounced, as for the arsenic-implanted samples.

The corresponding activation energy can be calculated to be about 3.3 eV. This calculation, however, is only a rough estimate, due to the results given in Fig. 6. Here, carrier concentration profiles are shown for the annealing times at which minimum sheet carrier concentration is reached. In contrast to the results with arsenic and phosphorus implantations, there is a diffusion broadening of the annealed profiles. This means that the reduction of the sheet carrier concentration in the relatively flat portion of the starting profile is caused both by relaxation of metastable boron atoms and by diffusion. Therefore, these concentrations do not correspond to the maximum stable electrically active concentrations of boron in silicon.

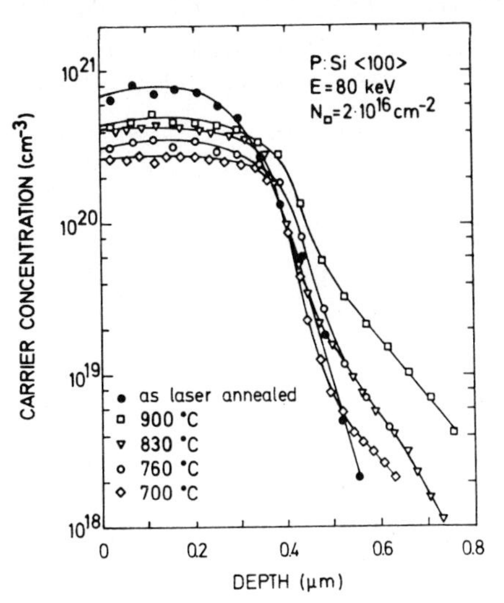

Fig. 4. Carrier concentration profiles of phosphorus-implanted silicon after annealing to maximum stable electrically active concentration at temperatures from 700 to 900°C

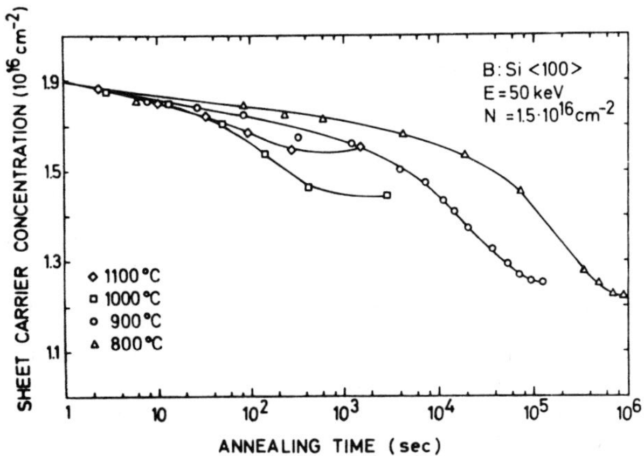

▲ Fig. 5. Dependence of sheet carrier concentration of boron-implanted silicon on the annealing time, for temperatures from 800-1100°C

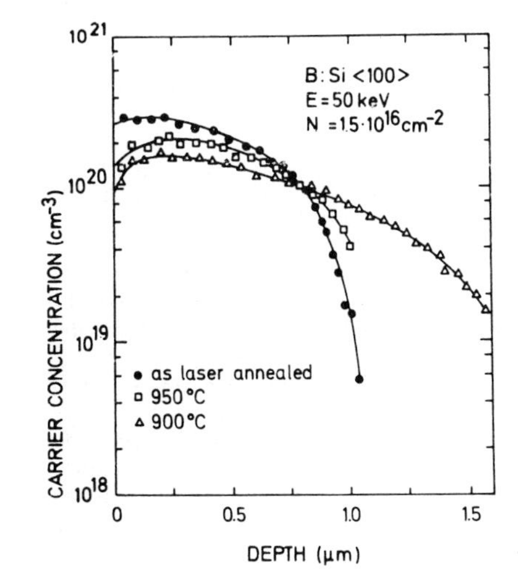

Fig. 6. Carrier concentration profiles of boron-implanted silicon after annealing to minimum sheet carrier concentration at different temperatures

Table 1. Activation energies for relaxation of metastable concentrations and maximum carrier concentration at thermal equilibrium, at different temperatures

Atom	E_a (eV)	C_{max} (cm^{-3})	T(°C)
As	3.4	>5×10^{20}	1100
		3.7×10^{20}	1000
		2.8×10^{20}	900
		1.9×10^{20}	800
		1.1×10^{20}	700
P	1.9	7×10^{20}	1000
		5×10^{20}	900
		4×10^{20}	830
		3.5×10^{20}	760
		2.7×10^{20}	700
B	≈ 3.3	diffusion broadening of profiles!	

4. Conclusions

High concentrations of electrically active arsenic, phosphorus, and boron atoms in silicon were produced by ion implantation and CO_2 laser annealing, and the relaxation behavior of these metastable solid solutions was investigated by post-activation temperature treatment. The results of our experiments are shown in Table 1. The activation energy of metastable arsenic concentrations is 3.4 eV, of phosphorus 1.9 eV, and the estimate for boron is 3.3 eV. The maximum electrically active concentrations at thermal equilibrium are between 3.7×10^{20} and 1.1×10^{20} cm^{-3} at 1000°C and 700°C, respectively, for arsenic; and between 7×10^{20} and 2.7×10^{20} cm^{-3} at 1000°C and 700°C, respectively, for phosphorus implantations. At 1100°C, the maximum active arsenic concentration is at least 5×10^{20} cm^{-3}.

References

1. C.W. White, S.R. Wilson, B.R. Appleton, and F.W. Young, Jr., J. Appl. Phys. 51, 738 (1980)
2. N. Natsuaki, M. Tamura, and T. Tokuyama, J. Appl. Phys. 51, 3373 (1980)
3. P.H. Tsien, S.C. Tsou, M. Takai, D. Röschenthaler, M. Ramin, H. Ryssel, I. Ruge, and K. Wittmach, phys. stat. sol. (a) 63, 547 (1981)
4. R. Stuck, E. Fogarassy, J.J. Grob, and P. Siffert, Appl. Phys. 23, 19 (1980)
5. A. Lietoila, J.F. Gibbons, and T.W. Sigmon, Appl. Phys. Lett. 36, 765 (1980)
6. P.H. Tsien, H. Ryssel, D. Röschenthaler, and I. Ruge, J. Appl. Phys. 52, 2987 (1981)

7. P.H. Tsien, J. Götzlich, H. Ryssel, and I. Ruge, J. Appl. Phys. 53, 663 (1982)
8. M. Miyao, K. Itoh, M. Tamura, H. Tamura, and T. Tokuyama, J. Appl. Phys. 51, 4139 (1980)
9. W.K.Chu, S.R. Mader, and E. Rimini, in Laser and Electron Beam Processing of Materials, C.W. White and P.S. Peercy, Editors, p. 253, Academic Press, New Work (1980)
10. M. Finetti, P. Negrini, S. Solmi, and D. Nobili, J. Electrochem. Soc. 128, 1313 (1981)
11. K. Itoh, Y. Sasaki, T. Mitsuishi, M. Miyao, and M. Tamura, Jap. Journ. of Appl. Phys. 21, L 245 (1982)
12. R.T. Young, C.W. White, G.L. Clark, J. Narayan, W.H. Cristie, M. Murakami, P.W. King, and S.D. Kramer, Appl. Phys. Lett. 32, 139 (1978)
13. D.K. Schroder, T.T. Braggins, and H.M. Hobgood, J. Appl. Phys. 49, 5256 (1978)
14. P.H. Tsien, H. Ryssel, D. Röschentaler, and I.Ruge, J. Appl. Phys. 52, 4775 (1981)
15. G.F. Neumark and D.K. Schroder, J. Appl. Phys. 52, 855 (1981)

Rapid Isothermal Annealing for Semiconductor Applications: Aspects of Equipment Design

C.J. Russo, D.F. Downey and S.C. Holden

Varian Associates/Extrion Division, Blackburn Industrial Park, Gloucester, MA 01930, USA

R.T. Fulks

Varian Associates/Central Research Laboratory, Palo Alto, CA 94043, USA

1. Introduction

Today, ion implantation is used where precise control of the dopant distribution in the device is important. In the future, rapid annealing will be used where dimensional control for very small geometry circuits is important. Rapid annealing techniques will probably have an impact on future device technology similar to that of ion implantation on present technology.

Minimal redistribution of implanted dopant will remove several restrictions on present device processing, allow more complicated device structures to be built, and reduce lateral and depth distribution effects. High temperature, short time activation will allow the separation of activation from the damage repair process. Some problems that minimized dopant redistribution and activation separated from damage repair can help solve are: uncontrolled gate spreading in short channel FET's; elimination of some parasitic-capacitances effects which limit device speed; fabrication of shallow hyperabrupt junctions with more control; reduction of diffusion induced effects like "emitter push"; and elimination of oxide caps now commonly required before furnace annealing high-dose, predeposition-type implants.

This paper will examine design models, data and process machine interactions used to provide improved process control with RIA.

2. Functional Design Considerations

Rapid Isothermal Annealing (RIA) is an annealing technology which activates the dopant by heating the wafer uniformly with a blackbody, graphite-radiation source held in vacuum. Details of the present RIA system are given in Russo [1].

The main features of RIA gained by using vacuum are excellent uniformity, energy efficiency, and controlled environment for the annealing process. Energy coupling from the heater to the closely spaced wafer is inherently uniform when radiation is the only method of heat transfer. The reflectors, the shutter and heat shields, and lack of conductive and convective heat transfer aid in reducing average heater power consumption to less than 3 KW for annealing a 100mm or 125mm diameter wafer under most conditions. The controlled environment provided by vacuum not only protects the heater and heat shields from oxidation, but also provides a contamination-free environment uncomplicated by ambient effects.

3. Theoretical Modeling

This section discusses modeling of the optical properties, heat transfer, diffusion, and sheet resistivity properties of rapidly annealed, implanted silicon. The optical absorption model considers the role of free carrier extrinsic absorption and intrinsic absorption at elevated temperatures. The heat transfer model simulates the radiation transfer to and from the wafer including the effects of: wafer and shield heat capacity, changes in emissivity, absorption, and reflectivity of the wafer and shields. The diffusion model considers diffusion of Gaussian implants, dopant loss and the effects of dopant solubility limits.

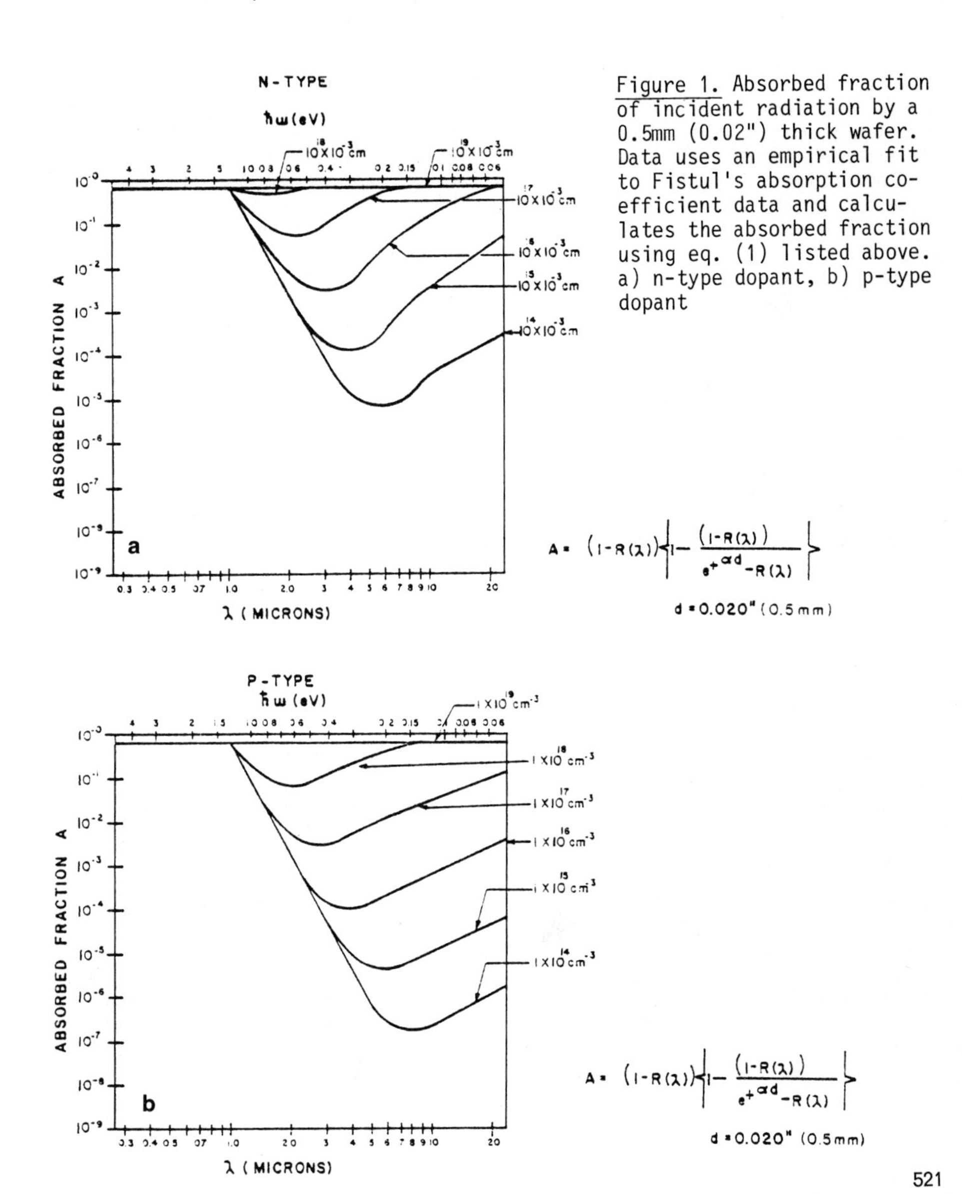

Figure 1. Absorbed fraction of incident radiation by a 0.5mm (0.02") thick wafer. Data uses an empirical fit to Fistul's absorption coefficient data and calculates the absorbed fraction using eq. (1) listed above. a) n-type dopant, b) p-type dopant

3.1 Optical Absorption

The silicon wafer is heated by optical absorption of the radiation emanating from the graphite plate heater. Since all semiconductor wafers are doped (both in the bulk and in the implanted layers), free-carrier, ionized-dopant states are available for absorption besides the band-gap transition states. Additional intrinsic free carriers become available as the wafer heats; and at temperatures on the order of 600 K, these intrinsic carriers become major contributors to the absorption [2][3]. Figure 1 shows optical absorption in a silicon wafer as a function of wavelength, λ, generated from an empirically derived fit of the absorption coefficient data[1].

Consideration is taken neither of the reflectivity changes due to interband-transition selection rules nor of impurity absorption bands such as the Si-O and the Si-P bonds in the 7-10 μ range. The absorbed fraction is calculated using techniques developed for thin film optics. The absorbed fraction, A, is given by (1) shown in Fig.1, where $R(\lambda)$ is the reflection coefficient, α the absorption coefficient and d is the thickness of the wafer. All data is from Fistul' [4]. Fistul' gives the following empirically derived dependencies of absorption coefficient for heavily doped semiconductors in the infrared, where N is the carrier concentration.

$$\alpha \approx N^{1.7} \tag{2}$$

$$\alpha \approx \lambda^{3.5} \quad \text{n-type dopant} \tag{3}$$

$$\alpha \approx \lambda^{2} \quad \text{p-type dopant .} \tag{4}$$

Kittel [16] gives the intrinsic carrier concentration for silicon as

$$N^2 = np = 4(2\pi KT/h^2)^{3/2} \exp(-E_g/kT) \tag{5}$$

Substituting (5) into (2) and comparison with Fig.1 reveals that the silicon wafer becomes opaque to the infrared during the anneal.

3.2 Thermal Radiation Model of RIA

Heating uniformity and temperature history are two important considerations in the radiant heating of silicon wafers using the RIA process. Uniformity of heating determines the degree of stress gradients at high temperatures which cause: wafer distortion and slips; and variations in activation, annealing and outdiffusion. Temperature history which influences the repeatability of the process can be predicted and controlled.

Radial uniformity is governed by: the temperature uniformity of the radiant heat source; uniformity of the radiant energy incident at all points of the wafer; and uniformity of the optical properties of the wafer and system components in the wavelengths around 2.0 microns; and the wafer's position relative to the heater. The geometry must make the heater appear as an infinite planar radiant source to the wafer. With a limited heater size, larger wafers will experience less radiant energy at the perimeter due to reduced view factor to the source. The worst case radiant view factor variation vs. radial position on a 100mm wafer is less than 3%. Refractory reflector rings surrounding the wafer during annealing, improve the apparent view factor and enhance the radiation at the perimeter. The result of this geometry and shielding is extremely uniform heating of the wafers.

A computer simulation of the RIA process considers: radiant heating of the wafer [6][7]; heat capacity of the wafer and of the shield used for support [8]; temperature-dependent emissivity for the refractory shields behind the wafer [9]; and variable emissivity for the heater and for the wafer [6][9]. The indicated temperature results from the infrared sensor system were corrected for an actual emissivity of 0.50, and the computer-simulated model assumed a silicon average emissivity also of 0.50, compensating for transmission in the infrared region at low temperatures, as described in Section 3.1, and for decreasing emissivity at higher temperatures. Final wafer temperature for these conditions is shown in Fig.2.

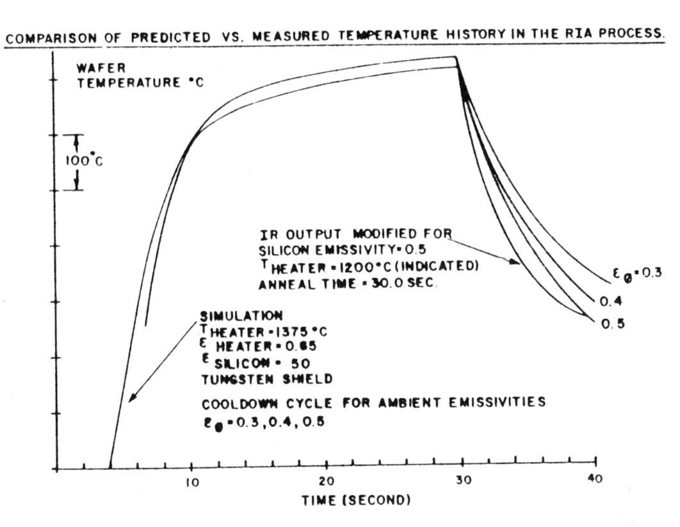

figure 2. Temperature histories of a RIA wafer from computer simulation considering: wafer and shield heat capacities; temperature-dependent emissivity of shield materials, and cooldown cycle for various assumed ambient emissivities. Also shown are emissivity corrected infrared measurements from the actual RIA process under similar conditions. Vertical temperature scale hash marks indicate 100°C per interval

3.3 Diffusion in Rapidly Annealed, Implanted Silicon

While annealing times for RIA are very short when compared with furnace annealing times, there is a limited amount of diffusion in rapidly annealed, implanted semiconductors. This diffusion and its effects can be seen by using a one-dimensional model of a Gaussian implant with subsequent diffusion. This model is capable of demonstrating the effects of the initial dopant distribution, subsequent diffusion, and loss of dopant through the surface of the material. The model is shown in equations 6-9. While the junction depths are given for this model, the

$$\omega = \sqrt{2Dt + \sigma_p^2} \qquad (6)$$

$$C(X,t) = \frac{N_s}{\sqrt{2\pi}\,\omega} \cdot \exp\left[-\frac{(X - R_p)^2}{2\omega^2} \right] \quad (7)$$

$$X_j = R_p \pm \omega \sqrt{2 \cdot \ln\left[\frac{N_s}{\sqrt{2\pi}\,\omega\, C_b}\right]} \quad (8)$$

$$F = \frac{1}{2}\left[1 - \text{erf}\left(\frac{R_p}{\sqrt{2}\,\omega}\right)\right] \quad (9)$$

ω = modified diffusion coefficient to account for Gaussian Implant (cm)
D = diffusion coefficient of dopant in silicon (cm^2-sec^{-1})
t = time that the wafer is at temperature (sec)
σ_p = projected standard deviation of implant (cm)
$C(x, t)$ = concentration of dopant in silicon (cm^{-3})
N_s = surface dose (ions-cm^{-2})
X = depth into wafer (cm)
R_p = projected range of implant (cm)
C_b = base level dopant of opposite dopant type in wafer (cm^{-3})
X_j = junction depth (cm)
F = fraction of dopant lost from surface during implant and anneal assuming diffusion limited dopant loss during anneal
C_p = peak concentration of implanted dopant (cm^{-3})
C_d = peak concentration of diffused and implanted dopant (cm^{-3}).

existance of non-Gaussian implant tails make the x_j values obtained from this model unreliable. This model does predict the point at which the concentration drops to $e^{-1/2}$ of the peak value. The model can only indicate the effects of very high dose arsenic or boron concentrations where dose-dependent diffusion occurs. The model needs extension to include D=D(C) to quantify the effect.

The peak atomic concentration can be found from dose and energy by using equation 7 to generate (10)

$$C_p\ (\text{atoms-cm}^{-3}) \approx 4000\ N_s\ (\text{atoms/cm}^2)/\ \sigma_p\ (\text{microns}). \quad (10)$$

Equation 10 and the projected range data from Gibbons et al. [10] give peak concentration information as a function of dose and energy.

Since carrier density is limited to the $2\text{-}4 \times 10^{20}\ cm^{-3}$ range for usable anneal temperatures [11], a series of charts can be constructed using equation (10) which will show regions of dopant controlled and carrier limit controlled resistivity as well as solubility limit effects. Such a chart for arsenic is shown in Fig.3.

3.4 Sheet Resistivity

Sheet resistivity has been modelled for Gaussian implants by Smith and Stephens [12]. They use Irvin's [13] mobility data and numerically integrate the equation for sheet resistivity. While there are some problems with Irvin's data at moderate to very high dose [14][15], the derived sheet resistivity from the calculations generally fits implants which are close to Gaussian with well characterized values of ω. The value of ω chosen for the theoretical values of sheet resistivity was σ_p. The calculations often fit driven implants at low to moderate dose. At high doses, driven implants remove the dopant from the peak

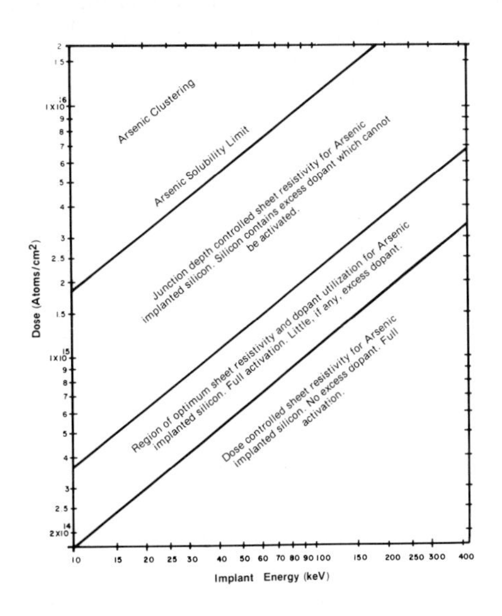

figure 3. Dose vs. Energy plot delineating maximum dose for highest carrier concentration. Plot assumes; LSS statistics; peak carrier concentration of 2 to 4 x $10^{20}cm^{-3}$, no redistribution and no outdiffusion

region where diffusion coefficient is high and mobility low to regions of lower concentration and higher mobility. As a result, a more rectangular non-Gaussian distribution results with lower sheet resistivity than predicted from the Gaussian model. In the case of rapid annealing, where the distributions rarely deviate far from Gaussian, the effects of very high peak concentrations are well approximated and the resulting data fits the model very well.

4. RIA Process Data

4.1 Activation and Uniformity

Sheet resistance data were obtained for 60 keV $^{11}B^+$, $^{31}P^+$ and $^{75}As^+$ implants with doses from 5 x 10^{12} to 2 x 10^{16} ions/cm^2 using both standard furnace anneals and 10 second rapid isothermal anneals [16]. The wafers were of the <100> orientation, having a bulk resistivity of 1-5 ohm-cm and no oxide caps. The sheet resistance was determined by a radial ASM four point probe.

Figure 4 is a plot of the sheet resistance vs. dose for both furnace anneals and rapid isothermal anneals. Plotted with these results are the theoretical values for Gaussian distributions of dopant obtained by Smith and Stephens [12]. Uniformity studies comparing the RIA and furnace annealing indicate that split-batch, sheet-implant, RIA anneals are more uniform by 10-50% [16].

4.2 Device Data, and Residual Damage

Previous studies [17][18] of infrared Rapid Isothermal Annealing have addressed device performance and residual damage. Bipolar transistors, MOSFETS and diodes have been fabricated and annealed by RIA, yielding comparable results to furnace-annealed control wafers. Diode structures annealed by RIA had excellent reverse I-V characteristics, indicating minimal defects in the junction depletion region. TEM analysis of residual damage for a standard RIA (1250°C heater thermocouple temperature, 10 second exposure) anneal on a 6 x 10^{15} ions/cm^2, 140 keV $^{75}As^+$ implant exhibited a high density of ~ 500 A diameter

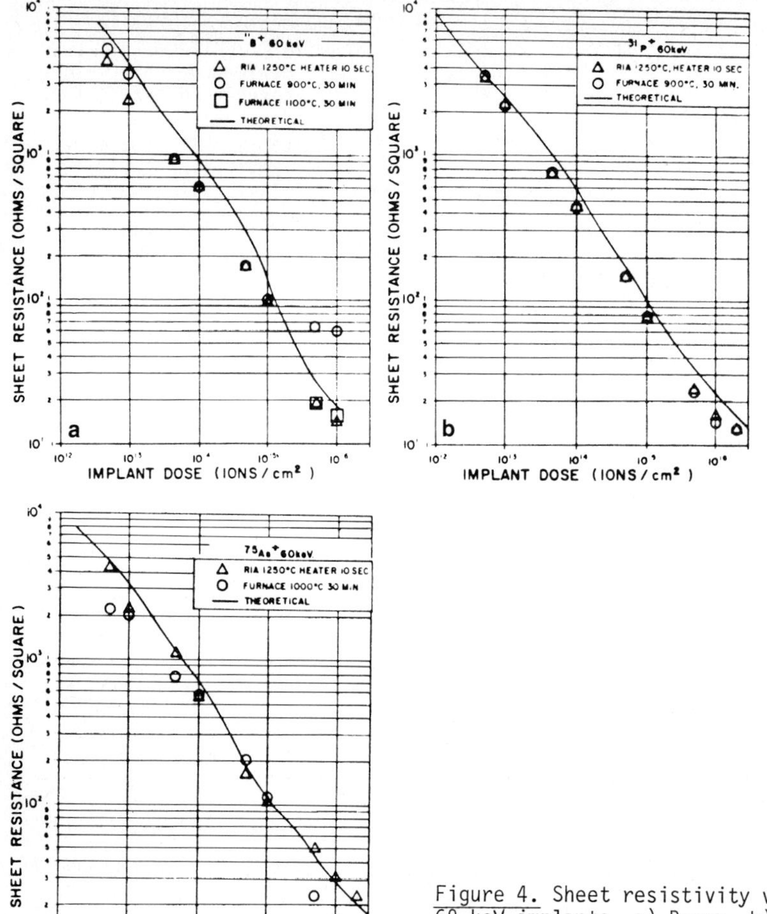

Figure 4. Sheet resistivity vs. dose for 60 keV implants. a) Boron, b) Phosphorous, c) Arsenic

dislocation loops extending 1000 A deep (determined by stereo pairs imaging). The comparable furnace anneal (1000°C, 30 minutes) produce dislocation loops, which have grown laterally to micron size and extend in depth approximately 3000 A.

4.3 BTS Data and Effects of the Ambient

Bias Temperature Stress (BTS) measurements performed on wafers annealed on the RIA system are comparable to those obtained on standard well-maintained furnace systems. There appears to be a significant effect of ambient gasses on flat band voltage shift ΔV_{FB} noted in the BTS measurements. Unprotected gate oxides can show significant ΔV_{FB} when exposed to high purity argon during the anneals. When a similar experiment is performed on pieces of the same wafer with no ambient, no ionic contaminants are found.

The experiments were performed in the test apparatus described in [17]. MOS capacitor structures were used in the experiments.To eliminate possible process variables after fabrication the 3" diameter wafers were quartered and one quarter of each wafer was used as a furnace control. The remaining quarters of each capacitor type were then exposed in the rapid isothermal annealer under the following conditions: Vacuum anneal, (1000°C, 12 sec); argon anneal, (900°C, 20 sec); and argon anneal, (1000°C, 12 sec). The temperatures noted above are actual wafer temperatures measured by an uncorrected optical pyrometer.

For the argon anneals, high-purity argon from a liquid source was introduced into the chamber by first pumping and then backfilling.

After exposure and metal electrode definition, all capacitor received a 450°C H_2 anneal to reduce interface states. C-V plots were then made using a PAR-410 (1MHz) C-V plotter. BTS (bias temperature stress) measurements using 2×10^6 V/cm positive stress at 200°C for 30 min. were made to determine the degree of ionic contamination.

For the case of bare gate oxides exposed to an argon environment, there is a significiant shift in the flatband voltage; for the 900°C anneal, ΔV_{FB} = 0.65 volts and for the 1000°C anneal, ΔV_{FB} = 1.2-1.8 volts. (Note: there is a 0.6-volt data spread for this anneal). At least five capacitors of each type were measured to obtain this data. For the worst case (1000°C, argon), the change in oxide charge is calculated to be $\Delta Q_s = 4.72 \times 10^{11}$ cm $^{-2}$. This is a quite high level of induced interface charge. Note from the data that the vacuum anneal is very close to the control sample (<0.1 V shift).

For the case of polysilicon-gate capacitors, the situation is greatly improved, and the variation of flatband voltage is about 0.15 volts for all samples. Since BTS measurements on all sample indicated minimal ionic contamination (<0.15 V shift), the excess charge is probably being induced by film stress due to convection cooling. Film stress induced bond disruption is somewhat reduced in a polysilicon overlayered "silicon sandwich" which may retard stresses and charge generation. Although bare-gate oxides would not typically be exposed during implant anneal (most MOSFETs use self-aligned polysilicon gates), the result indicates the advantages of vacuum annealing.

4.4 Minimal Redistribution

One of the major advantages to RIA vs. furnace techniques is minimal redistribution of the dopant. For small and intermediate dose levels RIA offers a significant advantage for the formation of shallow junctions devices; but the most dramatic example is for high-dose applications; e.g., short channel MOSFETs, where the depth of the source and drain implants and the lateral spread is critical. Figure 5 is a comparison plot of 2×10^{16}, 60 keV, $^{11}B^+$, implants annealed by RIA and the furnace.

4.5 Surface Topology

Surface topology changes have been checked by using a Tencor flat gauge instrument [19] and by a technique which measures mask superposition errors using van der Pauw resistor structures [20]. The wafer included unimplanted and implanted control wafers as well as RIA wafers annealed under several conditions. The max-to-min deviations on the annealed wafers were the same or less than the control wafers, and the wafer

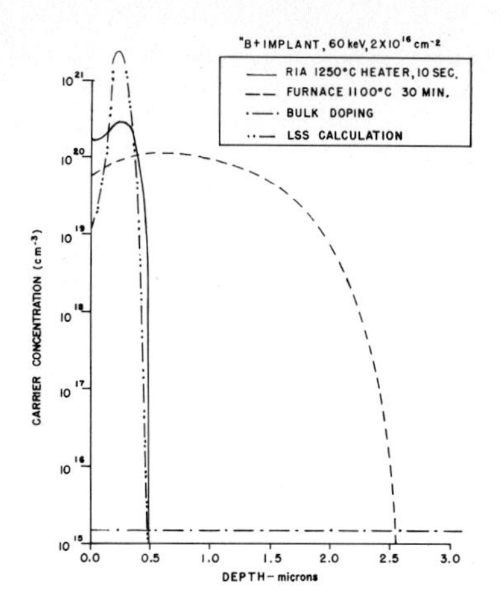

figure 5. Spreading resistance data for $2 \times 10^{16} cm^{-2}$ boron implant at 60 keV

profile differences appear to be due to wafer-to-wafer variations of the lot. Radial nonuniformities checked by Perloff's method [20] for <100> wafers were less than the mask alignment errors [21].

5. Comparison between data and models

The models of importance for interpreting the process data are: sheet resistivity; redistribution of a Gaussian implant; and the radiation simulation which gives temperature versus time. This section will discuss the comparison between model and data.

5.1 Sheet resistivity

The data in Figs.4 show an interesting trend with respect to the models for sheet resistivity and outdiffusion. At low to moderate doses, diffusion coefficients are not severely enhanced by concentration effects. The minimal diffusion which results, even for the case of furnace anneals, allows general agreement between the data and the theoretical curve. The experimental data shows slightly better activation than predicted by the theory. At moderate to high doses there is general agreement between the theory and the RIA sample. Neither significant out diffusion of the dopant nor apparant major changes from the preanneal Gaussian character are observed for RIA samples. Carrier density limits are most readily seen for: high-dose, rapidly annealed arsenic; for low-temperature, furnace annealed boron; and for very high dose boron.
The high-dose arsenic which was furnace annealed has significantly redistributed [17]. With more dopant at concentrations below the electron carrier limit, the activation fraction is higher and the sheet resistivity is lower than predicted. It has been shown in earlier work [1][16][18][22] that this lower sheet resistivity can only be gained at the expense of deeper junction depths. The deeper junction depths are often obtained during isochronal anneals due to concentration dependant diffusion effects [23].

The furnace annealed boron data shows the effect of improved carrier density limits with higher temperature anneals. Note that the 900°C anneals show much poorer activation than the 1100°C anneals or the RIA samples. The 1100°C furnace anneals usually do not produce sheet resistivities lower than the RIA wafers, possibly because of significant outdiffusion. The very high dose boron (fig.5) shows the effect of redistribution during a high-temperature furnace anneal which yields deep-junction, low-resistivity material vs. the shallow-junction, electron-carrier density limited material generated using RIA with $\simeq$2 x higher sheet resistivity.

5.2 Thermal modeling

The thermal modeling has successfully demonstrated the time-temperature relation within a constant. The uncertainties in the constant are due to uncertainties in the optical data for silicon and refractories at elevated temperatures. The modeling which predicts highly uniform heating of the wafers yields sheet resistivity and uniformities on wafers which are superior to those obtained in furnaces.

6. Machine - Process Interaction

There are several ways in which a rapid annealing system interacts with the process operated in it. These interactions include: the effects of uniform wafer heating on process uniformity; wafer warpage and slippage; wafer contamination by contact with the heating element; contamination transport by ambient gases and contamination by the materials which make up the system.

6.1 Wafer Warping and Slip

The authors have seen a qualitative correlation between the uniformity of wafer heating and the minimization of slips. Excellent uniformity will be an important consideration for successful PSG [24] reflow since elevated temperatures are required for a relatively long time. Data to date on wafer warpage indicates that <100> wafers show neither planer warping to the limits of lithographic error nor warping in the z direction to the limits of the basic flatness of the starting wafers.

6.2 Contamination

The main sources of contamination in any rapid annealing system come from the heating element, the ambient gases, the wall materials and from the wafers themselves. Mobile ion impurities are usually the most important contaminants to consider since they effect the flat-band voltage shift in MOS devices. As can be seen from Section 4.3, BTS shows that mobile ion contaminations in RIA are well controlled. In the same section, it is apparent that ambient gas has some effects on the annealing process itself and the use of vacuum for annealing may be advantageous for minimizing surface states in certain situations. The use of an ambient also has the effect of transporting contaminations from one part of the system to another. This contamination transport is a particularly insidious problem for a cold wall system which warms up with use. The nominally cool areas of the system become sinks for high vapor pressure material like water, phosphorous, arsenic or other dopants. When the ambient participates in the heat transfer, these materials can cause cross-contamination problems. Removal of the ambient gas eliminates this group of problems as the system slowly heats. The wall materials can contribute contamination by outgassing water or dopant as noted above or by outgassing high vapor pressure components such as magnesium from aluminum alloys. These contamination problems are typically controlled by careful design. The wafers are also a source of cross contaminations. As seen in equation 9, the fraction of outdiffused material may be relatively large. While nearly all of this contaminant can be pumped away in an RIA system, machines with a relatively stagnant ambient will have cross-contamination problems.

As can be seen, there are several sources of contamination in any rapid annealing system which has cold walls. If the system does not have well-designed cold walls, then nearly all of the precautions necessary for a hot-wall furnace will probably be required.

7. Summary

Several of the features of a rapid annealing system consisting of a graphite plate heater vertically mounted in vacuum have been modeled. Radiant heat transfer and optical absorption models have led to an annealer with excellent radiation coupling and uniformity. Radiation uniformity provides very uniform sheet resistivity with excellent activation for every wafer and no slips even at the temperatures required for standard PSG reflow. The diffusion and sheet resistivity models are useful for determining the proper conditions of implant and anneal, and provide tools for understanding sheet resistivity values obtained and the degree of dopant loss and redistribution during any anneal cycle. Several contamination issues were examined.

Rapid annealing has the capability of minimizing redistribution and of separating the low-temperature damage repair from the high-temperature activation of the dopant. The control given by minimal redistribution and fast activation in rapid annealing has the potential to impact future device processing in the same way that ion implantation impacts present device processing.

Acknowledgements

The authors would like to thank: R. Powell for useful discussions, J. Keyes, J. Rixon and M. Erickson for obtaining the process data, D. Barton and G. Ferraro for the machine-related data, I. Honjo for the computer calculation of figure 1., E. Seamonds, J. Favaloro and E. Smith typed and edited the paper, P. Mansfield and Julia Bonazoli provided graphic arts assistance.

References

1. C.J. Russo: Varian Semiconductor Equipment Operations Report No. 16, also Ionics (to be published)
2. S.M. Sze: Physics of Semiconductor Devices, 2nd ed. p.19 (Wiley, New York, 1981)
3. A. Bhattacharyya, B.G. Streetman: Solid State Communications 36, 71 (1980)
4. V. Fistul' Heavily Doped Semiconductors, Chapter 4.1 (Plenum Press, New York, 1969)
5. C. Kittel: "Introduction To Solid State Physics", 3rd ed., p. 305 (Wiley, New York, 1966)
6. W.R. Runyan: Silicon Semiconductor Technology, (McGraw-Hill, New York, 1965 pp. 187-212.
7. W.M. Rohsenow and H.Y. Choi: Heat, Mass, and Momentum Transfer,(Prentice-Hall, New Jersey 1961) pp. 332-371.
8. The Rembar Co., Inc., "Refractory Metals", March, 1981
9. D.E. Gray (ed.), American Institute of Physics Handbook, McGraw-Hill, New York, 1957, pp. 6-68 to 6-79.

10. J.F. Gibbons, W.S. Johnson, S.W. Mylroie: "Projected Range Statistics and Related Materials" 2nd ed. (Dowden, Hutchinson and Ross, Stroudsburg, Pa. (1975)
11. R.B. Fair, G.R. Weber: J. Appl. Phys. 44, 273 (1973)
12. B.J. Smith, J. Stephens: Radiation Effects 14 181, (1981)
13. J.C. Irvin: Bell Syst. Tech. J 41, 387 (1962)
14. W.R. Thurbur, R.L. Mattis, Y.M. Liu: J. Electrochem. Soc. 127, 2291 (1980)
15. W.R. Thurber, R.L. Mattis, Y.M. Liu: J. Electrochem. Soc. 127, 1807 (1980)
16. D.F. Downey, C.J.Russo, J. White: Solid State Technology, September, 1982 to be published.
17. R.T. Fulks, C.J. Russo, P.R. Hanley, T.I. Kamins: App. Phys. Lett. 39 604, (1981)
18. R.T. Fulks, C.J. Russo, D.F. Downey, P.R. Hanley, W.T. Stacey: Laser and Electron Beam Interactions with Solids-1981, ed. by B.R. Appleton, G.K.Celler (North Holland, New York, 1982) - to be published.
19. R.Fulks: Unpublished memo, Varian Central Research July, 1981
20. D.S. Perloff: IEEE J. Solid State Circuits SC-13, 436 (1978)
21. M. Current, H. Huff: Personal Communication, January, 1982, August, 1982
22. V. Wada, N. Hashimato: J. Electrochem. Soc. 127, 401 (1979)
23. R.B. Fair: "Concentration Profiles of Diffused Dopants in Silicon" in Impurity Doping, ed. by F.F.Y. Wang (North-Holland, New York, 1981)
24. D.F. Downey, U.S. Patent applied for.

Investigation of Polysilicon Implantation Under Thermal and Laser Annealing

W. Nachbauer, G. Schumicki

Valvo Röhren-und Halbleiterwerke der Philips GmbH, Stresemannallee 101, D-2000 Hamburg 54, Fed. Rep. of Germany

H. Schaumburg

TU Hamburg-Harburg, D-2000 Hamburg-Harburg, Fed. Rep. of Germany

Abstract

There is a great interest in the application of polysilicon in integrated circuit technology. But there is still a lack of data to characterize this layer.

This report deals with the sheet resistance for implantations of LPCVD poly with boron, phosphorus and rasenic under various heat treatments (laser and furnace anneal).

The depth distribution of phosphorus in a poly layer, either on silicon or oxide sublayer, has been studied with SIMS analysis. A comparison of implantation doping to phosphorus deposition is given.

1. Preparation

Monocrystalline silicon wafers were covered by an amorphous layer, either silicon nitride (100 nm) or a grown oxide (1100 nm). On top of this, a poly silicon layer of about 500 nm thickness was deposited by LPCVD at 600 °C.

This layer was implanted by boron, phosphorus and arsenic at different energies. The activation was accomplished at temperatures between 900 °C and 1150 °C in a nitrogen ambient for 30 minutes. Similar samples were annealed by a scanning argon laser. For comparison, some wafers were doped by a $POCl_3$ source. Van-der-Pauw systems were defined by photolithography, and the polysilicon etched by plasma etching.

2. Experimental Results

2.1 Thermal Anneal

Figure 1 shows the sheet-resistance dependence of polysilicon on implantation dose after a 30 minute heat treatment in nitrogen at 900°C. The samples were doped either by boron, phosphorus or arsenic. Arrows indicate the resistance of samples which were doped by a $POCl_3$ source. For comparison, the values for arsenic-doped monocrystalline silicon are shown.

There is nearly no dependence on implantation energy for high doses ($1\cdot10^{16}$ and $5\cdot10^{16}cm^{-2}$), and only minor dependence in the 10^{15} rage, as listed in Table 1.

The annealing behaviour over a wide temperature range is given in Fig. 2. For this reason, the same wafer was first annealed at 900°C, followed by 1000, 1100 and 1150°C for the same time. The sheet resistance decreases at lower temperatures and increases again after a high-temperature treatment. This increase is not seen in case of a $5\cdot10^{16}$ dose.

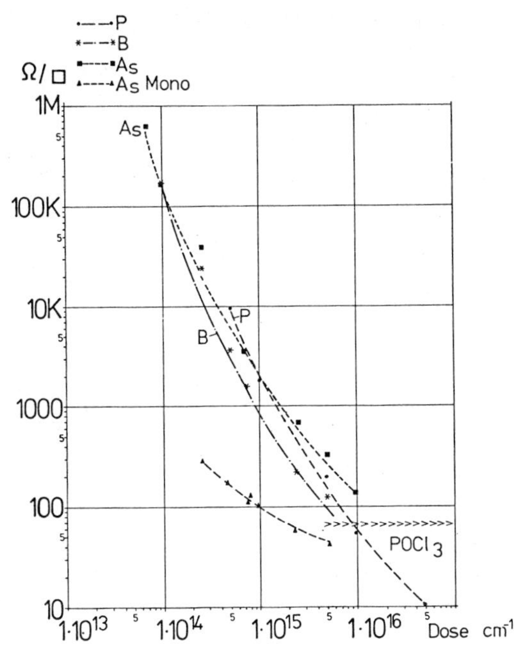

Fig.1: Sheet resistance of polysilicon for different implantations with B^+, P^+, As^+ after 30 minutes 900°C anneal

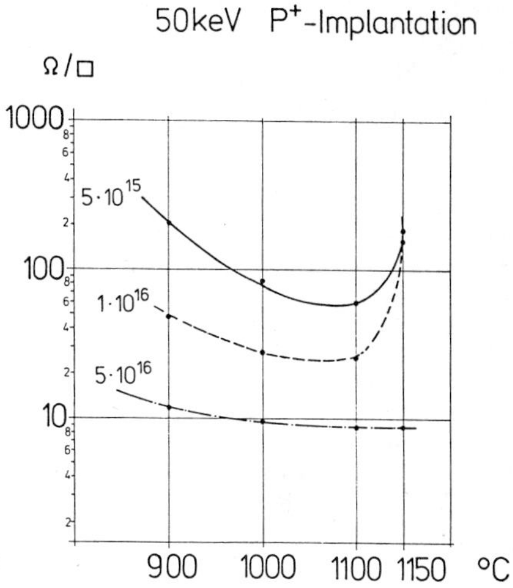

50keV P^+-Implantation

Fig. 2: Sheet resistance for different annealing temperatures and implantation doses ($5 \cdot 10^{15} - 5 \cdot 10^{16} cm^{-2}$)

Table 1: Sheet resistance dependence on dose and energy

		Dose cm^{-2}		
		$5 \cdot 10^{15}$	$1 \cdot 10^{16}$	$5 \cdot 10^{16}$
Energy	50	203 $\pm$ 2.7	47.5 $\pm$ 0.2	11.7 $\pm$ 0.1
keV	100	174.7 $\pm$ 2.4	44.9 $\pm$ 0.4	11.9 $\pm$ 0.1
	150	186.7 $\pm$ 3.2	48.9 $\pm$ 0.6	11.8 $\pm$ 0.1

2.2 Dopant Distribution

The distribution of the phosphorus doping in the polysilicon layer is shown by the SIMS profiles, Fig.3 - 5: a) indicates the concentration curve of thermally-annealed poly, which was deposited on silicon, and Fig. b) indicates poly on an oxide layer.
Conversion to concentration is done by multiplying the count/s with $2.0 \cdot 10^{16} cm^{-3}$. The depth calibration can be done by watching the Si signal of a known poly-layer deposited on oxide. Either implantation or furnace doping, Figs. 3 and 5, show constant concentration through the whole thickness. Only in those

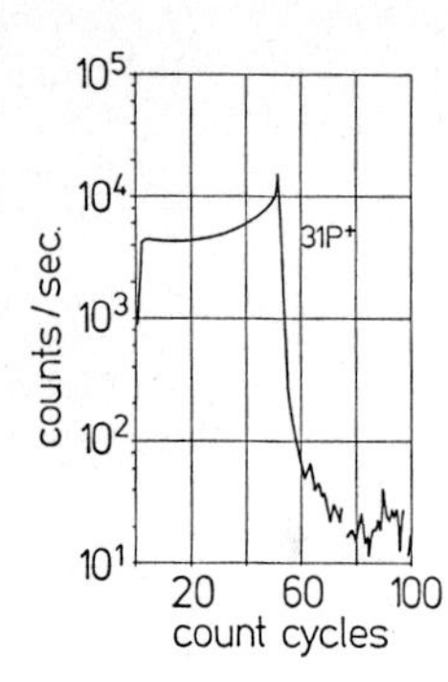

Fig. 3a: Implantation in Poly on Si
P^+ $5 \cdot 10^{15} cm^{-2}$ 150 keV
$N_{max\ impl.} = 3.2 \cdot 10^{20} cm^{-3}$
$\bar{N}_{ann.} = 9.2 \cdot 10^{19} cm^{-3}$

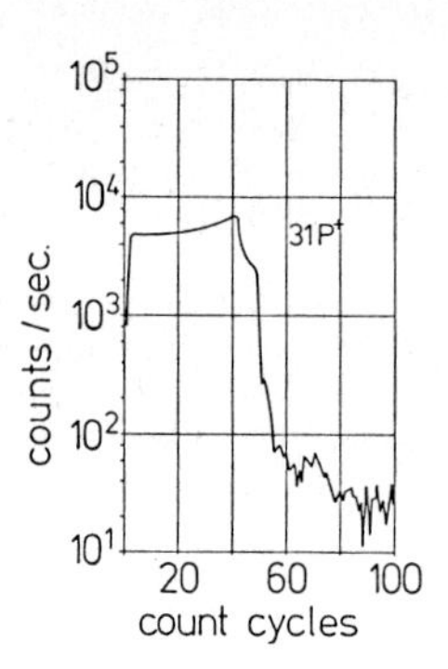

Fig. 3b: Implantation in Poly on SiO_2
P^+ $5 \cdot 10^{15} cm^{-2}$ 150 keV
$\bar{N}_{ann}$ $1.1 \cdot 10^{20} cm^{-3}$

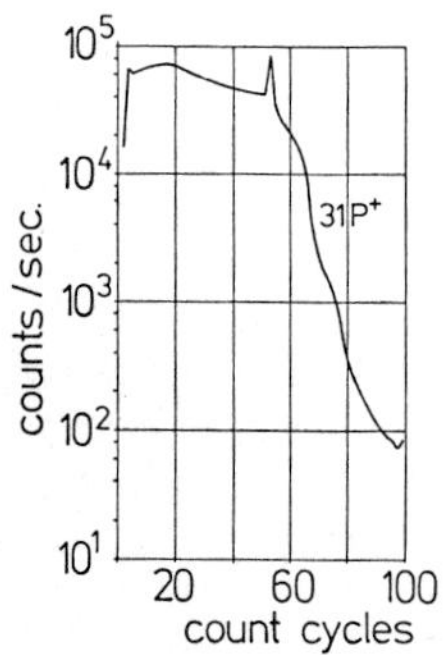

Fig. 4a: Implantation in Poly on Si
P^+ $5 \cdot 10^{16} cm^{-2}$ 150 keV
$N_{max\ impl.} = 3.2 \cdot 10^{21} cm^{-3}$
$\bar{N}_{ann.} = 9.5 \cdot 10^{20} cm^{-3}$

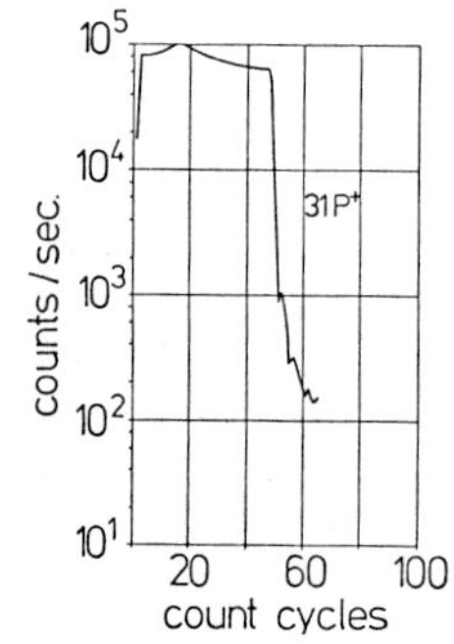

Fig. 4b: Implantation in Poly on SiO_2
P^+ $5 \cdot 10^{16} cm^{-3}$ 150 keV
$\bar{N}_{ann.}$ $1.6 \cdot 10^{21} cm^{-3}$

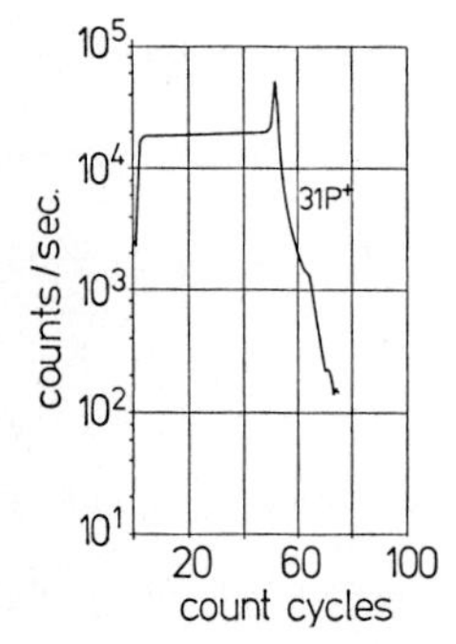

Fig. 5a: Doping with $POCl_3$
$\varrho_{sh} = 15.1^{\pm 1.2}$ Ohm / Sq
(Poly on Si)
$\bar{N}_{ann.}$ $4.0 \cdot 10^{20} cm^{-3}$

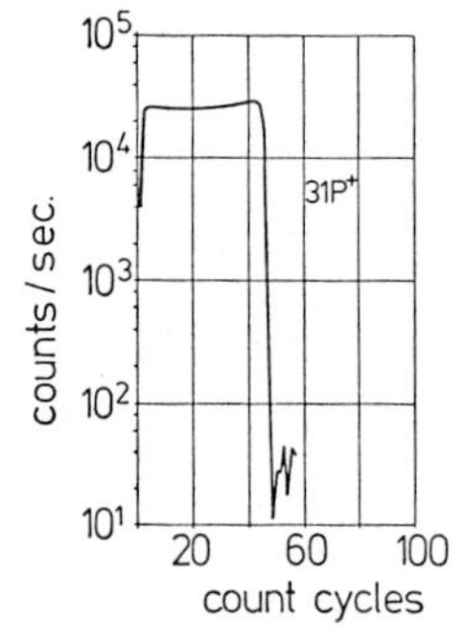

Fig. 5b: Doping with $POCl_3$
$\varrho_{h} = 17.2^{\pm 0.7}$ Ohm / Sq
(Poly on SiO_2)
$\bar{N}_{ann.}$ $5.8 \cdot 10^{20} cm^{-3}$

samples that were implanted with very high doses is the peak of the Gaussian distribution seen. In this wafer, the dopant extends deep into the silicon, which is not to be seen in all other doping curves. There is no extension of the doping curve across the interface of layers on top of silicon oxide, not even at high doses. The pronounced peak near the interface of polysilicon to monocrystalline silicon may be caused by precipitates of phosphorus on lattice misfits. Other reasons may be the structure of the poly near the interface or changes in sputtering rate.

In Table 2, the concentration and sheet resistance of different layers and dopants are compared.

Table 2: P concentrations in polysilicon for different doses

	doses	cm^{-2}	$5\cdot10^{15}$	$1\cdot10^{16}$	$5\cdot10^{16}$	$POCl_3$ (20 min)
Poly on Si	concentr.	cm^{-3}	$9.2\cdot10^{19}$	$1.8\cdot10^{20}$	$9.5\cdot10^{20}$	$4\cdot10^{20}$
	ϱ sh	$\Omega/\square$	195	50	8.2	15
Poly on SiO_2	concentr.	cm^{-3}	$1.1\cdot10^{20}$	$2.4\cdot10^{20}$	$1.6\cdot10^{21}$	$5.8\cdot10^{20}$
	ϱ sh	$\Omega/\square$	205	53	13	19

2.3 Laser-annealed Polysilicon

Figure 6 can be compared to Fig. 1. The boron-implanted wafer was scanned by a continuous-wave Ar laser with 10 W power on target.

Three different scan velocities were measured. The rear-side temperature of the wafers was kept constant at 300 °C. The sheet resistance is 2 to 4 times less than for the thermal anneal. The influence of laser power and scan velocity can be seen in Fig. 7. The higher the laser power, the lower the sheet resistance. The resistance increases with increasing scan speed. For higher laser powers, those samples with slow scanning could not be measured

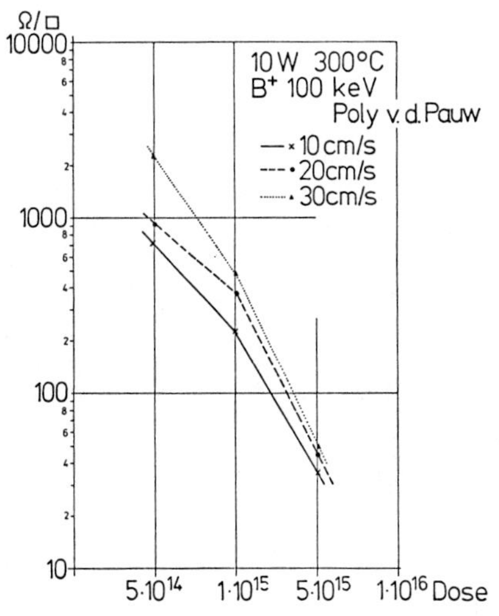

Fig. 6: Laser annealed Poly
Dependence of sheet resistance on implantation dose for different scan velocities

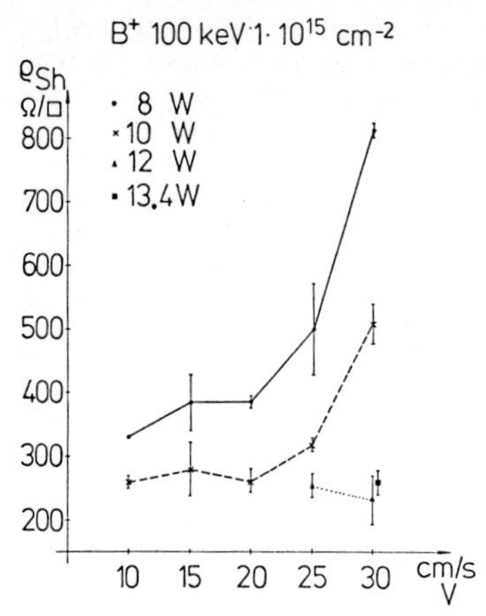

Fig. 7: Laser annealed Poly
Dependence of sheet resistance on scan velocity for different laser powers

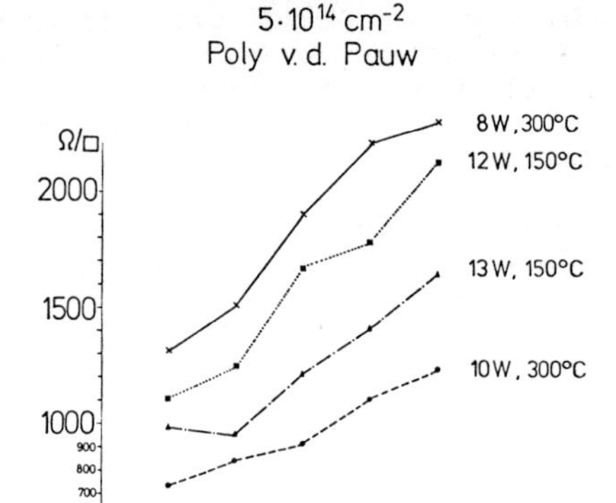

Fig. 8: Influence of scan velocity, laser power, and substrate temperature on sheet resistance of implanted poly

because the van-der-Pauw pattern was destroyed. Fig. 8 shows the additional influence of wafer rear-side temperature.

3. Discussion

If monocrystalline silicon is doped, the resistivity (ρ) depends on the amount of doping, the activated concentration, and the mobility of the charge carriers, as described by the following equation:

$$\rho=(\mu_n en+\mu_p ep)^{-1}$$

μ - mobility
p,n - concentration
e - unit charge

Polycrystalline silicon is composed of small crystallites joined together by grain boundaries. The grain boundaries are composed of silicon atoms with incomplete bonding, which form carrier-trapping and dopant-segregation sites. The dopant distributes uniformly within the grains, but some atoms segregate to the boundaries where they are trapped. Those in the crystallite can be ionized, but the others in the grain boundary are electrically inactive.

A Number of carriers which were released near the boundary are trapped by the dangling bonds, forming potential-energy barriers and a depleted region on both sides of the grain boundaries. Therefore, carrier transport in polysilicon may be accomplished by thermionic emission over these barriers or by tunneling through them, as well as by ohmic conduction along the grain boundaries. Complex models were proposed 1 2 3 to explain the current-voltage relationship. Without looking at the formulas describing the model, one can imagine that the resistance of a polysilicon layer depends on the grain size, which is the ratio of crystalline volume to amorphous grain-boundary volume.

SEM investigations revealed no grain-size dependence on the thermal anneal up to 1150 °C; the size was measured to be 100 to 150 nm. Laser annealing recrystallizes the poly layer, resulting in grain enlargement up to 4 µm.

The resistivity reduction shown in Fig. 6 is explained by this phenomenon. The higher the laser power, the deeper the layer recrystallizes; therefore the resistance decreases. The same argument holds for the scan velocity. Slower scan gives longer dwell times and therefore larger grains.

References

1. I.Y.W.Seto: J.Appl.Phys. 46, 5247 (1975)
2. T.I.Kamins: J.Appl.Phys. 42, 4357 (1971)
3. M.E.Cowher: J.Electrochem.Soc. 119, 1565, (1978)

CW-CO_2-Laser Alloying of Au-Ge-Ni Ohmic Contacts on GaAs

S. Tsou, W. Wang, C. Lin, and G. Xia

Shanghai Institute of Metallurgy, Chinese Academy of Sciences,
865 Chang Ning Road, Shanghai 200050, China

Abstract

Back-surface irradiation through the substrate with a CW-CO_2 laser (λ = 10.6 µm) has been used to produce Au-Ge-Ni ohmic contacts on n-GaAs wafers with different doping concentrations (6×10^{14} - 7×10^{17} cm^{-3}). Specific contact resistivity, as a function of irradiation time and bulk doping concentration, was measured. Data for conventional furnace alloying were also obtained for comparison. The laser-alloyed contacts showed good ohmic behaviour, having a contact resistivity one order of magnitude lower than that of the furnace-alloyed specimens, at a low bulk concentration of $\sim 5 \times 10^{15}$ cm^{-3}. The formation of a Ge-rich n-type GaAs layer during laser alloying, as indicated by AES analysis, is thought to be beneficial for improvement of the interface properties of the contacts. Preliminary results on dual-gate GaAs MESFET's consisting of these laser-alloyed ohmic contacts indicate good I-V characteristics.

1. Introduction

Laser irradiation has recently come into wide use for the fabrication of metal-semiconductor ohmic contacts. Previous investigators [1-3] have reported that the specific contact resistance resulting from front-surface irradiation with pulsed ruby lasers, Nd:YAG lasers, or CW-Ar lasers is lower than that in the case of furnace-alloyed specimens. However, the front-surface irradiation technique often leads to some undesirable effects in device performance. Moreover, before laser irradiation, a thin insulating film has to be deposited onto the metal layer, in order to cut down the high reflectivity of the latter. Though the absorption efficiency of the laser energy is thus improved, the fabrication process becomes more complex.

A new alloying technique for producing ohmic contacts through back-surface irradiation with a CW-CO_2 laser has been developed in the research reported upon in this paper. The CO_2 laser, having a photon energy of 0.12eV, penetrates deep into GaAs substrates with an energy gap of 1.4eV. Thus, if back-surface irradiation with a CO_2 laser is performed onto a GaAs substrate previously coated with a metal layer on the front surface, the absorbed laser energy is liable to be limited in the metal-semiconductor interface region. Such an effect has proven able to produce mixing in the interface layer without causing other detrimental electrical device properties.

2. Experimental Procedure

GaAs VPE n^+-n wafers, with (100) orientation and an electron concentration of 6×10^{14}-7×10^{17} cm^{-3}, were coated with a multilayer of Au-Ge-Ni alloy (88:12:5) as well as Au, with a total thickness of 2000Å. Test patterns of 8 µm diameter for specific-resistivity measurements were made. After cutting the wafer into small pieces, a CW-CO_2 laser was used to irradiate the samples from the back surface, with a power density of 350 W/cm² for different irradiation times. Similar samples were also furnace alloyed at 450°C for 1.5 min in a hydrogen ambient for comparison. Specific contact resistivities after alloying were measured by the four-point-probe method.

Atomic-concentration profiles within the front-surface layer of GaAs samples, before and after alloying, were determined by AES using a successive-layer-stripping technique. GaAs FET devices were produced on semi-insulating GaAs through Si selective implantation, followed by furnace annealing at 800°C for 30 min. Al gates with dimensions of 1.5x300 μm, 4000 Å thick, were used. An Au-Ge-Ni alloy with a thickness of 2000 Å was used for source and drain ohmic contacts, followed by back-surface irradiation with a CW-CO_2 laser.

3. Results and Discussion

Measurements regarding the dependence of the specific contact resistivity on the irradiation time, as shown in Fig. 1, indicate that a low specific contact resistivity can often be obtained with an irradiation time of 2 to 5 sec, for samples with different doping levels. A short irradiation time results in an insufficient interface reaction between the metal film and the substrate, while a long irradiation time causes the decomposition of GaAs and leads to a serious interdiffusion between different species at the metal-semiconductor interface. Both of these give rise to a high specific contact resistivity.

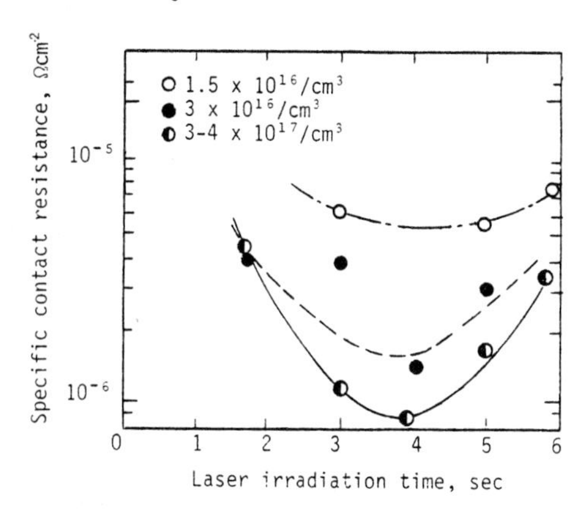

Fig. 1. Dependence of specific contact resistance on laser irradiation time

Experimental results shown in Fig. 2 demonstrate that specific contact resistivity depends strongly on the carrier concentration in the substrate. The higher the carrier concentration, the lower the specific contact resistivity. Specific resistivity for laser-alloyed contacts is nearly one order of magnitude lower than that of furnace-alloyed contacts at the low-carrier-concentration side ($\sim 5 \times 10^{15} cm^{-3}$).

Atomic concentration profiles of the implanted species in the samples, before and after alloying, were measured by AES analysis (Figs. 3-5).

Before alloying, a sharp interface is observed (Fig. 3). In comparison with the furnace-alloyed sample (Fig. 4), profiles of the laser-alloyed

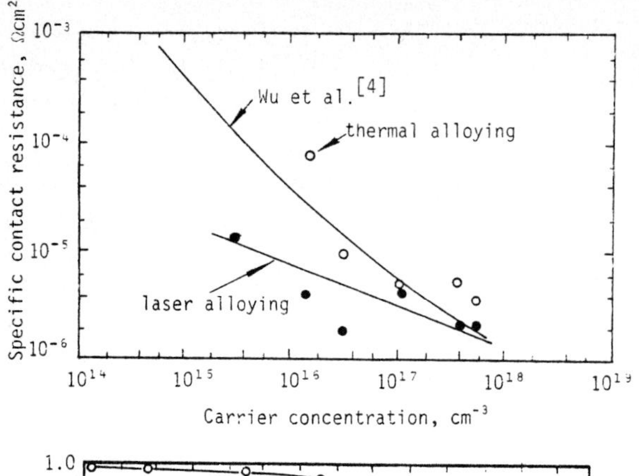

Fig. 2. Dependence of specific resistivity on carrier concentration, in the case of GaAs

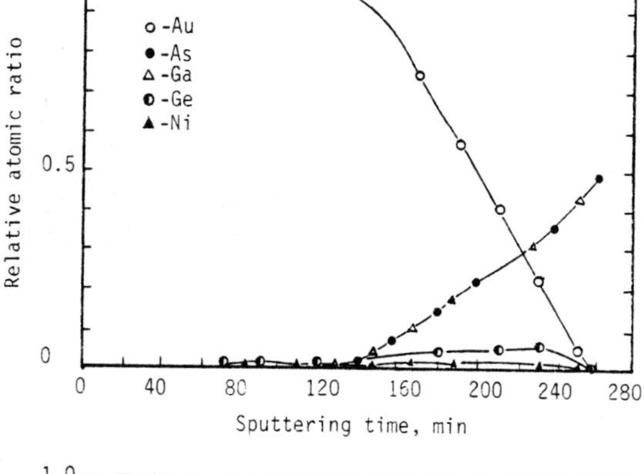

Fig 3. Atomic concentration profiles before alloying, as obtained by AES analysis

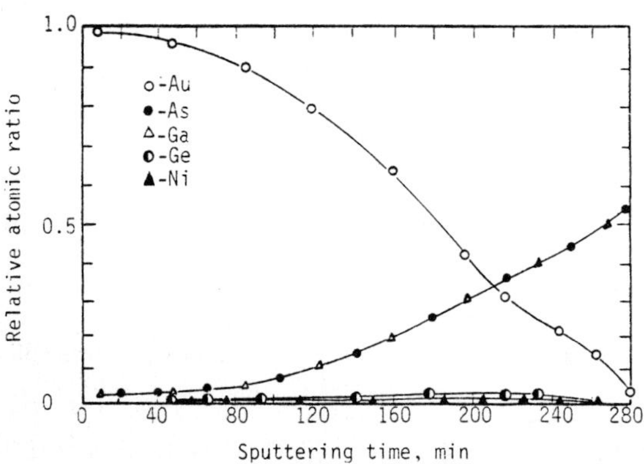

Fig. 4. Atomic concentration profiles after thermal alloying, as obtained by AES analysis

sample (Fig. 5) contain several important features. Owing to a very short irradiation time, the high-temperature region is limited to a thin layer near the interface. Consequently, the thickness of the alloyed layer is shallower than that in the case of a furnace-alloyed specimen. The increase in the Ge concentration induced by laser heating in the metal-GaAs interface region results in the formation of a heavily doped n^+ layer, due to Ge occupation of Ga lattice sites. A high carrier concentration at the interface means a high probability of tunneling, and a low specific contact resistivi-

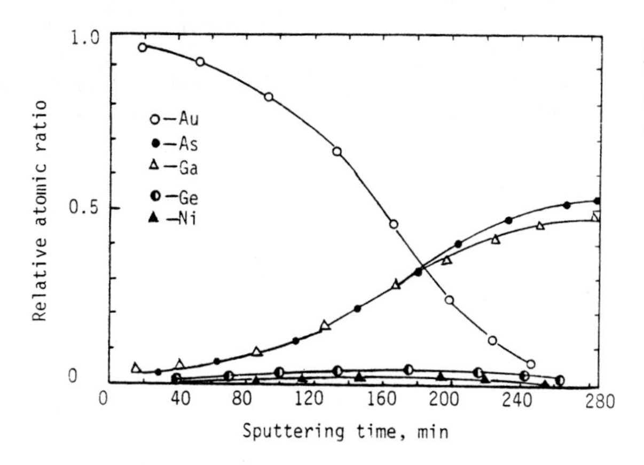

Fig. 5. Atomic concentration profiles after laser alloying, as obtained by AES analysis

ty can therefore be expected. This might explain the fact that the furnace-alloyed ohmic contact, with a low Ge concentration at the interface, has a high specific contact resistivity.

Figure 6 shows random Rutherford backscattering spectra of Au-Ge-Ni contacts before and after laser irradiation. A spectrum for a furnace-alloyed sample is also included for comparison. The latter shows good mixing of GaAs with the Au-alloy layer, as a result of complete etectic reaction. The spectrum of the laser-alloyed contact indicates incomplete mixing, in agreement witn AES analysis.

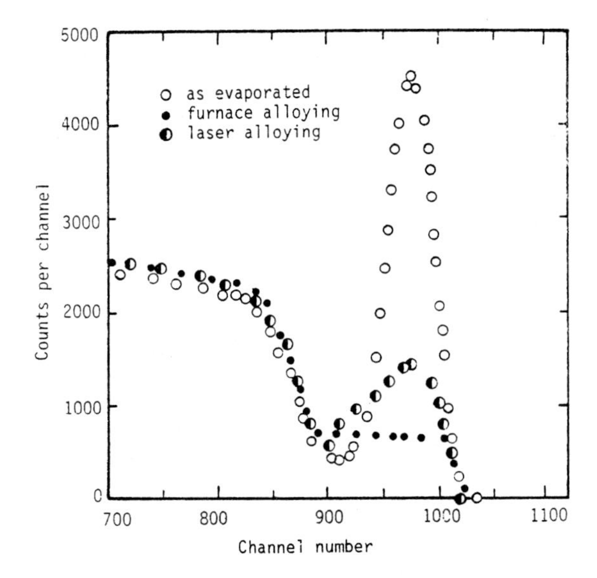

Fig. 6. 1.8 MeV He-ion RBS spectra before and after laser irradiation of Au-Ge-Ni contacts, compared with furnace-alloyed sample

A back-surface irradiation technique, applying a power density of 350W/cm² for 2-5 sec, has been employed to fabricate ohmic contacts for dual-gate Si - implanted GaAs FET's. Data for this device are shown in Fig. 7. The following electrical characteristics are observed: $V_P \sim -3V$, $I_{DSS} \sim 40mA$, and $G_{max} \sim 15mS$. No deterioration of aluminum Schottky contacts treated at the same time has been observed in any case.

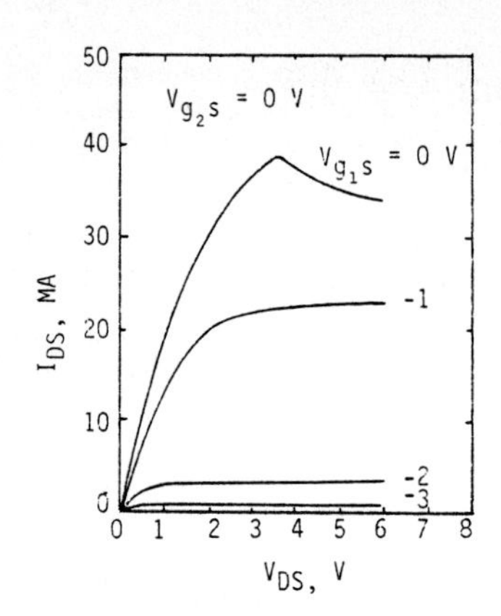

Fig. 7. I-V characteristics of fully Si-implanted dual-gate GaAs MESFET, with ohmic contact made by laser alloying

4. Conclusion

High-quality metal-nGaAs ohmic contacts can be fabricated through CW-CO_2 laser irradiation from the back surface. The specific contact resistivity thus obtained is considerably lower than that resulting from furnace alloying. At low carrier concentrations, the difference may amount to one order of magnitude. This technique has been successfully applied in fabrication of ohmic contacts for GaAs MESFET's.

Addendum: After completion of this study, experimental results reported by Oraby et al. [5] have come to the attention of the present authors. Oraby et al. have used a Q-switched Nd:YAG laser (λ=1.06μm) to irradiate the back surface of a GaAs wafer for fabrication of ohmic contacts. Their success ends further support to the feasibility of this technique.

Acknowledgements

Thanks are due to Mr. Gao Peide and Mrs. Lu Yuezhen in connection with AES analysis, and also to Mr. Fan Baohua in connection with the experimental phase in laser annealing.

References

1. S. Margalit, D. Fekete, D.M. Pepper, C.P. Lee, A. Yariv: Appl. Phys. Lett. 33, 346 (1978)
2. R.B. Gold, R.A. Powell, J.F. Gibbons: in Laser Solid Interactions and Laser Processing - 1978, ed. by S.D. Ferris, H.J. Leamy, and J.M. Poate (AIP Con. Proc., New York, 1979), p. 635
3. G. Eckhardt: in Laser and Electron Beam Processing of Materials, ed. by C.W. White and P.S. Peercy (Academic Press, New York, 1980), p. 467
4. Wu Dingfen, Chen Fenkou: private communication (1972)
5. A.H. Oraby, K. Murakami, Y. Yuba, K. Gamo, S. Namba, Y. Masuda: Appl. Phys. Lett. 38, 562 (1981).

Photoluminescence of Ion-Implanted Gallium Arsenide After Laser Annealing

M. Takai, S. Ono, Y. Ootsuka*, K. Gamo, and S. Namba

Department of Electrical Engineering, Faculty of Engineering Science, Osaka University, Toyonaka, Osaka, Japan

Photoluminescence measurements on unimplanted and zinc-implanted GaAs, after pulsed Rb, Nd:glass, and CW-Ar laser annealing, were performed to investigate laser-induced defects and optical activation of implanted impurities. It was found that the photoluminescence intensity at 77 K for unimplanted GaAs after Rb laser annealing with a pulse duration of 25 nsec was quenched, while it was not quenched or in some cases enhanced with a pulse duration of 0.4 msec. Optical activation of implanted zinc in GaAs was only attained for annealing by a CW-Ar laser with a dwell time of 40 to 1600 msec, in which the photoluminescence line due to the implanted zinc was observed.

1. Introduction

Effects of laser annealing on crystallographic and electrical characteristics in silicon and gallium arsenide (GaAs) have been intensively investigated to date. However, activation of low-fluence implants, especially in GaAs, still remains a problem in the case of pulsed-laser annealing. Furthermore, optical characteristics in GaAs, such as photoluminescence (PL), have not been studied in detail, and optical activation of ion-implanted impurities in GaAs by laser annealing has not been reported on until now.

In this study, PL of unimplanted GaAs after pulsed-laser annealing was measured to study laser-induced damage, which would affect the activation of low-fluence implants. Optical activation of implanted impurities in GaAs by laser annealing was attempted by using different cooling rates, i.e., different pulse lengths or beam-dwell times during annealing.

2. Experimental Procedures

GaAs samples used in this study were undoped, n-type, (100)-oriented, boat -grown wafers with carrier densities ranging from 10^{16} - $10^{18}/cm^3$. 150 keV zinc ions were implanted at room temperature with doses ranging from $10^{12}/cm^2$ to $10^{14}/cm^2$.

Pulsed-ruby lasers with pulse durations of 25 nsec and 0.4 msec, a pulsed Nd:glass laser with a pulse duration of 20 nsec, and a CW-argon laser were used for annealing. In the case of CW-laser annealing, a laser beam was focused to 0.08 mm and scanned using an X-Y stage. The temperature of the sample stage was varied from room temperature up to 500°C during CW-laser annealing, in order to decrease thermal gradients in a given sample. No encapsulation was used during laser irradiation.

* Soken Inc., Nishio, Aichi, Japan

Transient reflectivity measurements using a helium-neon laser (632.8 nm) during pulsed-laser annealing were performed to determine the threshold laser-energy density for the phase change from solid to liquid (i.e., melting).

PL was stimulated at 77 K by a focused 514.5 nm line from an Ar laser. The average incident power density during PL measurements was about 100 W/cm^2. The luminescence spectrum was measured using a grating monochromator and a photon-counting system coupled with an S-1 response photomultiplier.

Ion-channeling and backscattering measurements, using 2 MeV helium ions, were also performed to check the crystallinity of annealed layers and the stoichiometry of sample surfaces.

3. Results and Discussion

3.1 Effects of Pulsed-Laser Irradiation on PL Intensity in Unimplanted GaAs

Figure 1 shows PL spectra for unimplanted GaAs with a carrier density of $10^{17}/cm^3$, after irradiation with Rb laser pulses of 25 nsec. A PL spectrum for a virgin sample is also shown for comparison. PL spectra show a near-band-edge emission peak located at 1.507 eV, with a 25 meV FWHM before and after laser irradiation. The PL intensity decreases with increasing laser-energy density at and above 0.3 J/cm^2.

Figure 2 shows PL intensity as a function of Rb and Nd:glass laser-energy density for unimplanted GaAs with a carrier density of $10^{17}/cm^3$. The PL intensity is normalized to that of a virgin sample. In the case of Nd:glass laser irradiation, the PL intensity is constant before and after irradiation with energy densities up to 0.8 J/cm^2, while it decreases abruptly with increasing energy density at and above 0.3 J/cm^2 for Rb-laser irradiation, down to a level of 5 %. The GaAs samples with carrier densities of 10^{16} - 10^{18} $/cm^3$ showed the same result as that of

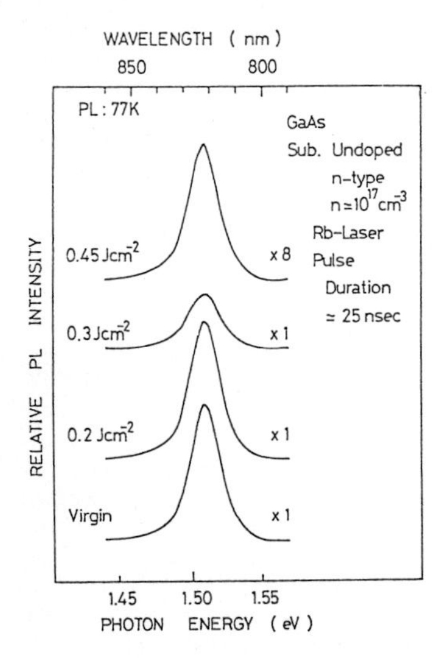

Fig. 1. PL spectra for unimplanted GaAs samples irradiated by 25 nsec pulses from a ruby laser

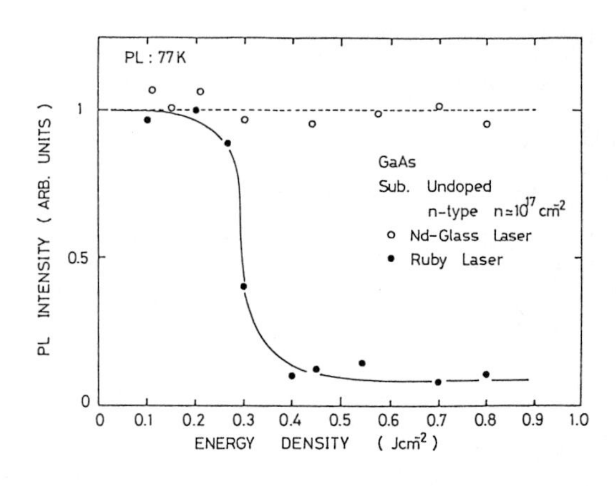

Fig. 2. PL intensity versus laser energy density for unimplanted GaAs samples

Fig.2. The PL intensity, once decreased by laser irradiation, was not recovered through thermal post-annealing up to 850°C.

This decreasing of the PL intensity is considered to be due to the increase of non-radiative centers by Rb-laser irradiation. The absorption coefficient for a 1060 nm line of a Nd:glass laser in single-crystalline GaAs is lower than that for a 694 nm line of a Rb laser by three orders of magnitude. Therefore, the light from the Nd:glass laser is not absorbed in GaAs, and nothing happens. In the case of the Rb laser, the light is absorbed in a near-surface layer, and melting occurs. Additional transient-reflectivity measurements using a probing beam during Rb-laser irradiation showed a high-reflectivity phase lasting more than 100 nsec when a sample was bombarded with an energy density at or above 0.3 $\pm$ 0.05 J/cm^2, which suggested the melting of a surface layer. Such a melting process would induce defects, killing radiative centers and/or acting as a non-radiative center in GaAs, since the cooling rate in melting and cooling processes is too high (about 10^{10} K/sec) for GaAs to retain local stoichiometry.

A similar PL-intensity reduction in single-crystalline GaAs due to Rb-laser irradiation was observed by Feldman et al.[1]. However, they observed only a gradual decrease with increasing laser-energy density. Laser-induced defects, observed through PL measurements, may account for loss of activation in low-fluence implants in GaAs after pulsed-laser annealing. Mooney et al.[2] and Yuba et al.[3] also found laser-induced defect centers in single-crystalline GaAs after Rb-laser irradiation on the basis of DLTS measurements; they estimated the defect concentration to be 10^{14} - 10^{16} $/cm^3$, which was even lower than that estimated from PL quenching or carrier activation loss in electrical measurements.

Figure 3 shows PL intensity as a function of Rb laser-energy density with a 0.4 msec pulse duration for unimplanted GaAs samples having carrier densities of 10^{16}- $10^{18}/cm^3$. The PL intensity is normalized to that of a virgin crystal for each carrier concentration. The change in the PL intensity depends on the carrier concentration of the sample. For 10^{18} $/cm^3$, the PL intensity does not change after laser irradiation with an energy density up to 6.2 J/cm^2, while it increases by a factor of 3 after irradiation with 2.5 J/cm^2 for 10^{16} $/cm^3$. Additional transient-reflectivity measurements did not show a high-reflectivity phase, and the power density in this 0.4 msec pulse irradiation is lower than that in the 25 nsec case by three orders of magnitude, which suggests that the GaAs-sample surface does not melt. Therefore, the increase in the PL

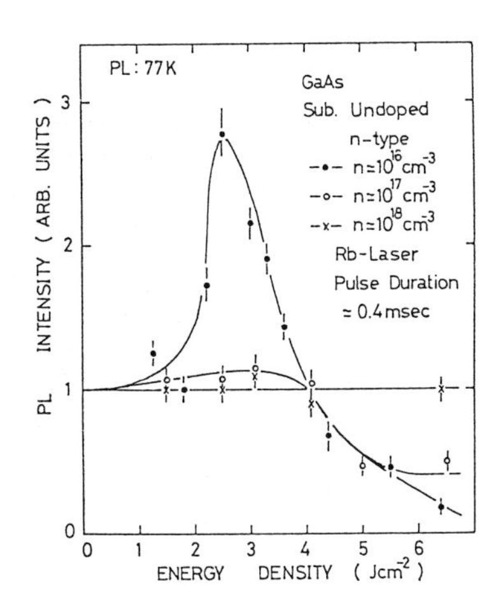

Fig. 3. PL intensity versus laser-energy density for unimplanted GaAs samples having various carrier densities

intensity observed in Fig. 3 is considered to be due to an increase in radiative centers, a decrease in non-radiative centers, and/or a decease in recombination centers because of the temperature rise below the melting point. Gallium-vacancy silicon-donor complexes, for example, are considered to be such centers, since the same phenomena were not observed in sulphur-doped GaAs. The effect of an increase in such centers on the PL intensity is usually more noticeable in low-carrier-concentration material, and is also dependent upon material quality. A similar result was obtained by Rostworowski et al. [4], in which they observed the increase of near-band-edge emission at 4.2 K by 3 orders of magnitude in Czochralski-grown single-crystalline GaAs with a carrier density of 10^{16} $/cm^3$, after 1 msec pulsed-Rb-laser annealing.

The results obtained in Figs. 1-3 indicate that the melting process in nsec pulsed-laser annealing of GaAs induces defects which reduce the PL intensity, while a moderate process using 0.4 msec pulsed-laser annealing does not induce such defects, but rather induces only small quantities of defects such as those found in furnace annealing. It is also apparent from the results that the cooling rate in GaAs annealing should be kept as low as possible, in order to retain local stoichiometry and avoid defect freezing.

3.2 Optical Activation of Implanted Zinc in GaAs by Laser Annealing

A series of PL measurements of zinc-ion-implanted GaAs after Rb-laser annealing, with pulse durations of 25 nsec and 0.4 msec, was performed to optically activate the implanted zinc. Nanosecond pulsed-laser annealing did not result in any enhancement of the PL intensity. The moderate annealing process, using 0.4 msec laser pulses with a cooling rate of 10^6 K/sec, was found only to increase the intensity of near-band-edge emission by a factor of 5. No spectral changes were observed.

CW-Ar-laser annealing was then used to activate optically the implanted zinc, in which case a more moderate annealing with a cooling rate of 10^3 K/sec occurred, and activation of low-fluence implants was probable. Figure 4 shows PL spectra for zinc-implanted GaAs with a dose of $1 \times 10^{13}/cm^2$, after furnace annealing at 400°C and laser annealing with 1.2 W and 2.0 W. The PL spectra, after furnace annealing at 400 °C or laser annealing at 1.2 W, show no spectral change and no enhancement of emission intensity, while the PL intensity is enhanced by a factor of 28 as compared with the as-implanted case, and a new emission line at 1.474 eV (841 nm) is observed for 2.0 W annealing. This new line at 841 nm is considered to be due to activated zinc, and the enhancement of the 841 nm line's emission intensity is due to increased activation of the zinc by laser annealing. An additional emission line at 1.37 eV is considered to be due to copper-related emissions. The emission intensity of the 841 nm line enhanced by laser annealing is still lower than that of the near-band-edge emission (827 nm) of virgin material.

Figure 5 shows PL intensity as a function of substrate temperature during CW annealing with 2.0 W. The PL intensity for near-band-edge emission (827 nm) and zinc-related emission (841 nm) was normalized to that of unimplanted material. The PL intensity for near-band-edge emission after furnace annealing, at temperatures from 100°C to 500°C for 20 min, was also investigated to distinguish the effects of furnace annealing from those of laser annealing. An enhancement of PL intensity through laser annealing is only found for a substrate temperature above 400°C, in which case the PL intensity increases up to 19 %, as compared with unimplanted material. Furnace annealing up to 500 °C does not increase the PL intensity. The substrate temperature in this case, therefore, reduces

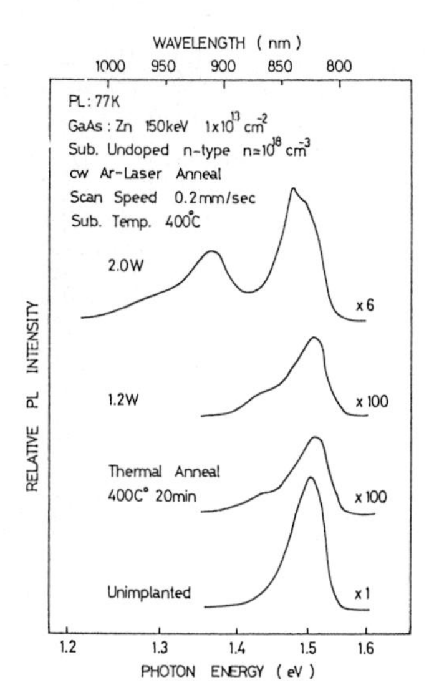

Fig. 4. PL spectra for zinc-ion-implanted GaAs samples after CW Ar laser annealing

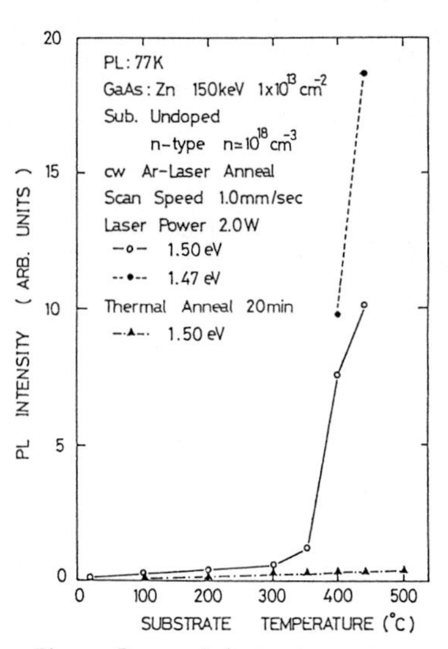

Fig. 5. Substrate temperature dependence of PL intensity for zinc-ion-implanted GaAs samples during CW Ar laser annealing

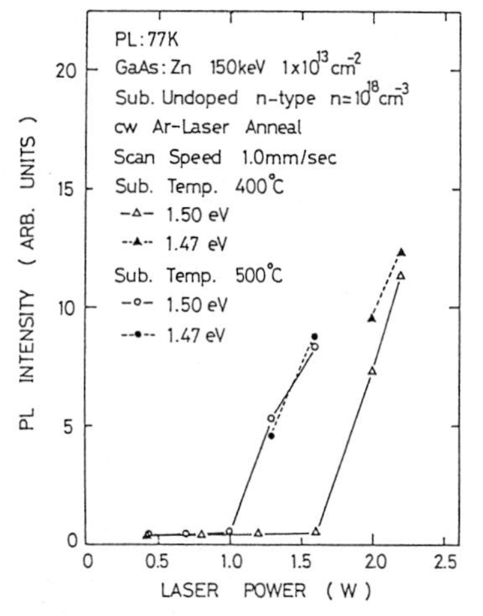

Fig. 6. PL intensity versus laser power for zinc-ion-implanted GaAs samples after CW Ar laser annealing with two different substrate temperatures

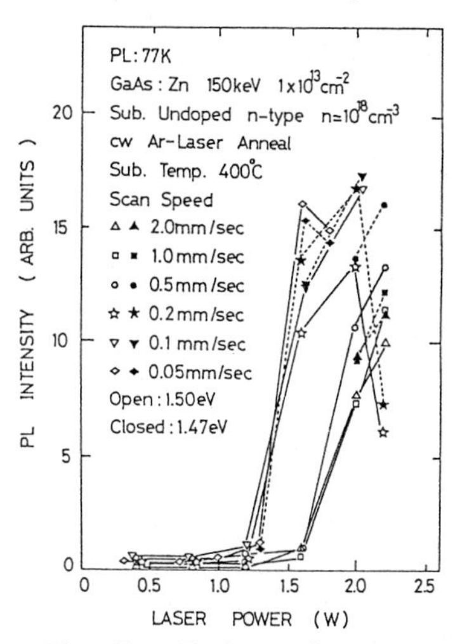

Fig. 7. PL intensity versus laser power for zinc-ion-implanted GaAs samples with various scanning speeds of a CW Ar laser beam

thermal gradients and thermal strains in the sample, and decreases the cooling rate.

Figure 6 shows PL intensity as a function of laser power for zinc-implanted GaAs, with a dose of 10^{13} /cm^2 and substrate temperatures of 400°C and 500°C. It is obvious that the higher substrate temperature yields the higher PL intensity. The maximum PL intensity is limited by the surface dissociation of a sample. Ion-backscattering measurements indicate such surface dissociation, i.e., arsenic and gallium evaporation during annealing.

Figure 7 shows PL intensity as a function of laser power for zinc-implanted GaAs, with a dose of 10^{13} /cm^2 and various scanning speeds. The substrate temperature was maintained at 400°C. The enhancement of PL intensity is found to be greater for a slower scanning speed. The decrease in PL intensity at 2.2 W is due to the surface dissociation mentioned before. The maximum PL intensity is also limited by this dissociation.

In the case of 10^{12}/cm^2 implantation, the same optical activation of implanted zinc was also attained as that shown in Figs. 5 - 7. These results indicate that moderate annealing with a CW laser, which does not melt the sample surface, does not induce destructive defects such as those in the case of nsec pulsed-laser annealing, and that an optical activation of implanted impurities in GaAs by this method is possible.

4. Conclusions

PL measurements on unimplanted and zinc-implanted GaAs, after pulsed-Rb, Nd:glass, and CW-Ar laser annealing, were performed to investigate laser-induced defects as well as optical activation of implanted impurities. From the obtained results, the following conclusions were drawn.

Rb-laser irradiation with a pulse duration of 25 nsec induces defects which decrease the PL intensity and are not removable by post-annealing at 850°C. Such defects are not induced by Nd:glass- and Rb-laser irradiation with a pulse duration of 0.4 msec, in which case a phase transition (to liquid) does not occur. Therefore, defects are considered to be produced by a liquid-phase epitaxy process with a fast cooling rate. Such defects may be responsible for loss of activity in the case of low fluence implants into GaAs.

Optical activation of implanted zinc was only attained through CW-Ar laser annealing, which does not produce destructive defects for reasons of the solid-phase epitaxy process and the moderate cooling rate.

Acknowledgements

The authors wish to thank Mr. K. Kawasaki for his technical assistance during the experiments, and Mr. Y. Yuba for helpful discussions concerning this study.

References

1. B. J. Feldman and D. H. Lowndes: Appl. Phys. Lett. 40, 59 (1982)
2. P. M. Mooney and J. C. Bourgoin: in Laser and Electron-Beam Solid Interactions and Materials Processing, ed. by J. F. Gibbons, L. D. Hess, and T. W. Sigmon(North-Holland, New York, 1981), p.255
3. Y. Yuba, K. Gamo, A. H. Oraby, K. Murakami, and S. Namba: Nucl. Inst. and Meth. 182, 699 (1981)
4. J. A. Rostworowski, R. R. Parsons, and D. G. Hutcheon: Appl. Phys. Lett. 35, 934 (1979)

Channeling and High-Resolution Backscattering Studies of Laser-Annealed Low-Energy Arsenic-Implanted Silicon

P.J. Scanlon, K.M. Barfoot, P. Skensved, J.L. Whitton,
Queen's University, Physics Department, Kingston, Ontario, Canada, K7L 3N6
I.D. Calder, F.R. Shepherd
Bell-Northern Research, 3K11, Ottawa, Ontario, Canada, K1Y 4H7

1. Introduction

The interest in smaller geometries of semiconductor devices has led to an increased need for reliable measurements of shallow implant profiles, both as-implanted and after annealing. The most sensitive and commonly used technique, Secondary Ion Mass Spectrometry (SIMS) has difficulties for very shallow implants, ~ 10 nm, because the range of the sputter-profiling ions is comparable to the implant range. Whitlow et al.(1) have used a grazing-angle rutherford scattering technique to examine low-energy indium and arsenic implants in silicon and the effect of thermal annealing up to temperatures of the order of 700°C. The present work examines the profiles, before and after laser annealing, of 15-keV arsenic in silicon. In addition, channeling measurements have been made to obtain information on the lattice location of the implanted ions and the effect of the annealing on the silicon crystal quality. Such information is not available with SIMS.

2. Experiment

Silicon wafers were implanted with arsenic at 15-keV to a fluence of 5E15/cm^2 at 7° to the normal of the (100) plane. Different areas of one wafer were laser annealed with a CW argon laser under varying conditions. For the work presented in this paper, the power was 4.0 watts, the sweep speed was 50cm/s, the beam width was 37 micro-meters and the step size was 10 micro-meters. The wafer was maintained at 500°C to reduce thermal shock. Profile and channeling measurements were made on the Queen's University 4-MV Van de Graaf accelerator.

Arsenic profiles were determined by a grazing exit-angle rutherford scattering technique as shown in Fig. 1. The angle relative to the surface normal was determined by rotating the goniometer until the scattered alpha particles were cut off by an edge on the goniometer which set a mimimum angle of 4.0 degrees. The angles were measured by optical encoders coupled through anti-backlash gears to the goniometer head. Angles were reproducible to 1 minute of arc. The operating pressure in the cryopumped target chamber was 3E-8 torr.

3. Results

Examples of grazing exit-angle spectra are shown in Fig. 2 for the unannealed sample and Fig. 3 for one of the annealed samples. The incident beam energy was 1 MeV. Also shown in each figure is a spectrum

Fig.1. Goniometer arrangement for grazing exit-angle measurements of shallow implant profiles

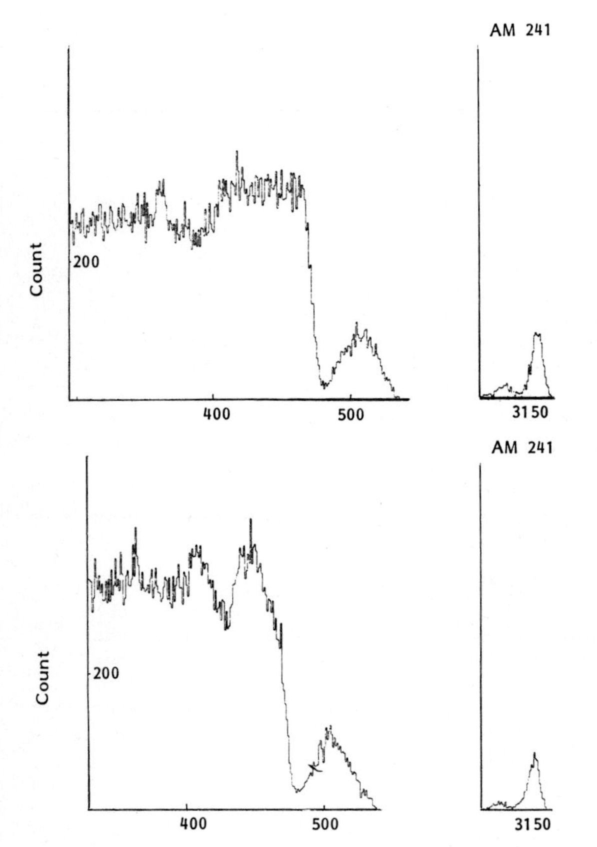

Fig.2. Alpha particle spectrum for 1-MeV incident energy on unannealed silicon implanted with 15-keV arsenic. The peak at 3150 is Am-241

Fig.3. Alpha particle spectrum for 1-MeV incident energy on laser annealed silicon, 15-keV arsenic implant. The peak at 3150 is Am-241

from an americium alpha particle source taken at the same time. The energy calibration was based on the source energy and the energy of the silicon edge. The yield of arsenic in the two cases was the same to within 6%.

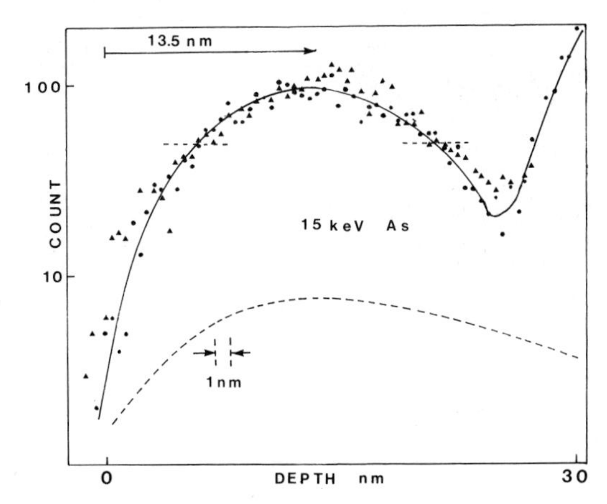

Fig.4. Depth profile for 15-keV, $5E15/cm^2$ arsenic in silicon; ● unannealed , ▲ annealed. The solid line shows the trend of the unannealed data. The dashed curve shows Phillips' (2) result with arbitrary normalization

In Fig. 4 are shown the depth profiles for the unannealed and annealed arsenic-implanted samples. The centroid position for the annealed sample was the same as for the unannealed and it can be seen that there is little change in the profile shape. The arsenic content, based on the surface silicon yield, is $4.3E15/cm^2$ in reasonable agreement with the nominal implant fluence of $5E15/cm^2$.

The line drawn to show the trend of the points in Fig. 4 is very close to gaussian, down to 10% of the peak height, with a mean projected range of 13.5 nm and fwhm of 14.5 nm. When corrected for the system resolution (17keV) the fwhm is 13.5 nm. The corresponding second moment is 5.7 nm. The measured value of the concentration is $3E21\ As/cm^3$.

Calculated values of these parameters using the Winterbon (3) procedure, with m=1/3, are: 12.6 nm for the projected range, 5.0 nm for the second moment and $4E21\ As/cm^3$ for the peak concentration.

The gaussian shape obtained in this experiment differs from that obtained by Phillips (2) with a SIMS system.

Examples of channeling spectra at a scattering angle of 170° are shown in Fig. 5 for the unannealed sample and Fig. 6 for the annealed sample, both for the ⟨100⟩ direction, together with the corresponding random

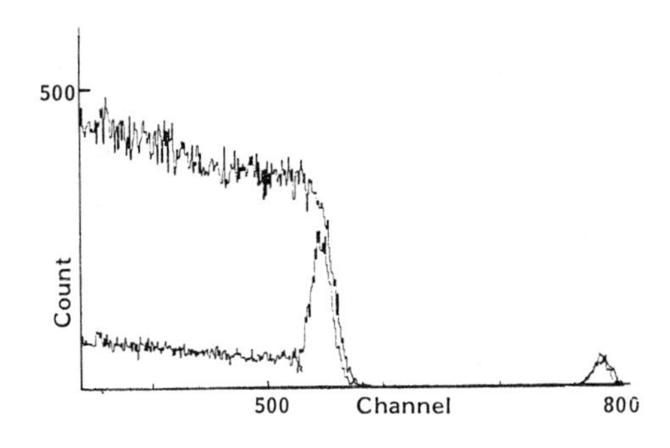

Fig.5. ⟨100⟩ channeling spectrum and superimposed random spectrum. Unannealed silicon, 15-keV arsenic implant

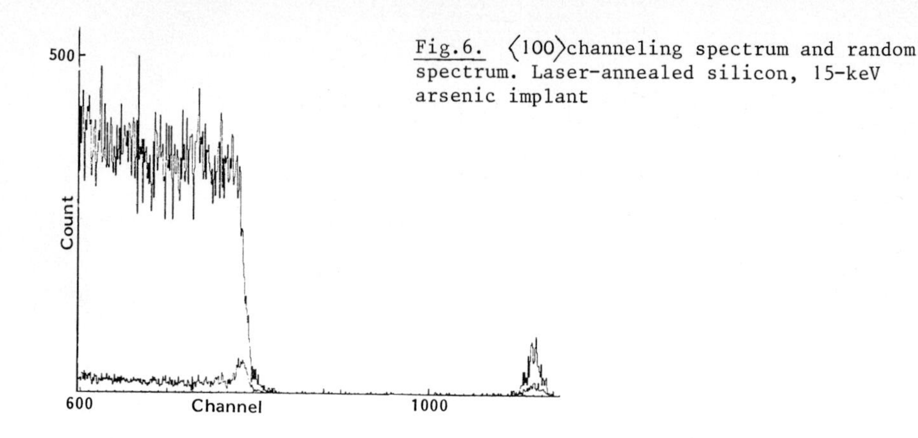

Fig.6. $\langle 100 \rangle$channeling spectrum and random spectrum. Laser-annealed silicon, 15-keV arsenic implant

spectra. The gain setting is different in the two cases. Similar results were obtained for the $\langle 110 \rangle$ and $\langle 111 \rangle$ axes. The chi-min values for the $\langle 100 \rangle$, $\langle 110 \rangle$, $\langle 111 \rangle$ directions are 0.036, 0.027, and 0.034, respectively.

Tilt angle scans for the $\langle 100 \rangle$ direction are shown in Fig. 7, 8 in which it can be seen that the arsenic is essentially randomly oriented before annealing. After annealing, approximately 75% of the arsenic is substitutional. That this value is not larger might be due to the high peak concentration of the arsenic.

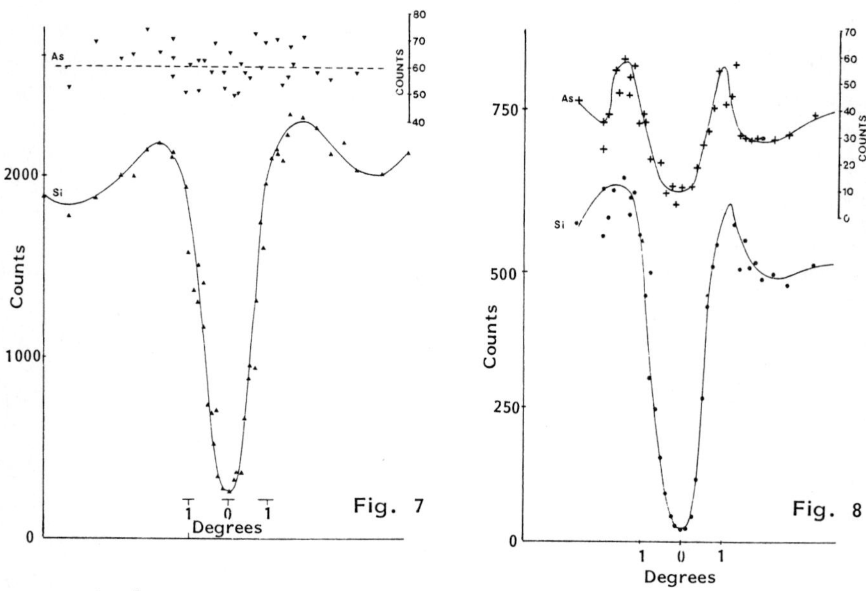

Fig.7. $\langle 100 \rangle$ tilt scan; unannealed arsenic in silicon.

Fig.8. $\langle 100 \rangle$ tilt scan; laser-annealed arsenic in silicon.

4.Summary

1. For 15-keV arsenic ions, implanted into silicon at a fluence of 5E15/cm^2, the mean projected range is 13.5 nm and the profile is gaussian (to 10% of the peak concentration) with a first moment of 5.7 nm. The estimated uncertainty is 10%. The maximum concentration is 3E21/cm^3.

2. Laser annealing at 1.3 W/cm does not significantly alter the shape of the profile.

3. No significant loss of arsenic occurs.

4. Good chi-min values are obtained for the annealed silicon.

5. Approximately 75% of the arsenic is substitutional after annealing.

Acknowledgements

It is a pleasure to thank H.W. Bowcock for work on the scattering chamber and S. Dzioba for the calculated profile data. This work was supported by a grant from the Natural Sciences and Engineering Research Council of Canada.

References

1 H.J. Whitlow, P. Blood, B.W. Farmery, D.J.O'Connor, J.M. Shannon and M.W. Thompson: Nucl. Inst. and Meth.

2 B.F. Phillips: J. Vac. Sci. Technol. 20,793 (1982)

3 K.B. Winterbon: Ion Implantation Range and Energy Deposition Distributions (Plenum, N.Y. 1975)

Index of Contributors

Magnetic Electron Lenses

Editor: **P. W. Hawkes**
1982. 240 figures. XIII, 462 pages
(Topics in Current Physics, Volume 18)
ISBN 3-540-10296-5

Contents: *P. W. Hawkes:* Magnetic Lens Theory. – *E. Kasper:* Magnetic Field Calculation and the Determination of Electron Trajectories. – *F. Lenz:* Properties of Electron Lenses. – *W. D. Riecke:* Practical Lens Design. – *T. Mulvey:* Unconventional Lens Design. – Appendix A: *P. W. Hawkes:* Some Earlier Sets of Curves Representing Lens Properties. – Appendix B: *P. W. Hawkes:* Bibliography of Publications on Magnetic Electron Lens Properties. – Subject Index.

Ion Implantation Techniques

Lectures given at the Ion Implantation School in Connection with the Fourth International Conference on Ion Implantation: Equipment and Techniques
Berchtesgaden, Federal Republic of Germany, September 13–15, 1982
Editors: **H. Ryssel, H. Glawischnig**
1982. 245 figures. XII, 372 pages
(Springer Series in Electrophysics, Volume 10)
ISBN 3-540-11878-0

Contents: Machine Aspects of Ion Implantation: Ion Implantation System Concepts. Ion Sources. Faraday Cup Designs for Ion Implantation. Safety and Ion Implanters. – Ion Ranges in Solids: The Stopping and Range of Ions in Solids. The Calculation of Ion Ranges in Solids with Analytic Solutions. Range Distributions. – Measuring Techniques and Annealing: Electrical Measuring Techniques. Wafer Mapping Techniques for Characterization of Ion Implantation Processing. Non-Electrical Measuring Techniques. Annealing and Residual Damage. – Appendix: Modern Ion Implantation Equipment: Evolution and Performance of the Nova NV-10 Predep™ Implanter. Ion Implantation Equipment from Veeco. The Series IIIA and IIIX Ion Implanters. Standard High-Voltage Power Supplies for Ion Implantation. The IONMICROPROBE A-DIDA 3000-30 for Dopant Depth Profiling and Impurity Bulk Analysis. – List of Contributors. – Subject Index.

Photoemission in Solids II

Case Studies
Editor: **L. Ley**
1979. 214 figures, 26 tables. XVIII, 401 pages
(Topics in Applied Physics, Volume 27)
ISBN 3-540-09202-1

Contents: *L. Ley, M. Cardona:* Introduction. – *L. Ley, M. Cardona, R. A. Pollak:* Photoemission in Semiconductors. – *S. Hüfner:* Unfilled Inner Shells: Transition Metals and Compounds. – *M. Campagna, G. K. Wertheim, Y. Baer:* Unfilled Inner Shells: Rare Earths and Their Compounds. – *W. D. Grobman, E. E. Koch:* Photoemission from Organic Molecular Crystals. – *C. Kunz:* Synchrotron Radiation: Overview. – *P. Steiner, H. Höchst, S. Hüfner:* Simple Metals. – Appendix: Table of Core-Level Binding Energies. – Additional References with Titles. – Subject Index.

Sputtering by Particle Bombardment I

Physical Sputtering of Single-Element Solids
Editor: **R. Behrisch**
1981. 117 figures. XI, 281 pages
(Topics in Applied Physics, Volume 47)
ISBN 3-540-10521-2

Contents: *R. Behrisch:* Introduction and Overview. – *P. Sigmund:* Sputtering by Ion Bombardment: Theoretical Concepts. –*M. T. Robinson:* Theoretical Aspects of Monocrystal Sputtering. – *H. H. Andersen, H. L. Bay:* Sputtering Yield Measurements. – *H. E. Roosendaal:* Sputtering Yields of Single Crystalline Targets.

Very Large Scale Integration (VLSI)

Fundamentals and Applications
Editor: **D. F. Barbe**
2nd corrected and updated edition. 1982.
147 figures. XI, 302 pages
(Springer Series in Electrophysics, Volume 5)
ISBN 3-540-11368-1

Contents: *D. F. Barbe:* Introduction. – *J. L. Prince:* VLSI Device Fundamentals. – *R. K. Watts:* Advanced Lithography. – *P. Losleben:* Computer Aided Design for VLSI. – *R. C. Eden:* GaAs Digital Integrated Circuits for Ultra High Speed LSI/VLSI. – *E. E. Swartzlander, Jr.:* VLSI Architecture. – *B. H. Whalen:* VLSI Applications and Testing. – *D. F. Barbe, E. C. Urban:* VHSIC Technology and Systems. – *R. I. Scace:* VLSI in Other Countries. – Addenda. – Subject Index.

Springer-Verlag
Berlin
Heidelberg
New York
Tokyo